$25.00

STARS AND STELLAR SYSTEMS

Compendium of Astronomy and Astrophysics

(IN NINE VOLUMES)

GERARD P. KUIPER, *General Editor*
BARBARA M. MIDDLEHURST, *Associate General Editor*

I
TELESCOPES

II
ASTRONOMICAL TECHNIQUES

III
BASIC ASTRONOMICAL DATA

IV
CLUSTERS AND BINARIES

V
GALACTIC STRUCTURE

VI
STELLAR ATMOSPHERES

VII
NEBULAE AND INTERSTELLAR MATTER

VIII
STELLAR STRUCTURE

IX
GALAXIES AND THE UNIVERSE

CONTRIBUTORS

H. W. BABCOCK

W. A. BAUM

W. H. VAN DEN BOS

I. S. BOWEN

A. D. CODE

W. J. ECKERT

ROBERT H. HARDIE

W. A. HILTNER

J. B. IRWIN

HAROLD L. JOHNSON

REBECCA JONES

PETER VAN DE KAMP

A. KÖNIG

A. LALLEMAND

WILLIAM C. LILLER

W. C. LIVINGSTON

J. D. McGEE

P. MULLER

R. M. PETRIE

STEWART SHARPLESS

FREDERIC R. STAUFFER

J. STOCK

JOHN STRONG

P. J. TREANOR

A. D. WILLIAMS

K. O. WRIGHT

ASTRONOMICAL TECHNIQUES

Edited by

W. A. HILTNER

THE UNIVERSITY OF CHICAGO PRESS

CHICAGO AND LONDON

This publication has been supported in part by the

NATIONAL SCIENCE FOUNDATION

Library of Congress Catalog Card Number: 62-9113

THE UNIVERSITY OF CHICAGO PRESS, CHICAGO & LONDON
The University of Toronto Press, Toronto 5, Canada

Preface to the Series

THE SERIES "Stars and Stellar Systems, Compendium of Astronomy," comprising nine volumes, was organized in consultation with senior astronomers in the United States and abroad early in 1955. It was intended as an extension of the four-volume "Solar System" series to cover astrophysics and stellar astronomy. In contrast to the "Solar System" series, separate editors have been appointed for each volume. The volume editors, together with the general editors, form the editorial board that is responsible for the over-all planning of the series.

The aim of the series is to present stellar astronomy and astrophysics as basically empirical sciences, co-ordinated and illuminated by the application of theory. To this end the series opens with a description of representative telescopes, both optical and radio (Vol. 1), and of accessories, techniques, and methods of reduction (Vol. 2). The chief classes of observational data are described in Volume 3, with additional material being referred to in succeeding volumes, as the topics may require. The systematic treatment of astronomical problems starts with Volume 4, as is apparent from the volume titles. Theoretical chapters are added where needed, on dynamical problems in Volumes 4, 5, and 9, and on astrophysical problems in Volumes 6, 7, and 8. In order that the chapters may retain a greater degree of permanence, the more speculative parts of astronomy have been de-emphasized. The level of the chapters will make them suitable for graduate students as well as for professional astronomers and also for the increasing number of scientists in other fields requiring astronomical information.

The undersigned wish to thank both the authors and the volume editors for their readiness to collaborate on this series, which it is hoped will stimulate the further growth of astronomy. The present plans call for the publication of Volumes 1, 2, and 6 during the academic year 1960–1961, with the remaining volumes to follow.

The editors wish to acknowledge the support by the National Science Foundation both in defraying part of the costs of the editorial offices and in providing a publication subsidy.

G. P. K.

B. M. M.

April 1, 1960

Preface to Volume 2

Astronomy, in contrast to most other sciences, depends upon observations, and the analysis and integration of newly observed data, rather than upon experimentation to gain new knowledge of the universe. Its progress is a function of the astronomer's ingenuity in the development of new instruments and the application of old as well as new techniques. Stars are point sources of radiation, and, in the final analysis, the astronomer has only the opportunity to measure their positions and to determine the radiation intensity versus wave length.

This volume is a collection of twenty-four essentially independent chapters written by twenty-six authors. Each author, actively engaged in the field about which he writes, presents the subject as he chooses. This has caused some overlap, many omissions, and a dispersion in the level of presentation. The overlap did not seem undesirable, and the editor made no attempt to correct for omissions or to reduce the level dispersion. As examples in overlap, a number of authors have discussed photocathodes, photomultipliers, and the noise in these receivers. On the other hand, one striking example of omission is the absence of any specific discussion of interference filter photometry. But the astronomer who wishes to work at narrow wave-length bands will find no less than six chapters, all by different authors, of significance to his problem. And yet none of the authors represented in this collection attempt to cover instrumentation for radio telescopes or the new technology being developed for telescopes beyond the atmosphere. This volume, instead, gives some of the concepts and principles for the design and application of basic instrumentation for optical earth-bound astronomy. A mastery of earth-bound techniques and their application to observational astronomical research is imperative for fruitful exploration with both old and new, unpredictable, developments.

Some of the areas are advancing so rapidly, especially the field of image intensification, that this volume is partially outdated before publication. Progress is, nonetheless, always welcome.

The editor wishes to acknowledge the co-operation and patience of the many authors who have generously contributed to this volume. Barbara M. Middlehurst gave invaluable assistance in editing and proofreading. Mrs. Elliott Moore assisted in the preliminary work, Mrs. David Norman checked many of the references, and Robert Hjellming checked references in page proofs. My special thanks are given to Mrs. Emil Niznik, who typed nearly all the manuscripts, prepared most of the figures, and organized the editorial work. The editor also thanks J. Tapscott for his generous assistance in the preparation of many difficult figures.

W. A. Hiltner

Table of Contents

3. RADIAL-VELOCITY DETERMINATIONS 63
   R. M. Petrie

4. SPECTROPHOTOMETRY 83
   K. O. Wright

18. MEASURING ENGINES 424

W. J. Eckert and Rebecca Jones

19. TECHNIQUES FOR VISUAL MEASUREMENTS 440

P. Muller

CHAPTER 1

The Detection and Measurement of Faint Astronomical Sources

W. A. BAUM

Mount Wilson and Palomar Observatories
Carnegie Institution of Washington, California Institute of Technology

§1. INTRODUCTION

No OBSERVATIONAL astronomer with a view to the future is ever completely satisfied with the instruments he has. The history of modern observational astronomy is a story of continuously pushing toward fainter and fainter limits. This has meant progressively bigger and bigger telescopes, more efficient spectrographs, improvements in photographic emulsions, and recently the rapid development of photoelectric devices. We are concerned in this chapter with the way in which various factors limit the threshold of detection. The considerations here are fundamental to all observational techniques: visual, photographic, photoelectric, and thermoelectric.

The detection of light in the optical range is often a quantum phenomenon. Photons strike a detector and produce "photo-events." For example, they can form latent images in photographic grains, liberate electrons from a photo-cathode, form color centers in alkali-halide crystals, and induce nerve impulses in the retina of the eye. Not all photons produce useful responses. Conversely, a single photon can sometimes produce an event which involves more than one registrable sub-event. For instance, the number of electrons liberated in a photoconductor might exceed the number of incident photons responsible for their release, but these electrons cannot all be considered to be independent photo-events.

In this chapter we shall be interested in the collection of information, in information rates, and in information-storage capacity. Consequently, we are interested in photo-events. In phenomena where it is not possible to ascribe a particular event to a particular quantum of light, we can turn the problem around to infer the equivalent efficiency of such a detector from its relative ability to collect information.

§ 2. THE PERFORMANCE OF A DETECTOR

Let us first suppose a photon detector whose performance is ideal in the sense that it will preserve all the information inherent in the train of photo-events induced in it. In other words, we suppose that each photo-event is counted, none is lost, and all are weighted equally. Let n photons per second from a light-source be incident upon a detector; then the number of photo-events produced in an exposure time t will be nqt, where q is the fraction of the photons that succeed in producing registrable photo-events. If this process is repeated many times, there will be a statistical fluctuation in the number of photo-events produced, despite the constancy of the light-source and despite the ideal performance of the detector. This minimum fluctuation is inherent in the random arrival of the incident photons and the random selection of those which yield photo-events. In a sequence of identical exposures, the standard deviation in the number of photo-events will be simply $(nqt)^{1/2}$.

The foregoing situation is stated in terms of a set of exposures applied sequentially to a single-channel detector such as a photocell. The same considerations apply to a set of exposures distributed over the surface of a multiple-channel detector such as a photographic emulsion, i.e., one which receives and distinguishes many parts of an image simultaneously. We can imagine that an image is divided, like a mosaic, into an array of tiny elemental areas of equal size. On a uniformly exposed photographic plate, for example, the number of blackened grains per image element will vary from one element to the next. If a photographic plate were an ideal detector, the standard deviation in grain counts per image element would be equal to the square root of the average grain count. Since a photographic plate is not an ideal detector, the actual fluctuation will be a little greater.

Whether the fluctuations are distributed over a surface or distributed in time, they represent "noise" against which a "signal" is to be detected. Thus, for an exposure time t with an ideal detector of quantum efficiency q, the signal-to-noise ratio is $(nqt)^{1/2}$, where n represents the number of photons per second incident upon each image element. This signal-to-noise ratio describes the performance of a detector for a particular choice of the elemental area. In the case of a detector producing a continuous output instead of a time-integrated accumulation, t has the meaning of a time-constant.

If we want to compare the performance of one detector with that of another, it is convenient to define a figure of merit which is relatively independent of test conditions. Jones (1947, 1949a, b) has shown that most detectors fall into two classes in this respect. They are distinguished by the way in which the noise-equivalent power depends on the area and the time-constant or integration time of the detector. The noise-equivalent power is the amount of radiant flux required to produce a signal response of the same size as the noise. The minimum value of the noise-equivalent power for detectors of Class I is given by

$$P_1(\text{min.}) = (4\sigma T^4 kT)^{1/2} \left(\frac{A}{t}\right)^{1/2},$$ (1)

where k is the Boltzmann constant, σ is the Stefan-Boltzmann radiation constant, T is the absolute temperature, A is the effective sensitive area per receiving channel or image element, and t is the time constant or the integration time. Class I detectors include all photoemissive tubes limited by shot noise, radio antennae limited by temperature noise, and the Golay pneumatic heat detector.

According to an empirical estimate made by Havens (1946), the minimum value of the noise-equivalent power for detectors of Class II at room temperature is given by

$$P_2(\text{min.}) \approx 3 \times 10^{-12} \left(\frac{A}{t^2}\right)^{1/2},$$ (2)

where P_2 is in watts if A is in square millimeters and t is in seconds. Class II detectors include photographic emulsions, bolometers, and thermocouples.

It is mainly the difference in dependence of $P(\text{min.})$ upon t that distinguishes the two classes of detectors. There are some subtleties in the assignment of detectors to these two classes and in specifying the limits under which the formulae hold; the reader is referred to the literature already cited.

The figures of merit for detectors of the two classes have been defined (Jones 1947, 1949a, b), respectively, by

$$M_1 = 2.76 \times 10^{-12} P^{-1} A^{1/2} t^{-1/2}$$ (3)

and

$$M_2 = 3 \times 10^{-12} P^{-1} A^{1/2} t^{-1}$$ (4)

for the observed noise-equivalent power P in watts, the area A in square millimeters, and the time constant t in seconds. The constant in equation (3) is chosen to yield $M_1 = 1$ for a perfect Class I detector at room temperature ($300°$ K). Figures of merit for various detectors as a function of wave length are illustrated in Figures 1a and 1b.

Relationships between the figure of merit and various familiar parameters can sometimes be derived. Jones (1955) finds, for example, that the figure of merit for panchromatic emulsions under monochromatic illumination at 4200 A is given by

$$M_2 = \text{Constant} \times \frac{1}{G} \frac{dD}{dE},$$ (5)

where G is the Selwyn (1930, 1950) granularity coefficient, D is photographic density, and E is exposure. By appropriate choice of units, the constant can be specified.

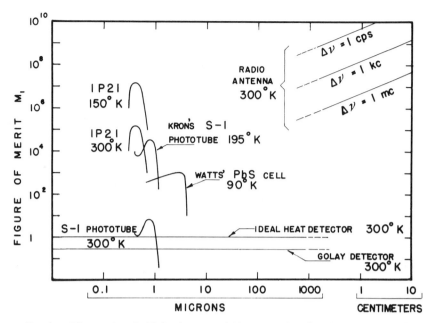

FIG. 1a.—Figures of merit M_1 for detectors of Class I as a function of wave length. The co-ordinate scales are logarithmic. Note the advantage gained by cooling the 1P21 and S1 photo-tubes. (From Jones 1953.)

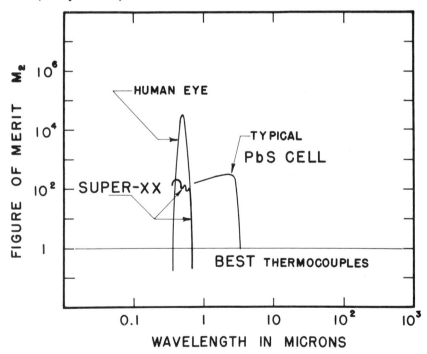

FIG. 1b.—Figures of merit M_2 for detectors of Class II as a function of wave length. The co-ordinate scales are logarithmic. (From Jones 1953.)

§ 3. ASTRONOMICAL LIMITATIONS

Neither the figure of merit nor the signal-to-noise ratio under an arbitrary condition is sufficient by itself to specify the threshold which a detector can reach in astronomical practice. Various parameters, some due to natural phenomena and some due to instrumental effects, must be taken into account. The natural phenomena affecting instrument thresholds are familiar to every astronomer. These include "seeing," scintillation, night-sky radiation, and atmospheric extinction. The general characteristics of these phenomena deserve mention because we shall want to deal with them quantitatively.

"Seeing" is the smearing and dancing of telescopic images caused by refractive deflection of starlight as it passes through turbulent strata in the earth's atmosphere. It is mainly a lower-atmosphere phenomenon, because the differential angles of refraction are dependent on air density as well as on the degree of turbulence. At elevations attained by balloons (Schwarzschild, Rogerson, and Evans 1958) the effect is much reduced. Typical amplitudes of refractive deflection encountered by earth-bound telescopes are 1 or 2 seconds of arc. The greatest amplitudes occur at frequencies around a few cycles per second. The refracting cells of air typically range in size from a few centimeters to perhaps half a meter in diameter. The consequent manifestation of seeing at the focus of a small telescope is a relatively sharp image which dances around, while that at the focus of a large telescope is a fuzzy mass composed of many superposed images dancing out of phase with one another. The smearing effect is the same in both cases if the exposure time is more than a second or two. For large telescopes, seeing is the principal factor determining the size of an image element, i.e., the area A occupied by a star image. It is also often a limiting factor in determining what fraction of a stellar image can be squeezed through the slit of a spectrograph.

"Scintillation" is the amplitude modulation of starlight caused by turbulent strata very high in the earth's atmosphere. At high levels, the air is thin, and the contribution to the angular deflection of rays (seeing) is small. There is, however, a very long "lever arm" between the high strata and the telescope— long enough that the lateral displacements of rays become appreciable. The frequencies involved range from a few cycles to a few hundred cycles per second. Since the light and dark patches of this dancing schlieren pattern are typically a few centimeters across, the amount of light from a star received through a small aperture varies up and down by large amounts. This is what makes stars twinkle when observed with the naked eye. A telescope of large aperture, on the other hand, encompasses many light and dark patches simultaneously, so that the over-all amplitude modulation of the light delivered to the focus is small. In ordinary photoelectric photometry by the direct-current method, for instance, scintillation is often the principal source of noise at a small telescope but is rarely important at a large telescope.

Night-sky radiation provides a background (more literally a "foreground") against which faint images must be detected. It is also a formidable factor in the spectroscopy of faint objects, because the night-sky spectrum is not smooth. A substantial fraction, perhaps half, of the total night-sky radiation on a moonless night is produced by photochemical processes in the earth's ionosphere, and it typically varies 5 or 10 per cent from hour to hour. The rest includes sunlight scattered by interplanetary matter in the solar system (the zodiacal light is a feature of this component), scattered starlight, diffuse radiation of the galaxy, light from subthreshold stars, and light from other galaxies and intergalactic matter. Altogether, night-sky radiation sheds more light on the surface of the earth than all the resolved stars, nebulae, and galaxies combined. In the visual region of the spectrum it averages about fourth magnitude per square degree or twenty-second magnitude per square second of arc. Moonlight at quarter-phase adds roughly an equal amount, but at full phase it makes the sky more than ten times as bright. The sunlit sky is about fourth magnitude per square second of arc.

Atmospheric extinction is a function of wave length and air mass. Near the zenith the extinction at sea level is about 15 per cent at 5500 A if the air is very clear. It rises steeply in the blue and ultraviolet, becoming more than 90 per cent below 3000 A. Below 2900 A, observations can be made only from rockets and space vehicles traveling above the ozone layer—say above about 50 km. In the red region of the spectrum the extinction falls to less than 10 per cent, but the infrared is chopped up by absorption bands due mainly to water vapor and carbon dioxide. There are relatively transparent "windows" from 1.9 to 2.3, from 3 to 4, and from 8 to 14 μ.

Another natural limitation is encountered in the observation of faint sources in the infrared, namely, ambient thermal radiation. At room temperature, for example, objects have their maximum radiation at a wave length of about 10 μ. In that region everything, including the optics of the telescope, becomes a significant radiant source.

Instrumental parameters affecting the detection and measurement of faint sources include quantum efficiency, integration time, storage capacity, background excludability, instrument noise, and optical geometry. These, together with the natural phenomena discussed in the foregoing paragraphs, can be used to predict thresholds attainable with various telescopes and detectors.

§ 4. THE DETECTION OF FAINT STARS AGAINST THE SKY BACKGROUND

Let us first consider the detection of a faint star against the sky background (Baum 1955a) and let us assume that the integration or exposure time is long in comparison with the fluctuations due to seeing and scintillation. The following quantities will be involved:

n = Average number of eligible unscattered photons per second received per unit area at the surface of the earth from a faint star.

N = Average number of eligible photons per second received per unit area at the surface of the earth from unit solid angle of the sky background.

t = Effective integration time.

q = Average effective quantum efficiency in terms of *independent* registered events per eligible photon received during an exposure. For a photoemissive cathode, q is not a function of t, but for a photographic emulsion it is.

β = Average number of instrument-background events per second per unit area (referred to the optical focus of the telescope) during an exposure—for example, thermionic emission from a photocathode or the time average of chemical fog in a photographic emulsion.

k = A coefficient of recognition, or a coefficient of certainty, which relates the actual threshold of recognition to the statistical uncertainty expressed as a standard deviation.

a = Angular diameter of a star image (due mostly to seeing if the telescope is large) or of an image element.

D = Aperture of the telescope.

f = Focal length of the telescope.

m = Magnitude of the star within the wave-length band of the system.

M = Magnitude per unit solid angle of the sky background within the same wave-length band.

It will be convenient to neglect the factor $\pi/4$ in the considerations which follow.

The total number of photo-events (such as blackened photographic grains or ejected photoelectrons) due to the faint star will be $S = nD^2qt$, and the average number of background events within an equal area (i.e., within each picture element) will be $B = (ND^2q + \beta f^2)a^2t$. Since these quantities will, in general, be numerically large, the threshold value of nD^2qt should be approximately

$$(n D^2 q t)_0 = k \left[(N D^2 q + \beta f^2) a^2 t \right]^{1/2} . \tag{6}$$

This simply says that a threshold image must stand out above the noise by a factor k; that is, $S_0 = kB^{1/2}$.

Equation (1) holds if all photo-events are truly independent and statistically effective. In a sense this is guaranteed by the definition of q, but the situation becomes complex when the photo-events are not all of equal size, as, for example, in photographic emulsions, photoconductors, and photomultipliers. In the case of a photomultiplier, this effect is rather pronounced and is evaluated later in the chapter; it is found, however, that the effective reduction in q on this account is less than a factor of 2. Equation (6) should therefore lead to predictions that are correct to within a fraction of a magnitude.

The threshold contrast of surface brightness between the picture element occupied by the star image and its surroundings will simply be equation (6) divided by the number of background events per picture element; hence

$$(\text{Contrast})_0 = \left[\frac{k^2}{(ND^2q + \beta f^2)a^2t} \right]^{1/2} = kB^{-1/2}. \tag{7}$$

The magnitude of a star whose image is at the threshold will be given by

$$m_0 = M - 2.5 \log \left(\frac{n}{N} \right)_0 = M - 2.5 \log \left[a^2 (\text{Contrast})_0 (1 + R) \right], \tag{8}$$

where R is the ratio of instrument background βf^2 to sky background ND^2q. The substitution of equation (7) in equation (8) yields

$$m_0 = \text{Constant} + 0.5M - 2.5 \log a - 2.5 \log k$$
$$+ 1.25 \log (D^2 qt) - 1.25 \log (1 + R), \tag{9}$$

which is the formula for the unsaturated threshold. This formula says, for example, that the threshold will be 1 mag. fainter if the sky background becomes 2 mag. fainter or if the image diameter due to seeing decreases by a factor of 2.51 (i.e., by 1 mag.). When expressed on a linear scale instead of a magnitude scale, the coefficient of one-half associated with the sky magnitude means that the threshold for image recognition depends on the *square root* of the surface brightness of the night sky, provided that the instrument background is small and that statistical saturation is not approached.

Equation (9) should apply to photoelectric photometry, to visual observations with the human eye, to unsaturated observations with image tubes, and to ordinary lightly exposed photographs. In the photoelectric case, a represents the diameter of the focal-plane diaphragm, and the formula is in good agreement with photoelectric experience, provided that the integration time is long in comparison with scintillation fluctuations (as specified above) but not so long as to be seriously affected by variations in night-sky brightness.

The threshold of visual detection has been examined by Bowen (1947), who made experiments with apertures ranging from 8 mm to 1.5 meters and used a broad range of magnifying power in order to vary the apparent surface brightness of the sky background. He found that the conventional formula for the visual threshold (m varies as $5 \log D$) should be modified to include the magnification. He found that the data fitted the relationship

$$m_0 = 5.5 + 2.5 \log D + 2.5 \log \mathfrak{M}, \tag{10}$$

where D is the aperture in centimeters and $\mathfrak{M}$ is the magnification. Actually, the magnification $\mathfrak{M}$ does not affect the sky brightness M as defined above, but it does determine the apparent angle a in the sky resolved by the eye. Until a sufficient magnification is reached for the eye fully to resolve the seeing disk of a star image, the $-2.5 \log a$ term in equation (9) could be replaced by $+2.5 \log \mathfrak{M}$. In other words, equation (10) is a special case of equation (9). As one would expect, Bowen found no further gain in threshold after the magnification became large enough to lose control of a.

The threshold for image-tube observations should be given by equation (9) if the exposures do not saturate the storage capacity of an image-tube system. If the integration time t can be made indefinitely long, one can reach any threshold desired simply by having the patience to continue the process long enough. Thus the problem becomes that of accommodating the amount of information accumulated without saturating the storage capacity of the system.

Since, depending on circumstances, the quantum efficiency q of a photo-emissive cathode is between 10 and 100 times greater than that of a photographic emulsion, the use of an ideal image tube in place of a photographic plate should theoretically be equivalent to a three- to tenfold increase in the aperture D. In equal exposure times it should theoretically be possible to attain the same magnitude threshold with an image tube at a 20-inch telescope as one can now reach by unaided photography with the 200-inch telescope. It should also be possible to extend the threshold of the 200-inch telescope and thereby reach objects never before observed. An actual practical gain amounting to only a small fraction of the theoretical goal will be worth a big effort.

Equation (9) is applicable to photography only for very light exposures in which the storage capacity of the emulsion is not approached. The information-storage capacity is set by the overlapping of photographic grains. This overlapping causes many of the grains to be ineffective statistically when appreciable densities are reached.

The ultimate threshold of a system is approached when the effective exposure t approaches its limiting value due to the finite storage capacity of the medium upon which the picture is registered. Let E represent the maximum number of statistically effective photo-events that can populate a unit area at the focus. This means that the saturated value of $B = (ND^2q + \beta f^2)a^2t$ is simply $B_s = a^2 f^2 E$. Substituting this in equations (7) and (8), we obtain the statistically saturated threshold,

$$m_s \approx M - 2.5 \log a - 2.5 \log k + 2.5 \log f$$
$$+ 1.25 \log E - 2.5 \log(1 + R). \tag{11}$$

In this case the threshold varies directly with sky brightness, but seeing has the same effect as before. The most remarkable feature of this saturated case is that the ultimate threshold does *not* depend on the telescope aperture; it is a function of focal length only. It also does not depend on the quantum efficiency of the receiver or on the time required for this statistical saturation to be reached, except insofar as the latter may or may not be attainable in practice.

Ordinary photographs provide a good quantitative test of equation (11). As an cxample, we can compute the theoretical threshold for an Eastman 103a-O plate which is "fully exposed" at the prime focus of the 200-inch telescope during good seeing on a moonless night. Take $M \approx -4.4$ mag. per steradian,

$a \approx 5 \times 10^{-6}$ radian, $f = 1855$ cm, and $E \approx 5 \times 10^6$ granulations per square centimeter. For a coefficient of certainty $k = 5$, the predicted threshold is $m_s \approx 23.7$ mag. (blue), which is in agreement with the photoelectrically checked value of the photographic threshold observed under the conditions cited.

For large telescopes, seeing is the predominant factor in determining the size of a stellar image. For small telescopes, however, the effective angular image diameter a depends on the focal length because of the finite resolving power of the detector; specifically, a varies as $1/f$. In equation (11) the a and f terms then combine to give $+5 \log f$, which is the threshold dependence most commonly quoted.

Figure 2 shows a rough comparison of saturated photographic thresholds for the principal telescopes at Mount Wilson and Palomar Observatories; they are plotted here against their focal lengths on a logarithmic scale. The three circles represent the 18-inch Schmidt, the 48-inch Schmidt, and the 200-inch reflector at Palomar, while the two crosses represent the 60-inch and 100-inch reflectors

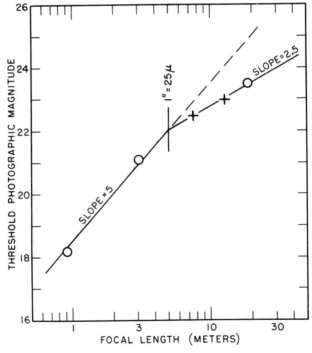

Fig. 2.—Relationship between the limiting photographic magnitude and the focal length of a telescope. The points represent the observed limits of the five telescopes at Mount Wilson and Palomar, while the solid lines represent theoretical prediction. The data were all adjusted to a particular set of standard conditions, namely, seeing = 1 second of arc; sky brightness, $m_{pg} = 22.2$ per square second of arc; and plates = Eastman 103a-O. (Fig. 5 from Baum 1955a.)

at Mount Wilson. The observed thresholds have all been chosen for (or adjusted to) a particular set of conditions, so that all parameters except focal length are effectively identical; specifically, these conditions include a night-sky brightness of 22.2 blue mag. per square second of arc, a seeing of 1 second of arc, a certainty of recognition close to 100 per cent, and the use of Eastman 103a-O emulsion. Owing to the proximity of the city lights of Los Angeles and Pasadena, the two Mount Wilson telescopes never actually reach the extrapolated thresholds necessarily assigned to them in this diagram. Although it is difficult to specify thresholds with any precision, the results here seem to be consistent with theory. It is certainly evident, for example, that the line of slope 5, representing the conventional 5 log f dependence for small telescopes, is grossly in error if extrapolated by the dashed line to long focal lengths. According to theory, the 2.5 log f dependence should commence when the focal length becomes long enough for the minimum image diameter to be determined mainly by seeing instead of by the resolving power of the emulsion, and this is indeed what Figure 2 shows.

Not only are we often up against the statistically saturated case in conventional photography, but we shall also need to be aware of it in predicting the performance of image-tube systems. Merely increasing the quantum efficiency q of the receiver without increasing its storage capacity will gain *nothing* toward discriminating fainter images against the sky; an increase in q is only a practical convenience which makes the reception of more information possible within reasonable exposure times.

§ 5. THE DETECTION OF DIFFUSE IMAGES

If the object is diffuse instead of stellar, equations (9) and (11) are not convenient to use unless the object happens to approximate a small disk of uniform brightness. In such a case, a can be taken to represent its diameter. Most extended astronomical objects, however, are neither uniform nor sharply bounded. It is necessary to detect and measure their fainter portions as well as their brighter portions. The signal-to-noise nature of the problem was recognized long ago by H. D. Curtis (1918), who correctly attached more importance to photographic granularity than to speed.

A good example of this problem is the familiar but difficult task of assigning integrated magnitudes to galaxies. The image of a typical galaxy consists of a bright nucleus surrounded by a diffuse body whose surface brightness tapers off to lower and lower values with increasing radius. In some types of galaxies, of course, various spiral or irregular features are superimposed upon this, but the underlying body always fades into tenuous outskirts having no definite boundary. It has often been tempting to examine the best photographs in hand at any particular time and to try assigning boundaries or diameters to the galaxy images on them. As better photographic plates have become available, larger and larger boundaries have been "discovered." Figure 3, which is a plot of the diameter assigned to Messier 32 as a function of the year of observation, shows in an amusing way how the data tell us more about the threshold of detection than about the object involved.

The limit of detection and the accuracy of measurement in the faint parts of a diffuse image, such as that of a galaxy, will be a function of the size of the area for which information is desired. If in a particular region of the image incident upon the detector there are Nq photo-events per second per unit area, then the total number of photo-events recorded in time t within an area A will be $NqAt$. For an ideal receiver the minimum distinguishable amount between two neighboring areas will accordingly be $k(2NqAt)^{1/2}$, where k is the coefficient of certainty as used earlier. The factor of 2 vanishes when many neighboring areas are intercompared.

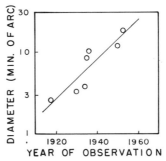

Fig. 3.—The assigned diameter of Messier 32 plotted against the year of observation

Let us apply this to the case of an E0 elliptical galaxy and let us assume, as available photoelectric measurements suggest, that the surface brightness in the outskirts tapers off roughly as the inverse square of the distance from the nucleus. In the outskirts the contribution of the galaxy will be small in comparison with that of the background; consequently, we are dealing with a uniform background illumination upon which small progressive increments are superposed. Let n represent the incremental number of photons per second per unit area. If n is to stand out with a coefficient of certainty k above the background, then

$$nqAt = k(NqAt)^{1/2} \tag{12}$$

Adopting $n = Cr^{-2}$, we find that

$$A = \frac{k^2 N r^4}{C^2 qt}. \tag{13}$$

Equation (13) says that, for a specified relative accuracy or coefficient of certainty k, the size of the area sampled with an ideal receiver would need to be made larger toward the outskirts in proportion to r^4 if the dwell time t is the same at all radii. This is very far from what is done when an ordinary microphotometer with a constant aperture is used for scanning the photographic image of a galaxy. It is no wonder in such a case that the tracing seems to vanish rapidly into the noise at large radii, where it gives a false impression of defining a boundary. Since it is not convenient to increase the size of the sampled area in proportion to so high a power as r^4, the practical means for obtaining a sufficiently large number of photo-events at large radii is to bring together the results from many photographs or to make direct photoelectric measurements in which a much greater integration time is spent at large radii than at small radii. If, for example, a certain integration time t_1 must be spent to determine the surface brightness with the desired accuracy at a radius r_1, then an integration time $16t_1$ must be spent to achieve the same accuracy at a radius $2r_1$ if a focal-plane diaphragm of the same size is used. Although the increase in required time is less extreme if larger diaphragm sizes are used at large radii, it is evident that the difficulty of measurement will increase steeply with increasing radius in objects of the kind described and that by far the biggest share of the observing time must be devoted to determining the outermost points.

§ 6. THE DETECTION OF SPECTRA

The limits of detection in spectroscopy can be broken down into two distinct problems. One of these concerns the faintness of objects reachable with various telescopes and spectrographs if the desired dispersion is specified. The other problem concerns the minimum strength of a feature which can be recognized within a spectrum. Since the characteristics of spectrographs are discussed by Bowen elsewhere in this volume, it will suffice here to state the threshold considerations very briefly.

When we speak of a threshold magnitude in connection with stellar spectra, we are concerned with a different kind of threshold than that which limits the detection of star images against the sky background. It is not sufficient merely to detect the barest trace of a stellar spectrum. We must also be able to recognize and measure features within it. A complete reduction of the problem to terms of photo-event statistics is possible but clumsy. It is simpler to make an analysis in terms of an operational threshold based on practical experience.

The magnitude threshold of a spectrograph can be defined by

$$m_0 = \text{Constant} + 2.5 \log(\mathfrak{S}\, g\, q t), \qquad (14)$$

where $\mathfrak{S}$ is the speed given by Bowen's (1952) formulae, g is the optical transmission of the telescope and spectrograph (not counting the slit), q is the effective quantum efficiency of the detector, and t is the exposure time. The constant must be chosen in accordance with the units used for various parameters. Bowen has shown that the speed $\mathfrak{S}$ must be differently defined under each of three different conditions of practical interest. These three are (1) star image broader than the slit of the spectrograph and the spectrum unwidened (i.e., star not trailed along the length of the slit during the exposure); (2) star image broader than the slit of the spectrograph and the spectrum widened by trailing; and (3) slit broader than the star image (so that most of the light passes into the spectrograph) and the spectrum widened by trailing.

The first of these is the case commonly encountered in high-dispersion spectroscopy of stars and in the spectroscopy of extended objects. Substituting Bowen's speed $\mathfrak{S}$ in equation (14) and adopting a notation consistent with the present chapter, we obtain, for the blue magnitude reachable in t seconds,

$$m_1 \approx -3 + 2.5 \log \left(\frac{\Delta d^2 K^3 g q t}{\psi^2 a^2} \right), \tag{15}$$

where Δ is the width (microns) of a monochromatic slit image at the detector, d is the aperture (centimeters) of the collimeter beam, K is the linear dispersion (A/mm) of the spectrograph, ψ is the angular dispersion (A/radian), and a is the angular diameter (radians) of the star image due to seeing and other effects. The angular dispersion ψ is Kf, where f is the camera focal length.

If the spectrum is widened to W microns, then

$$m_2 \approx -8 + 2.5 \log \left(\frac{\Delta d K^2 D g q t}{W \psi a} \right), \tag{16}$$

where D is the aperture of the telescope in centimeters.

In the third case, when all the light passes through the slit, we find

$$m_3 \approx +2.5 \log \left(\frac{K D^2 g q t}{W} \right). \tag{17}$$

In all three cases, g, q, and t play the same roles, but the other parameters enter in different ways.

The use of these formulae can be illustrated by an example. Let us consider Bowen's case 2 for an 8-hour photographic exposure with the 36-inch camera of the Palomar coudé spectrograph:

$\Delta = 20\,\mu, \qquad d = 30\text{ cm}, \qquad K = 9\text{ A/mm}, \qquad D = 500\text{ cm},$

$g = 0.2, \qquad q = 0.002 \text{ (long-exposure photograph)},$

$t = 3 \times 10^4 \text{ (about 8 hours)}, \qquad W = 100\,\mu, \qquad \psi = 8300\text{ A/radian},$

$a = 5 \times 10^{-6} \text{ radian (1 second of arc)}.$

From these we obtain $m_2 \approx 11.6$ mag. This is approximately the limit reached in practice under the conditions cited.

The other spectrographic problem, namely, that of discriminating features within a spectrum, can be expressed in the same terms as those applied above to the detection and measurement of extended objects. In other words, the ultimate threshold will be set by $k(nqAt)^{1/2}$. Thus, if the spectrum is scanned by an impartial detector such as a photoelectric photometer (or if the spectrum is photographed and later scanned by a microphotometer), the minimum depth of a feature that can be detected will be related to the area which it covers in the spectrum. One threshold feature twice as broad as another need be only 0.7 as deep, in order to be recognized with equal certainty. In the same way, a slower rate of spectrum scanning with a photoelectric photometer will gain accuracy in inverse proportion to the square root of the rate. If a spectrum is photographed and later analyzed with a recording microphotometer, the advantage of a wide spectrum as compared with a narrow spectrum will be roughly in proportion to the square root of the width. When the photograph of a spectrum is examined visually, the same principles continue to apply, but various factors, such as the magnification under which the plate is viewed, will influence the degree to which effective use is made of the information fundamentally available on the plate.

If a feature, such as an interstellar line, is both faint and narrow, the only way to improve the accuracy of its measurement with a particular instrument and detector is to increase the integration time t. For example, one can obtain several photographs and combine the results, one can scan the spectrum photoelectrically at a slower rate, or one can use photoelectric integrating methods with longer integration times. When a spectrum is photographed with an image-tube system having a higher quantum efficiency than an unaided photographic emulsion, the theoretically available gain will be proportional to the square root of the ratio of the quantum efficiencies if the exposure time is the same.

Another severe problem in spectrographic detection is that encountered when the redshifts of very distant galaxies are sought. A substantial portion of the light entering the slit of the spectrograph is then night-sky radiation. A photograph of a spectrum is covered over its full width by lines and bands of the night sky, the spectrum of the distant galaxy being only a faint superimposed stripe running along the center of this night-sky spectrum. Fundamentally, the limit is again set by the amount of information recorded, that is, by the number of photographic grains per unit wave length, but in this case there is the practical problem that the background has many features of its own.

An experiment was made to determine whether there was any significant gain in the recognizability of features in the spectrum of a faint galaxy when the spectrum of the night sky was canceled by photographic subtraction. Figure 4, a, is a reproduction of a faint galaxian spectrum kindly supplied by M. L. Humason. Figure 4, b, is a composite photograph prepared from Humason's plate by W. C. Miller. The original plate was first projected onto another plate at a much enlarged scale. A reversed copy of this enlargement was then contact-printed onto a third plate. The resulting positive and negative enlargements were superimposed with a small displacement at right angles to the direction of dispersion. Therefore, in Figure 4, b, the spectrum of the faint galaxy appears twice, in one case darker than its background and in the other case lighter than its background. The features of the night-sky spectrum have largely canceled themselves out. The uniform gray strip across the top of Figure

4, *b*, is the canceled image of an optical-density step wedge, which was combined with the first enlargement to check on the quality of the cancellation achieved. It is evident that the threshold gains attainable by a technique of this kind are relatively small in comparison with those that might be obtained by substantial increases in the quantum efficiencies and storage capacities of detectors. Nevertheless, in a problem of this kind it is important to squeeze out every possible bit of information in the observations available.

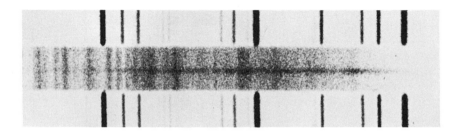

a

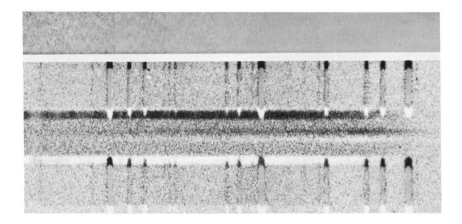

b

Fig. 4.—*a*, The spectrum of a very faint galaxy superimposed upon the spectrum of the night sky. Photographed at the prime focus of the 200-inch Hale telescope by M. L. Humason. Enlarged 27 times. *b*, Composite photograph prepared by W. C. Miller by combining a positive and a negative enlargement of the spectrum in *a*. The positive was displaced vertically with respect to the negative, so that the night-sky spectrum was canceled, while the galaxy spectrum was not. The uniformly gray strip across the top of the figure is the simultaneously canceled reproduction of a density step wedge.

§ 7. ASTRONOMICAL DETECTORS

Thus far we have been concerned with the thresholds attainable in various types of astronomical observations if detectors of certain characteristics are used. It remains now to discuss in more detail the characteristics of detectors appropriate for those applications.

Detectors which have been used in astronomical work include the human eye, photographic emulsions, photoemissive cathodes, photoconductive cathodes, thermocouples and thermopiles, bolometers, Golay cells, thermoluminescent phosphors, and photoionization counters. From Figures 1a and 1b we can see which detector should be the best to use at any desired wave length. The same problem has been discussed by Whitford (1955) on the basis of practical astronomical experience. His conclusions are summarized in Table 1. Perhaps the S4 and S11 photocathodes will soon be superseded by the multialkali photocathode, whose range of superiority over the S1 photocathode extends to about 0.73 μ.

TABLE 1

BEST PHOTOMETRIC DETECTORS IN VARIOUS WAVE-LENGTH RANGES
ACCORDING TO WHITFORD (1955)

Wave-Length Range (μ)	Best Detectors	Threshold
0.31– 0.60...	S4 and S11 photocathodes	Set by photo-event statistics
0.6 – 1.0....	S1 photocathode	Set by photo-event statistics
1 – 3.....	Lead sulfide cell	Factor of 10 short of ideal
8 –14.....	Heat-sensitive detectors	Factor of 10 short of ideal

Photoconductive cells, thermocouples and thermopiles, bolometers, and Golay cells are all primarily of value in the infrared part of the spectrum. Their properties and the techniques for their use have been discussed by Smith, Jones, and Chasmar (1957). Thermoluminescent phosphors and photoionization chambers are of specialized interest; they have been used for ultraviolet observations from high-altitude rockets (Newell 1953).

The human eye, photographic emulsions, and photoemissive cathodes are the detectors most widely used in astronomy. Their approximate quantum efficiencies are plotted as a function of wave length in Figure 5, and their properties are summarized in the pages which follow.

7.1. THE HUMAN EYE

The quantum efficiency of the human eye can be estimated in two ways, one based on the visual stellar thresholds of telescopes (Russell 1917) and the other based on laboratory experiments (Reeves 1918; Knoll, Tousey, and Hulburt 1946). Data from both methods lead to essentially the same result. If a time constant of 0.1 second is assumed, the detective quantum efficiency of the dark-adapted human eye is found to be about 3 per cent. This means that the signal-to-noise performance of the eye is equivalent to that of an ideal detector which produces one recorded photo-event for each 33 incident photons within the wave-length band to which it is sensitive. It is very probable that more than 3 per cent of the incident photons participate in producing visual response, but it is the over-all performance of the eye as a signal-to-noise detector with which we are concerned here.

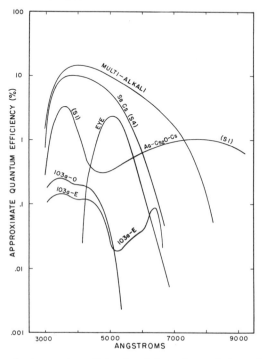

FIG. 5.—Approximate quantum efficiencies of three photoemissive cathodes, of the dark-adapted human eye, and of two photographic emulsions. These estimates are based on the use of these detectors under conditions typically encountered in astronomical practice.

Figure 5 shows that the maximum quantum efficiency of the dark-adapted eye occurs in the vicinity of 5100 A. Owing to the Purkinje effect, this value differs from the normally assigned wave length of maximum visual response. At extremely low light-levels the sensitivity of the eye to blue light becomes enhanced relative to its sensitivity to red light.

The eye performs as a photon detector in accordance with equation (9) when the field brightness is below 10^{-5} lambert. This value represents a brightness a little greater than that of the night sky under illumination by the full moon. For brightnesses above 10^{-2} lambert the eye behaves as though its information capacity is saturated in accordance with equation (11). Between 10^{-5} and 10^{-2}

lambert there is a transition region. The visual recognition of astronomical objects has been reviewed by Roach and Jamnick (1958).

A few other characteristics of the human eye may be of interest. The focal length is about 20 mm, and the maximum aperture under dark adaptation is about 8 mm. The fovea centralis, which is the region of highest acuity, covers a field of only $0°7$. Within that region the resolving power is about 1 minute of arc. At high brightness levels, where foveal vision comes into use, the threshold is determined by the minimum recognizable contrast in surface brightness. At the boundary between two extended areas, the minimum recognizable contrast is about 2 per cent. If the two areas are not immediately adjacent or if they subtend a very small angle, the contrast sensitivity of the eye is less favorable.

The time constant of the eye is a function of the brightness level. At very low brightness levels it is, as already noted, about 0.1 second. At higher brightness levels the time constant is shorter. It is only 0.025 second, for instance, at 10^{-2} lambert.

As an instrument, the eye behaves as though it had an arbitrarily variable gain control capable of adjusting itself automatically to a condition under which the output signal is of comfortable strength. This ability to adapt itself to the average brightness of a scene makes the eye a convenient instrument for ordinary daily needs, but it also robs us of the ability to use our eyes for judging absolute brightness. It is possible, for example, to vary the level of illumination in a room over a wide range without changing the visual appearance of the room.

7.2. PHOTOGRAPHIC EMULSIONS

Although photographic emulsions are among the commonest detectors of light, their quantum efficiencies have been the subject of much dispute. One reason for confusion is that the quantum efficiency of a photographic emulsion depends on the condition under which it is used. A single number does not suffice.

A typical photographic emulsion is a light-colored translucent layer about 25 μ thick. When light is incident upon it, a substantial fraction of the light is diffusely reflected, a similar amount is diffusely transmitted, and only about 10 per cent is actually absorbed by the photographic grains in the emulsion. Moreover, in order for a photographic grain to be rendered developable, it must absorb more than one photon. It has been estimated that several—perhaps as many as 10—photons must be absorbed by a grain if it is to turn black during development (Webb 1941, 1948; Webb and Evans 1941). Thus it is evident that one blackened grain is the end product of about 100 photons initially incident upon the photographic emulsion.

But this is not the whole story. In a typical application a photographic exposure might be carried to the point that 10 per cent of the total number of grains in the emulsion have absorbed enough photons to turn black upon development. This means that many of the incident photons are absorbed by grains which never reach their quotas for blackening. As a result, there will generally have been more than 100 photons incident upon the emulsion for every grain that is actually blackened. We can therefore expect the quantum efficiency of a photographic emulsion to be less than 1 per cent, perhaps sometimes as low as 0.1 per cent.

This prediction of photographic quantum efficiency can be verified directly by exposing a photographic emulsion to a known amount of light and counting the number of blackened grains that result. For long exposures to faint light, it is indeed found that "fast" emulsions of the type used in astronomical work have quantum efficiencies as low as 0.1 or 0.2 per cent (Argyle 1955; Baum 1955a).

Thus far we have concerned ourselves with a quantum efficiency judged from the average number of incident photons required to produce a blackened grain. Owing to the fact, however, that the grains are not all of exactly equal size and that many of them tend to hide or partly hide behind one another when appreciable densities are reached, the information content of an actual photograph will be a little less than that of an ideal receiver having the same number of recorded photo-events per unit area. Since the quantum efficiency is of interest insofar as it describes the ability of a detector to receive and record information, we can define the effective quantum efficiency of an actual detector as being that value which an ideal detector would need to have in order to yield the same amount of information under the same circumstances. Using data supplied by the Eastman Kodak Company, Jones (1958) has derived effective quantum efficiencies of several emulsions exposed to different densities. The quantum efficiencies of three typical emulsions are plotted as a function of photographic density in Figure 6. Similar studies of this problem include those by Fellgett (1953, 1958) and by Zweig, Higgins, and MacAdam (1958).

An interesting feature revealed by Figure 6 is that photographic emulsions reach their highest effective quantum efficiencies at densities less than 0.2. This is a much lower density than that of a "full exposure" in ordinary astronomical practice. In a so-called full exposure the average density within the area of interest is usually in the range between 0.5 and 1.0. In Figure 6 we note that a density of 0.6, for instance, corresponds to quantum efficiencies that are lower than the maxima by factors of 4 or more.

Why, then, do astronomers who seek faint thresholds make a practice of exposing plates to such high densities? The reason is that a typical photographic emulsion has its maximum contrast detectivity in the density range just below the linear part of the Hurter-Driffield curve (Branscomb 1951), say between 0.5 and 1.0. In other words, a full exposure is one which contains as much information as it is possible to cram into a single exposure. If the exposure is either lighter or darker, it has a poorer threshold of detection. It is evident from Figure 6 that an astronomer would theoretically be better off if, instead of making a full exposure, he devoted the same total time to a sequence of several short exposures yielding average densities around 0.2. If the results were then combined under proper circumstances by photographic superposition in the laboratory the information content of the composite picture would be several times that of a single full exposure requiring the same total exposure time.

There is, of course, no reason that the process of collecting a sequence of light-exposures need be terminated when a total time equal to that of a full exposure has been reached. In principle, the process can be continued without

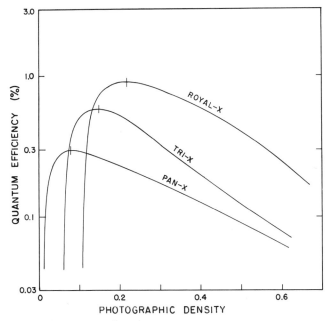

FIG. 6.—Quantum efficiencies of three photographic emulsions studied by R. C. Jones (1958). Maximum efficiencies occur at much lower densities than those to which astronomical plates are commonly exposed.

limit until the total accumulated information brings any desired threshold within reach. The only limitation is the amount of time and effort that the observer is willing to spend at the telescope. Ideally, the threshold of detection should vary inversely as the square root of the number of exposures combined. Although the process of superposition in the laboratory is tedious with present makeshift procedures, it should not be difficult to design convenient apparatus for initially exposing and later superimposing sequences of plates in proper registration; the threshold gains thus available may be substantial.

Since the purpose of combining an exposure sequence is to exceed the amount of information that can be crammed onto a single full exposure, it is evident that the plate onto which the composite picture is registered must be able to contain more information per picture element than the original plates do. This can be accomplished in either of two ways: either (1) the composite plate can have a fine-grained emulsion because its sensitivity does not matter, or (2) the composite plate can be produced on an enlarged scale.

At first sight it might appear that either a fine-grained emulsion or an enlarged scale could be used directly at the telescope to achieve the same result. There are, however, two practical difficulties that tend under most circumstances to make such a procedure less effective than the composite technique proposed above. In the first place, not only are fine-grained emulsions slower in terms of a density-exposure relationship, but they tend to have lower fundamental quantum efficiencies than coarse-grained emulsions. In the second place, extended exposures at a much enlarged scale are likely to incur a decrease in efficiency due to reciprocity failure.

To say that a photographic emulsion exhibits reciprocity failure is merely another way of saying that the quantum efficiency is dependent on the exposure time. The reciprocity failure is often an important factor in long astronomical exposures, and much effort has gone into the pre-exposure treatment of plates for the purpose of reducing the reciprocity failure (Bowen and Clark 1940). The refrigeration of plates to low temperatures during exposure is also known to have a beneficial effect in this regard (Fellgett 1955). Astronomical experiments with refrigerated photography have recently been made by A. A. Hoag (1961).

Not only is composite photography of interest in connection with achieving optimum photographic quantum efficiency and increasing the amount of information accumulated in a final picture, but it also provides a method for improving the recognizability of a signal against a non-uniform background. An example of this was cited earlier in connection with the spectrographic measurement of very large redshifts (see Fig. 4, a and b). Composite photography can also be used to display selectively the differences between plates taken under different circumstances, such as plates taken at different epochs, in different colors, or in different senses of polarization (see, for example, Zwicky 1956).

7.3. Photoemissive Cathodes

In the foregoing paragraphs we reviewed various factors affecting the thresholds of visual and photographic observations. The third important class of observations are those made with photoelectric techniques, and the remainder of this chapter will be devoted to a discussion of the factors affecting the thresholds of photoelectric detection.

The three types of photoemissive cathodes plotted in Figure 5 are the ones of greatest astronomical interest. The most common of the three is the antimony-cesium photocathode, which has its peak sensitivity in the blue part of the spectrum. It is probably fair to say that more than three-fourths of present-day astronomical photoelectric photometry is done with phototubes having antimony-cesium photocathodes. One of the most common tubes of this type is the 1P21 photomultiplier. Observations in the near infrared region of the spectrum can be made with phototubes having cathodes of the cesium-oxide-silver type. Beyond 12,000 A it is necessary to rely upon cathodes of the photoconductive type.

Multialkali photocathodes are a recent development and are of great future interest because of their high quantum efficiency and relatively low dark emission. They are also attractive astronomically because of their sensitivity in the red region. The multialkali photocathode makes it possible to do faint photoelectric photometry in four standard colors with one tube, namely, ultraviolet, blue, photovisual, and red. The addition of the red is of astrophysical importance because photovisual-red color indices $(V - R)$ are less sensitive to line-blanketing effects than $B - V$ indices and are therefore useful, along with $U - B$ indices, in determining intrinsic characteristics of the stars observed.

In the case of photoemissive cathodes, it makes very little difference whether the quantum efficiency is derived from over-all signal-to-noise performance or simply from the number of photoelectrons ejected by a given number of incident photons. The reason for this is that a good photocathode by itself is a nearly perfect detector. The photoelectron flux is an accurately linear function of the incident light-flux over a very broad range of light-levels. The photo-events (ejections of photoelectrons by incident photons) are independent of one another and are all of the same size. In other words, any incident photon is just as likely to eject a photoelectron as any other incident photon, and the photoelectrons all contribute equally to the cathode current.

§ 8.   PHOTOMULTIPLIERS

In a photomultiplier, however, the situation becomes a little more complicated. Each photoelectron undergoes cascade multiplication inside the tube and comes out of the tube as a pulse of many (often about 10^6) electrons. If all the photoelectrons were multiplied by this process into pulses of exactly equal sizes, they would continue to contribute equally to the signal current, but in actual photomultipliers the amount of multiplication is very different from one photoelectron to another. As a result, the stream of pulses coming out of a photomultiplier tube includes a very broad range of sizes, some of the pulses contributing ten times as much to the photocurrent as others. Since the pulses are not of equal size, it is evident that the signal-to-noise performance of a photomultiplier will be lower when used in combination with an ordinary current-measuring or charge-collecting (condenser-integrator) system than when used in a system that counts the pulses with equal weight regardless of their sizes. This is the fundamental difference between pulse-counting techniques and current-measuring or charge-collecting techniques.

It is worthwhile to investigate this problem in some detail because it has an important bearing on the detection and the accuracy of measurement of faint

sources. A quantitative comparison of the two techniques can be made on the
basis of data obtained from pulse counts. Let us suppose that the output pulses
from a photomultiplier, after undergoing a suitable amount of additional amplification, are passed through a pulse-height analyzer. The heights of the amplified pulses are proportional to the amounts of multiplication they have individually received in the photomultiplier. The pulse-height analyzer is a discriminator circuit which passes all pulses above a prescribed height and absorbs
all those that are below that height. Following the discriminator are scaling circuits which count the number of pulses passed on to them in a given interval of
time. As the discriminator setting is varied, we can observe the relative numbers
of pulses whose heights exceed the minimum height passed by the discriminator.
This procedure yields a pulse-height distribution function such as that shown for
a 1P21 in Figure 7. There are, of course, two curves of interest. One curve represents the number of pulses per unit time due to dark emission in the photomultiplier, while the other curve represents the additional number of pulses per unit
time when the photocathode is exposed to a faint light-source.

The abscissa of Figure 7 is labeled in units of electron heights. On this scale,

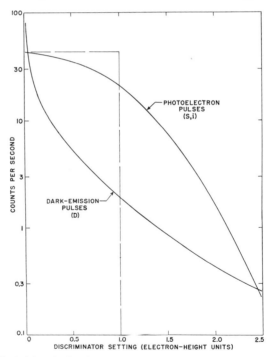

Fig. 7.—Pulse-height distribution function for 1P21 No. 2. The pulse count is plotted
against the discriminator setting. The amount of incident light was approximately equal to
that received from the moonless-sky background through a Corning 3384 yellow filter and a 10-
second-of-arc focal-plane diaphragm at the focus of a 30-inch telescope.

unity represents the height that all pulses would need to be if they were all identical with one another and if their combined charge were the same as that actually observed. In other words, if the ordinate were linear, the area under the dashed rectangle would be the same as the area under the curve due to photo-electrons.

The distribution of pulse heights due to dark emission is very different from that due to photoelectrons. One reason for this is that many of the dark-emission pulses originate at various stages along the multiplication chain and conse-quently undergo less multiplication than those which originate at the cathode. Photoelectron pulses, on the other hand, all originate at the photocathode, and they all undergo multiplication through the full length of the cascade multiplier. The curve representing photoelectron pulses can be extrapolated to a well-defined total at zero minimum pulse height. The curve representing dark-emis-sion pulses rises asymptotically as it approaches zero minimum pulse height, because the small pulses originating at later stages in the system become very numerous and blend eventually into ordinary amplifier noise. For this reason, one cannot actually operate a pulse-counting system with a discriminator set-ting of zero; the discriminator must be set at some low value that passes most of the photoelectron pulses but excludes the asymptotic rise of the numerous small dark-emission pulses.

When a very faint star is observed photoelectrically, much of the light reach-ing the photocathode is night-sky radiation admitted by the focal-plane dia-phragm of the photometer. We shall, in fact, be interested here mainly in the case of a star whose contribution to the photocurrent is small in comparison with that of the night sky.

Assuming, first, that the observation is made with a photomultiplier followed by a pulse-counting system, let S, i, and D represent the number of recorded pulses per second due, respectively, to night-sky radiation, to the faint star image, and to dark emission. Except for scale factors dependent on the bright-nesses of the sky and of the star, S and i vary with the setting of the discrimina-tor in accordance with the curve for photoelectrons in Figure 7, whereas D varies in accordance with the accompanying curve for dark emission.

When the faint star image is centered in the focal-plane diaphragm, the total pulse count in time t will be $(S + D + i)t$. When the focal-plane diaphragm is then offset to a vacant patch of sky neighboring the faint star image, the total pulse count will be $(S + D)t$. In practice (Baum 1955b), t is subdivided into a number of brief integration intervals taken alternately on $(S + D + i)$ and $(S + D)$. For large diaphragm sizes (large S) and long integration intervals, the non-constancy of the night-sky radiation will contribute appreciably to the error of measurement; but for small diaphragms and short integration intervals, the uncertainty in the difference $(S + D + i)t - (S + D)t$ will be

$$\epsilon it = (2S + 2D + i)^{1/2} t^{1/2} \tag{18}$$

in which ϵ represents the standard error. The probable error is 0.67 ϵ. If i is small in comparison with S and D, equation (18) yields

$$\frac{2}{\epsilon^2} \approx \left(\frac{i}{S}\right)^2 \left(\frac{S^2}{S+D}\right) t = \left(\frac{i}{S}\right)^2 \Re_c t \,. \tag{19}$$

For a particular star and a particular diaphragm (i.e., for a given value of i/S), the value of $2/\epsilon^2$ depends on an "information rate," $\Re_c$, and the total time, t. The photometer will be in optimum adjustment for the photometry of faint stars when the discriminator is set to yield the maximum value of the information rate $\Re_c$. It should be noted that this optimum adjustment is dependent on the diaphragm size selected. In other words, one first selects the minimum diaphragm size permitted by the quality of the seeing; there then exists an optimum setting of the discriminator which will minimize the error ϵ in the measurement of any faint star image ($i \ll S$).

The quantity $(i/s)^2 \Re_c$ in equation (19) is simply the square of the signal-to-noise ratio. The factor of 2 in the numerator on the left-hand side arises from the fact that a photoelectric photometer confines its attention to the amount of sky inscribed by the focal-plane diaphragm instead of simultaneously encompassing a large number of picture elements surrounding the star image as a photographic plate or an image tube does (see eq. [6]).

The time t represents the total amount of time devoted *each* to $(S + D + i)$ and to $(S + D)$. A two-channel photometer which receives these two quantities simultaneously enables one to attain a given value of t in half the total observing time required by a single-channel photometer. The effective saving in observing time will be even greater if the focal-plane diaphragm is large enough and if the integration intervals are long enough for bona fide sky-brightness variations to have a significant influence on the scatter in successive counts.

The shapes of the pulse-height distribution functions for 1P21 No. 2 in Figure 7 yield the information-rate curves in Figure 8a. The curve labeled "1.0" in Figure 8a is based on approximately the night-sky signal actually encountered when a focal-plane diaphragm subtending 6 seconds of arc and a Corning 3384 yellow (photovisual) filter are used at the prime focus of the 200-inch telescope on a moonless night. For this condition of observation we find that the maximum information rate, $\Re_c$, occurs at a discriminator setting of about 0.12 electron-height units.

The amount of night-sky signal associated with the foregoing example is relatively large. For similar observations with a smaller telescope, for work with narrow-band filters, or for many spectroscopic applications, one should assume a lower background light-level. If the background light-level is one-tenth of that assumed above, we see in Figure 8a that the optimum discriminator setting for 1P21 No. 2 occurs at 0.31 electron-height units; the ordinate scale of Figure 7 corresponds to this case. If the background light-level is only one one-hundredth, the optimum setting occurs at 0.62 unit. In this last case, for instance, a discriminator setting of 0.12 unit would result in an information rate only half as large as that available at the proper discriminator setting of 0.62 unit.

Figure 8b shows a family of information-rate curves for an infrared-sensitive photomultiplier kindly supplied by Professor A. Lallemand. The tube was in-closed in a sealed chamber filled with an atmosphere of water-free nitrogen, and the chamber was refrigerated with dry ice. The curves in Figure 8b indicate how the optimum discriminator setting and the maximum information rate depend on the potential applied to the tube. For the particular night-sky level investi-gated, we see that an operating potential of 2100 volts enables one to obtain information concerning faint images at a rate 2.5 times faster than at a potential of 1700 volts. We also see that there is little to be gained by using potentials above 2100 volts. These results are not readily apparent from a casual inspection of the raw data upon which Figure 8b is based; it is necessary to plot the infor-mation-rate curves before the situation becomes clear.

The performance characteristics of five infrared-sensitive photomultipliers are compared in Table 2. All five tubes have cesium-oxide-on-silver photocath-odes, and all were tested at the temperature of dry ice. The computation of the relative maximum information rates was based on the particular condition under

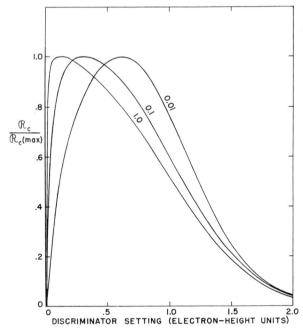

FIG. 8a.—Relative information rates of 1P21 No. 2 when used for the photometry of faint images or faint spectroscopic features against three different background light-levels (1.0, 0.1, 0.01). Note that the ordinate is a ratio; the absolute values of $\Re_c$ for the 0.01 level are much lower than those for the 1.0 level.

which infrared observations are currently being made at Palomar. Table 2 demonstrates clearly that photocathode sensitivities (or quantum efficiencies) do not by themselves tell us which tubes are better than others for a particular condition of observation. It is especially interesting to note that tube No. 3, whose photocathode sensitivity is less than one-third that of tube No. 1, has an information rate almost as high. Tube No. 3 is a Farnsworth 16-PM-1, and its dark emission is remarkably low; under most circumstances, the maximum information rate occurs at a discriminator setting below 0.1 electron-height unit, and the dark count at 0.1 unit is less than 10 electrons per minute!

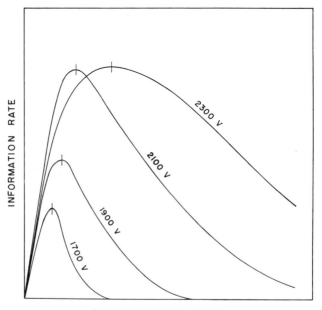

FIG. 8b.—Information rates of a Lallemand infrared-sensitive photomultiplier when various potentials are applied.

TABLE 2

RELATIVE PERFORMANCE CHARACTERISTICS OF FIVE
INFRARED-SENSITIVE PHOTOMULTIPLIERS

Tube No.	Relative Photocathode Sensitivity (q/q_3)	Relative Maximum Information Rate $[\mathfrak{R}_c(max.)/\mathfrak{R}_c(max.)_3]$	Tube No.	Relative Photocathode Sensitivity (q/q_3)	Relative Maximum Information Rate $[\mathfrak{R}_c(max.)/\mathfrak{R}_c(max.)_3]$
1........	3.2	1.1	4.......	2.3	0.4
2........	2.1	0.1	5.......	3.0	1.0
3........	1.0	1.0			

In conclusion, we now derive the information rate for a current-measuring or a charge-collecting system (Gardiner and Johnson 1955) and compare it with that of a pulse-counting system (Baum 1955b). For the purpose of this analysis we shall imagine the same photomultiplier to be used in both ways.

Let $\Delta S + \Delta D$ represent the number of sky-plus-dark pulses per unit time within an interval Δh at pulse height h. For a time constant or an integration time t, the root-mean-square fluctuation will be $(\Delta S + \Delta D)^{1/2}t^{1/2}$. The total "noise" in the anode current of the photomultiplier will be the combined effect of these fluctuations for all intervals Δh, the relative amplitude of the noise contributed to the anode current by each interval being proportional to h; therefore,

$$\text{Noise} = \left\{ \sum_{j} [h_{j}(\Delta S + \Delta D)_{j}^{1/2}t^{1/2}]^{2} \right\}^{1/2}. \tag{20}$$

Letting $\Delta h \rightarrow 0$, we have

$$(\text{Noise})^{2} = t \int_{0}^{S_{0}} h^{2}dS + t \int_{0}^{\infty} h^{2}d\,D. \tag{21}$$

By analogy with equation (18), we can write

$$\epsilon \left(\int_{0}^{i_{0}} h\,di \right) t = (2)^{1/2}(\text{Noise}), \tag{22}$$

from which it follows that

$$\frac{2}{\epsilon^{2}} \approx \left(\frac{i}{S} \right)^{2} \frac{\left(\int_{0}^{S_{0}} h\,dS \right)^{2}}{\left(\int_{0}^{S_{0}} h^{2}dS + \int_{0}^{\infty} h^{2}d\,D \right)} t. \tag{23}$$

Owing to the way in which the electron-height unit is defined, the integral of hdS is simply S_{0}. The information rate for current-measuring or condenser-integrating techniques, therefore, is

$$\Re_{d} = S_{0}^{2} \left(\int_{0}^{S_{0}} h^{2}dS + \int_{0}^{\infty} h^{2}d\,D \right)^{-1}. \tag{24}$$

The advantage of the pulse-counting method, then, is

$$\frac{\Re_{c}(\text{max.})}{\Re_{d}} = \left(\frac{S_{1}}{S_{0}} \right)^{2} \frac{\left(\int_{0}^{S_{0}} h^{2}dS + \int_{0}^{\infty} h^{2}d\,D \right)}{(S_{1} + D_{1})}, \tag{25}$$

which can be computed by graphical methods, using data such as those in Figure 7. In equation (25), S_{1} and D_{1} represent the sky count and dark count at the discriminator setting yielding the maximum value of the information rate $\Re_{c}$.

From the data in Figure 7 we can determine the manner in which $\Re_{c}$ (max.) and $\Re_{d}$ depend on the relative importance of the dark emission and the background light-level. While the pulse-height distribution-curve for photoelectrons is held fixed, the curve for dark-emission pulses can be shifted vertically by selected factors, and the corresponding values of $\Re_c$ (max.) and $\Re_d$ can be computed for each factor selected. The results are plotted in Figure 9 as a function of the discriminator settings (in electron-height units) at which the maximum values of $\Re_c$ occur. Also indicated on the abscissa of Figure 9 are the associated factors by which the dark emission was elevated relative to the background light-level; unity on this scale corresponds to the same case as that represented by the curve labeled "1.0" in Figure 8a.

Under the condition of operation mentioned in connection with the work at Palomar (200-inch telescope, Corning 3384 filter, and sky through a 6″ diaphragm), the values of $\Re_c$ (max.) and $\Re_d$ for 1P21 No. 2 are, respectively, 91 and 76 per cent of the theoretical $\Re_c$ (max.) for a perfect photomultiplier having no dark emission at all. In this particular case, the advantage of pulse counting (eq. [25]) is a factor of 1.2. If the same photomultiplier were used under different circumstances, the advantage of pulse counting would, in general, be a different factor; it could be either greater or less than 1.2.

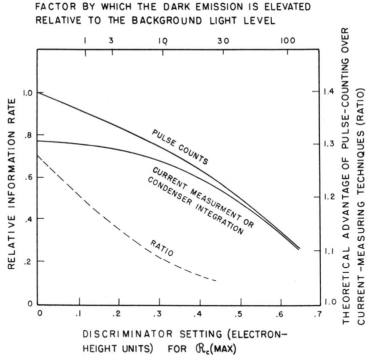

FIG. 9.—Theoretical advantage of the pulse-counting technique over current-measuring or condenser-integrating techniques for the photometry of faint images or faint spectroscopic features. These curves are based on data for 1P21 No. 2. Values of the abscissa depend on the relative importance of the dark emission and the background light-level (see the scale at the top).

For other kinds of photomultipliers, the advantage of pulse counting will tend to be greater than a factor of 1.2. This follows from the fact that the pulse-height distribution functions are usually less curved than the one in Figure 7. Factors approaching 2.0 have been found. An advantage of, say, 1.5 in the information rate is equivalent to a one-third saving in the observing time required to reach a desired accuracy. It is also equivalent to an advantage of 1.5 in quantum efficiency.

The theoretical advantage of pulse counting is, however, not the whole story. There are also some practical advantages. In the first place, the observations are directly available in digital form. No analogue conversion is required. In the second place, the actual performance of a pulse-counting system is so nearly perfect that the theoretical limits set by information rates and by sky-brightness variations can be taken essentially at face value. The truth of this can best be demonstrated by an example. Table 3 exhibits a list of 35 successive counts obtained with an EMI 6685 photomultiplier. Since the mean count was 42,301 per 100-second interval, the predicted theoretical value for the root-mean-square scatter in the counts is $(42,301)^{1/2} = 206$. The actual root-mean-square scatter is found to be 210, which is within 2 per cent of the theoretical prediction. It is doubtful whether either a current-measuring system or a charge-collecting (condenser-integrator) system could be made to perform as well. In the case of a

TABLE 3*

STATISTICAL FLUCTUATIONS IN REPEATED PULSE COUNTS WITH AN
EMI 6685 PHOTOMULTIPLIER AND A FAINT LIGHT-SOURCE

Source Count	Deviation from Mean	(Deviation)²	Source Count	Deviation from Mean	(Deviation)²
42229........	− 72	5184	42400........	+ 99	9801
42122........	−179	32041	42168........	−133	17689
42654........	+353	124609	42479........	+178	31684
42127........	−174	30276	42251........	− 50	2500
42074........	−227	51529	42522........	+221	48841
42657........	+356	126736	42230........	− 71	5041
42119........	−182	33124	42197........	−104	10816
42516........	+215	46225	42243........	− 58	3364
42204........	− 97	9409	42057........	−244	59536
41891........	−410	168100	42134........	−167	27889
42232........	− 69	4761	42147........	−154	23716
42172........	−129	16641	42563........	+262	68644
42454........	+153	23409	42465........	+164	26896
42589........	+288	82944	42282........	− 19	361
42080........	−221	48841			
42372........	+ 71	5041			
42811........	+510	260100	Mean.......	....	Mean
42360........	+ 59	3481	42301.......	....	44124
42319........	+ 18	324	√ =206......	....	√ =210

* Counting interval = 100 seconds each; dark-count contribution ∼ 1 per cent.

conventional current-measuring system which produces a graphical record, the results for a very faint star also depend critically on the personal judgment of the observer in extracting data from the record. Indeed, a star which is near the practical threshold of a pulse-counting system would yield a virtually unreadable record of the ordinary graphical kind.

REFERENCES

Argyle, P. E.	1955	*J.R.A.S. Canada*, **49**, 19.
Baum, W. A.	1955a	*Trans. I.A.U.*, **9**, 681.
	1955b	*Sky and Telescope*, **14**, 264 and 330.
Bowen, I. S.	1947	*Pub. A.S.P.*, **59**, 253.
	1952	*Ap. J.*, **116**, 1.
Bowen, I. S., and Clark, L. T.	1940	*J. Opt. Soc. America*, **30**, 508.
Branscomb, L. M.	1951	*J. Opt. Soc. America*, **41**, 255.
Curtis, H. D.	1918	*Pub. Lick Obs.*, Vol. **13**, Part I.
Fellgett, P. B.	1953	*J. Opt. Soc. America*, **43**, 271.
	1955	*Vistas in Astronomy*, ed. A. Beer (London and New York: Pergamon Press), **1**, 483.
	1958	*M.N.*, **118**, 224.
Gardiner, A. J., and Johnson, H. L.	1955	*Rev. Sci. Instr.*, **26**, 1145.
Havens, R.	1946	*J. Opt. Soc. America*, **36**, 355.
Hoag, A. A.	1961	*Pub. A.S.P.*, **73**, 301.
Jones, R. C.	1947	*J. Opt. Soc. America*, **37**, 879.
	1949a	*Ibid.*, **39**, 327.
	1949b	*Ibid.*, p. 344.
	1953	*Advances in Electronics*, ed. L. Marton (New York: Academic Press), Vol. **5**, Part I.
	1955	*Photog. Sci. Tech.*, Ser. II, **2**, 56 (No. 2).
	1958	*Photog. Sci. and Eng.*, **2**, 57 (No. 2).
Knoll, H. A., Tousey R., and Hulburt, E. O.	1946	*J. Opt. Soc. America*, **36**, 480.
Newell, H. E., Jr.	1953	*High Altitude Rocket Research* (New York: Academic Press).
Reeves, P.	1918	*Ap. J.*, **47**, 143.
Roach, F. E., and Jamnick, P. M.	1958	*Sky and Telescope*, **17**, 165.
Russell, H. N.	1917	*Ap. J.*, **45**, 60.
Schwarzschild, M., Rogerson, J. B., Jr., and Evans, J. W.	1958	*A.J.*, **63**, 313.
Selwyn, E. W.	1939	*Photog. J.*, **79**, 513.
	1950	*Photography in Astronomy* (Rochester, N.Y.: Eastman Kodak Co.), p. 72.

SMITH, R. A., JONES, F. E.,
   and CHASMAR, R. P.   1957   *The Detection and Measurement of Infrared Radia-
                                       tion* (Oxford: Clarendon Press).
WEBB, J. H.   1941   *J. Opt. Soc. America,* **31,** 348 and 559.
                               1948   *Ibid.,* **38,** 312.
WEBB, J. H., and
   EVANS, C. H.   1941   *J. Opt. Soc. America,* **31,** 355.
WHITFORD, A. E.   1955   *A.J.,* **60,** 22.
ZWEIG, H. J., HIGGINS,
   G. C., and MACADAM,
   D. L.   1958   *J. Opt. Soc. America,* **48,** 926.
ZWICKY, F.   1956   *Pub. A.S.P.,* **68,** 121.

CHAPTER 2

Spectrographs

I. S. BOWEN

Mount Wilson and Palomar Observatories
Carnegie Institution of Washington, California Institute of Technology

§ 1. INTRODUCTION

AN ASTRONOMICAL spectrograph is primarily an instrument for spreading out the light from a star or other object into a spectrum and for recording the intensity of the light in this spectrum as a function of wave length. The most important properties to be considered in the design of a spectrograph are the wave-length resolution or ability to separate close features in the spectrum and the speed which gives a measure of its ability to record the spectra of faint objects. The following three sections discuss the relationships of these properties to the optical design parameters of the spectrograph.

§ 2. WAVE-LENGTH RESOLUTION

The *wave-length resolution* is here defined as the minimum wave-length difference, $\Delta\lambda$, necessary for two features in the spectrum, such as two emission lines, to appear separate on the record. The theory of prisms and diffraction gratings and their optical resolving power is developed in many books on optics, spectroscopy, and astrophysics (Runge and Meissner 1933; Monk 1937; Harrison, Lord, and Loofbourow 1948; Jenkins and White 1950). However, photographic plates of moderate or high speed which are normally used to record the spectrum have a limit of resolution, R, in the range between 0.015 and 0.020 mm. Consequently, unless the spectrograph camera has a focal ratio greater than F 20 or F 30, the actual wave-length resolution is set by the plate rather than by the optical resolving power. Very few, if any, astronomical objects except the sun are bright enough to permit their spectrum to be recorded by cameras of greater focal ratio than this. In general, therefore, the wave-length

34

resolution, $\Delta\lambda$, expressed in angstroms, of a spectrograph for night observations is fixed by the photographic plate and is given by

$$\Delta\lambda = RK , \qquad (1)$$

in which K is the linear reciprocal dispersion of the spectrograph in angstroms per millimeter.

§ 3. SPEED

The other significant property of a spectrograph is its *speed*, which may be formally defined as the ratio of the energy impinging on unit area of the spectrum plate to the energy in a 1 A wave-length range received by a circular area on the telescope mirror of unit diameter. The exposure time required to record the continuous spectrum of a given star is therefore inversely proportional to this speed. Likewise, the limiting magnitude of a star of a given type that it is practicable to reach with a spectrograph is directly determined by its speed. The next sections will evaluate this speed in terms of the various parameters of the spectrograph.

3.1. OBJECTIVE PRISMS AND GRATINGS

The simplest type of equipment for the study of stellar spectra is a prism or grating placed in front of the objective of an astronomical camera. Each star image is then spread out into a spectrum which may be widened to any desired extent by drifting the image perpendicular to the direction of the dispersion. The great advantage of this arrangement is that the spectrum of all stars of sufficient brightness in a large field may be recorded on one exposure.

In practice, this method is limited to telescopes of small or medium size of the Schmidt or astrographic types that give good definition over a large field and whose apertures are small enough to be covered with a prism or grating. Another limitation on the telescope focal length that can be used effectively for this type of observation is caused by atmospheric "seeing." Thus, if "seeing" results in an image having an angular diameter of β radians, the linear diameter of the image formed by a telescope of focal length T is $T\beta$. When $T\beta$ becomes greater than the limit of resolution of the plate, R, the effective limit of resolution is set by the "seeing." Experience has shown that, at the better locations under conditions of good average "seeing," images having a diameter of 1–1.5 seconds of arc are observed, or $\beta \approx 6 \times 10^{-6}$ radian. If one also assumes the above-mentioned values of R for the plate resolution, it is evident that the limiting focal length T_0, beyond which "seeing" becomes the determining factor in resolution, is $R/\beta \approx 3000$ mm. For T greater than T_0, the wave-length resolution $\Delta\lambda$ is

$$\Delta\lambda = T\beta K . \qquad (2)$$

Or, if the wave-length resolution is to be retained, the linear reciprocal dispersion K must vary with T as follows:

$$K = \frac{\Delta\lambda}{T\beta} = \frac{K_0 T_0}{T} , \qquad (3)$$

in which K_0 is the linear reciprocal dispersion that would have been required if the resolution were determined by the plate.

If the telescope has an aperture D, the amount of light collected in a 1 A range is D^2 times that falling on the unit circle. If the spectrum has a width W and yields a linear reciprocal dispersion K A/mm, this energy is spread over an area W/K. As defined above, the speed is, therefore,

$$I = \frac{D^2 K}{W} = \frac{D^2 \Delta\lambda}{RW} . \qquad (4)$$

For telescopes having focal lengths greater than T_0, this becomes

$$I = \frac{D^2 \Delta\lambda}{T\beta W} . \qquad (5)$$

3.2 LIMITING MAGNITUDES

If the prism or grating is removed and the camera used to obtain direct photographs, all the light in the wave-length range $\lambda_1-\lambda_2$ to which the plate is sensitive is concentrated in an area slightly less than R^2. If we assume uniform intensity throughout the range from λ_1 to λ_2, the corresponding speed for direct photography becomes, approximately, for $T \lesssim T_0$,

$$I_d = \frac{D^2 (\lambda_2 - \lambda_1)}{R^2} . \qquad (6)$$

By spreading the light out into a spectrum, the intensity at the plate is therefore reduced in the ratio

$$\frac{I}{I_d} = \frac{KR^2}{W(\lambda_2 - \lambda_1)} . \qquad (7)$$

For equal exposure times, this causes a loss in limiting magnitude of

$$\Delta m = \tfrac{5}{2} \log \frac{W(\lambda_2 - \lambda_1)}{KR^2} . \qquad (8)$$

In direct photography a definite limit to the effective exposure time is set by the fogging caused by the night-sky (permanent aurora, zodiacal light, etc.). For a given telescope, essentially the same time limit is set for objective-prism exposures as for direct exposures. For the case in which the limit of angular resolution is set by the photographic emulsion rather than by "seeing" (focal length $T \lesssim 3$ meters), the extreme magnitude that can be reached on direct photographs with this limiting exposure is approximately

$$m = 18.5 + 5 \log T , \qquad (9)$$

in which T is in meters. For the maximum value of $T_0 = 3$ meters, this yields a magnitude of 21. This is the observed limiting magnitude of the Palomar 48-inch Schmidt telescope, which has a focal length of 3 meters.

For most classification and survey purposes it has been customary to use a linear reciprocal dispersion of 200–300 A/mm on a blue-sensitive plate which covers an effective range for λ_2–λ_1 of 1000–1400 A. Widening to 0.2 or 0.3 mm has also been considered desirable. When these values are inserted in equation (8), a Δm of 8–10 is obtained, i.e., the limiting magnitude that can be obtained for the 3-meter focal length is not appreciably beyond $m = 12$. By substantially narrowing the spectrum or by shortening it either by reducing the dispersion or by narrowing the wave-length range with filters, a gain of perhaps a magnitude or two might be made, at some loss, however, in effectiveness. Likewise, if the wave-length resolving power is maintained, increases in the focal length beyond T_0 produce relatively small gains in limiting magnitude. Thus, if $T/T_0 = 2.5$, an increase of 1 mag. is obtained.

3.3. SLIT SPECTROGRAPHS

If each exposure can be devoted to the spectrum of one star, the above limitation on magnitude may be eliminated by the use of a slit spectrograph. In the slit spectrograph an image of the star is focused by the telescope objective on a narrow slit. The light passing the slit is then rendered parallel by a collimator and dispersed by a prism or grating. The spectrum is then focused on the photographic plate by the camera lens. The slit eliminates most of the night-sky light that sets the limit to the exposure time of an objective-prism instrument. Furthermore, the slit can be narrowed to the point that its image on the plate is equal to, or less than, the plate resolving power, regardless of the telescope focal length, although this is done at the expense of wasting the light intercepted by the slit jaws.

In the consideration of the speed of a slit spectrograph when used to photograph the continuous spectrum of a star, the following parameters are needed:

D = Aperture of telescope.

β = Angular diameter of seeing image in radians. For this discussion it is assumed that the star image is square and is uniformly illuminated. The errors introduced by this assumption will be discussed later in this section.

c = Ratio of aperture of collimator to that of telescope, i.e., collimator aperture = cD.

f = Focal length of spectrograph camera.

F = Effective focal ratio of camera = f/cD.

P = Width of image of slit at photographic plate. This is normally set about equal to the limit of resolution of the plate, R.

W = Width of spectrum.

a = Angular dispersion of grating or prism in radians/A.

K = Linear reciprocal dispersion in A/mm, i.e., $K = 1/af$.

r = Ratio of change in angle of camera beam in direction of dispersion to change in angle of collimator beam. For a grating, r is equal to the ratio of the cosine of angle of incidence to the cosine of angle of diffraction. For a symmetrical prism system it is equal to unity.

The equivalent focal length of the telescope-spectrograph system is the same as that of an objective with the same aperture as the telescope and the focal ratio of the camera. If the slit is opened so that all light from the star passes the slit, then the star image at the plate has a linear size perpendicular to the dispersion of

$$S_1 = DF\beta = \frac{Df\beta}{Dc} = \frac{\beta}{caK}. \tag{10}$$

Parallel to the dispersion, this must be multiplied by r, or

$$S_2 = rS_1 = \frac{\beta r}{caK}. \tag{11}$$

Three cases must be considered, depending on the relative size of the star image and the proper slit image, i.e., on the relative values of S_2 and P and on whether the normal width of the spectrum S_1 is greater or less than the minimum necessary width of the spectrum W.

Case A: $S_2 < P, S_1 < W$.—In this case all the light collected by the objective passes the slit and is available to form the spectrum. Consequently, the speed is the same as that of an objective-prism spectrograph yielding the same width and dispersion of spectra. Formula (4) is still valid, and

$$I_A = \frac{K D^2}{W}. \tag{4}$$

If the spectrum is not widened, W is equal to the limit of resolution of the emulsion R, and equation (4) still holds if W is replaced by R.

Case B: $S_2 > P, S_1 < W$.—Under this condition, in order that the resolving power may equal that of the plate, it is necessary to narrow the slit to the point that the fraction of light passing the slit is

$$\frac{P}{S_2} = \frac{PcaK}{\beta r}. \tag{12}$$

The speed of the spectrograph is reduced in the same ratio and therefore becomes, for this case,

$$I_B = \frac{PcaK^2 D^2}{\beta rW}. \tag{13}$$

Case C: $S_2 > P, S_1 > W$.—This is the same as case B, except that the width S_1 is greater than W and therefore widening is not necessary. The speed is therefore obtained by substituting S_1 for W in equation (13), giving

$$I_C = \frac{Pc^2a^2K^3 D^2}{\beta^2 r}. \tag{14}$$

In the foregoing simplified theory a square, uniformly illuminated star is assumed rather than a star with the conventional "error-function" distribution of light given by the formula

$$i = i_0 \exp - \left(\frac{x^2 + y^2}{\psi^2} \right). \tag{15}$$

The results for this actual distribution are very close to those given in the above formulae except in the neighborhood of the boundaries between cases. In these boundary regions the precise theory gives a gradual transition from one case to the other rather than the sharp discontinuity implied by the formulae. In no case, however, does the simplified formula depart by more than about 20 per cent from the precise formula if β is set equal to 1.8 ψ. The variations in β are so large that a more precise formulation of the theory has little significance.

In the design of a spectrograph for use with a given telescope to carry out certain observational programs, P, K, D, β, and W are, in general, fixed by the telescope and the requirements of the program, while r rarely departs appreciably from unity. This leaves c and a for the designer to use in attaining the desired speed. From equations (13) and (14) it is evident that c and therefore the collimator aperture and a, the angular dispersion, should be made as large as practicable. This is especially important in spectrographs to be used with the large modern reflectors, since these formulae show that c must remain constant and therefore the collimator aperture must increase proportionally to the telescope aperture if the spectrographs on these new instruments are to retain the same efficiency as the spectrographs of the small, older telescopes.

Ideally, in order to achieve optimum speed in a slit spectrograph that is to equal the speed of an objective-prism instrument, it is necessary to satisfy the conditions for case A, that is, $S_2 \lesssim P$ or $DF\beta r \lesssim P$. The focal ratio of the spectrograph camera must therefore not exceed $P/D\beta r$. Assuming, as before, that r equals unity and that $P = R$, which with β have the values given in §§ 3.1 and 3.2, this means that F must not be greater than 3000/D, in which D, the aperture of the telescope, is in millimeters. In other words, the effective focal length of the telescope-spectrograph should not exceed 3 meters. This is, of course, equivalent to the limitation on the focal length of objective-prism instruments.

3.4. Extended and Emission-Line Sources

The above theory assumes stellar sources having a continuous spectrum in which the apparent angular diameter of the source is determined by atmospheric "seeing." In the case of extended sources such as planets, nebulae, or galaxies, the same formulae are valid if β is set equal to the angular diameter of the object. The large value of β of most of these objects throws them into case C.

In emission objects these formulae still apply if the dispersion is high enough that the emission lines are wide compared with P, the width of the slit image at the plate. A different set of assumptions must be made if the emission lines are narrower than P. In this case one assumes that the total energy in a line is spread over a width P instead of the former assumption that the energy in a 1 A band of the continuum is spread over a width $1/K$. Equations (4), (13), and (14) must, therefore, be modified by dividing the right side by PK, in order that they may apply to this case.

3.5. Photoelectric Scanning of Spectra

Formulae (4), (13), and (14) assume that the recording device is a photographic plate in which the response is proportional to the number of quanta falling on a unit area of the plate. If the plate is replaced by a scanning device in which the receiver is a photomultiplier tube placed behind a second slit in the plane of the spectrum, the response is proportional to the total number of quanta passing the second slit. In this case the speed has the same dependence on collimator aperture and angular dispersion as that given by equation (4) when the star image is smaller than the slit width and by equation (13) when the star is larger than the slit. When using the scanner, there is, however, no advantage in concentrating the light on a small area with spectrograph cameras of extremely low focal ratios. Indeed, all measurements can be made equally well with a single long-focus camera, the slits being widened when it is necessary to sacrifice resolution in order to obtain greater speed. It should also be noted that the ultimate resolution of a spectrograph using a scanning slit is no longer limited by the resolution of the photographic plate but, with appropriate slit widths, may reach the optical limit of resolution as set by the aperture of the collimator beam.

3.6. The Image-Slicer

From the discussion of the speed of the slit spectrograph in § 3.3, it is evident that, especially when the longer-focus cameras are used to obtain high dispersion, the slit must be narrowed to the point that a very large fraction of the light fails to pass the slit and is lost. Most of this light can be made to pass the slit by the use of an image-slicer, which is an optical device that slices the star image into strips whose widths are approximately equal to that of the slit and then rearranges these strips end to end along the slit without disturbing the collimation of the beam or changing the size of the incident cone of light. Several such devices have been designed, the one best suited for use with spectrographs having been described by Bowen (1938).

Such a device does not increase the intensity of illumination at any one point on the photographic plate but produces a number of parallel spectra on the plate equal to the number of slices, usually 5 to 20. If the speed of the spectrograph is to be increased, the light in these spectra must be brought together through the introduction of a cylindrical lens in front of the photographic plate. The aberrations of such a cylindrical lens limit its effective use to cameras having focal ratios greater than about F 2. Furthermore, the cylindrical lens produces an intensity distribution across the spectrum similar to the intensity distribution on the grating in a direction parallel to the lines. Unfortunately, because of the shadow cast by the secondary mirrors of a reflecting telescope, this distribution is far from uniform and therefore yields a spectrum that is not satisfactory for photometric purposes. The same distribution of light across the spectrum as in a normal unwidened spectrum may be obtained by the introduction of a lens system in front of the slicer which focuses on the grating the star image rather than an image of the telescope mirror.

When an image-slicer is used with a photoelectric scanning device, the speed of the spectrograph is increased by the same factor as the number of quanta passing the first slit, since, as noted above, the response of the photomultiplier tube is proportional to the total number of quanta passing the second slit and is independent of their distribution along the slit. The slicer has the further advantage in this case that, since it passes practically all the light of the star through the slit, fluctuations caused by seeing are substantially less than with a regular slit.

§ 4. OTHER LIGHT-LOSSES

The formulae of § 3 neglect all losses of light caused by absorption, reflection, and diffraction. Unfortunately, these losses may be very substantial in passing the many components of a modern spectrograph and the auxiliary mirrors necessary to bring the light to it.

4.1. REFLECTION LOSSES

Reflection losses are of two types, those that occur at metallic reflecting surfaces and those that take place when light passes through a glass-air surface. For front-surface mirrors of astronomical instruments, an evaporated aluminum coat is now customarily used. Pettit (1934) gives the reflective power of such an aluminum coat as ranging from 85 per cent at 3500 A to 88 per cent at 9000 A, that is, 12–15 per cent of the light is lost at each reflection from a clean, fresh aluminum surface. Old or dirty coats may result in substantially larger losses.

Each time a light-beam passes normally from air to glass or glass to air, a portion of the light equal to $(n - 1)^2/(n + 1)^2$ times the incident light is reflected and lost, n being the index of the glass. For ordinary glasses this represents a 4–5 per cent loss per surface. In the case of the prisms of a prism spectrograph, the loss per surface is substantially greater, 8–12 per cent, because of the higher index and large angle of incidence.

Theoretically, these glass-air reflection losses can be eliminated by depositing on the surface a coating $\lambda/4$ thick of material which has an index of $n^{1/2}$. In practice, complete elimination is unattainable because of the lack of suitably hard materials with indices in the range from 1.2 to 1.3. Furthermore, spectrographs are more and more being designed to cover the whole range from 3000 to 12,000 A, and it is impossible to satisfy even approximately the thickness criteria for all wave lengths. Nevertheless, by suitable compromises, substantial reductions in the reflection losses may be achieved by the coating of all glass parts.

4.2. Absorption Losses

Absorption losses are especially serious in prism instruments. In order to satisfy the conditions for high efficiency given by formulae (13) and (14), it is necessary to have high angular dispersion. This condition requires a prism train of at least two or three prisms of high-dispersion glass. For this glass, which is also of high index, the light-path along the base of each 60° prism is 1.5 to 2 times the aperture of the beam or 3 to 6 times the aperture for such a prism train. These same formulae also require the largest possible aperture, which, combined with the first condition, calls for a light-path of several decimeters in glass. The absorption of most high-dispersion glass is large, especially in the ultraviolet, and may result in a very substantial loss of light at the shorter wave lengths. Large-aperture, highly corrected lenses of low focal ratio may also have substantial light-paths through glasses that are far from transparent to the shorter wave lengths.

One of the main reasons for the present shift to grating–Schmidt camera designs is the impossibility of attaining high efficiency in a prism-lens system.

4.3. Diffraction Losses

Every grating is the cause of some light-losses because of the diffraction of part of the light into other orders than the one being recorded. Recent ruling techniques have come close to attaining the theoretical ideal of a grating consisting of a series of tilted plane surfaces. The order of the spectrum which falls in the direction of specular reflection from these surfaces receives practically all the light. In practice it has been possible to throw 60–70 per cent of the incident light into this order. Part of the loss is caused by the reflection losses at the aluminized surface, as discussed earlier in this section. In the case of a wave length which does not have an order in the direction of specular reflection, a correspondingly lower efficiency will be achieved (see also § 5).

Light-losses due to Rowland and Lyman ghosts are quite negligible (less than 1 per cent) in modern first-class gratings and, in general, do not have to be taken into account in speed calculations.

Another point at which diffraction may deflect light from the beam is at the slit. Thus, if the slit is set to give an image of width P at the plate, its own width is $f' P/f$, in which f' and f are the focal lengths of the collimator and of the camera, respectively. The angular distance from the central maximum to the first minimum of the diffraction pattern of such a slit is $\lambda f/f'P$. At the position of the collimator lens, i.e., at a distance f' from the slit, the linear distance between maximum and minimum is f' times this, or $\lambda f/P$. In most spectrographs the angle subtended by the collimator lens at the slit is made equal to that subtended by the telescope objective, i.e., if no diffraction were present, the cone of light from the telescope would just fill the collimator. In this case it can easily be shown by integration of the diffraction formula that the fraction of the light-loss because of diffraction is approximately $\lambda F/2\,P$, F being the focal ratio of the camera. Since P is normally set at about the resolving power of the photographic plate or 0.015–0.020 mm, $\lambda/2P$ usually falls between 0.01 and 0.03. For most modern spectrographs with cameras having focal ratios in the 0.5–12 range, it is evident that the loss is not very great. Furthermore, it should be noted that the loss is independent of the focal length of the collimator, i.e., there is no difference between a spectrograph at the prime focus or the coudé position as far as this loss is concerned.

Still additional losses may occur because of the obstruction of the beam by on-axis plateholders and their mounts.

Even in the more recent designs in which prisms have been replaced by gratings and lenses by Schmidt cameras, these reflection, absorption, and diffraction losses may be very serious. In the first place, most spectrographs are located at the Cassegrain or the coudé focuses. In addition to the reflection at the main mirror, these positions require from one to four reflections by secondary mirrors before the light is brought to the slit of the spectrograph. Additional reflections occur in the spectrograph at the collimator and camera mirrors and at the grating. Furthermore, the light passes two or four glass-air surfaces at the corrector plate, depending on whether the once- or twice-through designs are used. Additional glass-air surfaces may be introduced by field flatteners, image rotators, filters, or reflections by right-angle prisms changing the beam direction. Losses of 1 or 2 mag. are therefore to be expected and may be even larger if great care is not taken to maintain the mirrors and other surfaces in the best possible condition.

§ 5. EFFECTIVE WAVE-LENGTH RANGE

As already mentioned, the long glass light-path in prism spectrographs causes very large absorption in the ultraviolet. Indeed, for most spectrographs with

TABLE 1

RELATIVE VALUES OF DISPERSION OF FLINT GLASS

λ	$dn/d\lambda$ (Relative)	λ	$dn/d\lambda$ (Relative)
3800	1.0	7000	0.13
5000	0.38	9000	.07
6000	0.22	11000	0.05

prism trains of 2 or 3 prisms, this absorption is so great as to prevent effective observations in the regions short of 3600–4000 A, the exact value depending on the type of glass used in the prisms. On the other hand, the dispersion of glass falls off very rapidly at longer wave lengths. Table 1 lists the relative dispersions of the ordinary flint glasses at various wave lengths. From this it is evident that a prism system designed to give satisfactory dispersion in the violet and blue region does not provide adequate dispersion in the red or infrared. Indeed, work with prism instruments has normally been limited to the region shortward of 5000 A for this reason.

Gratings, on the other hand, give essentially constant dispersion throughout the range for which one order is used. In changing from one order to another, the linear reciprocal dispersion expressed in A/mm varies inversely as the order. Furthermore, with a modern blazed grating, the order that may be used with high efficiency is fixed by the wave length. Thus, with these gratings, the bottom of the groove is tilted to give maximum reflection in a given direction, and the order falling in this direction will receive nearly all the incident light. For example, if a given grating is blazed to have maximum speed in the third order at λ 4000 A, it will also have maximum intensity in the second order at λ 6000 A and in the first order at λ 12000 A. Reasonably satisfactory performance may be expected on either side of this maximum out to the point where two orders of a given wave length are equidistant from the intensity maximum. At these points the efficiency has fallen off to approximately half its maximum value. For example, consider the third order of the above grating. The second and third orders of λ 4800 and the third and fourth orders of λ 3429 are each equidistant from the center of the blaze at third-order λ 4000 A. Satisfactory operation in the third order may therefore be expected between about λ 3400 A and λ 4800 A. Similarly, the second order should be used between λ 4800 A and λ 8000 A. Since these orders fall on top of each other, they must be separated either by a small cross-dispersion or by the use of an appropriate emulsion-filter combination that is sensitive to one order only.

For the highest possible efficiency, several gratings should be available with different blaze angles. A grating can then be selected that will give maximum efficiency at the wave length under study. Since the spectra of a majority of stars fall off in brightness toward the ultraviolet, it is often advantageous to pick a grating with its blaze at a wave length near the short-wave-length end of the range under study. In going to longer wave lengths, the reduced efficiency of the grating tends to compensate for the greater brightness of the spectrum, thereby yielding a more uniform exposure throughout the spectrum than would otherwise be obtained.

§ 6. STABILITY OF THE SPECTROGRAPH

In order to investigate the spectrum of very faint objects, exposures of several hours or even nights are often required. Throughout these exposures it is essential that no movement of the spectrum with respect to the photographic emulsion shall exceed a few thousandths of a millimeter. Otherwise, resolving power will be lost, and the astronomical spectrum may be shifted with respect to the comparison spectrum, with a resultant error in wave-length measurements.

6.1. MECHANICAL FLEXURE

In the case of spectrographs mounted at the prime or Cassegrain focuses, the spectrograph is turned through a large angle with respect to the direction of gravity during such an exposure. If the spectrograph is not of the highest rigidity, large flexures will occur, causing serious shifts of the image. In any structure such as a spectrograph, the linear amount of the flexure varies as the square of the size, provided that all dimensions, including the thickness of all members, are increased proportionally. By careful attention to design, it has been found possible to provide the necessary rigidity for spectrographs having over-all dimensions up to 100 or 150 cm. For larger spectrographs the masses required become prohibitive, and the spectrographs should therefore be located in a fixed position at the coudé focus. Schmidt cameras in the movable spectrographs are therefore limited to focal lengths of about 50 cm and collimator focal lengths to

TABLE 2

THERMAL SHIFT OF SPECTRA

Prisms	$n_{G'} - n_F$	$10^5 \Delta n/\Delta t$ with Respect to Air	$\Delta\lambda/\Delta t$ at λ 4600 A (A/deg C)
Carbon bisulfide................	0.0222	−84	20
Light flint.....................	.0084	+ 0.42	0.26
Ordinary silicate flint..........	.0101	+ 0.54	0.28
Heavy silicate flint............	.0171	+ 1.27	0.39
Extra-heavy silicate flint........	0.0260	+ 2.05	0.41

Gratings	10^6 Coefficient of Expansion	10^6 Coefficient of Expansion $+\Delta n/\Delta t$ of Air	$\Delta\lambda/\Delta t$ at λ 4600 A (A/deg C)
Speculum metal................	18.6	17.7	0.081
Plate glass....................	8.9	8.0	.037
Pyrex........................	3.0	2.1	0.010

about twice this. In the case of a collimator, this may be extended by the use of a telephoto lens or a Cassegrain mirror system.

6.2. THERMAL DISPLACEMENTS

If the spectrograph frame is constructed entirely of one material, angles between various optical parts remain constant, even though changes in temperature occur. On the other hand, the index of refraction of prisms and the spacing of lines of a grating shift with temperature, thereby causing a movement of the lines if the temperature changes during an exposure. Table 2 lists the shift of the spectrum in angstroms per degree change in temperature for several types of dispersing systems at λ 4600 A. The table shows at once why liquids like carbon bisulfide are impractical as prism materials in spite of their high dispersion and ultraviolet transparency. Likewise, it is evident that the newer type of instruments using gratings ruled on aluminum evaporated on Pyrex can tolerate temperature changes during an exposure about 30 times as great as a prism spectrograph. In general, shifts during the exposure of up to 0.010 mm may be tolerated. For dispersions up to 10 A/mm, which is about the largest provided in instruments mounted on the telescope, this corresponds to a shift of 0.1 A or more. Temperature shifts in a prism instrument must therefore be held to somewhat less than 0.5° C, while, in a grating instrument, changes of 10° C may be tolerated. In a coudé instrument, in which dispersions may reach 2 A/mm the tolerance as to temperature changes is only one-fifth as great. However, coudé instruments are normally mounted in closed rooms on heavy piers with very large thermal inertia. Experience has shown that, under these circumstances, shifts of over 1° C per day very rarely occur.

Another result of temperature change is a shift in focus during the exposure. Thus, if the mirrors are made of a material whose coefficient of expansion is ρ_m and if the material of the spectrograph frame has a coefficient ρ_f and the focal length of the collimator is f' and of the camera is f, then a change in temperature Δt changes the focus by

$$\delta = f\left(1 + \frac{f}{f'}\right)(\rho_f - \rho_m)\Delta t. \tag{16}$$

If the exposure starts in focus, the diameter of the out-of-focus image, q after the change has taken place is δ divided by the focal ratio, f/d, or

$$q = d\left(1 + \frac{f}{f'}\right)(\rho_f - \rho_m)\Delta t, \tag{17}$$

in which d is the aperture of the collimator beam in millimeters. If a steel frame and Pyrex mirrors are used, $\rho_f - \rho_m = 0.000008$, and if a value of $q = 0.010$ mm is permissible, then temperature changes of

$$\Delta t = \frac{1250}{d(1 + f/f')} \tag{18}$$

are allowable. Obviously, for even the largest-aperture spectrographs, temperature changes of several degrees are permissible.

All these calculations indicate that thermostating is required for prism spectrographs but is not necessary for the newer grating–Schmidt camera instruments. When possible, it is desirable to eliminate thermostatic control, since the circulation of heated air across the light-beam almost invariably disturbs the internal seeing and causes a deterioration of the images.

§ 7. COMPARISON SPECTRA

A majority of spectroscopic problems require not only photographing the spectrum of an object but also measuring with high precision the wave lengths of various features in it. All astronomical spectrographs therefore make provision for placing the spectrum of a known source on both sides of the astronomical spectrum. For moderate and high-dispersion spectra an iron-arc comparison is normally used in the ultraviolet and blue regions and a neon-discharge tube in the yellow, red, and infrared. For very low dispersions a source with a simpler spectrum, such as He or Hg discharge tubes, is customarily used.

The light from the arc or discharge tube, after passing through suitable diffusers to reduce the intensity, is reflected through the slit by two quartz right-angle prisms placed immediately in front of it. Since it is desirable that the comparison spectrum be as close as possible to the astronomical spectrum, the prisms should be mounted with a variable separation to accommodate astronomical spectra of various widths. The whole prism assembly should also be easily removable, to facilitate location of the object during the original setting on it.

To avoid errors in wave-length measurements resulting from slight departures from exact focus, it is essential that the collimator be filled symmetrically by both starlight and light from the comparison source. This is usually accomplished by making the aperture of the collimator such that it subtends exactly the same angle at the slit as the telescope optics. The axes of the telescope and the collimator must also be made accurately coincident. The cone of light approaching the slit from the comparison source is made substantially larger than that subtended by the collimator at the slit. This procedure insures optimum use of the light collected by the telescope and the equal filling of the collimator with light from both telescope and comparison source.

Care must also be taken in the timing of the comparison exposures, to insure that no systematic shift occurs between astronomical and comparison spectra due to flexure or thermal changes. Thus, as indicated above, a shift during an exposure due to one or both of these causes of as much as 0.010 mm may occur without appreciably impairing the resolution of the plate. On the other hand, a relative shift of one spectrum with respect to the other by anything like this amount would result in serious wave-length errors. These errors may be largely avoided by distributing the two exposures similarly. For short exposures it is usually sufficient to give two comparison exposures, one near the beginning, the other near the end, of the astronomical exposure. For longer exposures, additional comparison exposures should be distributed uniformly through the astronomical exposure. However, no exposures of the comparison spectrum should be made until the plateholder has had an opportunity to come to the temperature of the spectrograph after being in the darkroom for loading.

§ 8. CALIBRATION SPECTRA

For an increasing number of problems it is also necessary to know quantitatively the relative intensity at various points in the spectrum. A calibration spectrum should be provided from which the relationship between exposing intensity and plate density may be determined at each wave length. These calibration data are usually obtained by exposing the plate in a spectrograph which provides a series of spectra with accurately known relative intensities. This is obtained by using a continuous source, such as an incandescent light, and a series of 6 to 10 short slits whose widths progress in accurately known, usually geometrical, ratios. The same result may also be obtained with an accurate V-slit, in which the width increases linearly from one end to the other. These slits may be mounted on the regular stellar spectrograph and make use of the same optics as the star spectrum. The calibration spectrum then occurs on the same plate as the star spectrum. An alternative procedure is to construct a simple spectrograph for calibration purposes. Before each exposure the plate is cut into two parts, one of which is exposed in the stellar spectrograph and the other in the calibration spectrograph. They are then developed simultaneously in the same developer.

In the design and construction of either type of calibration spectrograph, great care must be taken to insure uniform intensity of illumination over all steps of the step-slit or along the whole length of the V-slit. The usual procedure for this test of uniformity is to substitute a single long and accurately parallel slit for the step-slit or V-slit and to check the constancy of exposure over the whole width of the spectrum.

§ 9. LOCATION OF OBJECTS AND GUIDING

Present spectrographs have attained such speed that they may be success-fully used to study objects that cannot be seen in the finder telescope or in some cases even with the main telescope itself. Provision must be made for locating and identifying these objects and then guiding on them. For locating the object it should be possible to view the field of the telescope itself with a wide-field eye-piece. In the case of a coudé spectrograph this can be done with an eyepiece and field lens mounted 1 or 2 meters in front of the slit. The purpose of the field lens is to pull back the focus from the slit to the focal plane of the eyepiece, as well as to widen the field of the eyepiece. When the telescope is in focus for the finding eyepiece, it is therefore also in focus on the slit of the spectrograph. Since, because of the very large scale at the coudé focus, the field of the eyepiece may not be as large as the uncertainty of setting of the telescope, the eyepiece should be mounted in such a way that it can be moved about parallel to the focal plane. This makes it possible to search a much larger area than its own field of view. Once the object is located, the mount of the eyepiece should per-mit its being locked in such a position that an object on the cross-hair in front of the eyepiece falls on the slit when the eyepiece is removed from the beam.

In certain designs of prime-focus or Cassegrain spectrographs, either the spectrograph itself or the right-angle prism that is sometimes used to reflect the image to the slit is hinged in such a way that it may be removed from the direct beam. This permits examination of the field with a wide-angle eyepiece, which is provided with a cross-hair at the same place occupied by the slit or by its image in the right-angle prism.

In order to observe the object after it is located on the slit, the jaws of the slit are optically polished and are tilted at an angle of 80°–85° to the axis of the in-coming beam. The light striking the slit jaws is therefore reflected back at an angle of 10°–20° with the incoming beam and enters a guide eyepiece in which the observer can see the exact position of the image with respect to the slit. The guide eyepiece normally takes the form of a low-power compound microscope with one nearly right-angle reflection which permits swiveling the eye end to the point most convenient for the observer. An illuminated cross-hair is usually provided to assist in holding the object at the proper point along the slit. Several eyepieces of different power often help in following various types of objects.

For very faint objects the light reflected from the slit may not be sufficient for accurate guiding, and, if possible, a brighter star should be used. If the object can just barely be seen on the slit, it is first placed in the position desired. At the same time the cross-hair of a second movable eyepiece is carefully centered on another nearby star, of sufficient brightness for easy guiding, and then rigidly clamped in this position. Guiding proceeds throughout the exposure with this second guide eyepiece. In the extreme case in which the object under observation is so faint as to be completely invisible on the slit, an offset procedure must be used. For this procedure the guide eyepiece is provided with precise scales by which the cross-lines may be offset from the center of the slit in both right ascension and declination with an accuracy of at least 0.01 mm. A direct photograph of the field is taken in advance, preferably at the same focus of the same telescope. The co-ordinates of the object with respect to a suitable guide star are carefully measured on this plate. With this as a basis, the guide eyepiece is set off by the proper amounts, and, after identifying the guide star on the field, the cross-hairs are brought into coincidence with it. If this offset procedure is regularly used, provision is often made for taking the necessary direct photographs without removing the spectrograph. Because of the rotation of the field, this offset procedure cannot be used at the coudé focus. In general, however, objects faint enough to require this procedure cannot be reached with the higher dispersions available at this focus.

The very high sensitivity of photomultiplier tubes now makes it possible to guide automatically, and in several telescopes provision is made for this (Babcock, Rule, and Fassero 1956). The commonest form of guider consists of a knife-edge which rotates rapidly about the correct position of the image in the guide microscope. As long as the image remains in its correct position, the amount of light passing the knife-edge to the photomultiplier tube, mounted behind it, is constant. If the image drifts off from this position, however, the light fluctuates with the period of rotation of the knife-edge. The amplifier circuits connected to the photomultiplier tube are so designed as to transform the amount and phase of this fluctuation into the appropriate signals to the telescope-control system for bringing the image back to its proper position.

§ 10. WIDENING THE SPECTRUM

Many of the new high-speed spectrographs have so large a ratio of collimator-to-camera focal lengths that if the star image is held at one point on the slit during the exposure, the resultant spectrum is narrower than is desirable for photometric studies or for the certain recognition of faint lines. In order to widen the spectrum with the necessary uniformity, the usual procedure is to allow the star image to drift along the slit for the distance corresponding to the required width. If the slit is parallel to the right-ascension motion, this can be easily accomplished by rating the clock so that a drift of the proper amount occurs in from 1 to 5 minutes, or in any case in a very small fraction of the total exposure. At the end of each traverse it is brought back with the regular guide motions of the telescope. In case the slit is parallel to the declination motion, the same procedure may be followed if the telescope is provided with a slow drive in declination.

§ 11. MOONLIGHT ELIMINATOR

In photographing very faint objects in moonlight, this widening procedure has the disadvantage that the plate is exposed to the scattered moonlight throughout the exposure, while any given point on the plate is exposed to the starlight for only a small fraction of the time. Since the addition of even a small amount of moon spectrum to that of the star spectrum seriously complicates any photometric studies, it is important to eliminate this as far as possible. This may be accomplished with a second slit about as wide as the diameter of the star image and perpendicular to the regular slit. Provision is made for moving this at the same rate as the drift of the star image. One method is to move the slit with a motor-driven cam. A second procedure is the use of a slowly rotating disk with a series of radial slits of the proper width and spacing. The star moves along with one slit to the end of its run and then is rapidly moved back to pick up the next slit, which is spaced at a distance equal to the length of the star's run.

§ 12. IMAGE DEROTATOR

At the coudé focus the image rotates with respect to the slit once in 24 hours. A long exposure on the spectrum of an extended object may result in objectionable blurring of details. To avoid this, it is usual to provide an image derotator in the form of a large Dove prism, preferably of optical fused quartz, mounted in front of the slit and driven at the rate of one revolution in 48 hours. By properly setting the Dove prism at the start of the exposure, the image may be given any desired orientation with respect to the slit. This may be used to study the spectrum along any desired line across the object or to place the slit parallel to either the right ascension or declination motion for widening, using the method described in the preceding section. When observing near the horizon, it may be used to place the direction of atmospheric dispersion parallel to the slit, thereby insuring that all wave lengths enter the slit, thus simplifying the guiding for exposures in the ultraviolet. The same Dove prism without drive may be used on any spectrograph to change orientation of object with respect to slit.

§ 13. EXPOSURE METERS

Because of the variable amount of light which enters the slit during periods of changing seeing, it is often very difficult to give just the right amount of exposure required for many photometric studies. Some precise measure of the amount of light that has passed the slit is therefore very desirable. Such an exposure meter may operate by deflecting a small fraction of the light by a plane-parallel glass plate placed behind the slit, or preferably by intercepting with a mirror the light that would later be lost by on-axis plateholders or other obstructions. This light is then concentrated on a photomultiplier tube which is connected with some integrating circuit, such as a photon counter, which gives a measure of the amount of light that has passed the slit since the start of the exposure. Experience soon fixes the reading that should be reached for a correct exposure with a given camera.

§ 14. HISTORICAL DEVELOPMENT OF SPECTROGRAPHS

This final section traces the development of the designs of stellar spectrographs and notes how contemporary optical practice has been utilized to satisfy the conditions for maximum resolution and speed as outlined in the preceding sections.

All the very early observations of stellar spectra were made visually. The first observation of the spectrum of a star, Sirius, was made by Fraunhofer (1814), who used an objective prism mounted on a small transit telescope of about 3 cm in aperture. Later a much larger prism was mounted in front of a telescope with an aperture of 10 cm, and the characteristic features of the spectra of Sirius, Castor, Pollux, Capella, Betelgeuse, and Procyon were noted (Fraunhofer 1823).

The discovery of the significance of the absorption lines in the sun by Kirchhoff in 1859 stimulated very extensive visual observations of the spectra of a large number of stars by Huggins, Secchi, Rutherford, and many others. Both objective prisms and small spectroscopes at the focus of the telescope were used.

The first photographs of stellar spectra were made by Huggins and by Draper. After an abortive attempt to photograph the spectrum of Sirius in 1863, in which the continuous spectrum but no lines were recorded, Huggins continued with visual observations until better equipment was available. On returning to photographic procedures later, Huggins' chief interest was the extension of the spectrum into the ultraviolet. His first spectrograph, completed in 1876, therefore used a prism of calcite and lenses of quartz and was mounted at the prime focus of his 18-inch reflector at Tulse Hill. The optical specifications are listed in Table 3, item 1.

In 1872 Draper inserted a quartz prism in the converging beam of his newly completed 28-inch reflector and obtained a spectrum of Vega showing four absorption lines. After further experiments in which several arrangements of prisms and lenses were tried, he adapted a small slit spectroscope made by Browning and having flint prisms and achromatic lenses, the specifications being given in Table 3, item 2.

After 1880 the speeds of photographic emulsions were rapidly increased, and at the same time astronomers came to appreciate the great value of the per-

TABLE 3

SPECIFICATIONS OF SPECTROGRAPHS

(All Dimensions in Centimeters)

ITEM*	TELESCOPE	TYPE	APER-TURE	COLLIMATOR		DISPERSING ELEMENT	CAMERA		DATE
				Type	Apt.		Type	Focal Length	
1......	Huggins, Tulse Hill	Refl.	45	Quartz: Effective†	3.8	One 60° calcite prism	Single quartz	16.5	1876
2......	Draper	{ Refl. / Refr.	70 / 28	Achromat / Effective†	3.4 / 1.9 / 0.8–1.1	Two 60° flint-glass prisms	Achromat	15	1879
3......	Lick	Refr.	90	Achromat	3.74	Three 60° flint-glass prisms	Triple achromat / Achromat	40 / 80	1898
4......	Potsdam	Refr.	80	Achromat	3.2	Three 63° flint-glass prisms	Zeiss anastigmat / Triple achromat	56 / 41	1900
5......	Yerkes	Refr.	102	Achromat / Achromat	3.5 / 5.1	One 60° flint-glass prism / Three 66° flint-glass prisms	Triple achromat / Zeiss anastigmat	72 / 45	1901
6......	Newell	Refr.	63	Achromat	5.2	Four 56° flint-glass prisms	Triple achromat / Achromat / Telephoto	61 / 35.6 / 50.8 / 101.6	1899

* Items in this column are described in the following:

1. Sir William Huggins, *Proc. R. Soc. London,* **25,** 445, 1876; *Phil. Trans. R. Soc. London,* **171,** Part II, 669, 1880.
2. Henry Draper, *Am. J. Sci.* (3d ser.), **18,** 419, 1879; *Proc. Am. Acad. Arts and Sci.,* **19,** 231, 1883.
3. W. W. Campbell, *Ap. J.,* **8,** 123, 1898.
4. H. C. Vogel, *Ap. J.,* **11,** 393, 1900.
5. E. B. Frost, *Ap. J.,* **15,** 1, 1902.
6. H. F. Newall, *M.N.,* **65,** 608 and 636, 1905.
7. Paul Guthnik, *Sitz. Preuss. Akad. Wiss. Berlin, Phys.-math. Kl.,* **1,** 3, 1930.
8. J. S. Plaskett, *Ap. J.,* **49,** 209, 1919; **59,** 65, 1924.
9. M. L. Humason, *Ap. J.,* **71,** 351, 1930.
10. W. H. Wright, *Lick Obs. Bull.,* **9,** 52, 1917.
11. Paul W. Merrill, *Ap. J.,* **74,** 188, 1931.
12. W. S. Adams, *Ap. J.,* **33,** 64, 1911.
14. T. L. Page, *Ap. J.,* **116,** 65, 1952.
15,18. I. S. Bowen, *Ap. J.,* **116,** 1, 1952.
16. W. A. Hiltner, private communication.
17. W. S. Adams, *Ap. J.,* **93,** 11, 1941; T. Dunham, *Vistas in Astronomy,* ed. A. Beer (London, New York: Pergamon Press), **2,** 1223, 1956.
19. O. C. Wilson, *Pub. A.S.P.,* **68,** 346, 1956.
20. Ch. Fehrenbach, *Pub. Obs. Haute Provence,* **5,** 85, 1959.
21. A. B. Meinel, private communication.
22. Baustian, *Telescopes,* ed. G.P. Kuiper and B. M. Middlehurst (Chicago: University of Chicago Press, 1960), p. 16.

† Aperture of lens filled by cone of light from telescope.

TABLE 3—*Continued*

Item*	Telescope	Type	Aperture	Collimator Type	Collimator Apt.	Dispersing Element	Camera Type	Camera Focal Length	Date
7	Berlin-Babelsberg	Refl.	125	Achromat	5.0	One 66° flint-glass prism	Triplet Triplet Doublet	23.3 48 72	1930
8	Victoria	Refl.	185	Achromat	6.3	One 60° flint-glass prism	Petzval Triple achromat Triple achromat	22.8 42 71	1924
						Two to three 63° flint-glass prisms	Petzval Ross 4 lens	25.4 71	
9	Mount Wilson	Refl.	250	Achromat	3.8	Two 60° flint-glass prisms	Rayton	3.2	1930
10	Lick, Crossley	Refl.	90	Quartz	5.0	Two 60° cornu-quartz prisms	Single quartz	28	1916
11	Mount Wilson, Casse-grain	Refl.	250	Telephoto	6.3	Grating	Lens Lens Lens	15 25 45	1931
12	Mount Wilson, coudé	Refl.	150	Achromat	15.2	One 60° flint glass with mirror for second passage	Achromat auto-collimating	550	1910

53

TABLE 3—*Continued*

ITEM*	TELESCOPE	TYPE	APER-TURE	COLLIMATOR Type	Apt.	DISPERSING ELEMENT	CAMERA Type	Focal Length	Dispersion Blue A/mm	DATE
13......	Mount Wilson, Newtonian	Refl.	250	Mirror	5.1	Blazed gratings	Thick mirror Schmidt; Schmidt	3.2; 7.5	85 to 430	1948
14......	McDonald, prime focus	Refl.	205	Mirror	5.1	Blazed grating	Thick mirror Schmidt	3.3	330	1948
15......	Palomar, Hale prime focus	Refl.	500	Mirror	7.6	Blazed gratings	Thick mirror Schmidt; Thick mirror Schmidt	3.5; 7.2	85 to 750	1950
16......	McDonald, coudé	Refl.	205	Mirror	10	Blazed grating	Schmidt; Schmidt; Schmidt	20; 40; 80; 160	34; 17; 8.5; 4.3	1949
17......	Mount Wilson, coudé	Refl.	250	Mirror	15.2	Blazed gratings	Concentric mirror; Schmidts with twice-through corrector; Off-axis Schmidt; Off-axis Schmidt; Concentric mirror	20; 40; 80; 180; 285; 22	40; 20; 10 – 4; 4.5 – 1.8; 2.9 – 1.1; 38	1935–1956
18......	Palomar, Hale coudé	Refl.	500	Mirror	30.4	Composite of four blazed gratings	Aplanatic sphere Schmidt; Schmidts with twice-through correctors	47; 92; 184; 364	18; 9; 4.5; 2.3	1952
19......	Mount Wilson, Cassegrain	Refl.	150	Cassegrain mirror	10	Blazed grating	Concentric mirror; Schmidts with twice-through corrector and field flattener	10; 20; 40	80; 40; 20	1955
20......	Haute Provence, coudé	Refl.	193	Mirror	15	Blazed grating	Arnulf-Lyot-Schmidt; Arnulf-Lyot-Schmidt; Arnulf-Lyot-Schmidt; Concentric Mirror	16.5; 33; 67; 200	39 –50; 19 –25; 9.7 –12.4; 3.1 – 4.1	1959
21......	Kitt Peak, Cassegrain	Refl.	90	Mirror	7.6	Blazed grating	Flat-field Meinel-Schmidt; Flat-field Meinel-Schmidt	10.2; 6.1	160; 270	1960
22......	Lick, coudé	Refl.	300	Mirror	16.5	Blazed grating	Schmidt; Schmidt; Concentric Mirror	50; 100; 200; 400	6.8 –16.4; 3.4 – 8.2; 1.7 – 4.1; .85– 2.0	1961

manent record of the spectrum that the photograph provides. For these reasons the substantial number of large telescopes that were constructed in the period from 1885 to 1910 were regularly provided with spectrographic equipment. The specifications of several typical spectrographs of this period are listed in items 3 to 6 of Table 3. Many of these instruments were planned for radial-velocity programs on bright stars for which dispersions of 10–30 A/mm were necessary. To satisfy these needs, the usual arrangement had three prisms of flint glass and cameras of 35–100 cm in focal length. Since the range of wave lengths covered was small, the limited angular field of a simple achromat sufficed for most cameras, although in a few cases one of the early anastigmats was substituted. During this period the problem of flexure during long exposure was attacked and solved. Since the focal lengths of camera and collimator were about equal and since the usual three prisms produced a deviation of 180° in the beam, the slit and plate were very close together. By rigidly connecting these, partial compensation for flexure was achieved. Another device developed in this period to reduce flexure was the construction of a rigid spectrograph frame supported at its center of gravity rather than attached at one end to the telescope.

During the first two decades of the present century, telescope apertures increased very markedly with the advent of the large silver-on-glass reflectors.

FIG. 1.—Prime-focus spectrograph of the McDonald Observatory 82-inch reflector (item 14 of Table 3).

At the same time the great success of astronomical spectroscopy in opening up many new fields of investigation emphasized the need for instruments that could reach fainter and fainter objects and could record a wider range of wave lengths. As indicated in equations (13) and (14), this demanded the development of camera optics of larger aperture and lower focal ratio while maintaining the critical definition over a wide field necessary to take full advantage of the plate resolution.

The first step in the design of special camera lenses for this purpose was made in Germany by Hartmann (1904), who took advantage of the fact that a spectrograph-camera lens need not be achromatic, since chromatic aberrations may be compensated by plate tilt. By concentrating on the other aberrations, he was able to design a two-element lens which, at a focal ratio of F 12, gave good definition over a much larger field than a simple achromat. Later Schwarzschild

FIG. 2.—Prime-focus spectrograph of the Hale telescope with 3.5-cm camera (item 15 of Table 3).

(1912), taking advantage of this same property, designed a three-element lens that operated successfully at F 4.5 in apertures up to 6.0 cm. "Chromatic" camera lenses such as these have been used by Zeiss on the spectrographs constructed for a number of European observatories, including the Potsdam, Berlin-Babelsberg (see item 7 of Table 3), Hamburg-Bergedorf, Uccle, Merate, and Stockholm Observatories. For the spectrograph of the 72-inch Victoria telescope, J. S. Plaskett carried out a very extensive investigation of the lens designs available at that time. By carefully balancing the field curvature of lenses of the Petzval type against the opposite curvature of a spectral image caused by the secondary chromatic aberration, he was able to achieve satisfactory operation at focal ratios as low as F 3.6. Item 8 of Table 3 lists the camera-prism combinations finally selected for this instrument.

The demand for camera lenses of extreme speed but relatively small field, to permit effective use of the 100-inch Mount Wilson reflector in the measurement of the radial velocities of very faint galaxies, led Rayton (1930) to a new approach to the problem. Rayton made use of the design principles of the extreme-aperture lenses already developed for microscope objectives of high numerical aperture. By redesigning the 16-mm and 4-mm microscope objectives for use

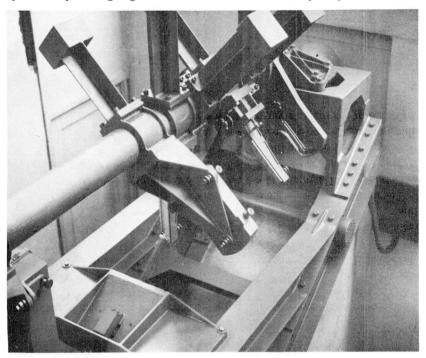

FIG. 3.—Coudé spectrograph of the McDonald Observatory 82-inch reflector. The three shortest cameras are mounted on a single turret for maximum stability and ease of operation (item 16 of Table 3).

without cover glass and for parallel incident light and by manufacturing the lenses with eight times the focal length of the corresponding microscope objectives, he produced two camera lenses of aperture 50 mm and having focal ratios of F 2.4 and F 0.59. The faster of these two lenses was mounted in a spectrograph, whose specifications are listed as item 9 of Table 3. Later Bracey (1936) adapted the design of the 2-mm oil-immersion microscope objective to attain a focal ratio of F 0.35.

Nearly all the spectrographs thus far listed made use of trains of flint-glass prisms of fairly large aperture. As discussed in § 5, the effective range of such a system is between about λ 3800 and λ 5000 A. With the rapid development of atomic-structure theory between 1910 and 1920, the interest in the whole observable range of wave lengths from the ultraviolet to the infrared became acute. In order to make observations at shorter wave lengths, Wright constructed a spectrograph for use either with a slit or as a slitless instrument with all-quartz optics at the Crossley reflector at Lick Observatory (see item 10 of Table 3). In order to attain satisfactory dispersion for observations in the red and infrared, Merrill built the grating instrument as detailed in item 11 of Table 3 for the telescopes on Mount Wilson.

During this same period there arose a demand for much higher dispersions for very detailed studies of the spectra of bright stars. Since weight increases as the

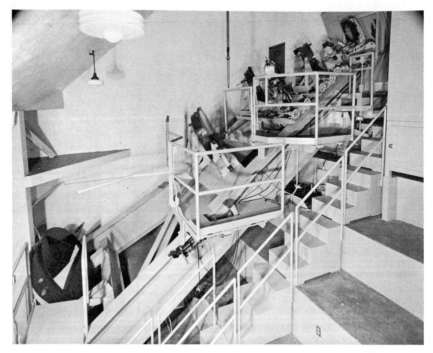

FIG. 4.—Coudé spectrograph of the Hale telescope (item 18 of Table 3)

cube and flexure as the square of the linear dimension of spectrographs, it was obviously impracticable to push to appreciably higher dispersion with spectrographs mounted on the telescope, and consequently such instruments must be placed in a fixed position at the coudé focus. The first of these was a prism-lens instrument constructed for the 60-inch telescope on Mount Wilson (see item 12 of Table 3); it yielded a dispersion of 1.4 A/mm at λ 4300 A. Later a similar instrument was installed at the coudé focus of the 100-inch telescope and modified from time to time as better lenses, prisms, and gratings became available.

The above instruments represent the development of spectrograph design up to the middle 1930's. Further progress in satisfying the conditions laid down by formulae (13) and (14) for the more effective use of the light collected by large telescopes was limited by two factors: (1) the failure of any lens design to pro-

Fig. 5.—Cassegrain spectrograph of the 60-inch telescope at Mount Wilson Observatory (item 19 of Table 3).

vide critical definition at apertures of over 6 or 8 cm and focal ratios of less than
F 3 and (2) the large absorption of any prism train having an aperture of over
6 or 8 cm.

Suddenly, however, the picture was completely changed by the advent of the
Schmidt camera and its various modifications (see Vol. **1,** chap. 4) and by the
development of the blazed grating, which permits the concentration of 60–70 per
cent of the light in one order. The efforts to exploit the Schmidt cameras for
spectrographs proceeded along two directions. The first of these was undertaken
at Mount Wilson to improve the performance of the extremely fast cameras for
the observation of the radial velocities of galaxies and of other very faint objects
by substituting a thick-mirror Schmidt for the Rayton lens. Originally, prisms
were used, but in a later modification these were replaced with blazed gratings,
and the instrument was redesigned for the Newtonian focus, thereby eliminating
the extra reflection of the Cassegrain focus. Item 13 of Table 3 lists the specifica-

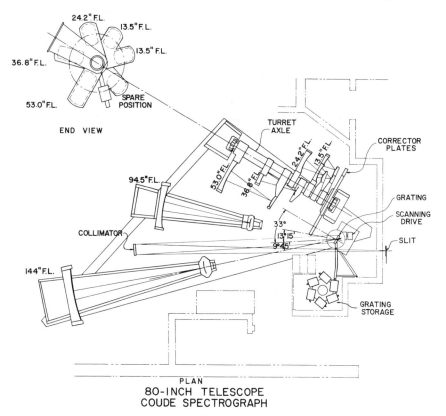

FIG. 6.—Design drawing of the coudé spectrograph for the 80-inch reflector of the Kitt
Peak National Observatory.

tions of this instrument in its final form. Later a similar instrument with a larger collimator beam was constructed for the prime focus of the Hale telescope. In order to make available a wide range of dispersions, this instrument is equipped with several gratings ranging from a 600-line/mm grating blazed in the second order to a 300-line/mm grating blazed in the first order (see item 15, Table 3).

The second application of the Schmidt camera was made by Adams and Dunham to improve the performance of the coudé spectrograph of the Mount Wilson 100-inch telescope. In this reconstruction the lens collimator was replaced by a parabolic mirror and the prism by a blazed grating ruled by Wood. Three off-axis Schmidt cameras having focal lengths of 80, 180, and 285 cm replaced the camera lens. Because of the large focal ratio, the corrector plate was omitted from the camera with the largest focal length. The original grating permitted a collimator aperture of 9 cm only. Later, as larger Babcock gratings became available, this was increased to 15 cm. In a further modification, provision was made for mounting four gratings in the spectrograph and for rapidly interchanging them. These included a 400-line/mm grating blazed at third-order λ 4200 A and second-order λ 6300 A; a 600-line/mm grating blazed at second-order λ 3500 A; and a 900-line/mm grating blazed in the third-order violet. At the same time it became evident that, even for the intermediate dispersions, the larger apertures at the coudé made possible substantial speed gains over any instrument that could be mounted on the telescope. Consequently, two on-axis Schmidt cameras with twice-through corrector plates having focal lengths of 20 and 40 cm were added to the battery of cameras. The 40-cm camera was constructed with a fused-quartz corrector plate, thereby permitting observations to the limit of transparency of the atmosphere. Item 17 of Table 3 lists the specifications of this instrument in its final form.

In making plans for the coudé spectrograph of the 200-inch Hale telescope it was obvious that if the efficiency was to be maintained at the same level as in smaller telescopes, it would be necessary to use a much larger collimator beam than any hitherto attempted. The final design has a 30-cm-aperture collimator beam and as a dispersing element a composite of four 14 × 17.5 gratings ruled with 400 lines/mm and blazed in the third order at λ 4200 A. These gratings are mounted on a heavy steel plate, the flexure of which is used as a fine adjustment. Cameras of 364, 184, 92, 47, and 22 cm in focal length are available. The longest is of the Schmidt type but, because of the large focal ratio, requires no corrector plate. The three intermediate cameras are of the Schmidt type with twice-through corrector plates. The shortest camera combines a quartz aplanatic sphere with the optics of the 47-cm camera to give the shorter focal length. Details are summarized under item 18 of Table 3.

Items 14, 16, 19, 20, 21, and 22 of Table 3 give the specifications of other postwar cameras making use of Schmidt cameras and blazed gratings. Three of these are coudé instruments (16, 20, and 22), one is for use at the prime focus (14), and two represent the application of these new procedures to Cassegrain instruments (19 and 21).

The author is indebted to Dr. Paul Merrill for many helpful suggestions made during the preparation of this article.

REFERENCES

BABCOCK, H. W.,
  RULE, B. H., and
  FASSERO, J. S.   1956   *Pub. A.S.P.*, **68**, 256.
BOWEN, I. S.   1938   *Ap. J.*, **88**, 113.
BRACEY, R. J.   1936   *Ap. J.*, **83**, 179.
FRAUNHOFER, J.   1814   *Denkschriften K. Akad. Wiss. München*, **5**, 222; *Gesammelte Schriften*, p. 25.

                           1823   *Gilberts Ann. d. Phys.*, **74**, 337; *Gesammelte Schriften*, p. 141.

HARRISON, G. R.,
  LORD, R. C., and
  LOOFBOUROW, J. R.   1948   *Practical Spectroscopy* (New York: Prentice-Hall, Inc.).
HARTMANN, J.   1904   *Zs. f. Instrumentenk.*, **24**, 257.
JENKINS, F. A., and
  WHITE, H. E.   1950   *Fundamentals of Optics* (2d ed.; New York: Mc-Graw-Hill Book Co., Inc.).
MONK, G. S.   1937   *Light Principles and Experiments* (New York and London: McGraw-Hill Book Co., Inc.).
PETTIT, E.   1934   *Pub. A.S.P.*, **46**, 27.
RAYTON, W. B.   1930   *Ap. J.*, **72**, 59.
RUNGE, C., and
  MEISSNER, K. W.   1933   *Hdb. d. Ap.*, **1**, 214.
SCHWARZSCHILD, K.   1912   *Sitz. Preuss. Akad. Wiss. Berlin*, p. 1220.

CHAPTER *3*

Radial-Velocity Determinations

R. M. PETRIE

Dominion Astrophysical Observatory

§ 1. INTRODUCTION

THE measurement of the line-of-sight component of stellar motion is one of the greatest achievements of astronomical spectroscopy. The technique reached a high degree of perfection in the first decade of the century, and it still ranks as one of the most versatile tools available to astronomers in the study of stellar motions and the exploration of the galaxy. It is of great value also in the study of the atmospheres of individual stars.

The principle of the dependence of the observed wave length of light on the relative motion of source and observer was announced by Christian Doppler in 1842 and extended by Fizeau in 1848, although publication was deferred until 1870. Huggins and Miller realized, in 1862, that an appreciable shift in spectral lines should be observable, and efforts to measure this were made by Huggins as early as 1866. His efforts were unsuccessful but were prophetic of the latent power of the spectroscopic method. It is of interest to note that, along with the experimental work, the subject appears first to have been presented in a definite analytical form by Clerk Maxwell in 1868 (Maxwell 1868).

The pioneers of the spectroscopic method were followed by a number of eminent students who strove assiduously to apply the Doppler principle to the measurement of stellar velocities. Their efforts were fruitless; the task was beyond the capabilities of human vision applied directly to the instruments of the time. It is instructive even today to examine the spectrum of a star visually in the focal plane of a powerful modern spectrograph attached to a large telescope. One is then not astonished at the negative results obtained by astronomers of pre-photographic days.

Toward the end of the nineteenth century one visual observer enjoyed a measure of success. Keeler, working with the 36-inch refractor under the favorable skies of Mount Hamilton, measured radial velocities of Arcturus,

Aldebaran, and Betelgeuse (Keeler 1894). These results, combined with Keeler's work on the more easily measured spectra of gaseous nebulae, represent the high mark of a method happily rendered obsolete by the introduction of photography. Beginning with Draper's experiments in 1872 (Draper 1877), a decade saw the photographic recording of stellar spectra firmly established and the way opened for the full development of the technique of measurement of Doppler shifts. The student interested in the history of the subject will find a fine account in Campbell's *Stellar Motions* (Campbell 1913), as well as a masterly description of the perfecting of the photographic method of obtaining radial velocities. The present chapter, being restricted to an account of the methods of determining radial velocities, will not include the full chronological story or the many applications of stellar radial-velocity data. The latter will be discussed in other chapters of this compendium.

§ 2. THE SPECTROGRAPH

The measurement of stellar radial velocities is generally difficult because of the smallness of the Doppler displacements. A typical single-prism spectrograph may be expected to give a linear dispersion, in the middle of the photographic region, of about 40 angstroms per millimeter. One millimeter on a spectrogram of this dispersion corresponds to a radial-velocity displacement of nearly 2900 km/sec. Radial velocities are ordinarily about 1 per cent of this amount, and we must therefore make significant measurements of a few microns on the photographic plate. It is, of course, relatively easy to obtain accurate velocities from high-dispersion spectrograms of the kind obtained with coudé instruments, but these powerful spectrographs cannot be used in extensive radial-velocity programs because of the prohibitively long exposures.

Leaving aside, for the moment, observations made with slitless spectrographs, the fundamental task is to photograph stellar and comparison spectra so that the wave-length system defined by the comparison lines is valid for the stellar spectrum. The comparison source is fastened to the spectrograph, and its light is passed into the slit by a combination of mirrors, lenses, and prisms, while the starlight is collected by the telescope optics. "Identity of source" must be maintained in the two beams within a few thousandths of an angstrom if systematic errors are to be avoided. This condition imposes severe restrictions upon the mechanical and optical tolerances in the design of a stellar spectrograph devoted to radial-velocity work.

Because of its faintness, one must use all the starlight passed by a necessarily rather wide slit. The collimating lens is to be filled by the stellar beam, but no more than filled. This condition requires that the spectrograph must not bend very much relative to the optic axis of the telescope for different positions of the telescope, or else "identity of source" is destroyed. The first instruments were fastened to telescopes by a single attachment and, like any cantilever, underwent appreciable bending. The introduction of a two-point support system

(Wright 1907) of counterbalancing devices, and of specially stiff construction, remedied the trouble, so that modern stellar spectrographs are adequately free from flexure. Necessary improvements in the methods of holding the optical parts firmly, yet without strain, were introduced about the same time as the advances in mechanical design.

Exposure times in stellar spectroscopy are usually long. This fact can be a source of error, in that temperature changes during exposure produce changes in the refractive index of the prism or prisms and tend to change the focus of the collimator-camera combination. The net result is a shift of the stellar absorption lines relative to the comparison spectrum. This source of error was eliminated in the early days of radial-velocity work, first, by insulating the spectrograph and, finally, by introducing controlled heating elements to offset the loss of heat during an exposure. The modern stellar spectrograph remains at a sensibly constant temperature even during an exposure lasting all night in a dome where the ambient temperature may drop 10° C or more. It is interesting to note that temperature controls may be dispensed with in large modern coudé spectrographs because the large heat capacity of the coudé room and the spectrograph itself, combined with the comparative thermal insensitivity of gratings, renders the use of a thermostat unnecessary.

Optical performance of a high quality is necessary for accurate results. The stellar lines appear in absorption and are measured relative to comparison lines in emission. Defects in the image caused by lens aberrations, inhomogeneity in the prisms, ghosts, or other irregularities in the lines from the grating are likely to displace the images of the comparison lines relative to the stellar absorption features. It follows also that the lenses and dispersive pieces must be mounted firmly enough to remain in alignment at all orientations of the telescope and yet be free from mechanical strain.

The strict requirements outlined above were appreciated and studied during the first years of this century, and, as they were met, the stellar spectrograph developed rapidly into an instrument of high precision. The pioneering work at Mount Hamilton (Campbell and Moore 1928), Potsdam (Vogel 1900), and Ottawa (Plaskett 1909), among others, are worthy of close study. A full account of the main developments, together with examples, is given by Eberhard (1933). The most recent trend in the direction of power and efficiency is demonstrated in the coudé spectrographs, principally at Palomar, Mount Wilson, and McDonald Observatories. These instruments have not yet been applied extensively to radial-velocity work, and it is not known whether the complex mirror system linking telescope and spectrograph has introduced difficulties and whether the use of a relatively wide slit has limited the accuracy. As an example of the potentialities of these great instruments, one may refer to Adams' measures of α Bootis and determination of solar parallax with the coudé spectrograph at Mount Wilson (Adams 1941). The internal probable error of a plate velocity, from twenty-five lines, was ± 0.05 km/sec, while the

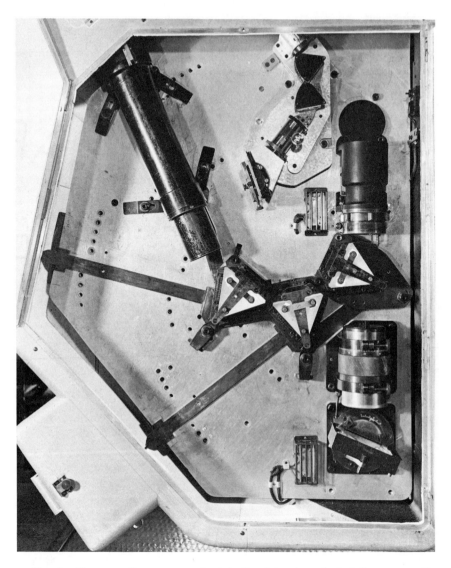

Fig. 1.—The new stellar spectrograph of the Dominion Astrophysical Observatory. The components of a three-prism spectrograph are shown fastened to the "optical table." Below the first prism (*right*) are shown the collimator-camera lens and the plane grating, which form a high-dispersion Littrow spectrograph. A complete two-prism ultraviolet instrument is shown at top center.

probable error of a single plate from the external agreement was found to be
± 0.03 km/sec, a remarkably small error!

During most of its existence, radial-velocity work has been performed
largely with prismatic spectrographs. An attempt to employ gratings was made
as early as 1913 by J. S. Plaskett (1913). His work plainly indicated the advantages of gratings, but the low reflecting power and lack of controlled blaze
available at that time were serious handicaps. The development of very
efficient blazed gratings and the invention of the Schmidt camera now make
obsolescent the conventional prism spectrograph, except possibly for small
apertures. The grating with its normal dispersion offers important advantages
in radial-velocity observations of stars of spectral types F5 and later. It allows
for effective work in the visual region where the spectrum is brighter and the
lines are more free from the blending that is so troublesome in the photographic
region.

An early use of a grating spectrograph of moderate dispersion was made by
Merrill (1931). Dunham (1956) pioneered in the use of gratings and Schmidt
cameras in the coudé spectrograph on Mount Wilson, and spectroscopists are
familiar with the magnificent instruments designed by Bowen (1952) for use
with the Hale telescope. Gratings are employed in a Littrow-type spectrograph
used at the Cassegrainian focus of the 72-inch reflector at Victoria (Beals,
Petrie, and McKellar 1946). Recently Bowen has designed a novel moderate-
dispersion spectrograph (Wilson 1956), employing gratings and all-reflection
optics (for the 60-inch reflector) which should be very efficient in radial-velocity
work.

§ 3. MEASURING THE SPECTROGRAMS

It was mentioned above that Doppler shifts are usually a few microns
on the single-prism spectrograms ordinarily obtained in extensive programs.
Defects in the measuring apparatus, photographic distortions, and human
frailties can produce errors of about the same size. Significant measures
are possible largely because the process is one of interpolation from comparison
to stellar spectrum. Every care must be exercised in the use of measuring
micrometers, and good judgment must be applied in making visual settings.
As remarked by Campbell, "an inexperienced or careless measurer will obtain
poor results from perfect plates."

Measurements were made at first by means of a traveling-plate carriage
under a microscope, the machine being equipped with an accurate screw, usually
of $\frac{1}{2}$-mm or 1-mm pitch. The setting of a reticle upon the absorption and comparison lines and the reading of the micrometer head were made with direct-
vision microscopes. The strain of looking for hours through a microscope was
later alleviated, to some extent, by the use of binocular eyepieces.

Direct measurement of the spectrogram, as described above, gives a series
of positions of stellar and comparison lines. The apparent wave lengths of the

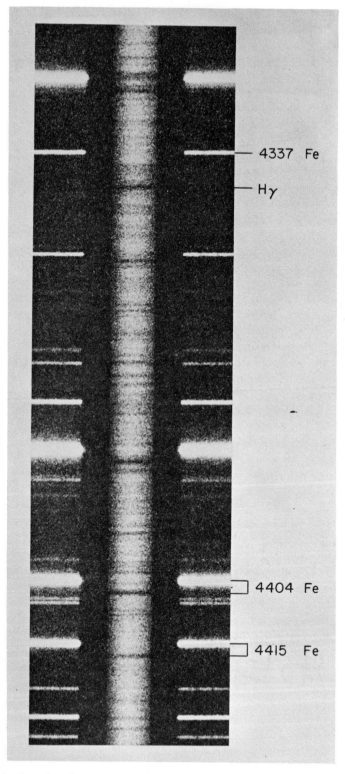

FIG. 2.—A portion of a spectrogram of HD 24421. The plate velocity is +130 km/sec. The redward displacement of the stellar lines is easily seen by comparison of the neutral iron lines in the stellar and comparison spectra.

stellar lines are then found from the known wave lengths of the comparison lines, using the well-known Hartmann interpolation formula,

$$R - R_0 = \frac{C}{(\lambda - \lambda_0)^a},$$

where R_0, λ_0, C, and a are constants for a plate. At first, the measurements made on each plate were analyzed by this formula to obtain values of λ for R, the setting, after the plate constants had been calculated from the settings and wave lengths of the comparison lines. The laborious method of treating each plate in this fundamental way was soon replaced by the use of a standard table computed once for each spectrograph and against which a plate could be "reduced" by a differential comparison. A good account of the application of the method, together with an illustrative example, is given by Moore (1935), while an example of the calculation of the plate constants is given by Stratton (1925).

Much of the computational labor associated with the "reduction" of plate measures was eliminated with the invention, by Hartmann (1906), of the spectrocomparator. Doppler shifts can be measured directly with the spectrocomparator, the spectrogram to be measured being compared in the field of view of the microscope with a standard spectrogram whose radial velocity is known. The ingenious instrument devised by Hartmann not only reduced computation to a minimum but also removed much of the uncertainty caused by "blends." This was accomplished by making comparisons between spectrograms of the same purity and spectral type. The spectrocomparator is very efficient in the measurement of spectra of types F5 and later but is not easily used for the earlier-type spectra in which the absorption lines are few in number, are often poorly defined, and vary in appearance from star to star. The measuring microscope remains the fundamental instrument for radial-velocity measures on early-type spectra and for investigating velocity differences among the spectral lines and other related problems.

The fatigue accompanying the use of visual microscopes limits the speed with which measurement can be carried out in an extensive radial-velocity program. Fatigue is decreased and efficiency increased by the adoption of projection methods introduced some twenty years ago in this application (Petrie 1937; Redman 1939). The effort required to convert measuring machines to the projection system is amply justified by improvement in efficiency and accuracy.

A further advance in measuring technique was made at Victoria in 1948 (Petrie and Girling 1948) with the invention of an all-projection machine which enables one to measure Doppler shifts directly for individual lines. An enlarged image of the spectrogram to be measured is projected onto a scale upon which are ruled the positions of the comparison lines and the zero-velocity positions of the stellar lines. Optical and mechanical adjustments allow one to match precisely the projected comparison spectrum with the corresponding scale rulings. The Doppler shift of the stellar absorption lines is then seen relative to the zero-velocity rulings and may be quickly measured. The projection comparator has proved to be extremely efficient when used in the measurement of large numbers of spectrograms of one dispersion and similar spectral class. The measurement and reduction of spectrograms need no longer be serious obstacles to the completion of an extensive radial-velocity program. Furthermore, the scales are ruled only for tested and accepted wave-length standards, so that the velocities are homogeneous and free from errors produced by the sporadic introduction of non-standard wave lengths.

The present development of measuring instruments is satisfactory as long as visual methods are used. The next advance, obviously, is the development of automatic, or semiautomatic, machines. Current progress in electronics and servomechanisms points the way, and already one or two ingenious devices have been constructed (Johnson 1949; Hossack 1953), although none has, as yet, been applied to routine production of radial velocities. It is likely, however, that measurement of spectrograms will eventually be relegated to impersonal,

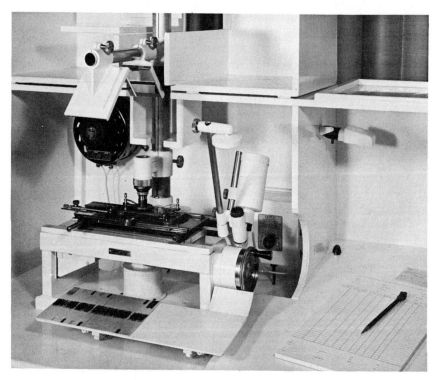

Fig. 3.—The projection micrometer of the Dominion Astrophysical Observatory. The projection systems for the spectrogram and micrometer head are readily seen. The appearance of the projected stellar spectrum is shown on the viewing screen.

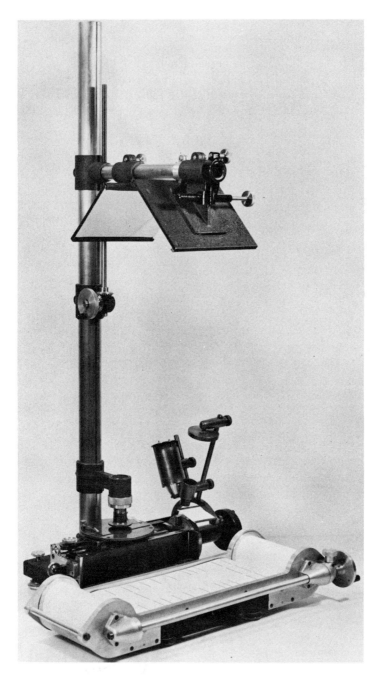

FIG. 4.—The projection comparator of the Dominion Astrophysical Observatory. The projection systems for the spectrogram and micrometer head are shown. A ruled scale is shown in position upon the scale transport mechanism.

automatic machines, and every encouragement should be given to experiments in that direction. It should be borne in mind that the ideal machine should supply the Doppler shift or, better, the radial velocity of each line measured. A tabulation of micrometer readings of the stellar and comparison lines is only half the task, since the lengthy process of "reduction" would then still remain to be done.

§ 4. EFFECTIVE WAVE LENGTHS

The determination of appropriate zero-velocity values of the wave lengths adopted in radial-velocity work is a matter of prime importance and considerable difficulty. An uncertainty of 0.05 A corresponds, in the photographic region, to an uncertainty of approximately 3.5 km/sec in radial velocity. Quantities of this size have received considerable attention in studies of stellar motion—for example, the K term and the redshift in early-type stars. We must be certain of the effective wave lengths before we can discuss alleged small velocity effects with confidence.

The accuracy of our wave-length systems determined in the laboratory is, of course, better than the requirements of stellar radial-velocity work. The problem is not the pure wave lengths of atomic lines but rather the equivalent wave lengths of absorption features observed in stellar spectra. Two effects generally prevent the use of laboratory data without investigation, as follows: (a) the blending of several pure absorption lines into a single feature and the asymmetrical broadening of a single strong line by adjacent absorption lines and (b) asymmetrical broadening such as that produced by the Stark effect, which influences the position of an absorption line in a complicated way. In addition, we must also consider the possibility of local atmospheric motions producing a false radial velocity, as, for example, in the spectra of "shell" stars. This matter cannot be investigated very well until the blending and broadening distortions are evaluated.

Wave-length problems have been given special attention at Victoria over the past decade (Petrie 1947, 1948, 1953; McDonald 1948; Wright 1951; Petrie, Andrews, and McDonald 1957). It has been found that, in spectra later than A0, practically all features are blends of two or more lines when observed with moderate dispersion. The effective wave lengths vary with linear dispersion and spectral purity, and, with a given spectrograph, a great many vary with spectral type, with absolute magnitude, and with the amount of broadening caused by rotation of the star. One cannot, without prior investigation, adopt wave lengths from the literature and be certain that the resulting velocities are, in fact, accurate motions in the line of sight.

The problem can be solved for spectral types F5–K8 inclusive by studying spectra of members of the solar system whose velocities are known independently of any spectroscopic information. Measures of lines in standard spectra of the sun, moon, and planets, when compared with the calculated radial velocities, and the powerful aid of the *Utrecht Solar Atlas* and the *Revised*

Rowland Table will enable one to select reliable features and assign effective wave lengths independently of instrumental and measuring errors. Spectra of standard velocity stars will allow one to extend the solar wave lengths to other spectral types between F5 and K8 and to eliminate features which vary strongly with spectral type.

The solar system velocities and spectra of solar type must form the basic standards and define the zero points of radial-velocity systems. Extension to other spectral classes must be by successive steps, since unfortunately we do not have velocity standards of types A, B, and M comparable to those of the solar system. Standards may be found, however, in components of visual binaries and in members of galactic clusters. If one member of a binary or one or more cluster members are solar-type stars, we can determine the radial velocities with wave lengths already verified from the solar system and proceed to test wave lengths in spectra of stars of other types. In doing this, we are assuming that both components of a visual binary have closely the same radial velocity and that members of a galactic cluster have a common radial velocity. Binaries selected for this work have long periods, and the assumption is a safe one. It is generally observed that the individual stars of well-known compact clusters, such as Taurus, the Pleiades, and Praesepe, have equal motions. The Taurus cluster is a good example. The four solar-type stars have radial velocities as follows (Petrie 1946): γ Tauri, $+38.6$ km/sec; δ Tauri, $+38.1$ km/sec; ϵ Tauri, $+37.8$ km/sec; θ^1 Tauri, $+37.8$ km/sec. The space motion of the cluster may be calculated from the radial velocities above and from the positions of the stars, and the space motion so derived may then be used to predict the radial velocities of the non-solar-type members. Thus A-type stars in the Taurus cluster become velocity standards homogeneous with those in the solar system. The visual binary μ Bootis, composed of stars of types G0 and late A, is a good example of a double-star control.

It is not usually possible to connect the B stars directly with the solar system because of the large difference in magnitude between G stars and B stars. The A stars have to be used as intermediate controls except in the few cases like the visual binary ADS 2559, which comprises a main-sequence star of type B2.5, $m_v = 7.4$, and a giant of spectral type G5, $m_v = 8.5$. Here we may compare a B and a solar-type star directly; in other cases the control velocities must, of necessity, depend on A stars.

The solar system until now has been used as the sole fundamental velocity standard, but one can visualize the future use of one or two moving clusters as primary standards for spectra of types A and B. We may calculate the radial velocities of members of the Taurus cluster, the Pleiades, and Praesepe, for example, from proper motions and trigonometric parallaxes when the latter are more accurately measured than at the present time. Even now the Ursa Major cluster may qualify as a "primary" control for A types. The space motion calculated from the proper motions and trigonometric parallaxes of the individual stars is 15.2 ± 0.8 km/sec (Petrie and Moyls 1953). Radial velocities obtained with a two-prism spectrograph (11 A/mm at Hγ) show the following residuals from the computed radial velocities: 8 A stars, mean residual = −0.3 km/sec ± 0.7; 2 F–G stars, mean residual = 0.0 km/sec.

The establishment of a homogeneous system of effective wave lengths, as described in the Victoria work, is extremely laborious, requiring the photography and measurement of several hundred spectrograms. Fortunately, this labor need not be repeated at other observatories, since we now have available standard stars between spectral classes B0 and K8 and, furthermore, we know which spectral features to accept and which to reject. The Victoria wave lengths will probably apply, with minor revisions, to spectra made with other instruments of comparable purity (Stibbs 1955). The verification should be made, however, and unsuitable lines should be eliminated before one embarks upon a program of radial-velocity work.

Effective wave lengths for O-type and M-type spectra have not yet been determined homogeneous with the other spectral intervals. The O stars are valuable in the study of galactic clusters, associations, and the question of the gravitational redshift; the M stars will be especially useful in investigating galactic structure and stellar populations. Radial-velocity measures of these very hot and very cool stars should be brought into the existing wave-length system as soon as possible.

§ 5. THE ACCURACY OF STELLAR RADIAL VELOCITIES

In spite of the development of powerful spectrographs of high mechanical and thermal stability and despite the care bestowed upon wave lengths, it is well to recognize that radial velocities are still subject to important errors. The following appear to be the principal causes.

5.1. DIFFERENTIAL FLEXURE

Flexure between optical axes of telescope and spectrograph can introduce systematic error, as described above. Although it is apparently not often troublesome in modern spectrographs, Jacobsen (1926) has reported errors produced by flexure in a two-prism spectrograph attached to the 36-inch refractor at Mount Hamilton. Extensive tests at Victoria (unpublished) have failed to reach differential flexure effects large enough to be measured with certainty. It is important to check flexure errors in coudé instruments, where the starlight undergoes several reflections before entering the slit, which, in long-focus instruments, is usually relatively wide.

5.2. GUIDING

Guiding errors, caused by non-uniform illumination of the slit, can be troublesome. They tend to increase with zenith distance and, for a particular telescope, with the width of the slit of the spectrograph. A slit-width of 0.075 mm in an ordinary single-prism spectrograph (linear dispersion at Hγ, 50 A/mm) projects into a rectangular area on the spectrogram about 100 km/sec wide. It is thus very easy to produce a spurious displacement in the stellar lines by uneven guiding. An example may be of interest. Deliberately bad guiding was used in photographing spectra of κ¹ Herculis and HD 168656, using a single-prism spectrograph at dispersion 51 A/mm at Hγ and a slit-width of 0.075 mm. Spectra were obtained by guiding on the extreme red and violet edges of the refracted images as well as by the usual central guiding. The following radial-velocity differences were found:

	κ¹ Herculis (Km/Sec)	HD 168656 (Km/Sec)		κ¹ Herculis (Km/Sec)	HD 168656 (Km/Sec)
Violet edge − central..	+10.2	+7.9	Red edge − central....	−8.7	−7.2

While this is an extreme example, it is obvious that careful attention must be given to guiding during an exposure.

The width of the slit image on the spectrogram, in kilometers per second, decreases as the angular dispersion is increased. Guiding errors are less, then, with multiprism, or large-grating, spectrographs for a given slit-width. The modern practice, however, is to employ high angular dispersion, short-focus cameras, and a wide slit, in order to increase efficiency. The problem of guiding is thus not avoided but may be even more important in large powerful spectrographs because a much larger fraction of the stellar image is covered by the slit.

5.3. Photographic Errors

Sporadic shifts of spectral lines, not explained by errors of measurement, are familiar to everyone experienced in measuring Doppler shifts. A recent paper (Gollnow and Hagemann 1956) demonstrates that large photographic distortions can occur, depending partly on the processing of the negative. On the average, the effect is minimized by the use of a large number of lines over a fairly large portion of the negative. Distortion contributes to the probable error of a plate and may, in certain cases, produce an erroneous mean velocity.

5.4. Measuring Errors

Errors of bisection are not serious with experienced measurers and with spectra showing a moderate number of reasonably well-defined lines. Measurement errors do become important, however, in spectra of early-type stars exhibiting only a few ill-defined features. The only way to obtain reliable velocities in such cases is to use six to ten spectrograms for the mean velocity.

It is worthwhile here to recall Campbell's remarks as to the care required in measuring even well-defined spectral lines. A certain background of experience and an understanding of the production of absorption lines are required for

successful radial-velocity measures. The practice of employing relatively inexperienced persons for the measurement of Doppler shifts cannot be approved
and should be abandoned. Modern measuring devices may now be made so
efficient that the astronomer working with radial velocities need no longer
relegate the measurement to others.

5.5. Discussion of Errors

The following paragraphs give some results on the accuracy to be expected
in radial-velocity work. The numerical values are obtained largely with the
spectrographs at Victoria; some comparisons indicate that similar results
will be obtained with other spectrographs giving comparable purity and dispersion. For an account of the errors found in early work with telescopes

TABLE 1

Probable Errors of Radial Velocity of One Spectral Line

Instrument	Linear Dispersion at Hγ (A/Mm)	Slit-Width (Mm)	Solar-Type Spectra			B-Type Spectra		
			Repeat Measures (Km/Sec)	Internal Agreement (Km/Sec)	Plate Error (Km/Sec)	Repeat Measures (Km/Sec)	Internal Agreement (Km/Sec)	Plate Error (Km/Sec)
Mount Wilson coudé.	3.5	0.025	±0.12	±0.43	±0.41	......	......	......
Victoria Littrow*....	3.5	.051	0.38	0.69	0.58	......	......	......
Victoria two-prism...	11.0	.051	0.6	1.7	1.6	±2.3	±5.4	±4.9
Victoria one-prism ...	30	0.051	1.3	2.6	2.2	2.7	8.5	8.1

* The Victoria Littrow spectrograph, while giving dispersions equal to the Mount Wilson coudé spectrograph,
provides much less spectral purity and resolving power than the Mount Wilson instrument.

of moderate power, one should consult the pioneering work of J. S. Plaskett
(1910).

It is evident at once that the errors of bisection or measurement need not
concern us because they are usually less than other causes. Table 1 lists probable
errors of average lines computed (a) from the internal agreement among lines
on a single plate and (b) from the differences between duplicate measures of
the same plates.

Spectra of solar-type stars with sharp lines were represented by α Bootis,
μ Herculis, and λ Serpentis. For the poorer, yet moderately well-defined, lines
of early-type spectra, average values were used from measures of spectra of
π^4 Orionis, π^5 Orionis, ν Orionis, and AR Cassiopeiae. It was possible to include
high-dispersion spectra of α Bootis taken with a coudé spectrograph through
the courtesy of the Mount Wilson Observatory.

The numbers in Table 1 demonstrate clearly that the error of measurement,
in velocity units, increases steadily as the linear dispersion is reduced and that

the bisection error is substantially greater on the rather diffuse lines of early-type spectra. These conclusions are, of course, to be expected. It is important to note that in every case the error of measurement is less than the error computed from the internal agreement. We may therefore dismiss the actual setting errors as unimportant compared with other sources, if measures are made by experienced persons. It is difficult to be certain about spectra with very poor lines, but it is suspected, from the comparisons that have been made, that errors of measurement approach those from the internal scatter in the worst cases. The technique of bisection may then become important.

The setting error has been removed from the error given by the internal agreement, assuming that the sources are independent and the errors distributed normally. The net results, which we may call the "plate errors," are listed under that designation in Table 1. It is seen that this error also increases with decreasing dispersion and is greater for the diffuse-line spectra.

The plate error probably arises from several causes. Errors in effective wave lengths certainly contribute, but the distortions and grain fluctuations in the emulsion itself are probably more influential. Fluctuations in density rather than actual displacements may explain, in part, the larger scatter found in the low-contrast lines. It is difficult to account for the full increase in scatter between solar-type and B spectra as emulsion effects, and some of it has very likely a physical origin. Spectral lines formed effectively at different levels in the stellar atmosphere may well show a velocity dispersion because of the violent local motions present in the outer layers of the hotter stars. The increase in plate error with decreasing dispersion in B-type spectra shows that only part of the error is physical: some of it must be ascribed to photographic effects, with perhaps a portion caused by uncertainties in effective wave lengths. It is clear from the entries in Table 1 that more refined methods of making settings upon spectral lines are unnecessary; improvement will come, if it comes at all, by reducing the emulsion errors themselves.

The material discussed above refers solely to the accidental errors inherent in a single spectrogram and has no bearing on the systematic error associated with the plate. This more serious matter makes the question of the internal scatter somewhat academic, at least until the errors now to be discussed can be reduced. Table 2 lists the probable errors of single plates determined from the internal agreement among the lines and, second, from the scatter of the plate values about the mean. Results are given for high-dispersion grating spectrograms as well as for the single-prism arrangements customarily used in radial-velocity programs at Victoria. The numerical values rest upon measures of several hundred spectrograms and are therefore representative.

The error calculated from external agreement exceeds in every case that calculated from the internal agreement. When we remove the latter error from the former, we are left with a source of error that is free from internal plate errors and is produced by causes other than those operative in the values

TABLE 2

PROBABLE ERRORS OF RADIAL VELOCITY FROM ONE SPECTROGRAM

INSTRUMENT	LINEAR DISPERSION AT $H\gamma$ (A/Mm)	SLIT-WIDTH (Mm)	SOLAR-TYPE SPECTRA			A SPECTRA			B SPECTRA		
			Int. Agreement (Km/Sec)	Ext. Agreement (Km/Sec)	Obs. Error (Km/Sec)	Int. Agreement (Km/Sec)	Ext. Agreement (Km/Sec)	Obs. Error (Km/Sec)	Int. Agreement (Km/Sec)	Ext. Agreement (Km/Sec)	Obs. Error (Km/Sec)
Mount Wilson coudé.......	3.5	0.025	±0.12	±0.19	±0.15	......	......	......	......	......	......
Victoria Littrow.........	3.5	.051	0.20	0.33	0.26						
Victoria two-prism.......	11.0	.051	0.35	0.70	0.60	±1.1	±1.4	±0.9	±1.8	±2.9	±2.3
Victoria one-prism.......	30	.051	0.7	1.3	1.1	1.2	1.9	1.5	2.4	3.7	2.8
Victoria one-prism.......	51	.076	1.2	2.0	1.6	2.2	3.4	2.6	3.7	4.3	2.2
Victoria one-prism.......	90	0.076	2.5	4.1	3.2	3.4	4.0	2.1	5.0	6.3	3.8

in Table 1. We shall call this the "observational error" and give its values
in Table 2. It will be noticed that the observational error increases as the slit
width is increased and as the dispersion is decreased and usually increases as
we proceed from solar-type spectra toward earlier types. The observational
error arises in instrumental effects, such as flexure, optical imperfections, and
thermal variation, and in guiding error, producing a non-uniform illumination
of the slit. It is probably affected in early-type stars by a small, real, velocity
variation not easily recognized because of the diffuse nature of the spectral lines.

Table 2 shows that the wave lengths and measuring techniques used in
obtaining the plate velocity are satisfactory. Improved mean radial velocities
may be obtained primarily by reducing the observational error. This may be
accomplished by increasing the number of spectrograms measured, by increasing
the dispersion, or by decreasing the slit-width. All these stratagems are expen-

TABLE 3

PROBABLE ERRORS OF A MEAN VELOCITY FROM THREE PLATES

Dispersion (A/Mm)	Solar-Type Stars (Km/Sec)	A-Type Stars (Km/Sec)	B-Type Stars (Km/Sec)	Dispersion (A/Mm)	Solar-Type Stars (Km/Sec)	A-Type Stars (Km/Sec)	B-Type Stars (Km/Sec)
10........	±0.4	±0.8	±1.7	50........	1.2	2.0	2.5
30........	0.8	1.1	2.1	90........	2.4	2.3	3.6

sive of light and can scarcely be contemplated in extensive programs on faint
stars. They may, however, be adopted with profit in shorter special investigations.

Extensive radial-velocity programs will in the future supply mean velocities
based on probably not more than three spectrograms of each star. Expected
probable errors of the mean velocities with various dispersions are given in
Table 3.

Even with the lowest dispersion, the values in Table 3 are satisfactory for
some investigations of stellar motions where the random motions will exceed
the probable errors.

§ 6. THE FUTURE OF RADIAL-VELOCITY OBSERVATIONS

Radial-velocity work with conventional slit spectrographs as a major astronomical activity is now restricted to relatively few observatories. Furthermore,
these institutions are now confronted with the principle of "diminishing
returns" in their efforts to obtain material to extend our knowledge to greater
distances from the sun. A step of several magnitudes in the stars to be observed
is required for rapid progress in galactic studies and is beyond the practical
resources of observatories now engaged in radial-velocity programs. The picture

is not encouraging, and astronomers may well pause to survey the prospects for the future. The above remarks apply, of course, to general stellar motion problems and do not include the many important observations to be made on special objects and relatively nearby stars.

Two possibilities are presently being developed which may bring about an improvement in the situation. The first is the recent advance in the application of the slitless spectrograph to radial-velocity determinations. The subject has a long history of attempts to utilize the great efficiency of the objective-prism method. Reviews by Millman (1930) and Fehrenbach (1947, 1948) cover work up to 1940 and indicate the lack of success to that time, the efforts of many investigators being nullified by, among other things, the existence of field distortions many times greater than the Doppler shift.

The most important and successful work to date has been by Fehrenbach (1947, 1948), who demonstrated that the distortions can be reduced to a tractable size by the use of a "normal," or "direct-vision," prism in front of the objective of a refracting telescope. The results published so far by Fehrenbach are promising, in that accidental errors are reduced to an acceptable amount, which appears to open the way to a significant extension to more distant parts of the galaxy. Studies and applications along similar lines have been made by Treanor (1948) and by Schalén (1954). Observatories with a background of experience in radial-velocity work and the necessary telescopic power should now consider exploiting the technical advances which have been made in the determination of velocities by the slitless method.

Perhaps the greatest advantage of the objective-prism method is its ability to cover an appreciable area on the sky and so, with a single exposure, to make available for measurement the spectra of numerous stars. This valuable property is lost if we remove the slit from a conventional spectrograph placed at the Cassegrain focus of a large reflector. Nevertheless, the great light-grasp of the large aperture, combined with the better temperature control available, makes it worthwhile to explore the possibilities in this direction, as suggested by Treanor (1948). Several arrangements using a grating with a strong blaze in a modified Littrow mounting suggest themselves as practicable and present the possibility of gaining 2 mag. or more in light compared with the slit spectrograph.

A second possibility of increasing efficiency is the replacement of the photographic plate by some photoemissive medium such as that employed in image convertors. Alternatively, a more direct method would be the reception of stellar and comparison spectra by one or more photoelectric cells. The quantum efficiency of such detectors is known to be high compared with that of the photographic emulsion; a gain of several magnitudes should ultimately be possible. The value of applications of photoelectric detectors to radial-velocity observations can scarcely be exaggerated.

The importance of radial-velocity data in studies of stellar motions, galactic structure, and other major astronomical problems continues. We may devote ourselves to the extension and improvement of this branch of observational astronomy, secure in the knowledge that carefully determined velocities will be a valuable and permanent contribution.

REFERENCES

ADAMS, W. S.   1941   *Ap. J.*, **93**, 11.
BEALS, C. S.,
  PETRIE, R. M., and
  McKELLAR, A.   1946   *J.R.A.S. Canada*, **40**, 349; *Contr. Dom. Ap. Obs.*, No. 5.
BOWEN, I. S.   1952   *Trans. I.A.U.*, **8**, 751.
CAMPBELL, W. W.   1913   *Stellar Motions* (New Haven: Yale University Press; London: Henry Frowde; Oxford: University Press).

CAMPBELL, W. W., and
  MOORE, J. H.   1928   *Pub. Lick Obs.*, **16**, 1.
DRAPER, H.   1877   *Am. J. Sci.*, **13**, 95.
DUNHAM, THEODORE, JR.   1956   *Vistas in Astronomy*, ed. A. BEER (London and New York: Pergamon Press), **2**, 1229.
EBERHARD, G.   1933   *Hdb. d. Ap.*, **1**, Part 1, 299.
FEHRENBACH, C.   1947   *Ann. d'ap.*, **10**, 306.
                             1948   *Ibid.*, **11**, 35.
GOLLNOW, H., and
  HAGEMANN, G.   1956   *A.J.*, **61**, 399.
HARTMANN, J. H.   1906   *Pub. Ap. Obs. Potsdam*, Vol. **18**, No. 53.
HOSSACK, W. R.   1953   *J.R.A.S. Canada*, **47**, 195.
JACOBSEN, T. S   1926   *Lick Obs. Bull.*, **12**, 138.
JOHNSON, H. L.   1949   *A.J.*, **54**, 190.
KEELER, J. E.   1894   *Pub. Lick Obs.*, **3**, 195.
McDONALD, J. K.   1948   *J.R.A.S. Canada*, **42**, 220.
MAXWELL, J. C.   1868   *Phil. Trans.*, **158**, 532.
MERRILL, P. W.   1931   *Ap. J.*, **74**, 188.
MILLMAN, P. M.   1931   *Harvard Obs. Circ.*, No. 357.
MOORE, J. H.   1935   *The Binary Stars*, by R. G. AITKEN (2d ed.; New York: McGraw-Hill Book Co., Inc.), chap. v.

PETRIE, R. M.   1937   *J.R.A.S. Canada*, **31**, 289.
                             1946   *Ibid.*, **40**, 325.
                             1947   *Ibid.*, **41**, 311.
                             1948   *Ibid.*, **42**, 213.
                             1953   *Pub. Dom. Ap. Obs. Victoria*, **9**, 297.
PETRIE R. M.,
  ANDREWS, D. H., and
  McDONALD, J. K.   1957   *Pub. Dom. Ap. Obs. Victoria*, **10**, 415.

PETRIE, R. M., and GIRLING, S. S.	1948	*J.R.A.S. Canada*, **42**, 226.
PETRIE, R. M., and MOYLS, B. N.	1953	*M.N.*, **113**, 239.
PLASKETT, J. S.	1909	*Report Chief Astronomer, Canada*, **1**, 161.
	1910	*Ibid.*, p. 110.
	1913	*Ap. J.*, **37**, 373.
REDMAN, R. O.	1939	*M.N.*, **99**, 686.
SCHALÉN, C.	1954	*Ark. f. astr.*, **1**, 545.
STIBBS, D. W. N.	1955	*M.N.*, **115**, 363.
STRATTON, F. J. M.	1925	*Astronomical Physics* (London: Methuen & Co), Appendix II.
TREANOR, P. J.	1948	*M.N.*, **108**, 189.
VOGEL, H. C.	1900	*Ap. J.*, **11**, 393.
WILSON, O. C.	1956	*Pub. A.S.P.*, **68**, 346.
WRIGHT, K. O.	1951	*Pub. Dom. Ap. Obs. Victoria*, **9**, 167.
WRIGHT, W. H.	1907	*Pub. Lick Obs.*, **9**, 50.

CHAPTER 4

Spectrophotometry

K. O. WRIGHT

Dominion Astrophysical Observatory

§ 1. INTRODUCTION

Accurate measurement of intensities in stellar spectra has long been known to be fundamental for the study of the physics of stellar atmospheres. Spectrophotometry in astronomy may be defined to include the measurement of intensities in stellar spectra, both relative and absolute, in all observable spectral regions. As such, it could include a discussion of stellar colors, including multicolor, and narrow-band filter photometry and also the techniques of infrared spectroscopy—subjects covered in this volume by others. The present chapter will be confined to a discussion of the basic techniques involved in making measurements on the continuum in stellar spectra and in determining the intensities of spectral lines relative to that continuum. We shall consider a very few applications of spectrophotometric observations to astrophysics, but, for a complete review, we must refer to reports of the Commission on Spectrophotometry of the International Astronomical Union and to texts on astrophysics, e.g., those of Aller (1953) and Unsöld (1955).

The problems of absolute spectrophotometry are very great, since all sources of absorption and scattering in the instrument must be considered, as well as, in the case of stellar sources, the important effects of atmospheric extinction. Extensive programs relating to the study of stellar continua, including these latter effects, have been carried out at Greenwich, Göttingen, Michigan, and Paris Observatories. Studies of line profiles may seem somewhat simpler, since the various points on a line are measured relative to the continuum and therefore differential atmospheric extinction and instrumental absorption may be neglected. However, even in this case, many problems arise, such as the determination of the position of the continuum in spectra where there are many lines and the elimination of the instrumental profile, which, except for a few stellar spectrographs giving the highest dispersion, determines the shapes of most lines observed in stellar spectra. Although great advances in the methods of measuring intensities have been made in the last thirty years, many difficulties remain, and, for accurate quantitative work, the greatest care must be taken to examine and allow for all possible sources of error.

The most direct method of studying the distribution of energy with wave length received from a star is to place a sensitive receiver at the focus of a spectrograph attached to a telescope and then to scan the stellar spectrum. Astronomical seeing is often a rapidly varying quantity, but methods have been developed to compensate for seeing fluctuations and several low- to moderate-dispersion photoelectric spectrophotometers have been constructed. The low intensity level of most stellar sources has, until very recently, prevented the use of high-dispersion instruments, but following intensive efforts by several workers at Mount Wilson, Oke and Greenstein (1961) have completed a high-dispersion scanning spectrophotometer which has permitted direct photoelectric measurements to be made on the bright stars which should be comparable to, or even better than, the results obtained by photography with the best stellar spectrographs.

Although photoelectric spectrophotometry will be used for special problems in the near future, it seems probable that most stellar-intensity measurements will be made by photographic methods for the next few years. The photocell, which term may be considered to include photomultiplier tubes, etc., is an excellent device for intensity measurement, since, with careful instrumentation, the response between energy received and current produced may be made linear and accurate intensities can be recorded directly on a recording potentiometer. Although the tubes must be carefully selected because commercial tubes and cells vary greatly in sensitivity and linearity of response (up to about 10 per cent), as well as in noise level and stability—i.e., freedom from drift and fatigue effects—it has been possible to make measurements accurate to better than 1 per cent and sometimes to 0.05 per cent on laboratory sources. The principal disadvantage of the photoelectric method is that the spectrum must be scanned wave length by wave length. Recent laboratory work has shown, however, that it is possible to install and record the response of several photocells simultaneously and thus to increase the total wave-length range studied per unit time. Dunham (1956) has recently made a comparison of photographic and photoelectric methods of recording a stellar spectrum. With reasonable assumptions for a grating spectrograph with resolving power of 80,000, he found that, although the spectrum of a sixth-magnitude star could be photographed with the 100-inch telescope over the range λλ 3400–4900 in 440 minutes, a single photocell could scan only about 30 A in that time. This difference is so great that, although the time required for the reduction of the photographic plate is much greater and the measures from several photographs should be averaged for comparable accuracy, it would seem that it would prove advantageous to use photographic plates when extensive regions of a spectrum were to be studied.

§ 2. PHOTOGRAPHIC SPECTROPHOTOMETRY

The principal advantages of a photographic plate in spectrophotometry are that it is panoramic because it covers a large range of wave lengths at one time; cumulative because it integrates the light received over a given exposure; stable because it is permanent and can be studied at any time, once the negative has been developed; fairly rapid, though not efficient in converting radiant energy into blackening of the photographic plate; and fairly sensitive over a wide range of wave lengths, since new emulsions are continually being developed and are now available from the shortest observable wave lengths to 12,000 A.

The principal disadvantage of a photographic plate is that its response is not linear, and therefore, for accurate work, a suitable calibration spectrum must be placed on each plate to be studied. It has many other lesser disadvantages, such as the reciprocity failure and intermittency effect which require that exposure of star and calibration be nearly equal. This is a difficult condition to meet exactly, since the star is usually trailed during an exposure, in order to broaden the spectrum. The variation of sensitivity with wave length requires that the characteristic curve obtained from the calibration correspond to the wave length studied in the stellar spectrum. In laboratory work it is generally recommended that the wave length used for the calibration be within 25 A of that for the spectrum being studied; however, in astronomical applications the accuracy is not so great, and it is usually found that it need be only within 100 A except where the plate sensitivity is changing very rapidly. There may be a latent image effect which makes it desirable that calibration and star spectrum be exposed simultaneously. This effect is usually small, but, when absolute measurements are to be made, development should be delayed for a few hours after the second exposure if simultaneous exposures are not possible. There may be variations over the plate in the emulsion and also in the glass, which make it desirable that calibration and stellar spectrum be placed as close together on the plate as possible. Fogging effects, particularly near the edge of the plate, produced as a result of storage, contact with the wrapping paper, etc., are found, and therefore regions within 1 cm of the edge of the plate should not be used for spectrophotometric measurements.

The choice of plate depends on the spectral region to be studied, the brightness of the star, the dispersion of the spectrograph, etc. The resolving power of the emulsion depends on the size of the grains; because fast emulsions are usually required for astronomical studies, the grains are large, and the resolving power is reduced. Fortunately, the fast emulsions have lower contrast than slow, fine-grained emulsions. Therefore, the slope of the characteristic curve is decreased, thus permitting a large range of intensities to be studied on a single plate, although the accuracy is correspondingly decreased. The contrast and graininess of the finished negative depend to some extent on the developer and time of development. It has been found that, for so-called "fine-grain" developers, any finer grain is obtained at the expense of decreased density of the plate, and no basic advantage is gained.

Developers and fixers are usually recommended by the manufacturers of the emulsions, but some experimentation is sometimes desirable to determine the proper contrast and grain for any given investigation. In spectrophotometry it is desirable to set up and maintain uniform conditions as far as possible, particularly in the development process. It has been found that development should be neither too fast nor too slow and that developers requiring 4–10 minutes are usually best. The principal error introduced during development is produced by the Eberhard effect. Where high- and low-density latent images are close together, the development reaction will take place at unequal rates,

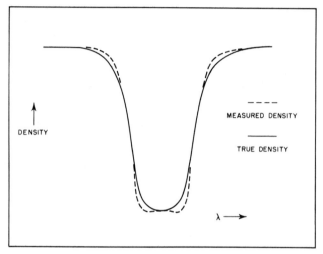

FIG. 1.—Qualitative diagram illustrating the Eberhard effect on a stellar absorption line

with the result that too dense an image may be formed in some regions and too weak an image in others (see Fig. 1). Rocking the tray during development, producing a continuous flow of liquid over the surface of the emulsion,˙may improve the results; but, since the effect is produced by a very thin layer of developer in close contact with the emulsion, it is strongly recommended that during development all spectrophotometric plates be brushed continuously with a camel's-hair brush or a fresh pad of absorbent cotton. This reduces the Eberhard effect considerably, although it has been detected occasionally even when it was thought that all necessary precautions had been observed.

§ 3. METHODS OF CALIBRATION

The conditions necessary for equal densities on a photographic plate to define equal intensities in a source were given by Hartmann (1899). With slight modifications, two regions of equal densities on the same photographic plate may be considered to have been produced by radiation having the same intensity if they have been given identical exposure and development, if they correspond in wave length and polarization, and if the same light-path and optics have been used to produce the spectra. For relative, rather than absolute, intensity measurements, the last three requirements may be relaxed, provided that the effects of stray light are the same. An important requirement in the photographic determination of intensities is that there should be *no extrapolation* of the characteristic curve.

Although it is very desirable that the calibrations required for spectrophotometric measurements be placed on the photographic plate at the same time and through the same optics as the stellar spectrum, this is possible in very few stellar spectrographs. Dunham (1956) described the method devised for the Mount Wilson 100-inch coudé spectrograph, but it may be noted that an auxiliary spectrograph is available and used both at Mount Wilson and at Mount Palomar.

If an auxiliary spectrograph must be employed to impress the calibration on the plate, its optics should be tested as thoroughly as those of the main stellar spectrograph. The dispersions of the two spectrographs should be comparable. It is important that all stray or scattered light be eliminated by means of stops and diaphragms within the spectrograph. It may be necessary to stop down the collimator lens to insure the quality of performance that is required. Such a stop decreases the resolving power somewhat, but the latter is not essential for most calibrating spectrographs. It need only be mentioned that sensitometer spots as usually employed are not recommended as an adequate calibration for accurate spectrophotometry. Such spots, which were widely used in the early days of spectrophotometry, were impressed on the plate with the aid of a set of tubes having equal apertures at the plate end and apertures of different diameters at the end near the source. The exposures were generally only a few seconds, and either white light or very broad-band filters were used. Thus the characteristic curve could not safely be assumed to have the same shape as that required for the study of the stellar spectrum.

The source for the calibration should, if possible, have spectral characteristics similar to those of the stellar spectrum. The source is usually an incandescent lamp set up behind suitable ground- or opal-glass screens, with a blue filter to produce a wave-length distribution as similar to that of the star as possible. It is essential that the slit of the spectrograph be uniformly illuminated. It may be necessary to test various combinations of screens, of stops for the collimator, and of lens systems used to focus the source on the slit before uniformity of illumination is achieved. The light from the source passing through the slit should just fill the collimator; otherwise the intensity variation produced by the calibrating device at the slit may be different at the plate. For astigmatic spectrographs it may be necessary to use a device that impresses the calibration at the plate itself (see Thiers 1951).

Numerous devices have been used for impressing intensity marks on a photographic plate. Probably the most complete list has been given by Harrison (1934), who also comments upon the requirements for their use. We shall consider only a few methods of calibration and, in the discussion, shall attempt to mention the requirements for a suitable photographic calibration.

1. The most nearly absolute method of calibration involves the use of the inverse-square law, by which the distance of the source from the spectrograph slit is varied and all other quantities are kept constant. The distances must be large compared with the size of the source, which may be a frosted incandescent lamp or, perhaps better, a slab of magnesium oxide, which, when freshly cleaned, is an excellent reflector. In recent years photocells that have been tested for linearity of response have been used to test other devices and have, to some extent, superseded the use of the inverse-square method.

2. Step-slits are valuable calibration devices. The narrowest slit must be wide enough not to be influenced by diffraction effects, and the widest slit must conform to the requirements of uniform illumination of the collimator. A range in slit-width of from 0.01 to 6 mm may be suitable for high-dispersion laboratory spectrographs. The width of each step can be measured accurately in the laboratory, and under ideal conditions the intensity is proportional to this width. Step-slits should have sharp, beveled edges; they can be made with random spacings and can be reversed in the spectrograph and thus provide valuable checks on the uniformity of illumination of the collimator, as well as on Eberhard effects. Spacers have sometimes been placed between each step to eliminate effects of photographic spreading and also to reproduce more accurately the conditions in many stellar spectra where the continuum is cut up by deep absorption lines.

3. Step-filters made by sputtering different thicknesses of platinum on optical quartz plates have been tested at Utrecht and elsewhere and found to be stable, although Harrison (1934) noted a small deviation from neutrality over the wave-length range λλ 3000–5500. Miss Banning (1947) studied several other substances for use as step-filters and found chromel A best for neutrality and stability. Photographic plates have been used as step-filters because they are stable and very nearly neutral; but there may be some scattering in the emulsion, and the plates should be calibrated and tested by photoelectric methods in the spectrographs where they are to be used.

4. The rotating step-sector is one of the most frequently used calibrating devices because of its convenience and because steps having the required intensity ratios can be cut accurately on a lathe or milling machine. The most intense step will be produced by radiation received at the plate during a full turn of the sector, and cuts can be made over successively smaller angles down to one or two degrees. A step ratio of 1.58 (0.2 in the logarithm) has been found quite satisfactory, and sectors can be made to cover a range of more than one hundred in intensity, which is more than can be measured accurately on

most photographic plates. Unfortunately, considerable controversy has arisen concerning this method of calibration because the problem of intermittent exposures is inherent in the operation of a rotating sector. Silberstein and Webb (1934) have shown from theoretical considerations that the density produced by intermittent exposures will approach asymptotically that produced by continuous exposures as the speed of a sector is increased; the frequency of flash required for effective equality depends on the size of the photographic grains and the intensity of the continuous source. Webb (1933) found earlier that if the flash frequency is approximately one photon per grain per flash, intermittency effects become negligible. Frequencies of approximately 1000 rpm give satisfactory results for most photographic plates. Webb (1933),

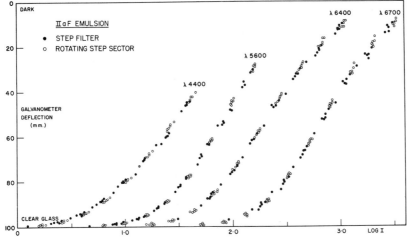

FIG. 2.—Characteristic curves obtained at Victoria for the IIa-F emulsion, using rotating step-sector and step-filter.

Petrie and McKellar (1937), Cousins and Stoy (1947), and Thiers (1951), among others, found that rotating sectors were suitable for the plates they used, but Sawyer and Vincent (1943) arrived at conflicting results for different emulsions. Tests have been made recently at Victoria by comparing a rotating step-sector with a Hilger step-filter of sputtered platinum on quartz. The results, for the IIa-F emulsion, based on six plates and shown in Figure 2 as galvanometer deflections plotted against log (intensity), indicate that for this emulsion the rotating step-sector produces a calibration identical, within the probable errors, with that of the step-filter. It seems that when rotating sectors are to be used, tests of each type of emulsion should be made to check whether the calibrations are valid. Errors may be introduced by the synchronization of the speed of the sector motor with the a.c. frequency of the power supply, and this factor should be examined.

A valuable check on the self-consistency of a calibration system is obtained by impressing two or more sets of calibration marks on a given plate when all conditions are the same except the intensity of the light-source. If identical calibration-curves are obtained at each wave length, even though the intensities of each mark are different, the system is, in all probability, adequate. If the characteristic curves are not the same, some source of error, such as fogging of the emulsion by stray light, must be sought and eliminated.

These calibrating devices have been described on the assumption that discrete densities are desired which, when measured with a microphotometer, may be plotted against the known relative intensities to give the characteristic curve applicable to the problem under investigation. Many modern instruments permit intensities to be derived directly from the photographic plate. These instruments are usually based on the null method of spectrophotometry, in which equivalent densities on the stellar spectrum and on the calibration are found by some method involving a light-chopping device or two matched photo-cells, one of which searches the calibration at the correct wave length. This null method fulfils Hartmann's requirement for equal photographic intensities; but the determination of the characteristic curve from discrete points is probably more accurate, since each density is derived from a strip on the photographic plate from which the grain effect can be eliminated. Where null methods are employed, the calibrations must provide a continuous variation of intensity. Photographic wedges, continuously varying platinum weakeners, triangular slits, and logarithmic sectors have been used, each of which can be made to reproduce intensities on a linear scale by means of suitable cams or other arrangements on the instrument.

§ 4. METHODS OF MEASURING AND RECORDING INTENSITIES

Although the term "densitometer" is preferred in physical laboratories for instruments used to measure densities on photographic plates, the same instruments are ordinarily called "microphotometers" in astronomical observatories. The latter term is employed in astronomy because the first microphotometers were extensions of the photometers used to measure densities of star images before the art of spectrophotometry was developed. A typical microphotometer, developed by Beals (1936), is shown in Figure 3. The source, A, usually an automobile headlight run from storage batteries, is focused on a slit B, which is lined up perpendicular to the direction of the dispersion of the spectrogram D, on which the light is focused by lens C. The spectrum is focused by a lens E on the analyzing slit F, behind which is a photocell. An amplifying system increases the photoelectric current and causes a deflection of the galvanometer, which is recorded by a light-beam from lamp H on the galvanometer mirror, which is focused by a cylindrical lens K on a roll of photographic paper inclosed in a light-proof box. As the spectrum is driven in the direction of the dispersion, the paper travels past the cylindrical lens at a speed which is increased by a set of gears to magnify the motion 20 or 100 times. An auxiliary system permits

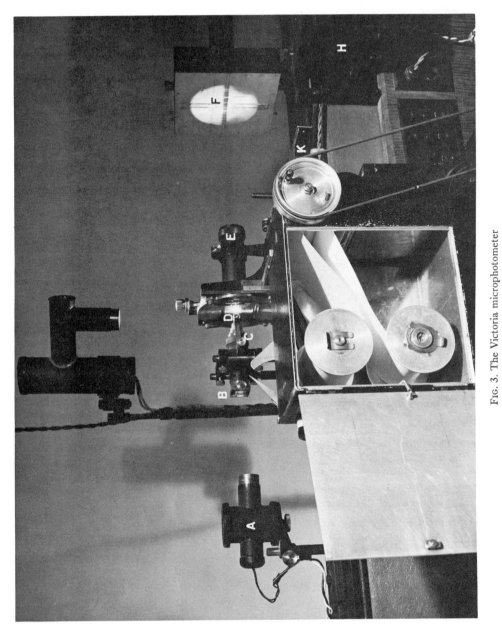

FIG. 3. The Victoria microphotometer

the spectrum to be viewed, so that correct alignment may be achieved and the desired region selected. Under favorable conditions, when calibrations as well as clear-glass and zero deflections are repeated after as much as an hour's run, no differences in observed deflections can be detected.

One of the first microphotometers, designed by Moll (1921), employed a thermopile as the light-sensitive element, and, with minor modifications, many of these instruments are still in use. Koch was among the first to use a photocell to measure densities as a voltage measured by an electrometer; this instrument was improved by Goos (Goos and Koch 1927) and was standard equipment in many laboratories for many years. Knorr and Albers (1937) designed a high-speed pen-recording photoelectric microphotometer marketed by Leeds and Northrup that is also an excellent instrument. Other physical laboratories have developed photoelectric densitometers for their own needs, which may include automatic wave-length measurement, as well as intensity records. A few of these have been described by Harrison and Bentley (1940), Grossman *et al.* (1949), Dieke, Dimock, and Crosswhite (1956), and Lundin (1952).

The best instruments in physical laboratories are claimed to reproduce intensity data with an error of less than 2 per cent. In these cases the charac-teristic curve is usually obtained from spectra calibrated by means of the same source as the spectra being studied. They are photographed under ideal condi-tions with fine-grained plates using very high dispersion. In astronomical spectra such accuracy is rarely achieved.

The two principal sources of error in microphotometry are probably caused by the use of too wide slits. If the first slit (*B* in Fig. 3) is too wide, there may be scattered light from the emulsion and glare produced by the lenses (the Schwarzschild-Villiger effect), which will vary with the density of the emulsion and thus produce an incorrect calibration-curve. If the analyzing slit (*F* in Fig. 3) is comparable in width to the lines in the spectrum being studied, there may be serious integration effects, since a large range in intensity may be covered by the analyzing slit at a single setting. This error was first discussed by Langseth and Walles (1934) and more recently by Hardy and Young (1949), by Broderson (1954), and by Deutsch (1954). Corrections can be made for this effect, but it is generally better to use slits as narrow as possible but such that the deflections produced by the plate grains do not hide the spectroscopic features that are being studied. As long a slit as possible should be used for the stellar spectrum, so that the grain effect on the microphotometer tracing may be minimized. The focus of the microphotometer may be important where highly corrected microscope lenses are used, since focusing in the visual region may not be the same as in the infrared region, to which the older photocells and thermopiles are most sensitive. Errors due to too rapid motion of the plate have been found in the past, but sensitive receivers, short-period galvanometers, and other recording devices make such errors less likely to occur now.

Different types of microphotometers may prove to be best suited to different problems. As an example, low densities are well recorded with the Moll micro-photometer, and therefore this instrument will give good results for plates that are relatively weakly exposed. On the other hand, the Victoria microphotometer with its amplifying system records high densities well and thus is very suitable for studying spectra with deep absorption lines. With it, spectra can be exposed to bring the stellar continuum on the shoulder of the characteristic curve, but the bottoms of strong absorption lines with central intensities only a few per cent of the continuum are still measurable. Beals (1940) has compared the response of several microphotometers.

The reduction of microphotometer tracings to intensities was a very laborious task when it was necessary to reduce each point on a line profile through the several stages. Instruments to decrease this labor by mechanical means were de-veloped by Wouda (1932), Dunham (1933a), and others. Pannekoek (1940), Koelbloed, and Walraven (1940) devised a method of converting a continuous microphotometer trace into an intensity trace by following the characteristic curve manually. Beals (1944) improved this instrument, and the versatile Victoria intensitometer shown in Figure 4 was the result. The principal advantage of the intensitometer is that, although it is operated manually, it can be used to obtain direct-intensity traces, or rectified intensities (in two stages, using first a loga-rithmic characteristic curve and repeating the process with an antilogarithm curve) to separate two spectra, such as occur in composite eclipsing binaries, or merely to change the scale of a tracing. The characteristic curve is drawn, by means of the calibration marks on the microphotometer tracing, on an illuminated ground-glass screen, G, whose image is projected back to the tracing. As a motor slowly moves the tracing, the operator keeps the projected charac-teristic curve at the intersection of the microphotometer tracing and a standard index line, I. Intensities are recorded on a moving paper roll by a pen, which moves with the plate containing the characteristic curve. The scale of the tracing depends on the scale used for the characteristic curve, and the magnification of the intensity tracing may be changed by a set of gears, X. Other transforma-tions are achieved through motion of the box containing the microphotometer tracing and by using straight lines on the ground-glass screen rather than the characteristic curve.

Instruments have been designed to convert intensities on the photographic plate directly into intensities. Minnaert and Houtgast (1938) introduced a template cut to the shape of the correct characteristic curve, combined with an additional galvanometer and photocell, which were added to the conventional Moll microphotometer, when they recorded their pioneer *Photometric Atlas of the Solar Spectrum* (Minnaert, Mulders, and Houtgast 1940). Williams and Hiltner (1940) developed a direct-intensity instrument based on the null method. Calibration and star spectrum were photographed on separate halves of the same plate and placed on carriages that could move independently. A light-beam was passed through each plate, and the calibration carriage was

so adjusted that the density at each point on the stellar spectrum was successively matched on the calibration at the same wave length. The motion of the calibration carriage was converted into intensities by means of a cam. The most
elaborate recording direct-intensity microphotometer for stellar work was built
by H. W. Babcock at Mount Wilson Observatory (see Dunham 1956). The
calibration is produced by a triangular slit, and a servomechanism, driving a
photographic wedge to make the density equal to that of the star spectrum,
causes a pen to record the intensity directly. This instrument records intensities
quite rapidly; using high-dispersion Mount Wilson spectra, 11 A can be
traced on the scale of the Utrecht *Atlas* in 1 minute. For spectra with only
a few lines, the instrument can be made to record regions of the continuum
quickly and regions containing lines more slowly.

Intensity tracings of representative stellar spectra have been published by

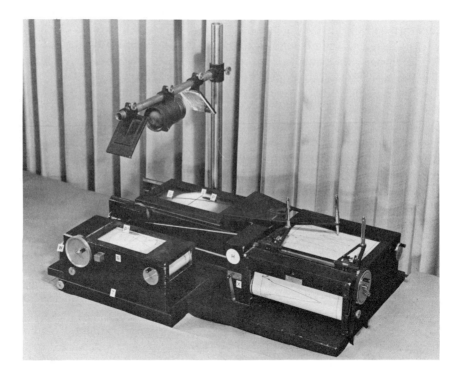

Fig. 4.—The intensitometer. A tracing on a logarithmic scale, shown in the box, B, is being
converted to the intensity tracing shown at the right. The pointer, P, and its projected image,
P', are kept at the level of the continuum by motion of the box, B, along the track, T, by means
of the wheel, W.

Hiltner and Williams (1946). These records and others, such as are shown in Figure 5, gave to many people a completely new picture of the intensities of lines in stellar spectra, since microphotometer tracings so often distort the intensity co-ordinate. They also showed the great difficulty in locating the position of the continuum for stars later than type F. This difficulty also appeared when studies of the Utrecht *Photometric Atlas of the Solar Spectrum* were made. This *Atlas*, derived from spectra taken at the center of the solar disk with the spectrograph attached to the Mount Wilson 150-foot tower telescope with a dispersion of 3.0 and 1.5 mm/A, is the best record of the com-

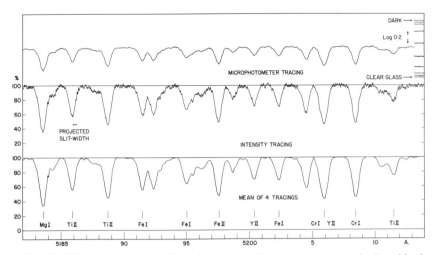

Fig. 5.—Microphotometer and direct-intensity tracings of the spectrum of α Persei in the region λλ 5182–5214. The microphotometer tracing has been converted into a rectified intensity tracing in two stages; the intensity steps, which differ by 0.2 in the logarithm, were used to obtain a logarithmic intensity tracing, and the latter was then converted into intensities using an antilogarithmic curve, as shown in Fig. 4.

plete observed intensity profile of any star over the region λλ 3332–8771 and has been used for many investigations. Even though the continuum for the *Atlas* was derived from studies of high points on the intensity profiles, many of which cover only a few hundredths of an angstrom and therefore cannot be detected on spectra taken with lower dispersion, Michard (1950) has shown that, at wave lengths shorter than 4000 A, the continuum adopted for the *Atlas* should be raised. For example, at λ 3785 he suggests that, because of overlapping hydrogen lines, the continuum should be set at 132 instead of the adopted 100. It seems probable, however, that the continuum adopted for the *Atlas* is approximately correct at longer wave lengths.

An example of how additional information can be obtained from intensity tracings is shown in Figure 6, in which the derived spectrum of the secondary component of the system 31 Cygni is shown. The upper spectrum shows the composite, out-of-eclipse spectrum of the star, while the lower spectrum, taken during total eclipse, is the spectrum of a K5 star. Intensity tracings of these spectra are shown in the third and fourth panels. Since the adopted continuum of the K star contributes 0.45 of the total intensity in this region, the intensities in panel four were reduced to this amount and superposed on the out-of-eclipse tracing. A simple subtraction of the intensities on these tracings at each wave length produces the spectrum of the secondary component, which is shown to be a B3 star with hydrogen and helium lines. The 1952 spectrum shows less

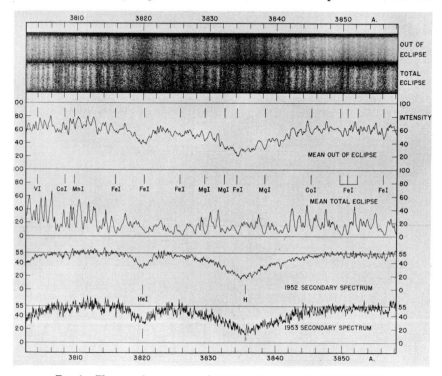

Fig. 6.—The secondary spectrum in 31 Cygni in the region λλ 3802–3858

grain effect because three plates were used in the reductions, whereas only a single plate was used to obtain the 1953 secondary spectrum.

§ 5. MEASUREMENTS OF LINE INTENSITIES

It is important that true stellar-line profiles be obtained because the absorption relative to the continuum at each point on the profile is proportional to the absorption coefficient at that wave length and therefore is required for studies of the distribution with depth in the stellar atmosphere of the number of atoms producing a line. Many problems arise in connection with the theoretical interpretation of such profiles. Since all but solar-line profiles are obtained from the flux integrated over the stellar disk, the effect of limb darkening must be considered. Rotation changes the profile very markedly. Although the theory for a rotationally broadened line has been worked out, including the coefficient of limb darkening, it is probable that the projected rate of rotation is the only quantity that can be obtained from such a profile. Large-scale turbulent motions broaden the lines of many stars, especially those with extensive atmospheres; these effects cannot readily be included in the usual model-atmosphere calculations. Even for sharp-lined stars it is difficult to define a given profile uniquely according to one distribution of temperatures and pressures for given abundance ratios and surface gravity; but it is hoped that the development of the theory of model atmospheres, combined with the capabilities of modern computing machines, will permit the appropriate calculations to be made.

The problems of determining line profiles empirically are almost equally great. For most stellar spectrographs the shape of the observed lines is determined almost entirely by the instrumental profile. Broad lines, such as those of hydrogen or the resonance lines of calcium and chromium in late-type stars, are almost free from instrumental effects. Lines such as those in the spectrum of ϵ Aurigae, which are broadened presumably by turbulence, require little correction when the resolving power is 50,000–80,000, such as is achieved by several large stellar spectrographs. Metallic lines in the spectrum of α Persei require some correction, while those in the spectrum of α Canis Minoris are so sharp that they are defined by the instrumental profile.

If the instrumental profile $h(x)$ of a spectrograph is known, the true profile $f'(x)$ and the observed profile $f(x)$ are related by the integral equation

$$f(x) = \int_{-\infty}^{\infty} h(x-y) f'(y) \, dy.$$

If $h(x)$ has a half-width comparable to $f'(x)$, the true profile is difficult to determine. Several authors have attempted to derive the true profile by solving this integral equation; for example, van de Hulst (1941) examined the problem in connection with work on the Utrecht *Atlas*, and Kremer (1941) devised a machine to reduce the laborious computations required. Later van de Hulst and Reesinck (1947) showed that both instrumental profiles and those of stellar lines could be represented by Voigt profiles and that the reductions could therefore be simplified; Elste (1953) has given further examples of this method. Righini (1941) developed an optical method for solving the integral equation which gives a good approximation to the true profile. Recently Bracewell (1955) has presented a simple graphical method for the solution of this problem.

For most stellar and solar spectrographs the instrumental profile has been determined photographically from the shapes of weak comparison emission lines, usually Fe I and sometimes Kr I. Redman (1935, 1937) at Cambridge and ten Bruggencate, Houtgast, and von Klüber (1939) at Potsdam incorporated a monochromator in front of the slit, in order to reduce the effects of scattered light. The above methods were used to determine the instrumental profile for the records of the Utrecht *Atlas*, where it was found that the profile was asymmetrical. Allen (1937) used the terrestrial O_2 B band to study the instrumental profile given by the Mount Wilson solar spectrograph.

Recently pure Hg^{198} has become available for laboratory investigations; the freedom from isotopic constituents and the high atomic weight of mercury make it suitable for studies of the instrumental profile. Pierce's analysis (1957) of the results obtained with the Michigan solar vacuum-grating spectrograph has been one of the most accurate studies of this problem. He found that, when the spectrum was scanned photoelectrically point by point, seeing effects inside the spectrograph produced errors, and therefore the vacuum system was installed. An 8-inch, 600 grooves/mm Babcock grating used in the fifth order with a dispersion of 8 mm/A gives a resolving power of 630,000, total ghost intensities of only 1.8 per cent in that order, and general scattered light of 0.7 per cent.

§ 6. PHOTOELECTRIC SPECTROPHOTOMETRY

There is a great need for photoelectric intensity measurements of all types, but particularly for high-dispersion studies of selected line profiles. Hiltner and Code (1950), among others, have solved the problem of compensating for variable seeing by having one cell monitor the seeing over a wide range of spectrum while another analyzes the desired strip of spectrum. This method has been used by Oke and Greenstein (1961) to scan 100 A regions of the spectrum of a few early-type stars with a dispersion of 2.8 A/mm at the coudé focus of the Mount Wilson 100-inch telescope. Their equivalent-width measurements of the lines λ 4471 and λ 4481 in the spectra of τ Scorpii, 10 Lacertae, and 9 Sagittae, and those obtained photographically by other observers, are listed in Table 1. The differences between equivalent widths measured photographically and those measured photoelectrically are certainly not larger than those measured photographically by different observers. For the same resolution, the photoelectric scanning of spectra should be more accurate than photographic measurements, although the problem of defining the continuum may be more difficult with the scanner because of the shorter region observed. The good agreement of most of the measurements listed in Table 1 increases the confidence to be placed in the best results obtained by photographic means.

The pioneer work on photoelectric solar-line profiles was done by Dunham (1933b) at Mount Wilson and by Brück (1939) at Cambridge, who reproduced profiles of the Ca II K line. Further work is being done by Kuprevitch (1952) at Pulkovo and by Pierce (1957) at Michigan, among others. A few moderate-dispersion photoelectric spectrometers have been put into operation, including those of Code (1952) and of Oke (unpublished) at Toronto. Low-dispersion instruments have been employed by Guerin and Laffineur (1954) for scanning stellar spectra to study the continuum and by Liller and Aller (1954) and Liller (1957) to study planetary nebulae.

In the infrared region of the spectrum the development of the lead sulfide cell by Cashman and others has permitted considerable extension of the observable spectrum by photoelectric methods. Kuiper, Wilson, and Cashman (1947) have described the Cashman spectrometer at the McDonald Observatory that has been used to study the sun and planets, and McMath and Mohler (1949) have described the instrument at the McMath-Hulbert Observatory with which the Michigan atlas of the solar spectrum from 8465 to 25,242 A (Mohler *et al.* 1950) was made. These developments are discussed more fully by Strong and Stauffer and by Code and Liller elsewhere in this volume.

TABLE 1

MEASURED EQUIVALENT WIDTHS

STAR	LINE (A)	SCANNER OKE AND GREENSTEIN (1961) (A)	PHOTOGRAPHIC			
			Jugaku (1959) (A)	Unsöld (1942) (A)	Underhill (1958) (A)	Oke (1954) (A)
τ Sco.........	{4471 {4481	1.23 0.110	1.24 0.105	0.98 0.105	....	....
10 Lac........	4471	0.96	....	....	0.93	....
9 Sge.........	4471	0.67	....	....	0.95	0.72

§ 7. SPECTROPHOTOMETRY OF CONTINUOUS SPECTRA

The intensity distribution of the continuous spectrum is in some respects more important than the line spectrum. Its measurement is difficult, especially for stars of later spectral type, and the theoretical interpretation of the results may be equally so. Since the stars do not radiate as black bodies, the color temperatures or gradients that are measured must not be regarded as true temperatures; but they are definite measurable quantities and give information concerning the sources of the continuous radiation, chiefly H, H⁻, He, and electron scattering. It is of great interest that recent observations of the photographic region require at least three color temperatures to define the observed variation in the continuous spectrum over the regions λλ 3000–3650, 3650–5000, and 5000–7000. However Kienle (unpublished) has suggested that the break at 5000 A is not real and the apparent discontinuity is the result of rapid changes in sensitivity of photographic emulsions at this wave length.

Most measurements of stellar continua have been made with spectrographs of low dispersion (30 A/mm or lower). The reason for this is that exposures should be short, numerous spectra should be obtained on the same plate in a short time interval and at approximately the same zenith distance (to minimize the effects of differential extinction), and also because high dispersion has not been considered necessary when stars with few lines and long stretches of continuous spectrum are being studied. Further, since the spectrographs must be effectively slitless, so that the whole of the radiation transmitted by the atmosphere and optics can be received without further distortion at the photographic plate, the resolution is much diminished by the size of the star image. Recently Westerlund (1957) has shown that high-dispersion spectra give approximately the same color temperatures as low-dispersion spectra for spectral types B–F in the regions λλ 4200–4500 and 5500–6100.

Since the extinction factors vary with wave length and with conditions of the sky, it is very important that a series of spectra of one or more stars be photographed at several zenith distances each night. Even then, weather disturbances barely perceptible to the eye may produce discordant results. Therefore, color-temperature observations should be made only on nights of excellent seeing and transparency. Since the color temperature or gradient depends on the spectral region studied, it is important that the same wave lengths be studied for each spectral type. This should also be done for a range of spectral types, since it is from a comparison of results for stars of different spectral types that the nature of the stellar continuum can be deduced. Because regions of the continuum cannot always be detected on low-dispersion spectra, high-dispersion slit spectra should be available for each spectral type, so that the high points that define the continuum may be checked. If, for a given study, sufficient points at the continuum cannot be found, it may be possible to estimate the effect of weak absorption lines at a few additional points and thus improve the values of the gradients. Fortunately, the Hiltner and Williams *Atlas of Stellar Spectra* (1946) provides a good selection of stars suitable for this purpose. However, the intensities and breadths of lines differ for each spectral type and for giants and dwarfs of the same type, and such corrections may be uncertain.

The relative gradients discussed above can be obtained without great difficulty by making long series of observations and intercomparing standard stars. Absolute stellar gradients are much more difficult to obtain. Greaves, Davidson, and Martin (1932, 1952) made numerous attempts to determine the absolute zero point of the Greenwich system of color temperatures by determining the atmospheric extinction of a standard source over long optical paths. Williams (1940) made somewhat similar observations at Michigan, as well as Barbier and Chalonge (1940) at Paris; but the zero point, defining the color temperature of an A0 star, cannot yet be considered definitive. Similarly, results for the color temperature of the sun on either side of the Balmer discontinuity obtained by Labs (1957) do not agree exactly with those of Canavaggia and Chalonge (1950), but here the difficulty of determining the true continuum is probably the principal problem.

Chalonge (1952) at Paris and Kienle *et al.* (1938, 1940, 1957) at Göttingen and Heidelberg and their collaborators have been developing improved methods for determining stellar gradients. Chalonge (1952) constructed a special spectrograph to give approximately the same density in the blue as in the red region of the spectrum by widening the spectrum at the shorter wave lengths. He and Guerin (Guerin 1954) also made up a special combination of fluorescent powders—a mixture of crystalline mineral salts deposited between quartz slides and illuminated by ultraviolet radiation from a mercury lamp—to provide a standard source for all his stellar spectra. Although these powders do not give a truly continuous source and the energy-curve does not vary monotonically, nevertheless they provide a stable source, and the energy-curve can be determined accurately in the laboratory. Kienle (1957) has found a high-pressure xenon lamp suitable as a standard for his gradient observations over the range λλ 3000–7000. Earlier, Minnaert (1935) and his collaborators at Utrecht had observed that a tungsten-ribbon lamp gave off energy very similar to that of a black body. However, these lamps require recalibration after 100 hours; a blue filter is often used to make the observed energy distribution more similar to that of most stars. Kienle (1957) has recently established a laboratory at Heidelberg that is available for the purpose of testing and calibrating standard lamps and other calibrating devices.

An application of Chalonge's (1955) spectrophotometric measurements on the continua of low-dispersion spectra has been his three-parameter system of stellar classification based on the magnitude of the Balmer discontinuity, D, its position, λ_1, and the gradient in the blue, ϕ_b. On the other hand, Ramberg (1957), among others, has classified stellar spectra using absorption features observed on microphotometer traces of objective-prism spectra obtained at Stockholm, and the Walravens (1960) have classified over a thousand stars according to luminosity and spectral type by means of a photoelectric spectrum analyzer attached to the 36-inch telescope of the Leiden Southern Station.

§ 8. SUMMARY OF SOURCES OF ERROR IN SPECTROPHOTOMETRY

In previous sections numerous sources of error in spectrophotometry have been pointed out. Sources of error may occur anywhere during the progress of the stellar radiation from the time it enters the earth's atmosphere until it falls onto the photographic plate or photocell. Scattered light in the spectrograph has undoubtedly been a source of error that has not always been thoroughly investigated. Although photographic plates have been greatly improved both in speed and in grain, their use must always be subject to numerous tests concerning intermittency effects, latent image and background fogging, and variations in sensitivity. Great care must be taken in their treatment to prevent Eberhard and other development effects. In the analysis, broad slits and scattered light in the microphotometer may produce systematic errors. The characteristic curve is subject to errors, both those inherent in the calibration system and those that occur in estimating the mean position of a series of galvanometer deflections.

In stellar spectra the position of the continuum must usually be considered an unknown. As Miss Underhill (1960) and others have shown, weak lines may be present even in early-type spectra at nearly every wave length, though on most dispersions they are lost in the fluctuations produced by the photographic grains. The problem becomes much more difficult in late-type spectra, where the wings of the strong lines extend over many angstroms, where numerous weak lines of the metals are present, where molecular bands affect large wave-length regions, and where additional sources of continuous absorption may be present.

The effect of the grains in the emulsions used for photographing stellar spectra is often comparable to the effect produced by weak lines. In order to minimize the grain effect, it is desirable that mean values be obtained by averaging the results of several similar spectra. For this purpose it has often been found desirable to derive a logarithmic intensity profile on which the continuum can be drawn and, in a second stage, to derive the intensity profile with the continuum drawn at a constant value. Even then, the drawing of the continuum and of mean profiles by eye through the mean of several superposed tracings may not be quite so accurate as the Edinburgh system devised by Baker (1949) of a mathematical point-by-point determination of the intensity profile in the neighborhood of each stellar line. The Edinburgh system of defining the continuum of an individual star as the mean continuum derived from many stars of similar spectral type undoubtedly has many advantages when results of the highest accuracy are desired and is particularly useful in studies of weak lines. This method requires many measurements and a great deal of time. It seems possible that intensity-recording instruments could be combined with modern computing methods whereby spectra could be measured point by point and mean values for several plates derived automatically. This problem is being investigated by Fellgett at Edinburgh.

Some investigators have claimed that spectrophotometric measurements of sources in the physical laboratories can be obtained with probable errors of ± 2 per cent or less. It is doubtful whether such accuracy can be achieved for stellar observations at the present time because of the low light-levels involved and the consequent use of lower dispersions and coarse-grained photographic plates. Comparisons of equivalent-width measurements determined from high-dispersion spectra obtained at Mount Wilson and at Victoria indicate that the systematic differences are small. For 15 Vulpeculae—an A5 star with numerous weak lines and a well-defined continuum—Mount Wilson measures of 124 lines with $W > 50$ mA were, on the average, 2.5 per cent greater than similar Victoria measures. For σ Bootis, a dwarf F2 star, measures of 47 lines on a single Mount Wilson plate and on three Victoria plates showed that the Mount Wilson data were, on the average, 9 per cent smaller than the Victoria values. Comparisons of the calibration devices at the two observatories showed that the calibration-curves were identical. Greenstein (1956) noted that he sometimes found a range of 20 per cent in the equivalent width of a line measured on several plates, but he considered that the differences arose from uncertainties in drawing the continuum and from slight variations in allowing for blending of other lines rather than from photometric causes. It would seem that the estimate made many years ago that errors up to 10 per cent might occur in measures of stellar equivalent widths is still of the correct order of magnitude. Modern techniques have resulted in a great reduction in the time and labor of deriving the intensities, but the fundamental accuracy has not been markedly increased. Fortunately, this accuracy is sufficient to obtain much essential information concerning the physics of stellar atmospheres.

§ 9. FUTURE NEEDS AND DEVELOPMENTS

Accurate data concerning intensities in stellar spectra are required for most phases of astrophysics. We now have what seem to be reasonable estimates of the composition of representative stellar atmospheres, their temperatures, pressures, and internal motions. More accurate data for many more stars are required. We know that the current models of stellar atmospheres do not uniquely define the shape and intensity of all lines in a spectrum. As accurate line profiles become available, more accurate models of atmospheres that could produce these lines will become necessary, as well as further research into differential motions in the atmospheres that could produce these lines.

There is a great need for high-dispersion studies of stellar spectra of all classes, of giants and dwarfs, and of the different types of stellar populations. There is also a great need for much more laboratory data concerning atomic transition probabilities and damping constants. Many types of objects, such as planetary nebulae, white dwarfs, etc., have no bright representatives, and low-dispersion studies must suffice. However, there seems to be no reason why the scale of such intensity observations should not be related to those of other objects obtained with high dispersion, and in this way it should be possible to obtain a homogeneous set of intensities for stellar spectra of all types.

Although it is hoped that new developments, such as photoelectric image tubes, will revolutionize stellar spectroscopy in the future by improving the quantum efficiency by a factor of 10 to 100, as suggested by Hiltner (1955), it seems probable that present methods of intensity measurements will be employed for some years to come. The use of photoelectric methods will undoubtedly increase, and such methods in special problems, such as studies of individual line profiles in selected stars and the recording of low-dispersion spectra, will considerably improve the accuracy of photometric measurements. Nevertheless, it seems probable that the photographic methods discussed in this chapter will remain the principal source of stellar spectrophotometric measurements for some time. By increasing the care now being taken and by continuously guarding against all possible sources of error in reducing the observed data to intensity profiles, consistent results free from systematic errors should become available to aid in extending our knowledge concerning the physics of stellar atmospheres.

REFERENCES

ALLEN, C. W.	1937	*Ap. J.*, **85**, 156, 165.
ALLER, L. H.	1953	*Astrophysics: The Atmospheres of the Sun and Stars* (New York: Ronald Press).
BAKER, E. A.	1949	*Pub. R. Obs. Edinburgh*, **1**, 15.
BANNING, M.	1947	*J. Opt. Soc. America*, **37**, 686.
BARBIER, D., and CHALONGE, D.	1941	*Ann. d'ap.*, **4**, 30.
BEALS, C. S.	1936	*M.N.*, **96**, 730.
	1940	*Pub. A.S.P.*, **52**, 267.
	1944	*J.R.A.S. Canada*, **38**, 65.
BRACEWELL, R. N.	1955	*J. Opt. Soc. America*, **45**, 873.
BRODERSEN, S.	1954	*J. Opt. Soc. America*, **44**, 22.
BRÜCK, H.	1939	*M.N.*, **99**, 607.
BRUGGENCATE, P. TEN, HOUTGAST, J., and KLÜBER, H. VON.	1939	*Pub. Potsdam Ap. Obs.*, Vol. **29**, No. 3.
CANAVAGGIA, R., and CHALONGE, D.	1950	*Ann. d'ap.*, **13**, 355.
CHALONGE, D.	1952	*Ann. d'ap.*, **15**, 142.
	1955	*J. d. Obs.*, **38**, 85.
CODE, A. D.	1952	*Observatory*, **72**, 201.
COUSINS, A. W. J., and STOY, R.	1946	*M.N.*, **106**, 286.
DEUTSCH, A. J.	1954	*J. Opt. Soc. America*, **44**, 492.
DIEKE, G. H., DIMOCK, D., and CROSSWHITE, H. M.	1956	*J. Opt. Soc. America*, **46**, 456.
DUNHAM, T., JR.	1933*a*	*Pub. A.S.P.*, **45**, 204.
	1933*b*	*Phys. Rev.*, **44**, 329.
	1956	*Vistas in Astronomy*, ed. A. BEER (London and New York: Pergamon Press), **2**, 1223.
ELSTE, G.	1953	*Zs. f. Ap.*, **33**, 39.
GOOS, F., and KOCH, P. P.	1927	*Zs. f. Phys.*, **44**, 855.
GREAVES, W. M. H., DAVIDSON, C., and MARTIN, E.	1932	*Colour Temperatures of Stars* (Greenwich: Royal Observatory).
	1934	*M.N.*, **94**, 488.
	1952	*Colour Temperatures of Stars*, II (Greenwich: Royal Observatory).

GREENSTEIN, J. L.   1956   *Vistas in Astronomy*, ed. A. BEER (London and New York: Pergamon Press), **2**, 1299.

GROSSMAN, H. H., PETER-
SON, E. W., SAUNDERSON,
J. L., and CALDECOURT,
V. J.   1949   *J. Opt. Soc. America*, **39**, 261.

GUERIN, P.   1954   *Rev. d'opt.*, **33**, 137.

GUERIN, P., and
LAFFINEUR, M.   1954   *C.R.*, **238**, 1692.

HARDY, A. C., and
YOUNG, F. M.   1949   *J. Opt. Soc. America*, **39**, 265.

HARRISON, G. R.   1934   *J. Opt. Soc. America*, **24**, 59.

HARRISON, G. R., and
BENTLEY, E. P.   1940   *J. Opt. Soc. America*, **30**, 290.

HARTMANN, J.   1899   *Ap. J.*, **10**, 321.

HILTNER, W. A.   1955   *Trans. I.A.U.*, **9**, 687.

HILTNER, W. A., and
CODE, A. D.   1950   *J. Opt. Soc. America*, **40**, 149.

HILTNER, W. A., and
WILLIAMS, R. C.   1946   *Photometric Atlas of Stellar Spectra* (Ann Arbor: University of Michigan Press).

HULST, H. C. VAN DE   1941   *B.A.N.*, **9**, 225.

HULST, H. C. VAN DE, and
REESINCK, J. J. M.   1947   *Ap. J.*, **106**, 121.

JUGAKU, J.   1959   *Pub. A. S. Japan*, **11**, 161.

KIENLE, H.   1957   *Sitz. Heidelberg Akad. Wiss.*, p. 353.

KIENLE, H., STRASSL, H.,
and WEMPE, J.   1938   *Zs. f. Ap.*, **16**, 201.

KIENLE, H., WEMPE, J.,
and BEILEKE, F.   1940   *Zs. f. Ap.*, **20**, 91.

KNORR, H. V., and
ALBERS, V. M.   1937   *Rev. Sci. Instr.*, **8**, 183.

KREMER, P.   1941   *B.A.N.*, **9**, 229.

KUIPER, G. P., WILSON,
W., and CASHMAN, R. J.   1947   *Ap. J.*, **106**, 243.

KUPREVITCH, N. F.   1952   *Pub. Pulkovo Obs.*, No. 142.

LABS, D.   1957   *Zs. f. Ap.*, **44**, 37.

LANGSETH, A., and
WALLES, E.   1934   *Nature*, **133**, 210.

LILLER, W.   1957   *Pub. A.S.P.*, **69**, 511.

LILLER, W., and
ALLER, L. H.   1954   *Ap. J.*, **120**, 48.

LUNDIN, L.   1952   *Ark. fys.*, **4**, 391.

McMATH, R. R., and
MOHLER, O. C.   1949   *J. Opt. Soc. America*, **39**, 903.

MICHARD, R.   1950   *B.A.N.*, **11**, 227.

MINNAERT, M.   1935   Reported in *Trans. I.A.U.*, **5**, 231.

MINNAERT, M., and
  HOUTGAST, J.   1938   *Zs. f. Ap.*, **15**, 354.
MINNAERT, M., MULDERS,
  G. F. W., and HOUT-
  GAST, J.   1940   *Photometric Atlas of the Solar Spectrum* (Amster-
                               dam: Schnabel, Kampert, and Helm).

MOHLER, O. C., PIERCE,
  A. K., McMATH, R. R.,
  and GOLDBERG, L.   1950   *Photometric Atlas of the Near Infrared Solar Spec-
                               trum* (Ann Arbor: University of Michigan
                               Press).
MOLL, W. J. H.   1921   *Proc. Phys. Soc.*, **33**, 207.
OKE, J. B.   1954   *Ap. J.*, **120**, 22.
OKE, J. B., and
  GREENSTEIN, J. L.   1961   *Ap. J.*, **133**, 349.
PANNEKOEK, A.   1940   *B.A.N.*, **9**, 155.
PETRIE, R. M., and
  McKELLAR, A.   1937   *J.R.A.S. Canada*, **31**, 130.
PIERCE, A. K.   1957   *J. Opt. Soc. America*, **47**, 6.
RAMBERG, J. M.   1957   *Stockholm Obs. Ann.*, **20**, 1.
REDMAN, R. O.   1935   *M.N.*, **95**, 290.
                       1937   *Ibid.*, **97**, 552.
RIGHINI, G.   1941   *Pub. Ap. Obs. Arcetri*, **60**, 27.
SAWYER, R. A., and
  VINCENT, H. B.   1943   *J. Opt. Soc. America*, **33**, 247.
SILBERSTEIN, L., and
  WEBB, J. H.   1934   *Phil. Mag.*, **18**, 1.
THIERS, R. E.   1951   *J. Opt. Soc. America*, **41**, 273.
UNDERHILL, A. B.   1958   *Étoiles à Raies d'Émission*, Report of Liège Sym-
                               posium No. 8, p. 91.
                       1960   *Pub. Dom. Ap. Obs.*, **11**, 283.
UNSÖLD, A.   1941   *Zs. f. Ap.*, **21**, 1.
                       1955   *Physik der Sternatmosphären* (2d ed.; Berlin:
                               Springer).

WALRAVEN, T., and
  WALRAVEN, J. L.   1960   *B.A.N.*, **15**, 67.
WEBB, J. H.   1933   *J. Opt. Soc. America*, **23**, 157.
WESTERLUND, B.   1957   *Pub. Dom. Ap. Obs.*, **10**, 425.
WILLIAMS, R. C.   1940   *Pub. Michigan Obs.*, **8**, 37.
WILLIAMS, R. C., and
  HILTNER, W. A.   1940   *Pub. Michigan Obs.*, **8**, 45.
WOUDA, J.   1932   *Zs. f. Phys.*, **79**, 511.

CHAPTER 5

Measurement of Stellar
Magnetic Fields

H. W. BABCOCK

Mount Wilson and Palomar Observatories
Carnegie Institution of Washington, California Institute of Technology

§ 1. INTRODUCTION

THE study of electrodynamics in astronomy was initiated by George E. Hale (1908) with his discovery of the magnetic fields of sunspots. About 1912 he began a long series of attempts to detect the general magnetic field of the sun, but, as this was much weaker than he had supposed, its measurement required refined photoelectric equipment and techniques that were not available during his lifetime. Hale further envisioned the possibility of detecting magnetic fields in stars (1915) and began the development of apparatus suitable for such investigations. The possibility of detecting stellar magnetic fields was also foreseen by Minnaert (1937).

In astrophysics the direct detection of stellar magnetic fields and the measurement of their intensity and polarity depend on the Zeeman effect, which is familiar to every student of spectroscopy and atomic structure. An up-to-date discussion of this effect is given by van den Bosch (1957). We give here only a brief review of certain fundamentals and a discussion of their application in stellar spectroscopy, where the Zeeman splitting of lines is usually observed in absorption (the inverse Zeeman effect). The technique and instruments for detecting and measuring stellar magnetic fields are then discussed. Such fields, first detected in 1946, have now been measured in about 100 stars (Babcock 1958); the interpretation of the observations is treated in Volume **6,** chapter 10.

§ 2. THE ZEEMAN EFFECT

In a magnetic field the atomic energy levels are split, and electron transitions between these split levels, according to the selection rules, result in a division of

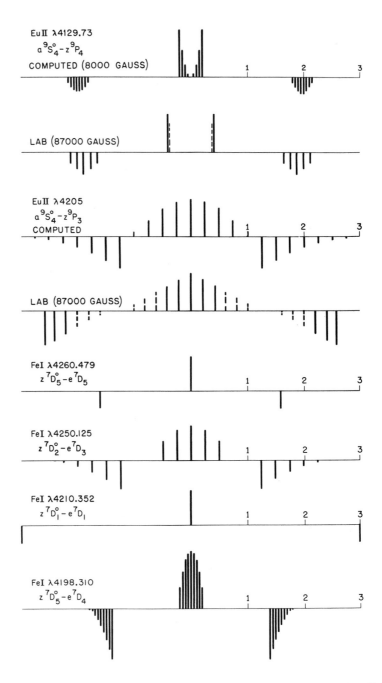

FIG. 1.—Zeeman patterns. The unit of displacement is the normal "Lorentz triplet." As is customary, the π components are shown above the axis, the σ components below. For the two lines of Eu II, computed (LS) patterns and observed laboratory patterns are shown.

otherwise single spectral lines into Zeeman patterns of components that are pre-
dictably spaced and polarized. The number of components, relative spacing,
intensity, and polarization depend on the Landé g-values of the two spectroscopic terms involved, while the scale of the pattern is proportional to the intensity of the field.

It was shown by Lorentz, in a classical treatment of a simple, one-electron
system, that if $\bar{\nu}_0$ represents the wave number without a magnetic field, the
wave number in the presence of a field of H gauss will be given by $\bar{\nu}_0 \pm \Delta\bar{\nu}$, where

$$\Delta\bar{\nu} = \frac{eH}{4\pi m c^2} = 4.67 \times 10^{-5} H \text{ cm}^{-1}. \tag{1}$$

The shift in wave length for the normal triplet is, correspondingly,

$$\Delta\lambda = \pm 4.67 \times 10^{-13}\lambda^2 H \text{ angstroms} . \tag{2}$$

The normal triplet, so defined, establishes the scale in terms of which the more
complicated anomalous patterns are generally expressed.

The displaced components of the triplet pattern, called the "σ components,"
are circularly polarized in opposite senses when observed in the direction of
the magnetic field (the longitudinal effect), while the undisplaced (π) component
is absent. In the transverse effect, on the other hand, the σ components are
linearly polarized perpendicular to the field, and the sum of their equal intensities is equal to the intensity of the π component, which is linearly polarized
parallel to the field. In the more elaborate patterns, the σ and π components split
up into groups, all components of a group showing the same characteristic
polarization. Certain representative Zeeman patterns are shown in Figure 1.

If one observes a source in which there is a magnetic field directed toward the
observer (positive polarity), then electrons revolving in a counterclockwise direction and resulting in left-hand circularly polarized radiation will produce
the higher-frequency σ component, or components, of the pattern, and these
components, either in emission or in absorption (the inverse Zeeman effect), will
be transmitted by a left-hand analyzer. The right-hand polarized components,
of lower frequency, will be totally suppressed by the analyzer.

When, in the vector model of the atom, LS coupling prevails, the Landé g-
values of the respective terms are given by

$$g = 1 + \frac{J(J+1) + S(S+1) - L(L+1)}{2J(J+1)}. \tag{3}$$

For example, the g-values for $^5F_3$ and $^5G_4$ are 15/12 and 23/20. For $^5F_3$ the magnetic quantum number runs from -3 to $+3$ ($-J$ to $+J$) and for $^5G_4$ from -4
to $+4$. The mg-values for each term are given in the table on page 110. ·

By subtracting the figures of the lower row from those above, first vertically
and then diagonally, we obtain, respectively, the components of the Zeeman
pattern for which $\Delta m = 0$ and $\Delta m = \pm 1$. The collected results, expressing the

positions of the components of the pattern for the $^5F_3$–$^5G_4$ transition, are given in the usual notation as $\pm$ (**0.00**, 0.10, 0.20, 0.30), **0.85**, 0.95, 1.05, 1.15, 1.25, 1.35, 1.45. The parallel (π) components are inclosed in parentheses, with the perpendicular (σ) components following. The most intense component of each group, as determined by the selection rules, is printed in boldface.

					m				
	-4	-3	-2	-1	0	$+1$	$+2$	$+3$	$+4$
$^5F_3$........	....	-3.75	-2.5	-1.25	0	$+1.25$	$+2.5$	$+3.75$	....
$^5G_4$........	-4.6	-3.45	-2.3	-1.15	0	$+1.15$	$+2.3$	$+3.45$	$+4.6$

The calculation of Zeeman patterns and the intensity rules are treated at length in the standard texts. Tables of theoretical Zeeman patterns, in LS coupling, have been published by Kiess and Meggers (1928) for all term combinations likely to occur in the spectra of elements other than the rare earths. For certain elements, there is evidence that g-values different from those given by the formula for LS coupling are required, largely because jj coupling tends to prevail among the heavier elements. In current work on the Zeeman effect in stellar spectra, the tables of Kiess and Meggers have been used, except that these computed patterns have been superseded by observed laboratory values when available. Laboratory Zeeman patterns for Fe ɪɪ have been published by Weeks (1944), for Cr ɪɪ by Kiess (1951), and for Eu ɪɪ by Russell, Albertson, and Davis (1941). Because there is often doubt whether LS or jj coupling prevails, additional laboratory determinations of Zeeman patterns would be of value.

§ 3. ZEEMAN EFFECT IN STELLAR SPECTRA

In stars, numerous magnetic fields have been measured with intensities ranging up to 5000 gauss. While these may be regarded as strong fields, the Zeeman broadening is measured only in tenths of an angstrom, which is usually of the same order as, or less than, the line width due to Doppler effects of axial rotation, hydromagnetic turbulence, or other causes. Consequently, the Zeeman patterns are not resolved, and one has to deal with a line profile made up of a number of overlapping components. The Zeeman components, although blended, occur in the π and σ groups, each group having its characteristic polarization. Only one star, HD 215441, has been found that has a field sufficiently strong and uniform that several lines are clearly resolvable into the π and σ components of their Zeeman patterns. The effective field sometimes reaches 34 kilogauss (Babcock 1960).

Two conditions are rather clearly required for the measurement of stellar magnetic fields. It is necessary to select stars with narrow spectral lines, generally no greater in width than about 0.4 A. Further, the field of the star should be "coherent"; i.e., the contributions to the line profiles from the various parts of the star should exhibit one outstanding magnetic polarity. Usually, it is assumed that the main field of the star has a predominant dipolar component. If the star is so oriented that the field is largely longitudinal, a differential circular analyzer can be used to show relative line displacements between the line profiles in the right-hand and left-hand modes of polarization. This is, in fact, the method actually used. If the star has a coherent field that is predominantly transverse in character, a differential analyzer for linear polarization in two azimuths differing by 90° would, when properly oriented, yield line profiles differing in sharpness, although without displacements. Since it is far simpler to measure displacements than to measure differences in line sharpness, the detection of the longitudinal Zeeman effect, using differential circular analyzers, is the method relied on. Tests to detect the transverse Zeeman effect have been made, but without marked success.

If a star is affected by a magnetic field of mixed polarity, so that polarization cannot be detected, a selective broadening of line profiles, in proportion to the field intensity and to the specific Zeeman patterns, may nevertheless be expected. But, because Zeeman broadening is comparatively small, there are few stars in which its presence can be definitely established unless the field is longitudinal and coherent, permitting line offsets to be detected in polarized light.

§ 4. LONGITUDINAL COMPONENT OF THE FIELD

The magnetic field affecting the radiation from any surface element of a star is characterized by an intensity, H, and by an angle, γ, between the field vector and the line of sight. F. H. Seares (1913) showed that the relative intensities of the three components of a normal Zeeman triplet in emission or weak absorption, for any value of γ, as seen through a circular analyzer, are as follows:

$$I_v = \tfrac{1}{4}(1 \pm \cos \gamma)^2 ; \qquad I_m = \tfrac{1}{2} \sin^2 \gamma ; \qquad I_r = \tfrac{1}{4}(1 \mp \cos \gamma)^2 . \quad (4)$$

The sum of the three intensities is independent of γ.

By setting up an equation of moments, it is readily shown that, for independent but blended and overlapping components, the displacement of the blend is proportional to $H \cos \gamma$, the longitudinal component of the field in the line of sight (Babcock 1947).

§ 5. THE z-VALUE OF THE ZEEMAN PATTERN

In the measurement of the effective longitudinal magnetic field of a star, the significant parameter of the blended Zeeman pattern of a particular line is the mean displacement of the σ group of components, to one side of the center, in terms of the displacement of the σ component of a normal Zeeman triplet. This has been designated the "z-value of the pattern." If, within a group of σ components, the strongest is in the middle of the group, the z-value of the pattern is simply the displacement of the strongest component. But if the strongest component occurs at the end of the group, the empirical rule of H. N. Russell has

TABLE 1

PARTIAL ZEEMAN PATTERNS AND z-VALUES OF SELECTED LINES

λ	Element	Mult. No.	σ Components			No. of σ Comps.	z (Computed)	z (Laboratory)	z (Empirical)
(1)	(2)	(3)	(4)	(5)	(6)	(7)	(8)	(9)	(10)
3853.657	Si II	1	0.53	**1.07**	1.60	3	1.07	......	.....
56.021	Si II	1	**1.00**	1.13	1.27	4	1.10	......	.....
59.913	Fe I	4	.....	1.50	.....	1	1.50	1.52	
62.592	Si II	1	.....	0.73	**0.87**	2	0.84		
3900.546	Ti II	34	.....	1.11	.....	1	1.11		
3905.527*	Si I	3	.....	1.00	.....	1	1.00		
05.64*	Cr II	167	0.83	0.89	**0.94**	4	0.90		
33.664	Ca II	1	**1.00**	1.67	.....	2	1.17		
35.942	Fe II	173	**1.00**	1.03	1.06	8	1.05		
38.289	Fe II	3	1.57	**1.63**	1.68	5	1.63		
3938.969	Fe II	190	0.83	0.89	**0.94**	4	0.90	......	.....
4071.740	Fe I	43	.....	0.67	.....	1	0.67	0.69	
77.50*	Cr II	19	**0.63**	1.12	1.62	4	1.00		
77.714*	Sr II	1	**1.00**	1.67	.....	2	1.17		
82.30	Cr II	165	0.94	**1.11**	1.28	5	1.11	1.10	
4128.053	Si II	3	0.83	0.89	**0.94**	4	0.90		
28.735	Fe II	27	1.40	1.80	**2.20**	4	1.90		
29.712	Eu II	1	**1.95**	.....	**2.00**	8	1.98	1.88 R	2.66
30.884	Si II	3	.....	.....	.....	.....	1.05?		
45.77	Cr II	162	.....	1.20	.....	1	1.20	1.23	
4161.796	Sr II	3	.....	1.33	.....	1	1.33		
63.644	Ti II	105	**1.00**	1.06	1.11	6	1.07		
78.855	Fe II	28	**0.35**	0.70	1.06	6	0.80		
79.43	Cr II	26	**1.00**	1.17	1.34	6	1.22		
87.044	Fe I	152	1.25	1.50	1.75	5	1.50	1.46	
4187.802	Fe I	152	1.35	1.45	1.55	7	1.50	1.40 m	
95.337*	Fe I	693	1.27	.....	**1.40**	10	1.34	1.40 m	
95.41*	Cr II	161	1.00	**1.40**	1.80	5	1.40	1.28	.....
4204.989	Eu II	1	1.25	1.50	1.75	7	1.63	2.34 R	1.95
06.375	Mn II	7	**1.00**	1.10	1.20	9	1.20		
4207.35	Cr II	26	1.26	**1.48**	1.72	5	1.48		
10.350	Fe I	152	.....	3.00	.....	1	3.00	3.05	.....
15.524*	Sc II	1	.....	1.33	.....	1	1.33		
15.77*	Cr II	18	.....	1.33	.....	1	1.33		
26.728	Ca I	2	.....	1.00	.....	1	1.00		
4233.167*	Fe II	27	**1.00**	1.17	1.34	6	1.22		
33.25*	Cr II	31	1.14	**1.33**	1.52	7	1.33	1.36	
33.608	Fe I	152	**1.00**	2.00	3.00	3	1.50	1.53	
35.942	Fe I	152	.....	1.65	.....	1	1.65	1.68	
42.38	Cr II	31	**1.00**	1.10	1.19	8	1.17	1.12 A	
4246.41	Cr II	31	0.88	1.86	**2.83**	4	2.10	......	
46.829	Sc II	7	.....	1.00	.....	1	1.00		
50.125	Fe I	152	1.25	1.50	1.75	5	1.50	1.46	
51.733	Gd II?	15	1.50	1.66	1.82	6	1.70		
52.62	Cr II	31	0.86	**1.20**	1.54	5	1.20		
4253.02	Mn II	7	**0.75**	1.00	1.25	5	1.00	......	
56.16	Cr II	192	.....	1.11	.....	1	1.11	1.10	
59.203	Mn II	7	0.90	1.05	1.20	7	1.12		
61.92	Cr II	31	0.91	1.04	1.17	6	1.07	1.00 A	.....
69.28	Cr II	31	0.00	**0.80**	1.60	3	0.80	0.80	
4271.159	Fe I	152	1.35	1.45	1.55	7	1.50	1.43	
73.317	Fe II	27	.....	0.87	**2.60**	2	2.17		
74.803	Cr I	1	1.92	.....	**2.00**	6	1.96	......	
75.57	Cr II	31	**0.77**	0.94	1.12	4	0.90	0.77	.....
89.364*	Ca I	5	.....	1.50	.....	1	1.50	......	

* Sometimes blended.

TABLE 1—*Continued*

λ (1)	Element (2)	Mult. No. (3)	σ Components (4)	σ Components (5)	σ Components (6)	No. of σ Comps. (7)	z (Computed) (8)	z (Laboratory) (9)	z (Empirical) (10)
4289.721*	Cr I	1	1.33	1.67	2.00	5	1.67	......	.....
90.222	Ti II	41	0.83	1.19	1.55	4	1.10	......	.....
92.246	Mn II	6	.....	1.25	.....	1	1.25	......	.....
98.986	Ca I	5	.....	1.50	.....	1	1.50	......	.....
4299.242	Fe I	152	1.40	1.45	1.50	9	1.50	......	.....
4300.052	Ti II	41	1.00	1.17	1.34	6	1.22	......	.....
00.197	Mn II	6	1.45	1.55	1.65	7	1.50	......	.....
01.928	Ti II	41	0.47	1.93	.....	2	0.84	......	.....
02.527	Ca I	5	.....	1.50	.....	1	1.50	......	.....
03.166	Fe II	27	0.93	1.47	2.00	3	1.47	......	.....
4305.447	Sr II	3	1.00	1.47	.....	2	1.17	......	.....
75.932	Fe I	2	.....	1.50	.....	1	1.50	1.52	.....
83.547	Fe I	41	1.30	1.32	1.33	9	1.30	1.16 A	.....
85.381	Fe II	27	.....	1.33	.....	1	1.33	......	.....
4386.858	Ti II	104	0.90	0.94	0.97	6	0.93	......	.....
4394.057	Ti II	51	.....	0.93	1.47	2	1.33	......	.....
95.031	Ti II	19	1.00	1.06	1.11	6	1.07	......	.....
95.848	Ti II	61	1.00	1.17	1.34	6	1.22	......	.....
99.767	Ti II	51	1.35	1.39	1.43	4	1.40	......	.....
4404.752	Fe I	41	1.22	1.28	1.35	7	1.25	1.17 B	.....
4415.125	Fe I	41	0.92	1.17	1.42	5	1.17	1.14	.....
16.817	Fe II	27	0.47	1.93	.....	2	0.83	......	.....
17.718	Ti II	40	0.40	0.93	1.47	4	0.80	......	.....
27.312	Fe I	2	.....	1.50	.....	1	1.50	1.53	.....
34.960	Ca I	4	0.83	1.17	1.50	3	1.00	......	.....
4435.60*	Eu II	4	1.80	1.85	1.90	7	1.88	......	2.47
35.688*	Ca I	4	0.50	.....	1.50	2	1.00	......	.....
42.343	Fe I	68	1.50	.....	1.83	4	1.66	1.68	.....
43.802	Ti II	19	0.83	0.89	0.94	4	0.90	......	.....
49.663	Fe II	222	0.94	1.01	1.07	8	1.06	......	.....
4450.487	Ti II	19	0.69	1.03	1.37	5	1.03	......	.....
59.121	Fe I	68	1.50	.....	1.67	6	1.58	1.59	.....
65.78	Cr II	191	1.00	1.02	1.04	10	1.04	......	.....
68.493	Ti II	31	1.00	1.03	1.06	8	1.06	......	.....
72.921	Fe II	37	0.71	1.34	1.97	4	1.50	......	.....
4481.228 {129 / .327}	Mg II	4	0.83	0.89	0.94	4	0.90 / 1.05	......	}0.98
88.319	Ti II	115	1.00	1.06	1.11	6	1.07	......	.....
89.185	Fe II	37	1.34	1.55	1.76	6	1.50	......	.....
91.401	Fe II	37	.....	0.40	.....	1	0.40	......	.....
4496.862	Cr I	10	1.00	1.33	1.67	5	1.33	......	.....
4501.270	Ti II	31	0.90	0.94	0.97	6	0.93	......	.....
08.283	Fe II	38	.....	0.20	0.60	2	0.50	......	.....
20.225	Fe II	37	1.48	1.57	1.67	8	1.50	......	.....
22.634*	Fe II	38	0.77	0.94	1.12	4	0.90	......	.....
22.62*	Eu II	4	2.00	.....	2.25	6	2.12	2.25	2.08

been used, according to which the effective center of the group lies at a point one-quarter of the way from the strongest toward the weakest σ component. Within a group, the spacing is constant.

Alternatively, the z-value may be obtained from formulae given by Shenstone and Blair (1929). Two cases are distinguished:

$$J_2 = J_1 + 1 , \qquad z = \tfrac{1}{2}(g_2 - g_1)J_1 + g_2 , \qquad (5)$$

$$J_1 = J_2 , \qquad z = \tfrac{1}{2}(g_1 + g_2). \qquad (6)$$

The z-values for several hundred lines in the photographic region of the spectrum have been tabulated by Miss Sylvia Burd. Table 1 is an abbreviated list of selected lines, found by practical experience to be useful in the measurement of magnetic fields of the sharp-line stars of type A. The wave length and identification are followed, in column 3, by the multiplet number in the multiplet tables

TABLE 2

UNUSUAL ZEEMAN PATTERNS OF ASTROPHYSICAL INTEREST

λ	Element	Multiplet No.	Components	z
3677.477.....	Fe I	125	(0.00, 0.75, 1.50) − 0.75, 0. 00, 0.75, 1.50, 2.25	0.00
3767.194.....	Fe I	21	(0.00) 0.00	0.00
3849.969.....	Fe I	20	(0.00) 0.00	0.00
3936.95......	Cr II	128	(0.20, 0.58, 0.96, 1.34, 1.72) −0.61, −0.23, +0.15, 0.53, 0.92, 1.31, 1.69, 2.07, 2.45	+0.92
4000.02......	Fe I	360	(1.17, 2.34), −0.84, +0.33, +1.50, +2.66	+0.92
4016.432.....	Fe I	560	(0.00, 1.17) −0.83, +0.33, 1.50	−0.25
4065.402.....	Fe I	698	(0.00) 0.00	0.00
4122.522......	Fe I	356	(0.00, 0.83) −0.17, +0.67, 1.50	+0.25
4150.258.....	Fe I	695	(0.00) 0.00	0.00
4210.350.....	Fe I	152	(0.00) 3.00	+3.00
4246.41......	Cr II	31	(0.49, 1.46) −0.09, +0.88, 1.86, 2.83	+2.10
4256.212.....	Fe I	690	(0.00, 2.00) −1.00, +1.00, 3.00	0.00
4258.155.....	Fe II	28	(0.67, 2.00) −0.27, +1.07, 2.40	+1.07
4263.141.....	Cr I	247	(0.00, 0.02, 0.04, 0.06, 0.08, 0.10, 0.12, 0.14) 0.98, 1.00, 1.02, 1.04, 1.06, 1.08, 1.10, 1.12, 1.14, 1.16, 1.18, 1.20, 1.22, 1.24, 1.26	+1.05
4278.128	Fe II	32	(0.18, 0.54, 0.90) −0.24, +0.12, 0.49, 0.85, 1.21, 1.57	+0.21
4284.425.....	Mn II	6	(0.00) 0.00	0.00
4314.356.....	Ti I	45	(0.00, 0.60, 1.20, 1.80) −0.45, +0.15, 0.75, 1.35, 1.95, 2.55, 3.15	+2.25
4327.125.....	Gd II	15	(0.20, 0.60) 2.60, 3.00, 3.40	+3.00
4339.718.....	Cr I	22	(0.00) 0.00	0.00
4430.618.....	Fe I	68	(0.00) 2.50	+2.50
4456.612.....	Ca I	4	(0.00, 1.00) 0.50, 1.50, 2.50	+2.00
4462.774.....	Cr I	127	(0.00) 0.00	0.00
4491.401.....	Fe II	37	(0.00) 0.40	+0.40
4508.283.....	Fe II	38	(0.20) 0.20, 0.60	+0.50
5247.564.....	Cr I	18	(0.00) 2.50	+2.50
5250.216.....	Fe I	1	(0.00) 3.00	+3.00
6173.343.....	Fe I	62	(0.00) 2.50	+2.50

of Mrs. Moore-Sitterly (1945), where the spectroscopic terms are given. In the next three columns, up to three components are listed, including always the strongest component of the group, even though the number of components, as indicated in the next column, may exceed three. In column 8 is the computed z-value, and in column 9 the laboratory value, if one is available. The lines in Table 1 are generally free of serious blending in sharp-line A-type spectra, but those occasionally subject to blending are marked by asterisks. A few lines having Zeeman patterns of exceptional interest are listed in Table 2. The preparation of the tables is due to Miss Burd.

Even though Zeeman displacements increase as λ^2, while the Doppler effect varies as the first power of the wave length, most of the practical measurements of stellar fields have depended on lines in the region between λ 3900 and λ 4600. While useful measurements can sometimes be made in the yellow and red, there are fewer suitable lines of the metals in these regions of the spectrum, where photographic emulsions tend to be more grainy and slower.

§ 6. ANALYZERS FOR STELLAR POLARIZATION

The double or differential analyzer shown schematically in Figure 2 has proved to be efficient for observation of the Zeeman effect in stellar spectra (Babcock 1947). A similar analyzer was used by Zeeman (1913) for laboratory spectra. Essentially, it consists of a quarter-wave plate of mica, selected for the

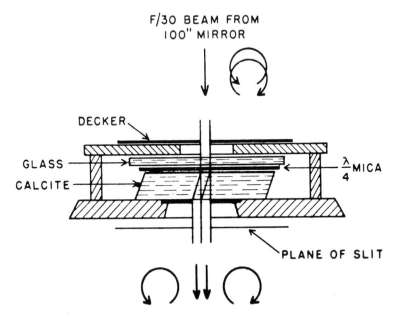

FIG. 2.—Differential analyzer for right- and left-hand rotatory polarization. Essential optics are a quarter-wave plate and a calcite crystal.

desired region, usually near λ 4300, in combination with a calcite crystal several millimeters thick. The calcite is plane-parallel and doubly refracting; the parallel emergent rays, ordinary and extraordinary, are orthogonally plane-polarized. The fast axis of the mica is oriented so as to bisect the right angle between the polarizing planes of the calcite. When mounted in the proper azimuth, a few millimeters in front of the focus of the telescope, the device produces two images of the star, side by side on the slit of the spectrograph, and it functions as a circular analyzer of opposite sign for the two images. Thus two closely spaced, parallel spectra are photographed simultaneously, and differential measurements of line shifts due to the longitudinal Zeeman effect are readily made on the resulting plate.

To prevent overlapping of the two spectra if the seeing is poor or the guiding imperfect, the analyzer is provided with windows or deckers, front and rear, of width a and $2a$, respectively, where a is the separation of the ordinary and extraordinary rays. The mica and calcite crystals, together with a glass cover plate, are assembled into a unit with a thermo-setting plastic cement and are mounted in a hinged holder so that the analyzer can be swung to one side when the comparison spectrum is to be photographed. The slit jaws are highly reflecting and are slightly tilted, so that the automatic photoelectric guider (Babcock, Rule, and Fassero 1956) can function on the light reflected back through the analyzer from the slit jaws.

The phase shift introduced by a mica plate of thickness t, with indices n_0 and n_e, is

$$\delta = \frac{2\pi}{\lambda} t (n_0 - n_e). \qquad (7)$$

Thus, for wave lengths differing from λ_0, for which the phase shift is strictly a quarter-wave, the shift is approximately

$$\delta = \frac{\pi}{2} \frac{\lambda_0}{\lambda}, \qquad (8)$$

and the undesired component of circularly polarized light will be transmitted with intensity nearly proportional to $\sin^2 (\delta - \pi/2)$. Neglect of this factor is usually permissible over a spectral range of a few hundred angstroms centered on λ_0.

The use of a Fresnel rhomb in place of the mica plate would provide a retardation essentially independent of wave length, but it would entail practical drawbacks in fragility and in the offset of the optical axis.

Depending on the relative orientation of crystal axes, there is ambiguity in the sign of the double analyzer. The first such analyzer was therefore standardized by photographing with it the spectrum of a laboratory source in a magnetic field of known polarity. In applying it to the determination of the polarity of stellar magnetic fields, the reversal of the sign of circular polarization at each reflection in the telescope must, of course, be taken into account. A field directed toward the observer is taken to be of positive polarity. Thus, to an external observer looking at the north geomagnetic pole, the earth's magnetic polarity would be negative. This polarity rule, without implying anything regarding the physical origin of cosmic magnetic fields, provides that, for a rotating body with a positive electric charge, the induced magnetic-field vector is parallel to the vector representing angular velocity.

§ 7. PHASE-SHIFTING COMPENSATORS

Coudé optical systems, with one or more oblique reflections, are required in large telescopes to direct the light to the large, immobile grating spectrographs customarily used for high-dispersion spectroscopy. With the 200-inch Hale reflector, the three-mirror coudé system involves two nearly normal reflections and one oblique reflection, for which the angle of incidence is half the sum of 90° plus the declination. This system is used for objects south of declination +45°;

TABLE 3

PHASE SHIFT PROVIDED BY MICA PLATES ($\delta = \lambda/8$)
CROSSED AT ANGLE 2ϕ

ϕ	Δ	ϕ	Δ
0°.........	90°	25°.........	55°47′
5°.........	88°34′	30°.........	42°24′
10°.........	84°18′	35°.........	28°30′
15°.........	77°10′	40°.........	14°09′
20°.........	67°33′	45°.........	0°

for more northerly objects, a five-mirror system with three oblique reflections is used. When the telescope is directed to the north pole, the angles of incidence are $69\frac{1}{2}°$, $44\frac{1}{2}°$, and 65°, respectively.

Oblique reflections from metallic (evaporated aluminum) mirrors produce changes in the quality of polarized light because a phase shift is introduced between vibrations of the electric vector in the plane of incidence and in the orthogonal plane and also because the reflectivity is different in the two planes. These effects are discussed in texts on physical optics (e.g., Jenkins and White 1950). The phase shift at oblique reflection is the more important of the two effects; compensation for it is generally required in the observation of stellar magnetic fields if the angle of incidence is greater than about 50°.

The expressions for the phase changes at metallic reflection of the p and s components of vibration involve n, the index of refraction, and κ, the absorption index. In general, n and κ depend on the thickness, quality, age, and condition of cleanliness of the evaporated surface; if they are measured, the phase retardation can be computed for any angle of incidence. But the physical characteristics of such a mirror change to some extent with time, and it has been found that the best practical procedure is a direct empirical calibration of a phase-shifting compensator in the telescope, using an artificial source of circularly polarized light that is reflected from the coudé mirrors at various declination settings.

A Soleil compensator, with uniform and adjustable phase shift over the field, nicely fulfils the requirements, but a simpler device, first proposed by I. S. Bowen, has been used satisfactorily. It consists of two retardation plates of mica ($\delta = \lambda/8$), in series, mounted so as to be mutually adjustable in azimuth. When

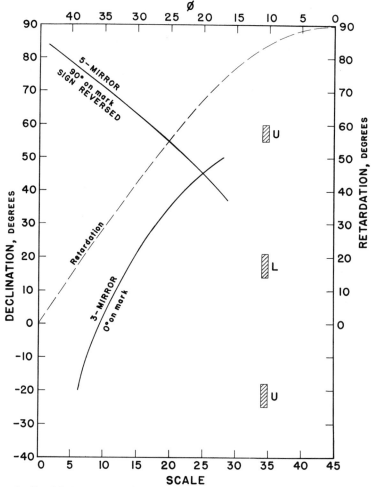

Fig. 3.—Empirical curves showing the setting of the crossed-plate compensator as a function of declination of the star, for the three-mirror system and the five-mirror system. With the latter, which involves three oblique reflections, the retardation is nearly 180° at the north pole; this reverses the indicated polarity as compared with the three-mirror system. For declinations between +45° and +90°, the compensator is rotated 90° and is set to restore the total retardation to 180°.

crossed, the plates give no phase shift; when parallel, a quarter-wave. The compensator is mounted a few inches in front of the analyzer and is equipped with a separate hour circle and synchronous motor drive so that it can be set to follow the telescope in hour angle. It should be noted that the optical performance of composite quarter-wave and half-wave plates differs from that of single plates with the same phase shift (Childs 1956).

If the calibration is strictly empirical, an analytical expression for the phase shift of the crossed plates is not essential, but it can be shown, following the methods of Mascart (1889), that the phase shift, Δ, is given by

$$\tan \Delta = \frac{4\gamma \cos 2\phi (\gamma^2 - \cos 4\phi)}{\gamma^4 - \gamma^2 (1 + 2 \cos 4\phi) + \cos 8\phi}, \tag{9}$$

where $\gamma = \operatorname{ctn} \delta/2$ and ϕ is the angle through which the plates are turned, in opposite directions, from the position of maximum retardation. The phase shift for several values of ϕ is given in Table 3.

Figure 3 gives empirical calibration-curves for the crossed-plate compensator as used with the three-mirror and five-mirror coudé optical systems of the 200-inch telescope.

§ 8. SPECTROGRAPH AND TECHNIQUES

The coudé grating spectrograph of the 200-inch telescope is described in Volume 2, chapter 2. When possible, a dispersion of 4.5 A/mm is employed, as given by the Schmidt camera of 6-foot focus. On a 10-inch plate, the useful range for magnetic-field measurements extends from beyond the K line (λ 3933) to Hβ (λ 4861). The equivalent slit-width is customarily about 0.07 A. Eastman IIa-O plates, baked in an oven for 3 days at 50° C, yield satisfactory speed and fine grain. With average seeing and a moderate degree of widening, the double spectrum of a star of magnitude 7 can be photographed in 3 hours. Figure 4 is an example of a short section of a spectrum of an A-type star, 53 Camelopardalis, showing the offsets of the lines due to the Zeeman effect of a strong (5-kilogauss) stellar magnetic field. The two spectrograms, at different phases, show the reversal of polarity, which occurs in a period of about 8 days.

§ 9. MEASUREMENT AND REDUCTION

Spectrograms are measured much as for radial velocity, except that, in addition to recording the mean setting for stellar lines, the offset, Δs, in microns, between the upper and lower spectrum is noted. Blends are avoided as far as possible. From 30 to 40 metallic lines are generally measured if the richness of the spectrum permits. Table 1 is a useful guide to the selection of lines in A-type spectra. The comparison lines of the iron-arc spectrum are made long compared with the stellar lines, so that the wire in the eyepiece of the comparator can be accurately aligned.

After the "direct" measurement, the plate is reversed by turning it end for

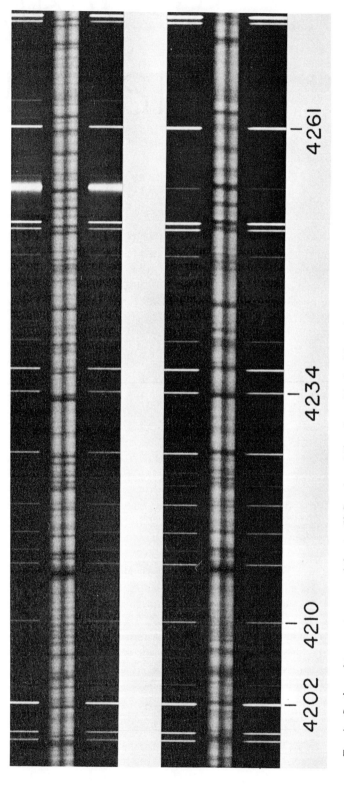

FIG. 4.—Sections of two spectrograms of the star 53 Camelopardalis, taken with the differential analyzer at different times. Offsets, due to the Zeeman effect, are visible in many of the lines, and variations in width and number of the lines can be seen, in addition to the reversal of polarity. The magnetic field of this star varies between the approximate limits +3700 and −5100 gauss in a cycle of about 8 days.

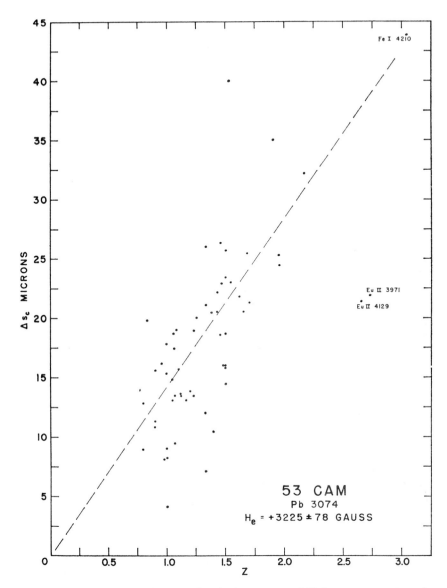

Fɪɢ. 5.—A plot of Δs_c against z for lines in the spectrum of 53 Cam as measured on plate Pb 3074. The slope of the line is a measure of field intensity, which for this plate is $H_e = +3225 \pm 78$ gauss. Note the displacement of 43 μ for Fe ɪ λ 4210.

end and also turning it over, so that the "reversed" measurements are made through the glass. This reverses the sign of the apparent Zeeman displacements, thus minimizing the effect of any personal bias toward right or left.

It follows from equation (2) that, if F is the dispersion in A/mm,

$$H_e = 52.7 \left(\frac{4500}{\lambda}\right)^2 F \frac{\Delta s}{z} \text{ gauss}. \tag{10}$$

In practice, the offsets, Δs, are individually corrected to the value Δs_c that would obtain at a standard wave length, λ 4500, by multiplying by the factor $(4500/\lambda)^2$. The effective magnetic-field intensity is then found from the formula

$$H_e = 52.7F \frac{\Sigma \Delta s_c}{\Sigma z} \text{ gauss}. \tag{11}$$

Usually the effective field is computed for each element individually, as well as for all measured lines, and the radial velocity is also derived.

The effective field, H_e, is the component in the line of sight on the simplifying assumption that the field is uniform and unidirectional. This avoids unnecessary assumptions as to the distribution of the field, of surface brightness, and of equivalent line width over the surface of the star. The results of measurements of stellar magnetic fields are given in terms of H_e, together with its probable error (Babcock 1958). For ultra-sharp-line A-type spectra, probable errors of about ± 30 gauss are customarily obtained.

Figure 5 is a plot of the Zeeman-effect measurements on a single plate, where, for each line, Δs_c is plotted against z. The slope of the straight line passing through the origin and best representing the data is a measure of the H_e. The deviations of the points from a straight line are not entirely accidental errors of measurement. In part, the deviations are systematic, deriving from the fact that for some lines the appropriate z-values are not known. Laboratory values have been used where available; otherwise it has been assumed that LS coupling holds. In many instances, particularly for the heavier atoms, either jj coupling or an intermediate coupling must be assumed to prevail, but, in the absence of laboratory measurements in a field of suitable intensity, accurate z-values are not available. Another important source of error is that saturation effects in the profiles of stellar absorption lines, as affected by the magnetic field and as viewed through the circular analyzer, will necessarily alter the effective z-values, particularly for strong lines. While these factors limit the absolute precision of measurement of stellar fields, the current techniques have been sufficient to delineate the gross features of these fields and of their variations.

§ 10. PHOTOELECTRIC METHODS

The photoelectric method of measuring small Zeeman displacements is the only one that has proved adequate for the very weak magnetic fields (0.5–30 gauss) of the sun (Babcock 1953). The possibility of applying a modified photoelectric device to the measurement of stellar fields has been considered and tested in a preliminary way (Babcock 1955).

In outline, such a system employs, in front of the spectrograph, an electrically excited oscillating analyzer for circular polarization that varies, at a fixed frequency, ψ, between the right-hand and the left-hand states. Thus all the lines in the spectrum of a magnetic star synchronously undergo slight oscillations in effective wave length. The amplitudes are proportional to the individual z-values and to the effective field, H_e. In place of a photographic plate in the spectrograph, an opaque template, with slits corresponding to the spectral lines, transmits the significant part of the radiation, which is in the line profiles, to a condensing system and thence to a multiplier phototube. The resulting electrical

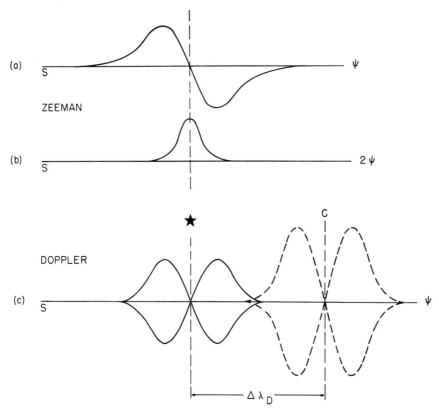

Fig. 6.—Output as a function of template displacement for (a) frequency ψ, and (b) frequency 2ψ, where ψ is the frequency of the electro-optic retardation plate as it is made to oscillate between $+90°$ and $-90°$. The curves represent the integrated effect of the Zeeman shifts of all lines. In c the analyzer is not used, but the optical spectrum is made to oscillate by the angular vibration of a plane-parallel plate behind the slit. Crossover of the curves represents coincidence of (C), the comparison spectrum, and $(*)$, the stellar spectrum, with the appropriate set of slits in the template. The difference, $\Delta\lambda_D$, is a measure of the Doppler effect.

signal, after amplification, is demodulated by a synchronous rectifier and recorded on a strip chart. If the template, under the control of a screw, is made to traverse a short range, permitting the respective slits to scan the corresponding lines in the optical system, curves such as those of Figure 6, *a*, *b*, result. Upon imparting an angular oscillation to a plane-parallel glass plate behind the main slit of the spectrograph, the whole optical spectrum can be made to oscillate, also at frequency ψ, in the direction of dispersion, 180° out of phase with the Zeeman oscillations. The amplitude of the oscillating glass plate can then be adjusted to nullify the effect of the latter. This permits one to derive a mean Zeeman displacement, for all lines, by a null method that is independent of the magnitude of the star. If the mean effect is once calibrated, the photoelectric template system can then be used for the observation of the magnetic-field intensity and polarity of the same star at any subsequent time.

With the polarizing analyzer removed from the beam, the system is capable of yielding, with high precision, the setting of the template for coincidence with the optical spectrum either of the star or of the comparison source. Thus stellar radial velocities can be obtained. When the optical spectrum is made to oscillate by means of the vibrating plane-parallel plate, coincidence-curves such as those of Figure 6, *c*, are obtained. A traverse in each direction, with reversal of phase of the oscillating plate, yields an accurate crossover or coincidence position. Templates for such an instrument can be made by photographing the spectrum of a suitably chosen bright star on a plate of very high contrast.

An experimental system of the kind described has been tested in connection with the coudé spectrograph of the 200-inch telescope. Fellgett (1955) independently proposed a "radial-velocity photometer" based on the template principle, for measurement of velocities, and analyzed the signal-to-noise problem in detail.

The photoelectric template method of observing radial-velocity and magnetic fields has the following advantages over the conventional photographic methods: (1) it utilizes the much greater quantum efficiency of the photocathode as compared with the photographic emulsion (a factor of 10–100); (2) the contributions of all spectral lines are integrated, yielding at the telescope an indication of the result. Subsequent measurement of spectrograms is eliminated.

Disadvantages include (1) no permanent record of the spectrum is obtained; (2) templates must be carefully produced, with optimum slit-widths for good efficiency; (3) because of the diversity of sharp-line stellar spectra, a large stock of templates may be required; and (4) unsuspected variations in line intensity or in profiles can produce spurious results. Variations are not uncommon, at least among the sharp-line A-stars.

REFERENCES

Babcock, H. W.   1947   *Ap. J.*, **105**, 105.
                    1953   *Ibid.*, **118**, 387.

	1955	Reported in *Carnegie Inst. Washington Yearbook*, No. 54, p. 27.
	1958	*Ap. J. Suppl.*, **3,** No. 30, 141.
	1960	*Ap. J.*, **132,** 521.
BABCOCK, H. W., RULE, B. H., and FASSERO, J. S.	1956	*Pub. A.S.P.*, **68,** 256.
BOSCH, J. C., VAN DEN	1957	*Hdb. d. Phys.*, ed. S. FLUGGE (Berlin, Göttingen, and Heidelberg: Springer-Verlag), **28,** 296.
CHILDS, W. H. J.	1956	*J. Scient. Instr.*, **33,** 298.
FELLGETT, P. B.	1955	*Optica acta*, **2,** 9.
HALE, G. E.	1908	*Ap. J.*, **28,** 100, 315.
	1915	*Ten Years' Work of a Mountain Observatory* (Washington, D.C.: Carnegie Institution), p. 45.
JENKINS, F. A., and WHITE, H. E.	1950	*Fundamentals of Optics* (2d ed.; New York: McGraw-Hill Book Co., Inc.), p. 574.
KIESS, C. C.	1951	*J. Res. Bur. Stand.*, **47,** 385 (No. 5).
KIESS, C. C., and MEGGERS, W. F.	1928	*J. Res. Bur. Stand.*, **1,** 641 (No. 23).
MASCART, M. E.	1889	*Traité d'optique* (Paris: Gauthier).
MINNAERT, M.	1937	*Observatory*, **60,** 292.
MOORE-SITTERLY, C. E.	1945	*A Multiplet Table of Astrophysical Interest* (rev. ed.); *Contr. Princeton U. Obs.*, No. 20.
RUSSELL, H. N. ALBERTSON, W., and DAVIS, D. N.	1941	*Phys. Rev.*, **60,** 641.
SEARES, F. H.	1913	*Ap. J.*, **38,** 99.
SHENSTONE, A. G., and BLAIR, H. A.	1929	*Phil. Mag.*, **8,** 765.
WEEKS, D. W.	1944	*Trans. Amer. Phil. Soc.*, **34,** Part II, 181.
ZEEMAN, P.	1913	*Researches in Magneto-Optics* (London: Macmillan & Co., Ltd.), p. 150.

CHAPTER 6

Photomultipliers

A. LALLEMAND
Observatoire de Paris

§ 1. PRINCIPLE OF THE PHOTOMULTIPLIER

A PHOTOMULTIPLIER is the combination of a photoemissive cell and a current amplifier in one envelope that makes possible a very large multiplication of the electron current emitted by the photosensitive layer. External photoelectric emission is the property possessed by certain substances that emit electrons, generally in vacuum, when they receive light or photons. In an ordinary phototube these electrons are collected by an anode. The number of electrons emitted by the photocathode can be determined by measuring the electric current flowing into this anode by means of a galvanometer or through the intermediary of an electronic amplifier.

In a photomultiplier the electrons liberated by the action of the light are directed onto targets called "dynodes," which possess the property of emitting under electron bombardment many more electrons than they receive. One designates by δ the ratio of the average number of secondary electrons emitted by a target to the number of primary electrons received by it. The secondary electrons emitted by the first dynode can be directed onto the second dynode, which functions in the same manner as the first. This process can be repeated many times. If the photomultiplier has n dynodes, each with the same multiplication factor δ, the total gain or multiplication factor for the tube will be $M = \delta^n$.

§ 2. SUPERIORITY OF THE PHOTOMULTIPLIER OVER THE PHOTOELECTRIC CELL FOLLOWED BY AN AMPLIFIER— STUDY OF THE SIGNAL-TO-NOISE RATIO

Consider a photoelectric substance illuminated by a luminous flux Φ_0 that yields a saturation current I_0. This current, often very weak (e.g., $\sim 10^{-17}$ amp.), cannot be measured directly; it must be amplified. One customarily uses an electron-tube amplifier, but, since these amplifiers respond to voltage rather

126

than to current, one transforms the current into a potential drop $I_0 R$ through a resistance R. The larger R becomes, the more advantageous this transformation is. However, difficulties are encountered when R becomes excessively large: the response of the electron-tube amplifier is slow (because of the grid-cathode capacitance), and the grid current in the first tube interferes with its operation. A special tube called an "electrometer tube" largely overcomes the latter difficulty.

The current I_0 is not a perfectly steady current. Since the current is a flow of a finite number of individual charges, the current will fluctuate. The fluctuation is called "shot noise" and was first discussed by Schottky (1918). These fluctuations are also amplified and limit, in a fundamental fashion, the smallest light-flux measurable. But there exists another very important source of disturbance in the resistance R which behaves as a generator of emf, of perfectly random character, which is to say that all frequency components are equally probable and of the same amplitude. If one considers a band of frequencies Δf, the mean-square voltage disturbance, or Johnson (1928) noise, is

$$\langle v^2 \rangle = 4kTR\Delta f,$$

where k is the Boltzmann constant, 1.38×10^{-23} watt seconds per degree; R is the resistance in ohms; T is the ambient absolute temperature.

Furthermore, the mean-square photocathode current fluctuation (shot noise) is

$$\langle i^2 \rangle = 2eI_0\Delta f,$$

where $e = 1.60 \times 10^{-19}$ coulomb, the charge of the electron. It is necessary to compare the magnitudes of these two disturbances.

The current i gives rise to a potential drop of iR in the external resistance. If γ is defined as the ratio of shot noise to Johnson noise, it follows that

$$\gamma = \frac{\langle i^2 \rangle R^2}{\langle v^2 \rangle} = \frac{I_0 R}{2(kT/e)};$$

at room temperature,

$$\gamma = \frac{I_0 R}{5 \times 10^{-2}},$$

which is to say that the Schottky noise is equal to the Johnson noise if the current delivered by the tube gives rise to a potential drop of 0.05 volt across the input resistance. Thus the smallest measurable light-flux is limited by the Johnson noise in the external resistance. It is principally for this reason that the electron multiplier was developed, since it gives current amplification without the use of a resistance.

We have seen that if I_0 is the current from the photocathode, n the number of multipliers, and δ the multiplication factor, the current output from the tube with multipliers is

$$I = I_0 \delta^n.$$

But the current still contains fluctuations. We attempt to calculate the smallest light-flux measurable in the ideal case where there are no other sources of disturbance except that arising from the discrete nature of electricity. We assume that (1) the electron emission from any multiplier follows the Schottky law, $\langle i^2 \rangle = 2eI_0\Delta f$; (2) the Schottky noise is multiplied by the successive stages in the same manner as the signal (all the frequencies are amplified equally).

If I_0 is the current from the photocathode, its fluctuation is given by

$$\langle i_0^2 \rangle = 2eI_0\Delta f .$$

At the output of the first multiplier stage the current is $I_1 = \delta I_0$, and its fluctuation $\langle i_1^2 \rangle$ is

$$\langle i_1^2 \rangle = 2e\delta I_0\Delta f + \delta^2(2eI_0\Delta f) = 2eI_0\Delta f(\delta + \delta^2) .$$

At the output of the nth multiplier stage, one finds a total fluctuation

$$\langle i_n^2 \rangle = 2 I_0\, e\Delta f\, [\,\delta^n + \delta^{n+1} + \ldots + \delta^{2n}]$$

$$= 2 I_0\, e\Delta f\, \delta^n\, [1 + \delta + \ldots + \delta^n]$$

$$= 2 I_0\, e\Delta f\, \delta^n \left(\frac{1 - \delta^{n+1}}{1 - \delta}\right).$$

If S is the initial signal, the signal will be $S\delta^n$ at the output of the nth stage of multiplication. The disturbance (mean-square fluctuation) at the input is given by $\langle i_0^2 \rangle = 2eI_0\Delta f$; the mean-square noise at the output of the nth stage is

$$\langle i_n^2 \rangle = 2 I_0\, e\Delta f\, \delta^n \left(\frac{1 - \delta^{n+1}}{1 - \delta}\right).$$

Therefore,

$$\frac{(\text{Signal/noise})_{\text{input}}}{(\text{Signal/noise})_{\text{output}}} = \left[\frac{1 - \delta^{(n+1)}}{\delta^n(1 - \delta)}\right]^{1/2} = A .$$

This expression enables one to calculate the noise added by the multiplier. For example, when

$$\delta = 2, n = 1; A = \sqrt{1.5} ; \qquad \delta = 4, n = 1; A = \sqrt{1.25} ;$$

$$\delta = 2, n = 7; A = \sqrt{2} ; \qquad \delta = 4, n = 7; A = \sqrt{1.3} .$$

It is evident that the signal-to-noise ratio at the input to the multiplier is always greater than the signal-to-noise ratio at the output. Therefore, a multiplier can never improve the signal-to-noise ratio of the initial photoelectric current. The multiplier introduces less degradation to the signal-to-noise ratio as δ becomes greater and the number of stages of multiplication becomes fewer. But, for all practical purposes, the additional disturbances introduced by this method of amplification are negligible for $\delta > 2$, regardless of the number of stages (in the ideal case we have been considering).

The great interest in tubes with electron multipliers is due to their capability of measuring extremely weak photoelectric currents without adding appreciable

noise. But if one can make the luminous flux sufficiently intense to permit measurements of the current without amplification or if the current produces a voltage drop greater than 0.05 volt in the external resistance, the multiplier tube
loses its importance.

In measuring weak light-fluxes we shall presently show that a high multiplication cannot compensate for a low photocathode sensitivity. Consider a tube with
an ideal multiplier, together with a photocathode with a well-defined quantum
efficiency. The minimum luminous flux that this tube can detect is ϕ_m; when this
photocathode is used without multiplication but its output is measured directly
with a classical electron-tube amplifier, the minimum detectable flux is ϕ_ν. The
advantage or *gain* of the multiplier over the amplifier is defined as

$$G = \frac{\phi_\nu}{\phi_m}.$$

Assume that the amplification by secondary emission is sufficient to permit
measurement of the currents without further amplification and that the current
fluctuations due to secondary emission are negligible in comparison with the
Schottky noise of the photoelectric emission (which will be true if the multiplication factor of the first dynode is greater than 2). Under these conditions the
photocathode yields a current I_a whose mean-square noise component is

$$\langle i^2 \rangle = 2eI_a\Delta f.$$

The current I_a is made up not only of photoelectrons from the light to be
detected but also of thermionic electrons emitted from the photocathode and
any photoelectrons from background light-flux (e.g., sky-background light). A
modulation factor Γ is defined for the current from the photocathode such that

$$\Gamma = \sqrt{2}\,\frac{I_m}{I_a},$$

where I_m is the photoelectric current that contains the information of interest.
If we assume that the current is detectable when the signal-to-noise ratio has a
value ρ (approximately 2), it follows immediately that

$$I_m = \rho \sqrt{(2\,eI_a\Delta f)}.$$

In the case where an ordinary phototube is followed by an electron-tube
amplifier, the noise arises from the input resistance R of the amplifier, and the
mean-square noise voltage generated by this resistance (Johnson noise) is

$$\langle \Delta E^2 \rangle = 4kTR\Delta f.$$

If we require that the signal-to-noise ratio take the same value ρ as before, it
follows that the current emitted by the photocathode must have a value

$$I_\nu = \rho \sqrt{\left(\frac{4\,kT\Delta f}{R}\right)},$$

where I_ν is the signal.

If C is the input capacitance of the amplifier, it can be shown that

$$\Delta f \approx \frac{1}{2\pi RC} \cdot$$

Therefore,

$$G = \frac{I_\nu}{I_m} = \frac{\Gamma}{e\rho} \sqrt{(\pi kTC)} = 7 \times 10^8 \frac{\Gamma}{\rho} \sqrt{C},$$

where the numerical coefficient is calculated for room temperature (300° K) with C expressed in farads. Taking $C = 20~\mu\mu f$ and $\rho = 2$, one has

$$G = 1600\Gamma .$$

For a signal modulated 100 per cent, $\Gamma = 1$. That is to say, with a very well-refrigerated tube and without any background illumination, the multiplier tube can detect, under these conditions, a signal 1600 times weaker than a vacuum photocell followed by an electron-tube amplifier. But when thermionic emission is superimposed, which has the same effect as a stray light-flux, the factor Γ decreases, and the performance of the photomultiplier rapidly approaches that of an ordinary photocell.

As long as the luminous flux to be measured is sufficiently intense or the photomultiplier has a sufficiently large number of stages, one can measure the output current with a galvanometer. But if it is desirable to obtain the greatest possible sensitivity from the tube, one is obliged to use either an impedance transformer or an amplifier. Assume for this case that the value of the input resistance is R and the amplifier band width is Δf. The fluctuation at the output of the multiplier is

$$\langle I_t^2 \rangle = 2eI_0 \Delta f M^2 ,$$

where M is the over-all multiplication of the photomultiplier. The Johnson noise in the input resistance is $4kTR\Delta f$, and this must be smaller than the noise from the multiplier, which leads to the inequality

$$2eI_0 \Delta f M^2 R^2 \geq 4kTR\Delta f$$

or

$$M^2 \geq \frac{0.05}{I_0 R}$$

at room temperature. As an example, assume that the photocathode current $I_0 = 10^{-15}$ amp. With $R = 10^6$ ohms, which does not offer any difficulty with amplifier instability because of grid current, the minimum multiplier gain is $M = 7000$. A photomultiplier with a gain of 10,000 is adequate. The amplifier itself must, of course, have sufficient gain to make the photomultiplier noise override the fluctuations in any following apparatus. If the tube can be cooled, I_0 is reduced. It then becomes necessary to increase the number of stages of multiplication in the tube for a given resistance R.

We shall see shortly that it is necessary for the last dynode to deliver no more than approximately 10^{-7} amp. if the photomultiplier is to give a linear response. Thus, if one selects a photomultiplier with a large number of stages, one will rapidly approach an upper limit to the measurable luminous flux. On the other hand, if one uses a photomultiplier with a relatively small number of stages, one will be able to measure much greater light-fluxes before the current from the last dynode reaches its limiting value. This same multiplier can also observe very weak fluxes by making the amplifier input resistance very large, e.g., 10^{10} ohms.

We shall next determine the multiplication necessary to make use of the ultimate sensitivity of the photocathode. The assumption will be made that secondary electron multiplication permits accurate measurement of the photocurrents without the addition of any perturbations itself. Let $I\phi$ be the signal component of the photocathode current and $I\Phi$ this same component at the output of the multiplier. The signal, then, is $I\Phi = MI\phi$. If the extraneous component of the photocathode current is i, it will appear in the multiplier output as a background current $I = Mi$. At the output, the Schottky noise is given by

$$M[2e(i + I\phi)\Delta f]^{1/2},$$

and the signal-to-noise ratio is

$$\text{Signal/noise} = \frac{MI\phi}{M[2e(i+I\phi)\Delta f]^{1/2}} = \frac{I\phi}{[2e(i+I\phi)\Delta f]^{1/2}}.$$

It is seen that the multiplication, M, disappears and that the signal-to-noise ratio increases (i.e., the measurement becomes better) under the following conditions: (1) When $I\phi$ is largest; that is to say, when, for a given light-flux, the quantum efficiency of the photocathode is greatest. In a photomultiplier it is well known that photocathodes with the highest quantum efficiencies permit measurement of the weakest light-fluxes. The amplification obtained from the dynodes does not enter; it is necessary only that it be great enough to make the Johnson effect of the load resistance negligible compared with the Schottky effect of the photocathode. (2) When i is smallest. There is a great advantage in reducing i (i.e., by cooling the tube). But i can also arise from photoelectric currents caused by extraneous illumination—for example, that of the night sky. It is important not to allow a photomultiplier to receive background light other than the minimum necessary. Otherwise, its performance will be greatly degraded by this extraneous light, which has the effect of adding noise to the output. It is also important that the first few dynodes do not give significant thermionic currents. This is one advantage of dynodes made from silver-magnesium alloys, since their thermionic emission is negligible. (3) When Δf is smallest. An improvement in signal-to-noise ratio can be obtained very effectively by reducing Δf, that is, by increasing the time constant of the measuring circuit. The typical time constant used in astronomical observations is between $\frac{1}{2}$ and 2 seconds. Under some circumstances, integration circuits (Gardiner and Johnson 1955) are used to extend the time constant to several minutes. However, the

time constant cannot be extended indefinitely without possible loss of phenomena of interest, such as variations in atmospheric transmission and in the sky
background.

§ 3. CONSTITUENT ELEMENTS OF A PHOTOMULTIPLIER

3.1. PHOTOCATHODES

A metal contains a very large number of free electrons, of the order of 10^{22} per
cubic centimeter. The energies of these electrons obey the Fermi-Dirac statistics. At absolute zero the kinetic energies cannot exceed a definite energy, W,
which is characteristic of the metal. When the temperature is raised, a small
fraction of these electrons can acquire additional energy. At low temperatures
these electrons are unable to leave the metal spontaneously, their energy W
being insufficient to overcome the surface potential barrier or work function. If
the temperature is raised further, the additional energy acquired will eventually
become great enough to allow the electron to escape from the metal as thermionic emission, which obeys Richardson's law.

At absolute zero an electron can be liberated from the metal with zero kinetic
energy outside by receiving an amount of energy Φ_0. This energy can be given
to the electron by a photon of frequency ν_0 such that

$$\Phi_0 = h\nu_0 ,$$

where h is Planck's constant.

The number of electrons liberated is proportional to the intensity of the light.
If the frequency is greater than ν_0, the electrons can be emitted with a certain
energy and with velocity v, and the energy balance is given by the Einstein
formula,

$$h\nu = \tfrac{1}{2}mv^2 + \Phi_0 .$$

The maximum energy of the emitted electrons is proportional to ν and does not
depend on the intensity of the light.

The yield of this photoemission can be large. Photocathodes with a 40 per
cent yield have been made. But what is most remarkable is that the emission
arises from the interaction of elementary particles, each photon acting individually and capable of producing on its own the emission of an electron by
virtue of the quantization of luminous energy. The exterior photoelectric effect
thus gives the possibility of detecting a single photon, that is to say, it offers the
possibility of realizing the most sensitive receiver of luminous energy that it is
possible to conceive, and the photomultiplier is capable of exploiting this possibility.

The experimental values of Φ_0 for different metals in electron volts: $\Phi_0 = eV$,
where e is the charge on the electron, are as follows: Na, 2.5 volts; K, 2.3 volts;
Cs, 1.8 volts; Zn, 3.4 volts; Ni, 5.1 volts; Mo, 4.1 volts. The values of Φ_0 can be
determined either by the photoelectric threshold ν_0, the frequency below which

photoelectric emission ceases, or by the study of thermionic emission. In the case of metals the values found by these two methods are in good agreement.

Photoelectric surfaces with high efficiency are not generally obtainable with metals but rather with semiconductors. From the point of view of their external photoelectric effect, the behavior of a semiconductor is very similar to that of a metal. However, the work function determined from thermionic emission by Richardson's law can differ appreciably from the value given by the photoelectric threshold frequency.

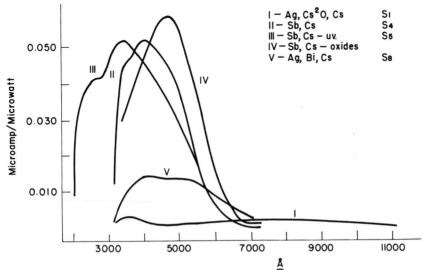

FIG. 1.—Spectral response-curves for photosurfaces of various compositions. *I:* Ag, Cs_2 O, Cs, the commercial S1 type photosurface; *II:* Sb, Cs, the S4 surface when on an opaque substrate; *III:* Sb, Cs, the UV S5 surface, similar to S4 but in a UV transmitting tube; *IV:* Sb, Cs, oxidized; *V:* Ag, Bi, Cs, the S8 photosurface.

Great effort has been expended to make photosurfaces with the highest possible efficiency over a broad spectral region. A great many factors enter into the results obtained: the nature of the constituents, the impurities, the heat treatment, the state of order or disorder of the layer, probably the crystal system of the microcrystals, the thickness of the layer, the direction and polarization of the light, and the transparency of the glass envelope. Temperature, which plays a basic role in thermionic emission, has very little influence on photoelectric emission except that when it is raised, it makes the threshold frequency more indefinite.

The alkali metals play an important role in the fabrication of photoelectric surfaces. Figure 1 gives the spectral responses in microamps per microwatt for surfaces of different compositions. The numbers given are only orders of magnitude. In a given fabrication procedure these numbers may vary by a factor of 2, and appreciable changes can take place with time. This is why a photosurface cannot replace a standard of luminosity.

Commercially the custom has been adopted of designating the spectral sensitivities of the various types of phototubes as S1, S2, S3, S4, S5, etc. The different sensitivities result either from the different compositions of the photosurfaces or from differences in the transmission of the glass envelope. For example, the surface S1 is formed from silver, oxygen, and cesium. Its spectral sensitivity extends to about 12,000 A. The surface S4 has for its principal constituents antimony and cesium. The S5 surface is sensitive to ultraviolet as a result of using a special glass envelope.

A. H. Sommer (1955) has developed several new photosurfaces that contain two or more alkali metals. These surfaces are particularly interesting because of their high quantum efficiencies. Figure 2 gives the spectral responses of these surfaces with various constituents.

The curves given in Figures 1 and 2 are representative of the semitransparent photosurfaces, that is, the light arrives from one side (through the transparent support), and the electrons are emitted from the opposite side into the vacuum. Semitransparent photosurfaces are widely used because they greatly facilitate the construction of a photomultiplier. For example, they simplify the collection

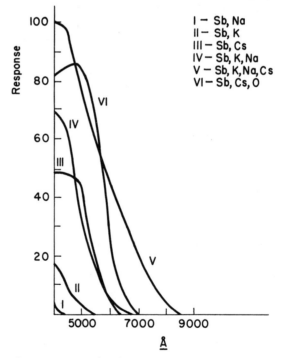

FIG. 2.—Spectral response-curves for photocathodes, including representative multialkali photosurfaces (after Sommer 1956).

of photoelectrons and the concentration of these electrons onto the emitting surface of the first dynode. The precision of assembly can be much greater with the semitransparent photosurfaces than with the opaque surfaces. Generally, in the case where the sensitive layer is prepared upon an opaque support, the surface is a highly reflecting metal. Because of this reflecting surface, these layers can have very high efficiencies, nearly twice those of the semitransparent ones. It was shown previously that a good photomultiplier is characterized from the beginning by good photocathode efficiency. Consequently, in spite of several difficulties, the best photomultipliers are realized with opaque photosurfaces.

3.2. DYNODES

Certain substances are capable of emitting in a vacuum several electrons when struck by an electron with sufficient velocity. This is the phenomenon of secondary electron emission. The number of secondary electrons emitted depends on the nature of the surface, on the energy of the primary, and on the angle of incidence of the primary electrons. The ratio of the number of electrons leaving the surface to the number arriving is designated as the "secondary emission ratio, δ." Among the emitted electrons it is possible to distinguish three groups of electrons: primaries elastically reflected without loss of energy, back-

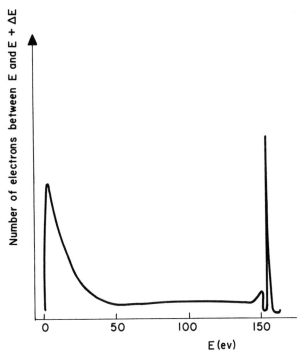

FIG. 3.—Energy distribution of secondary electrons from a typical secondary emission surface.

diffused primaries which have lost varying amounts of energy, and the low-energy group of true secondary electrons. If the energy distribution of emitted electrons is measured, for example, by deflection in a magnetic field, the result is similar to the example shown in Figure 3, which gives the number of electrons with energies between E and $E + \Delta E$ as a function of the energy E in electron volts for a primary electron energy of 150 ev.

It is found that the true secondary electrons with energies in the neighborhood of 2–50 ev have approximately a Maxwellian distribution. Between 50 and 150 volts one finds diffused primaries which have lost energy, while near 150 volts appear the primaries reflected without loss of energy. There is no true secondary emission for primary energies less than approximately 10 ev, for only reflected primaries are observed. When the primary electron energy is sufficiently large, no further increase in primary energy will affect the energy distribution of the true secondaries. If one considers only the true secondary electrons, the maximum emission is perpendicular to the surface.

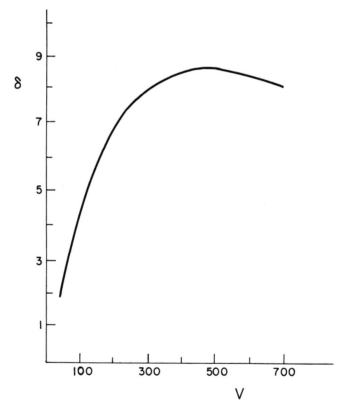

Fig. 4.—Secondary emission ratio as a function of primary electron energy for a silver-magnesium alloy surface treated with cesium vapor.

The value of δ depends on the energy of the primary electrons. Figure 4 gives this variation for a silver-magnesium alloy treated with cesium vapor. For all substances, δ has a maximum whose position lies between primary energies 200 and 1000 ev. At higher primary energies, more and more secondary electrons are produced so deep in the substance that they cannot escape; so δ begins to decrease. The value of δ depends on the nature of the surface. The accompanying table gives approximate values of δ for the substances most commonly used.

Substance	Maximum δ	Primary Energy at δ_{max} (Volts)
Silver-magnesium..........	10	600
Antimony-cesium..........	8	500
Copper-beryllium..........	5	700

The combination of cesium and antimony has often been used, but it cannot withstand the elevated temperatures frequently necessary during fabrication of the photomultiplier, and it also possesses a thermionic emission that is not negligible for the first dynodes. The oxides of the alkali metals or alkaline earths possess remarkable properties. MgO and BeO are stable at high temperatures and, with certain precautions, can be prepared outside the photomultiplier.

It is necessary that the emitting surface have some electrical conductivity. Otherwise, under bombardment by the primary electrons, the surface can charge up sufficiently to cause field emission, making secondary emission unstable, if not impossible. The emitting substance is therefore not a pure oxide but must contain an excess of metal, and the dosage is one of the problems in the fabrication of the layers. Actually, the best method is to make an alloy of some metal not readily oxidized, such as silver, copper, or nickel, with an alkali metal or an alkaline earth. Magnesium is widely used for this purpose. This alloy, when heated in an oxidizing atmosphere (oxygen or water vapor), becomes covered with an oxide layer of the more oxidizable metal with a suitable structure. The operation is carried out in such a way as to obtain an electrical conductivity that is not too small. If one attempts to obtain very large δ's, one encounters undesirable effects, such as the Malter effect, which is characterized by unstable emission and the phenomenon of persistence of emission after the primary current has been interrupted.

There is no close relation between the values of δ and the work functions. This is not surprising, since the energies of the primaries and most of the secondaries greatly exceed possible variations in work functions, but generally the best substances have a low work function. Atoms of an electropositive metal absorbed on the surface of the emitter can play an important role, as in the case of thermionic or photoelectric emission. The value of δ is independent of the temperature of the emitter.

Poor conductors or insulators can possess high secondary emission ratios. This can give rise to serious disturbances in the operation of a photomultiplier, since it must contain glass walls and insulating supports. If the walls and supports are bombarded by electrons, they can assume a variable and uncontrolled potential which can give rise to serious difficulties in the performance of the multiplier. Generally, for these insulating materials, δ is greater than unity, and if they are bombarded by electrons, they approach the potential of the electrode that collects the secondary electrons. In this way the potentials of insulators in the vicinity of the cathode may be raised to levels near anode potential. This gives rise to very high potential gradients in the tube—often high enough to produce cold-field emission and ionization of residual gas in the tube.

§4. STRUCTURE OF A PHOTOMULTIPLIER

In a photomultiplier the system of dynodes must multiply the number of photoelectrons emitted by the photocathode by a statistically constant factor. It must, as far as possible, also satisfy the following conditions:

a) Each dynode surface must receive the largest possible fraction of secondaries emitted by the preceding dynode. To accomplish this, an electric field must be established in such a manner as to direct the electrons onto the multiplier surfaces without loss, while at the same time preventing electron bombardment of the insulators within the tube.

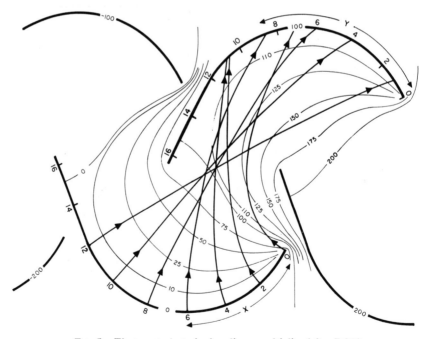

FIG. 5.—Electron trajectories in a linear multiplier (after RCA)

b) The secondary electrons must be emitted into an accelerating, rather than a retarding, electric field.

c) The system must be as insensitive as possible to perturbing fields, such as the earth's magnetic field.

d) Ionic feedback must be eliminated. Ions liberated by ionization in the interior of the tube must be prevented from reaching the cathode, where they could produce parasitic electron emission, which would be amplified through the entire multiplication chain. In turn, these amplified parasitic electrons can produce further ionization of the residual gas in the tube. These ions may then take part in the feedback process, leading to enormous over-all multiplication factors; such high-gain tubes should be mistrusted, as they may prove unstable.

e) Electron cold-field emission must be avoided. Surface asperities, sharp edges, and large potential gradients must be eliminated. The last tend to require tubes of large dimensions.

Much effort has been devoted to realizing these conditions. Generally these efforts have led to a linear assembly of dynodes in which the low and high voltages are widely separated. The first conception of this arrangement is due to Rajchman (1938) and developed by RCA (Figs. 5 and 6). DuMont has developed a linear structure of different form (Fig. 7) and E.M.I. Electronics Ltd. has a Venetian-blind type of linear multiplier (Fig. 8).

At the Paris Observatory we have also developed photomultipliers of the Venetian-blind type (Figs. 9 and 10). The multiplying surfaces are formed of parallel inclined slats of silver-magnesium alloy. A spherical-shaped grid of fine wire surmounts each dynode. This grid serves to concentrate the electrons toward the axis, to insure that they do not miss the surfaces and strike the insulating parts of the tube. It also facilitates extraction of the secondary electrons by replacing a retarding with an accelerating electric field at the dynode surfaces. To eliminate field emission, it is necessary to eliminate all roughness and sharp points or edges. The disposition of the supports must be such that electrons pulled from the borders of the electrodes cannot participate in the multiplication process. It is also necessary that conductors or electrodes with very different potentials be separated as widely as possible from each other. We have met these requirements most successfully in a large 19-stage tube (Fig. 11). Our experience has shown that the electric current of ohmic leakage is of surface origin at the tube base. Consequently, we have lengthened surface leakage paths between all electrodes to the maximum, as is done in "high-tension" insulators. Multiplier tubes make use of extraordinarily high voltages relative to the weak signals that are measured. It is not reasonable to make the tube small, for this ultimately leads to insufficient insulation and excessively high potential gradients, both sources of parasitic emission. However, one of the early successful photomultipliers (RCA 1P21) used a small, compact multiplier structure (see Figs. 12 and 13).

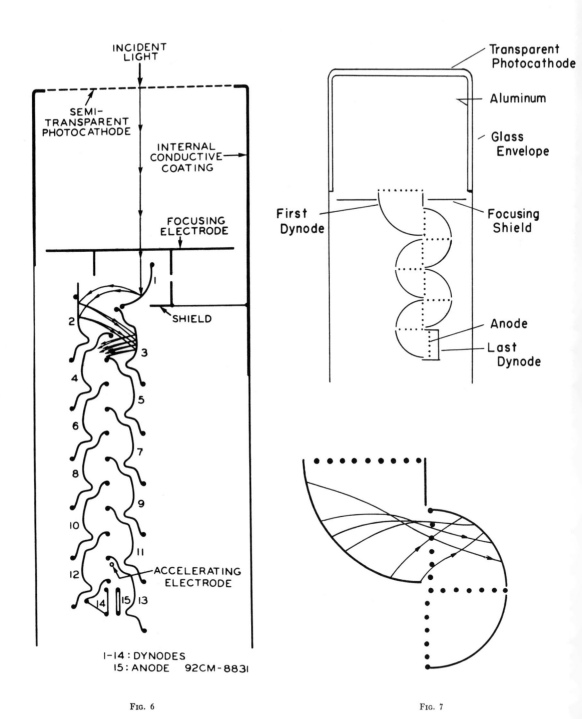

FIG. 6.—A linear photomultiplier (after RCA)

FIG. 7.—A "bucket-type" photomultiplier with typical electron trajectories (after DuMont)

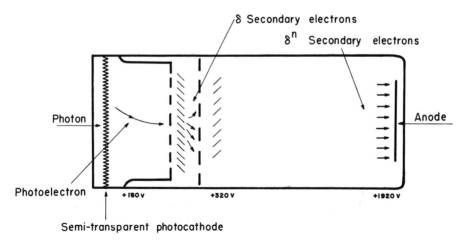

FIG. 8.—The Venetian-blind type of photomultiplier (after E.M.I.)

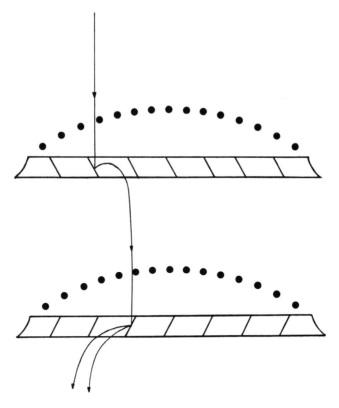

FIG. 9.—Electron trajectories in the Paris Observatory type of Venetian-blind multiplier (after Lallemand).

141

Fig. 10.—A linear photomultiplier, using the Venetian-blind structure of Fig. 9
Fig. 11.—A 19-stage linear photomultiplier developed at the Paris Observatory

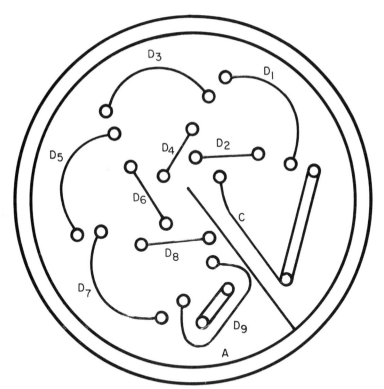

FIG. 12.—Compact photomultiplier design (after RCA)

FIG. 13.—RCA 1P21 photomultiplier (see Engstrom 1947)

§ 5. DISTURBING PHENOMENA IN PHOTOMULTIPLIERS

5.1. THERMIONIC EMISSION

Thermionic emission from the photocathode depends on the work function, that which is on the photoelectric threshold of the layer. For example, photocathodes of the antimony-cesium type, which are much less red-sensitive than layers of the Ag-Cs$_2$O-Cs type, have a much smaller thermionic current. Even so, the thermionic current at ordinary temperatures, amplified by the dynode system, is far from negligible, and, as we have seen, this dark current limits the minimum light-flux that can be measured.

Figure 14 gives, according to Lenouvel (1957), the variation of thermionic current as a function of temperature for a tube of the antimony-cesium type with silver-magnesium dynodes. The accompanying table gives the numerical values. The emission does not follow the Richardson law at lower temperatures, a fact pointed out earlier by Rajchman (1938) and by Duchesne (1953).

	TEMPERATURE (° C)								
	+28	+23.1	+20	+16	+11	+5	0	−4.1	−19.1
Current (amp.)..	9.9×10^{-9}	3.3×10^{-9}	1.8×10^{-9}	9.5×10^{-10}	3.9×10^{-10}	1.3×10^{-10}	6.5×10^{-11}	4.2×10^{-11}	1.1×10^{-11}

To decrease this thermionic emission and thus improve the effectiveness of the photomultiplier, the tube can be refrigerated. Dry ice or liquid nitrogen are convenient refrigerants, but it is necessary to observe certain precautions. In the case of photocathodes sensitive to the infrared, cooling is often insufficient. A further improvement is possible by using a photomultiplier with a very small photocathode. It has been impossible, however, to realize in a photomultiplier a very small photocathode with good sensitivity. One therefore makes a photocathode of normal dimensions and forms an electron-optical image of the photocathode on a diaphragm with the desired dimensions. This is arranged so that only the photoelectrons and the thermionic electrons from the same part of the photocathode are passed on to the multiplier, while all other extraneous electrons are intercepted by the diaphragm. In this way the active surface of the photocathode is artificially limited. The dimensions cannot be limited excessively because it is necessary to form the entire image of the objective upon the active surface of the photocathode with a Fabry lens. For a telescope this image is circular and also often large because the focal length of the Fabry lens cannot be made sufficiently short. It often becomes necessary to have the Fabry lens firmly fixed mechanically to the photocathode.

Figure 15 shows a tube of this type constructed at the Paris Observatory. One can observe near the photocathode a cone that is part of the electron lens for forming the image of the photocathode. With this arrangement it is still necessary to cool the photomultiplier to low temperatures to achieve high sensitivity.

Figure 16 shows, after I.T.T. Laboratories, a photomultiplier sensitive to the infrared with an effective sensitive area in the form of a circle $\frac{1}{8}$ inch in diameter at the center of the photocathode.

5.2. COLD-FIELD EMISSION

Cold-field emission is produced by a high electric field at the surface of some part of the photomultiplier, generally at the tip of the point. This phenomenon can give rise to very troublesome effects, for field emission is facilitated by the presence of cesium inside the tube and the electrons emitted can be multiplied by the dynodes by a very large factor. All photomultipliers have this effect to a greater or lesser degree. To reduce field emission, the electric fields must be reduced by applying smaller potential differences between dynodes. It should be remarked that there is often the tendency, in order to obtain a large amplification, to operate the photomultiplier with too high voltages. Often it is better to have less secondary emission amplification and to compensate the loss of gain by an electron-tube amplifier than by trying to achieve the full amplification of the signal in the photomultiplier.

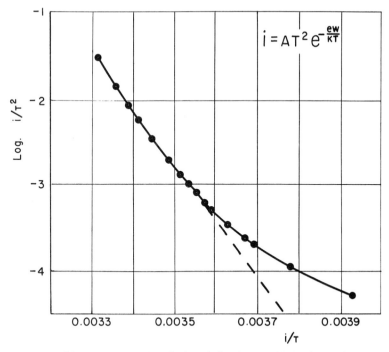

$$i = AT^2 e^{-\frac{ew}{kT}}$$

FIG. 14.—Richardson plot of thermionic emission from an Sb-Cs photocathode

FIG. 15.—Paris Observatory photomultiplier with provision to reduce thermionic emission dark current.

5.3. Ion Feedback

Even though the vacuum in a tube may be very good, there always exists some ionization of the residual gas, particularly around the last dynodes, where the electron current is most intense. Bombardment of surfaces in the tube by these ions can give rise to emission of electrons, which, multiplied by the dynodes, can cause a strong, fluctuating residual current. Photomultipliers which have this defect must be rejected. A photomultiplier which functions normally improves with use because the ions are absorbed and therefore the vacuum becomes better. When one has had a photomultiplier that has given good results and has not suffered any mechanical accidents (breakage, cracks, etc.) and has

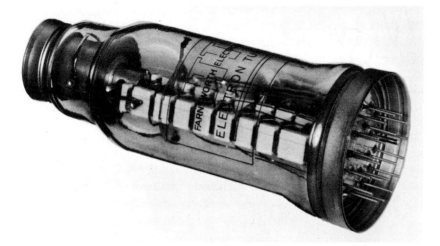

Fig. 16.—Infrared sensitive photomultiplier (after I.T.T. Laboratories)

not been exposed to excessively strong light or too much heat, but ceases to give good results, the cause of the malfunction should first be sought outside the photomultiplier, i.e., in the mounting, the voltage source, the measuring apparatus, etc. Cooling the tube improves the vacuum and therefore reduces the ionic feedback. In certain photomultipliers the manufacturer places in front of the last dynodes metal grids made of metals such as titanium, zirconium, and tantalum,[1] having a large capacity for absorbing ions. These grids play the role of ion pumps, and the performance of such a photomultiplier improves with time.

5.4. Ohmic Leakage

We have seen how the photomultiplier should be constructed to minimize leakage currents. An ohmic leakage should give a constant current without troublesome fluctuations. In practice, it never behaves this way because the leak-

[1] Patent of the Schlumberger Well Surveying Corporation.

age usually arises from a thin conductive film produced inside the tube by cesium vapor and outside by humidity. The conductivity of these films is variable and can produce disastrous effects. These fluctuations can give rise to sudden variations in potential on the insulators within the tube and especially on the glass envelope, with attendant ionization that gravely disturbs the operation of the tube. In practice, nothing can be done about leakage paths inside the tube, except to select a photomultiplier which has been properly constructed; but much can be done about external leakage. Unsatisfactory performance is very often due to external conductive films. The photomultiplier should be mounted in a perfectly dry and water-tight chamber. Under these conditions, experience shows that even when very active desiccants are used, such as activated alumina, it is often necessary to wait several weeks before the photomultiplier performs correctly. Care must be taken that the glass walls of the tube do not touch anything but high-quality insulators, such as polyethylene or araldite.

Figure 17 shows the design of the chamber that is used at the Paris Observatory. It is perfectly tight, since it is constructed in a vacuum-tight manner with O-rings as seals. The chamber is made of soft iron to provide magnetic shielding.

Figure 18 gives a recording of output current, signal plus noise, of an excellent photomultiplier correctly mounted. In the same figure is given a recording of the currents for the same signal, when the same photomultiplier was inadequately sealed in the same chamber. The mounting problem becomes more delicate when the tube is to be cooled. It is not necessarily that cooling leads to a defective seal, as is often the case with heterogeneous assemblies, such as metal to rubber, but that condensation of water vapor becomes important. Lenouvel (1957) has proposed a solution that consists of attaching a "respirator" (Fig. 19), which is a long tube connected at one end to the photomultiplier chamber, the other end open to air through a 1-mm hole. The tube is filled with desiccant. The pressure inside the chamber is the same as the pressure outside. This lack of airtightness does not increase the tube leakage because the air entering the chamber must pass through the desiccant, which is renewed periodically.

5.5. FLUORESCENCE AND RADIOACTIVITY

In the interior of a photomultiplier, electrons bombard the dynodes and, to some extent, other parts as well. This bombardment often produces a weak light-emission which can be sufficient to excite the photocathode. From the point of view of stability, it is always of interest to limit the intensity of the currents in a tube as much as possible.

There always exists in the glass envelope of the tube some radioactive potassium, K^{40}, which can give spurious pulses (Labeyrie 1956). Other causes of radioactivity and emission of photons can be presented. However, it is difficult to see what precautions can be taken to reduce the photocurrent from these sources to less than a few electrons per second.

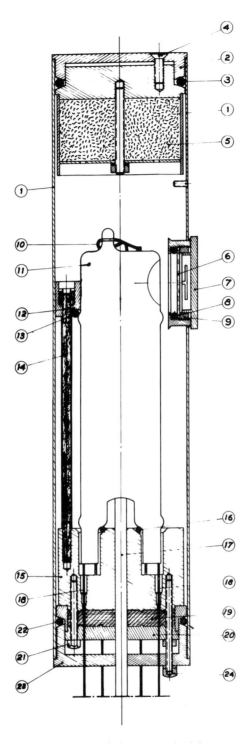

Fig. 17.—Mounting chamber for photomultiplier. *1:* Box of soft iron; *2:* cover made of light metal; *3:* O-ring; *4:* one of three screws for compression of O-ring; *5:* desiccator; *6:* transparent window; *7:* removable metal cover; *8:* O-ring; *9:* clamping ring; *10:* photocathode connection; *11:* photocathode; *12:* araldite collar; *13:* rubber collar in contact with the photomultiplier; *14:* one of three rods that support the araldite collar; *15:* block of araldite that supports the photomultiplier; *16:* rubber ring in contact with the glass of the photomultiplier; *17:* passage for the anode lead; *18:* dynode leads; *19:* block of compressed rubber to insure tightness of the wire leads; *20:* block of araldite to compress rubber block; *21:* screws for compressing rubber block; *22:* O-ring; *23:* cover; *24:* screws for compressing O-ring.

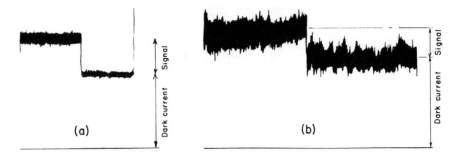

Fig. 18.—Output current recording of a photomultiplier (*a*) properly mounted, (*b*) in a mounting chamber with a defective seal which allowed moist air to enter.

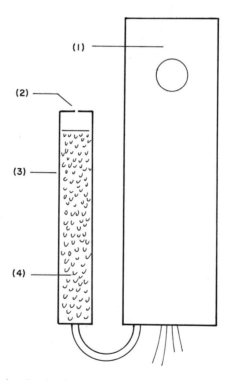

Fig. 19.—Mounting chamber for cooled photomultipliers. *1:* Mounting chamber; *2:* 1-mm-diameter hole; *3:* respirator tube; *4:* silica gel.

5.6. Magnetic Field

The electrons which travel through an electron multiplier are relatively slow and thus quite sensitive to the presence of a magnetic field, which can deflect them sufficiently to miss a dynode surface. Tubes with precise focusing are more sensitive to magnetic fields than those of the Venetian-blind type, for example. A magnetic field of 1 gauss does not change the response of the photomultipliers made at the Paris Observatory more than 1 per cent when mounted in a soft-iron shield. Figure 20 shows, according to RCA, the effect of a magnetic field on an RCA type 5819 photomultiplier. It should be pointed out that in an astronomical dome the variations in magnetic field can become very important when the photomultiplier approaches objects constructed of magnetic metal, as, for example, the iron observation ladder. Under some circumstances, it is necessary to shield the photomultiplier with mu-metal.

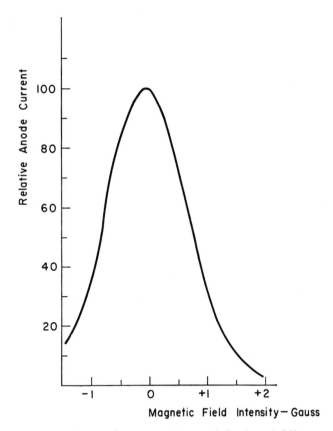

Fig. 20.—Effect of magnetic field on a photomultiplier (after RCA)

5.7. Saturation Fatigue

A space charge exists around the collecting anode of a photomultiplier in operation. A saturation current is obtained from this space-charge region with a voltage that can be comparable with that of the preceding dynode. Since this anode current produces a potential drop in the measuring apparatus or in the input resistance of an amplifier, one must be careful that this potential drop does not lower the anode voltage below the saturation potential.

By way of illustration (Lenouvel 1953), a 19-stage photomultiplier, operated at 70 volts per stage and delivering a current of 4×10^{-8} amp. at the output, had a variation in anode current of 1 per cent when the output was fed into a resistance of 67 megohms.

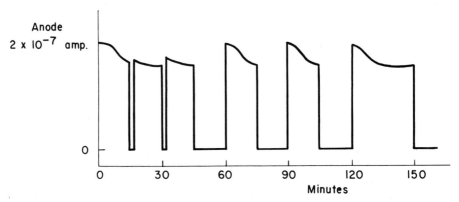

FIG. 21.—Photomultiplier output current showing effects of space charge between the anode and final dynode.

A photomultiplier that gives a signal proportional to the light flux which it receives is required. This condition can never be realized if the current delivered by the last dynodes is excessive. Experience at the Paris Observatory suggests that a current of the order of 10^{-7} amp. represents a practical upper limit, which in turn limits the number of dynodes in a photomultiplier. Lenouvel (1953) gives as a limit 4×10^{-8} amp., and M. Walker (1958) gives 10^{-7} amp. as the limiting current for E.M.I. type 5659 and 6094 tubes. Figure 21 reproduces the output current of a photomultiplier delivering 2×10^{-7} amp. as a function of time. The dynodes are of silver-magnesium alloy. This phenomenon does not arise from the photoelectric effect at the photocathode but from the final dynode, as can be shown by recording the currents delivered by the different dynodes. The explanation, in all likelihood, rests with the variation in potential of the active surface of the dynode, which moves in the direction of the potential of the collecting anode with the creation of a space charge. This effect is produced by insufficient electrical conductivity in the secondary emission layer on the dynode surface. This phenomenon presents a serious inconvenience because it limits the range of fluxes that can be measured with precision for a given supply voltage.

One can broaden this range by varying the interstage voltages and obtain, in this way, a range of 4–5 orders of magnitude. This method has been found convenient by some observers, but M. Walker (1958) has pointed out the possibility of errors, since the electron trajectories in the photomultiplier will be somewhat modified by changing the potentials between dynodes. To maintain a large δ at the first dynode, the potential between the cathode and first dynode should be held constant in any case. It may be more reasonable to use a photomultiplier with few stages which is thus capable of measuring relatively intense fluxes, followed by a linear amplifier whose input resistance can be varied between very wide limits (Kron 1958).

5.8. Miscellaneous Effects

The frequency response of a photomultiplier is very high, and a response of 10^8 cycles/sec is easily obtained. In astronomical observations one is rarely concerned with these limitations except in the broadening of the signal produced by a single photon. This broadening is due to the fact that the electrons emitted from the cathode and re-emitted from the different dynodes do not all have the same transit time through the tube. This is especially true for tubes that make little use of precise focusing, such as the Venetian-blind multiplier.

We have seen that ionization of residual gas in the tube can exist. The ions so produced can lead to the generation of parasitic electrons, which are received by the anode a certain time after the normal secondaries. A signal, called the *after-pulse*, will then be recorded. This phenomenon is not observable except during pulse operation, as in the case of scintillation counting.

The procedure for putting a photomultiplier into operation poses once more a number of unresolved questions. If one suddenly applies the working voltage to the different dynodes, the residual current can become very large. Generally it will decrease to a normal value in about 20 minutes for a good photomultiplier. It is highly advantageous to raise the voltage very gradually until the voltage slightly exceeds the working voltage. Kron (1958) has obtained better performance by first applying voltage followed by cooling than by carrying out these operations in the reverse order. These phenomena are probably caused by the redistribution of electric charges on the internal parts and insulators of the photomultiplier, particularly on the walls of the glass envelope. It should not be forgotten that, in view of the extremely minute electric currents brought into play and the large potential differences used, the concepts of conductors and insulators lose their customary significance, and the glass of the envelope, through its conductivity, helps to establish the equilibrium potentials inside the photomultiplier.

§ 6. REMARKS ON THE USE OF PHOTOMULTIPLIERS

6.1. Choice of the Voltage per Stage

We have seen that there is always a tendency to make the voltage too high, in order to simplify the problem of recording the signal. The signal-to-noise ratio always increases when one lowers the voltage. At the same time, a voltage sufficient to assure saturation of the photocathode and a multiplication at least as large as 2 on the first dynode must be used, and to assure anode saturation, the electrons must not be allowed to drift between dynodes. Taking into account all these factors, it is difficult to operate a multiplier properly with less than approximately 60 volts between dynodes. With multipliers which do not require precise electron focusing from stage to stage, an attempt can be made to find the best distribution of voltages between dynodes for a given over-all voltage. However, this is a complicated operation and does not greatly improve the results.

6.2. Voltage Stability

Figure 22 gives the total multiplication as a function of the voltage. The very large variation in gain produced by a small variation in voltage makes it absolutely essential, in order to assure constant gain during measurements, to use a very well-regulated voltage supply with the multiplier. For a photomultiplier with 20 stages operated at 103 volts per stage, a variation of only 0.08 volt per stage produces a 1 per cent variation in gain. To measure to about 1 part in 1000, it is necessary to regulate the voltage supply to about 1 part in 10,000.

We have seen that precaution must be exercised in mounting a photomultiplier, in order to avoid external leakage. Precautions of the same nature must also be taken with its voltage supply. This must be mounted with insulators of

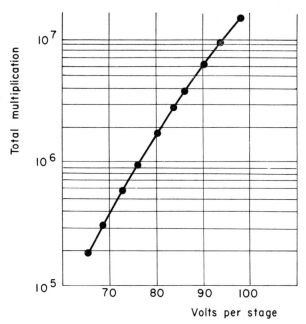

Fig. 22.—Over-all gain of a photomultiplier as a function of the voltage between dynodes.

highest quality, with care taken at every step to minimize the possibility for an electrical discharge, however microscopic, to occur. Similar care must be taken with the voltage divider and the wiring. The factor which causes the disturbances is the high electric field, i.e., volts per centimeter. The voltage on a 20-stage photomultiplier is about 2000 volts, and it is of great advantage to separate points at different potentials in the tube base by as much space as possible. In particular, voltage dividers in the form of a ring such that their points of extreme voltage difference are in proximity usually lead to trouble. The various ground connections should be made with good contacts and should be joined together at a single point.

6.3. Tests for Proper Functioning

A good photomultiplier possesses a good photocathode. The photocathode sensitivity can be measured with the photomultiplier connected as a diode (the whole dynode assembly connected together) and a known light-flux. At the same time, the current saturation-curve as a function of voltage can be determined. The saturation voltage must be well below the voltage normally applied between the cathode and the first dynode. The measurement is generally made with a lamp having a color temperature of 2870° K and standardized in lumens. For tubes sensitive to the infrared, a filter—e.g., Corning No. 2540—is interposed. The ratio of the responses with and without the filter is then measured.

Precise measurement of the multiplication factor is not of much interest, but it may be useful to know its order of magnitude, particularly to check whether the mounting is correct—for example, to determine whether two dynode connections are reversed. To do this, the output signal of the multiplier functioning normally is first measured. Then the last dynode is connected to the anode so that the two act together as an anode, and the signal output is measured with the new connection. These two measurements serve to determine the gain of the last dynode. Proceeding in this fashion, the gain of each dynode in turn, up to the first, may be determined. Naturally, it is necessary to have the signal suitably increased from time to time during the series of measurements. This is done by increasing the light-flux on the photocathode by a known amount.

When the photomultiplier is put into service and provision made to record the currents it delivers during time intervals as long as one desires, examination of the magnitude and constance of the dark current yields valuable information. Fluctuations of this current should not show evidence of "flicker effect." For cesium-antimony photocathodes cooled to dry-ice temperature, it is possible to have dark currents as low as 10^{-19} amp. ($\sim$1 electron per second). For tubes of the Ag-Cs_2O-Cs type, one can reach 10^{-17} amp. It may be useful for the laboratory to have extremely weak light-sources made of fluorescent materials activated by radioactive materials, but the results with such light-sources are always qualitative.

A photomultiplier functioning properly shows the following behavior: the dark current has a certain value and the noise a certain amplitude; on illumination of the tube with a very weak light-flux, the signal increases, and the amplitude of the noise should also increase.

A photomultiplier is, in principle, a very simple device, since it requires only the application of a constant voltage to each electrode to make it function, but this functional simplicity is only apparent. The very high gains of which it is capable demand as much care in its use as a corresponding electron-tube amplifier.

REFERENCES

DUCHESNE, M.	1953	*Bull. Astr.*, **17**, 67.
GARDINER, A. J., and		
JOHNSON, H. L.	1955	*Rev. Sci. Instr.*, **26**, 1145.
ENGSTROM, R W.	1947	*J. Opt. Soc. America*, **37**, 420.
JOHNSON, J. B.	1928	*Phys. Rev.*, **32**, 97.
KRON, G. E.	1958	Private communication.
LABEYRIE, J.	1956	*J. de phys. et radium*, **17**, 577.
LENOUVEL, F.	1953	Thesis, Paris.
	1957	*Electronique*, **123**, 15.
RAJCHMAN, J.	1938	*Arch. d. sci. phys. et naturelles*, **20**, 231.
SCHOTTKY, W.	1918	*Ann. d. Phys.*, **57**, 541.
SOMMER, A. H.	1955	*Rev. Sci. Instr.*, **26**, 725.
	1956	*I.R.E. Trans. Nuclear Sci.*, NS-3, p. 8.
WALKER, M.	1958	Personal communication.

CHAPTER 7

Photoelectric Photometers
and Amplifiers

HAROLD L. JOHNSON

*McDonald Observatory, University of Texas**

§ 1. INTRODUCTION

THIS chapter is devoted to a discussion of photoelectric photometers and other associated apparatus, such as are used for astronomical photometry. A detailed discussion or description of the many photoelectric photometers that have been constructed and used during past years or a discussion or reference to the many publications and experiments on the underlying physics of the photoelectric effect cannot be given here. The reader is referred to the exhaustive bibliography given by Linnell (1953) for such matters. Instead, this chapter contains general design data for photoelectric photometers and recommendations for their construction. Included are comparisons and specifications of photomultipliers and photocells and a circuit diagram for a recommended d.c. amplifier.

§ 2. THE GENERAL DESIGN OF A SIMPLE PHOTOMETER

In the design of an astronomical photoelectric photometer, there is a minimum of five essential components. These are (1) finding-guiding eyepiece; (2) a focal-plane diaphragm containing at least one hole of a size suitable for isolating the desired objects; (3) a field (or Fabry) lens; (4) suitable filter or filters for isolating the desired spectral region(s); and (5) a suitable detector (including amplifier) for the radiation being measured. Additional components may increase the convenience or usefulness of the photometer.

The schematic layout of a photoelectric photometer intended for use at the Cassegrain focus of a reflecting telescope is shown in Figure 1. The figure is drawn for a focal ratio of 14:1. The various components are identified in Figure 1, and it will be noted that the five essential components listed above are in-

* Now at the Lunar and Planetary Laboratory, University of Arizona.

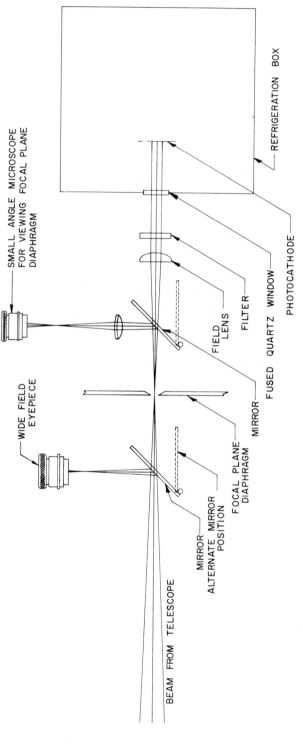

FIG. 1.—The schematic diagram for a Cassegrain-focus photoelectric photometer. See text for further description

cluded. In addition, there is a small-angle microscope for viewing the focal-plane diaphragm. This additional eyepiece, while not absolutely necessary, is sometimes convenient; if it is not included, the wide-field eyepiece must be such that it can double for both finding and guiding purposes. The phototube has been shown in a refrigeration box, since refrigeration is required for many astronomical observing programs. The mirrors for reflecting the light to the two eyepieces have been arranged so that they may be removed from the light-beam, for observation of the star with the phototube, by rotation about a pivot at one end of the mirror. This method works quite satisfactorily, but a good alternative is to move the mirrors perpendicular to the plane of the paper; since such motion is parallel to the mirror surface, it is not necessary to provide accurate stops for the mirror motion. A simple plano-convex fused-quartz field lens usually suffices. This design, or slight variations upon it, has been used for photometers at many observatories, for example, at the Lick, Washburn, Yerkes, McDonald, and Lowell Observatories.

Operation at the Newtonian or prime focus ($f/5$ or $f/3$) of such an instrument is not feasible for the design in Figure 1 because of the rapidly divergent beam beyond the focus, which makes it necessary to place the photomultiplier very near to the focal-plane diaphragm. These small focal ratios require a photometer of the design similar to that shown in Figure 2. In this design the phototube

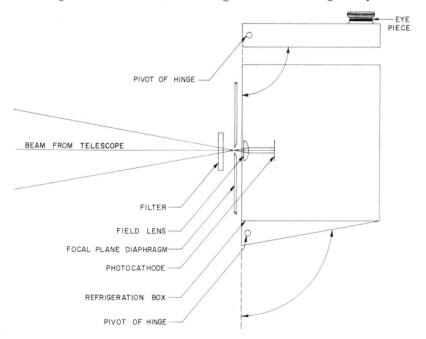

Fig. 2.—The schematic diagram for a Newtonian or prime-focus photoelectric photometer. See text for further description.

refrigeration box can be removed from the telescope beam by rotation about the pivot shown at its lower left edge; the eyepiece may then be rotated into place for viewing the image. The diaphragm and filters may have to be removed at this time. The filters are placed in front of the focal-plane diaphragm because there is no space for them elsewhere; such placement does, of course, require that the filters have fairly good optical quality and that all filters have the same optical thickness. Photometers of the design of Figure 2 have been used at the Mount Wilson and Palomar observatories and elsewhere.

A comparison of the photometer designs of Figures 1 and 2 makes apparent some of the advantages of photoelectric photometry at the Cassegrain focus of a large reflecting telescope, with regard both to flexibility in the design of the photometer and to convenience in its use.

§ 3. INDIVIDUAL COMPONENTS

While certain of the components of a photoelectric photometer (see Figs. 1 and 2), such as the focal-plane diaphragms or the field lenses, need no further comment, others may profitably receive further discussion. Among those components which require disquisition is the detector, which, in the terms of this chapter, includes the amplifier.

3.1. PHOTOMULTIPLIER

The light-sensitive element in all photoelectric photometers is a photoelectric cell of some kind, which, in the range of wave lengths from 3000 to 11000 A, is nowadays almost universally a photomultiplier. Ordinary photocells, both vacuum and gas-filled, have seen considerable use in astronomy, but such use is almost entirely of the past, and the reader is referred to the bibliography of Linnell (1953) for reference to such work.

The first photomultiplier to be used in astronomical photoelectric photometry was the RCA 1P21 (or its low-priced version, the RCA 931-A), and it is still the most sensitive one in the wave-length range from 3000 to 6500 A. The principal disadvantage of the 1P21 is its construction with the cathode inside the tube, near the center. This makes it difficult in some applications, such as a photometer for an $f/3$ telescope beam, to get the light to the photocathode. The greater sensitivity and superior performance of the 1P21 are, however, sufficient to counterbalance, for most astronomical uses, the disadvantage of its construction. Selected 1P21's can be obtained which have cathode sensitivities exceeding 80 microamperes per lumen and with dark currents less than one thermal electron per second with refrigeration. Experience has shown that only RCA 1P21's (among all the types of blue-sensitive photomultipliers) are further improved by refrigeration below the temperature of dry ice ($-80°$ C). Upon refrigeration with liquid nitrogen, many RCA 1P21's, even those with very sensitive cathodes, have dark currents well under one electron per second referred to the cathode (i.e., the output dark current divided by the gain of the multiplier). Only in RCA 1P21's is the efficiency of collection of the photo-electrons into the multiplier approximately 100 per cent, although other photo-multipliers, such as those made by DuMont, have collection efficiencies in the neighborhood of 80 per cent. On the other end of the scale, a collection efficiency of only 25 per cent has been measured. It goes almost without saying that, to be useful, a sensitive photocathode must be accompanied with high collection efficiency. All the phototubes with which the 1P21 has been compared are of the type in which the photoelectrons are collected into the first dynode structure by means of some type of electron lens system, while in the 1P21 the photoelectrons are generated right inside the multiplier structure. Thus it may be that the very structure of the 1P21, which makes it difficult to get the light into the cathode, is also partly responsible for its superior performance.

The placement of the anode pin next to the cathode pin in the 1P21 and the resultant possible leakage across this small space have worried some investigators. While one might very well suppose that such construction could lead to serious problems, in actual practice the leakage between these two pins is insignificant. The material of which the socket holding the 1P21 is composed is important; it is essential to use a socket made either of ceramic or of mica-filled bakelite, not the ordinary black bakelite.

For the range of wave lengths from 6000 to 11000 A, a different photosensitive surface from that used in the 1P21 (SbCs) is required. The only photoemissive surface available for this entire spectral range is the S-1 (CsOAg) surface, and there are several manufacturers of photomultipliers having this surface. Among the available tubes are the Farnsworth (ITT Laboratories) 6836/16 PMI and FW-118, the RCA 7102, and custom-built tubes made by Lallemand. W. A. Baum (1957) has used the Farnsworth tubes at the 200-inch telescope; K. L. Hallam has used a selected preproduction prototype of the RCA 7102 in the observational work for his doctoral thesis; and G. E. Kron (1958) and R. H. Hardie have used several Lallemand tubes in their work. The lack of extensive experience with these infrared-sensitive tubes precludes specific recommendations, but it seems likely that the best choice at present is among the three manufacturers mentioned above.

3.2. REFRIGERATION OF THE PHOTOMULTIPLIER

For most astronomical photometry, it is convenient and often necessary to refrigerate the photomultiplier. Even in cases in which it is not necessary from the standpoint of phototube sensitivity and dark current, refrigeration may be desirable in order to produce constant-temperature conditions, independent of outside ambient-temperature conditions. For this purpose, a suitable refrigeration box is required. A successful design of such a box is illustrated in Figures 3 and 4. In this design, the 1P21 phototube is inclosed within a brass or copper tube, which is itself inclosed within another brass or copper tube. The only connections between these inner tubes and the outside container, other than the

wires leading to the 1P21, are two thin-walled Inconel tubes, one for leading the
light to the 1P21 and the other for inserting the refrigerant (either dry ice or
liquid nitrogen) into the larger inner tube. These two Inconel tubes are made
poor conductors of heat by thinning down the walls to 0.006-inch thickness.
These two tubes are, nevertheless, sufficiently strong to provide the entire
mechanical support for the inner structure of the box. Brass (or, preferably,
copper) is used for the inner structure because of its high thermal conductivity.

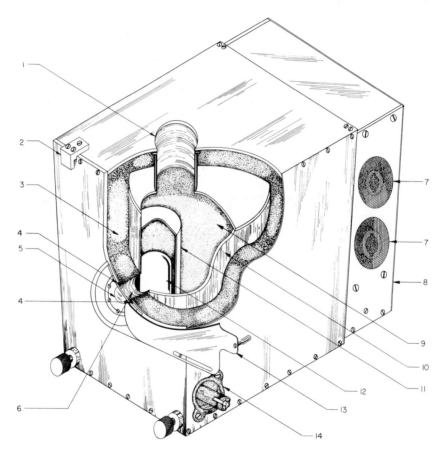

FIG. 3.—The 1P21 refrigeration box, showing the internal structure. The numbers designate
the following components: *1*, Refrigerant intake tube. This is 0.006-inch-wall Inconel tubing.
2, Clip for attaching refrigeration box to rest of photometer. *3*, "Santocel" insulating material.
4, Rubber "O-ring" for sealing window (No. *5*). *5*, Fused-quartz window. *6*, Light-inlet tube.
This is 0.006-inch-wall Inconel tubing. *7*, Pulse amplifier tubes. *8*, Amplifier and voltage divider
box. *9*, Space for refrigerant. *10*, Outer tube. This holds the refrigerant (No. *9*). *11*, Inner tube.
This holds the 1P21 photomultiplier (No. *12*). *12*, 1P21 photomultiplier. *13*, Dark slide. *14*,
Power connector for heater to prevent frosting of window (No. *5*).

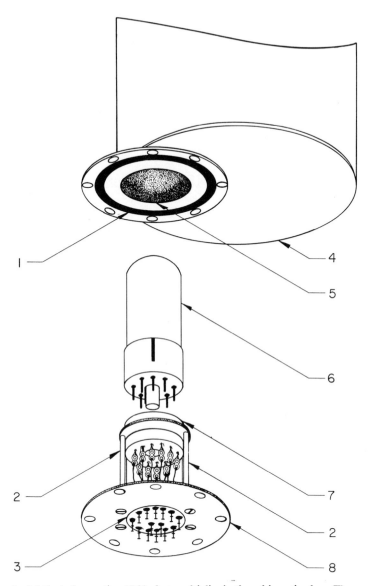

FIG. 4.—Method of mounting 1P21 photomultiplier in the refrigeration box. The numbers designate the following components: *1*, Groove for silicon-rubber "O-ring." *2*, Posts for holding socket (No. *7*). *3*, Airtight feed-through connectors for the electrical supply to the photo-multiplier. Wires for the voltage divider attach here. *4*, Outer tube (see Fig. 3, No. *10*). *5*, Inner tube (see Fig. 3, No. *11*). *6*, 1P21 photomultiplier. *7*, 1P21 socket. This must be ceramic or mica-filled bakelite. *8*, Mounting flange. This bolts to flange attached to outer tube (No. *4*).

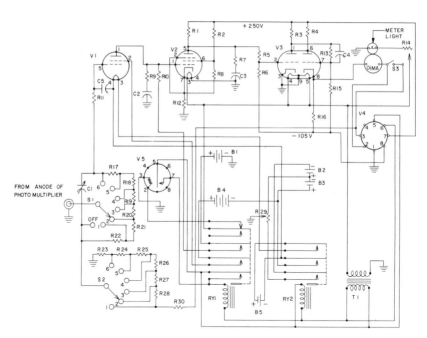

Fig. 5.—The schematic circuit diagram of the recommended d.c. amplifier. The parts are as follows:

Resistors ($\frac{1}{2}$ watt, 10 per cent tolerance unless otherwise specified):

R1—470 K ohms
R2—220 K ohms, 1 watt
R3—100 K ohms
R4—27 ohms, 1 watt
R5—4.7 meg. ohms
R6—4.7 meg. ohms
R7—33 K ohms
R8—33 K ohms
R9—470 K ohms
R10—9 meg. ohms, 1 per cent
R11—350 meg. ohms
R12—8.2 K ohms
R13—18 meg. ohms
R14—100 ohms rheostat
R15—10 meg. ohms
R16—47 K, 2 watts

R17—9000 meg., 1 per cent
R18—900 meg., 1 per cent
R19—90 meg., 1 per cent
R20—9.0 meg., 1 per cent
R21—900 K, 1 per cent
R22—100 K, 1 per cent
R23—100.00 ohms, 0.1 per cent
R24—58.49 ohms, 0.1 per cent
R25—92.70 ohms, 0.1 per cent
R26—146.92 ohms, 0.1 per cent
R27—232.85 ohms, 0.1 per cent
R28—369.04 ohms, 0.1 per cent
R29—2 K helipot, 10 turns, 0.5 per cent linearity
R30—1000 ohms, 1 per cent

Capacitors (400-volt, 20 per cent tolerance unless otherwise specified):

C1—140 $\mu\mu$f max., ceramic insulated, variable
C2—270 $\mu\mu$f, mica insulated

C3—0.15 μf, paper
C4—0.01 μf, paper
C5—100 $\mu\mu$f, mica insulated

Batteries:

B1—Eveready No. 416 (67.5 volts)
B2—Eveready No. E-340-E (1.5 volts)
B3—Eveready No. E-340-E (1.5 volts)

B4—Eveready No. E-163 (4.2 volts)
B5—Mallory No. RM 42 (1.3 volts)

Relays:

RY1—115-volt a.c. coil, 3 normally open contacts, one normally closed.

RY2—115-volt a.c. coil, 3 normally open contacts.

Transformer:

T1—115-volt a.c. to 6.3-volts, 2 A

Tubes:

V1—Raytheon CK-5886
V2—6AU6
V3—12AT7

V4—Power connector
V5—Amperite 6N020

Switches:

SW1—One-pole 7-throw ceramic insulated rotary switch
SW2—One-pole 6-throw rotary switch

SW3—Single-pole single-throw toggle switch

Meter: Triplett 0–1 ma., illuminated

The box will maintain the 1P21 at a nearly constant temperature until the refrigerant is almost completely evaporated. One filling of dry ice is sufficient for an entire night, but it is necessary to refill with liquid nitrogen approximately every 4 hours in order to maintain constant-temperature conditions. The entire inner structure should be silver-soldered and airtight. This box is designed for a focal ratio of 14:1 or longer. The preamplifier-voltage divider box contains the voltage divider for the 1P21 and a pulse preamplifier for use with pulse-counting amplifiers.

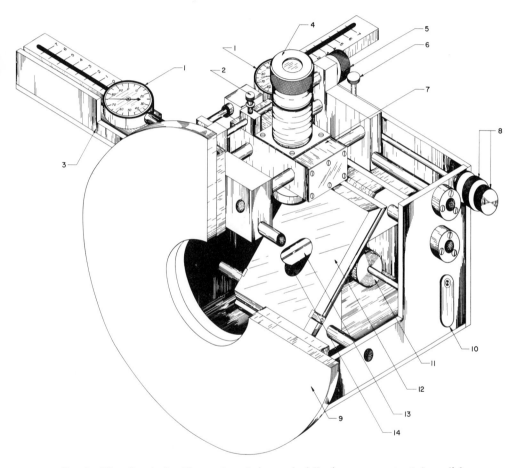

Fig. 6.—The offset device. The numbers designate the following components: *1*, Ames dial-indicators (0.01 mm per division). *2*, Clamp for declination motion of eyepiece carriage. *3*, Mechanical shield for dial indicator. *4*, Eyepiece (Erfle, 1¼-inch focal length). *5*, Slow-motion in declination for eyepiece carriage. *6*, Clamp for right-ascension motion of eyepiece carriage. *7*, Eyepiece carriage. *8*, Slow-motions in right ascension for eyepiece carriage. *9*, Front plate for bolting to telescope. *10*, Handle for translating large mirror (No. *12*) back and forth. *11*, Counterweight for the large mirror (No. *12*). *12*, Large mirror. *13*, Light shield. *14*, Hole in mirror through which the starlight passes when it is measured by the photomultiplier.

3.3. Amplifiers

Suitable d.c. amplifiers for use with the 1P21 are manufactured by various American corporations. These commercial amplifiers, however, do not have gain-control switches in the $\frac{1}{2}$-magnitude steps which astronomers have found to be convenient, and several astronomers have, for this reason, built their own d.c. amplifiers. A satisfactory design is given by Borgman (1960). However, it suffers from excessive sensitivity to instability of the voltage regulator tube, V_2. It is more satisfactory to use battery operation of the first stage. A circuit for a d.c. amplifier is given in Figure 5, which is essentially the same as that described by Gardiner and Johnson (1955).

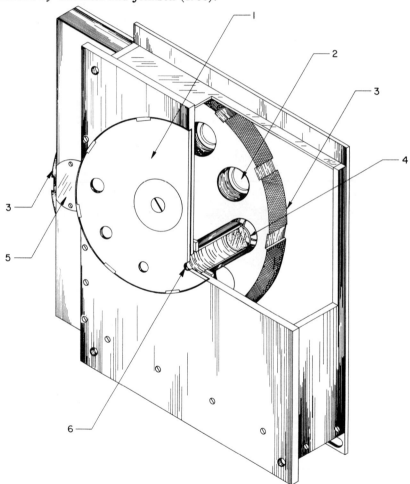

Fig. 7.—The filter box. The numbers designate the following components: *1*, Diaphragm disk. *2*, Hole for filter. *3*, Filter disk. *4*, Field lens. *5*, Cover plate (after removal of this plate, filters may be removed or inserted). *6*, The hole in the diaphragm disk that is being used.

For faint stars, it is convenient to use a capacitor-charging integrator with this amplifier. Two circuits have been published—one by Gardiner and Johnson (1955) and the other, of somewhat different design, by Weitbrecht (1957). Satisfactory high-voltage supplies with stability up to 3 parts per million are manufactured by many American companies.

3.4. GUIDING MECHANISM

The next components to be discussed are the eyepieces for finding and guiding. It was noted above (see Fig. 1) that it is sometimes convenient to have separate eyepieces for finding and guiding. It is, however, quite satisfactory to use only one eyepiece for this purpose, and the devices to be described here have only one. Such construction imposes a small inconvenience during the alignment and adjustment period, but, provided that the eyepiece assembly is properly made, there is no disadvantage thereafter. Since astronomers often want to be able to measure objects which are too faint to set on visually, only devices which contain provision for offsetting will be described.

One method of construction for an offsetting eyepiece device is illustrated in Figure 6. When this device is used for stars that are bright enough to set on visually (non-offset operation), the eyepiece is centered on the position of the hole in the focal-plane diaphragm, and the switching of the object from the eyepiece to the phototube is accomplished by translating the large mirror back and forth parallel to its surface. For offset use, the large mirror is set so that the phototube looks out through the hole in the mirror, and the eyepiece is offset to the position of a suitable guide star, whose co-ordinates with respect to the object to be observed are known from measures of a direct photograph of the region. A variation upon this design has been constructed by Hiltner, who has used a self-locking cam for translating the large mirror (instead of the cable drive) and screws and counters for recording the position of the eyepiece (instead of the Ames dial-indicators).

The offset eyepiece device which has been described above and illustrated in Figure 6 is intended for operation at the Cassegrain focus, where the focal ratio is about 14:1 or larger. For shorter focal ratios, a different arrangement for offsetting has been used. At the Mount Wilson and Palomar Observatories, where the general photometer design of Figure 2 is employed, an additional guiding eyepiece displaced some distance from the focal-plane diaphragm is employed. Centering of brighter stars is accomplished by use of the eyepiece that looks through the focal-plane diaphragm, while offsetting is accomplished by use of the guiding eyepiece and its calibrated position scales.

3.5. FILTER BOX

The last component of a simple photometer is the filter box, one version of which is illustrated in Figure 7 (the filter box also contains the focal-plane diaphragms and the field lens). In this box, both the focal-plane diaphragm and

FIG. 8.—The complete single-channel photoelectric photometer. An earlier design of the filter box is shown, instead of the improved design of Fig. 8; a spacer for use with an $f/32$ telescope beam is shown between the filter box and the refrigeration box. Photograph by the W. L. Richards Company.

the filter holder are disks which may be rotated to select the desired hole or filter; these positions are established by accurate detents. There are eight different holes in the diaphragm disk and twelve positions for filters in the filter disk.

A complete photoelectric photometer, constructed according to the design principles illustrated in Figures 3, 4, 6, and 7, is shown in the photograph of Figure 8.

§ 4. MULTICHANNEL AND MULTICOLOR PHOTOMETERS

Almost all the photoelectric photometers that have so far been constructed have been of the single-channel type. With these, it is necessary to measure the light of each object and the appropriate sky successively in each of the filter bands. It is evident that the simultaneous measurement of at least some of these quantities can significantly improve the speed and precision of measurement.

A two-channel photometer, developed from the design principles illustrated in Figures 3, 4, 6, and 7, has been described by Johnson (1958). A schematic diagram of this photometer is shown in Figure 9, and a photograph of this photometer is shown in Figure 10. The simple photometer of Figure 8 can be converted into the two-channel photometer of Figure 9 by removing the single-channel filter box (Fig. 7) and substituting a two-channel box. Two identical refrigeration boxes are then installed. The design of the two-channel filter box is very similar to that of the single-channel one; there is added an aluminized prism to split the star and sky beams and a removable eyepiece to facilitate alignment procedures.

The addition of the second channel doubles the efficiency of observation on very faint stars. There is, however, an additional dividend. Experience has shown that the variation in the brightness of the night sky between successive sky and star exposures with a single-channel photometer is enough to reduce significantly the precision of a measure of a very faint star. Computation from actual observations indicates that simultaneous recording of star and sky improves the accuracy by 20–100 per cent, depending on the amount of variation of the night sky at the time. This multiplies the weight of an observation by an additional factor of 1.4–4. Thus it can be expected that the use of a two-channel photometer of the design of Figures 9 and 10 will increase the efficiency of observation of very faint stars up to a factor of nearly 8 in comparison with a single-channel photometer.

A six-channel photometer, which measures not only the sky and star simultaneously but also, at the same time, the amount of light in three filter bands corresponding approximately to the U, B, V system, has been constructed by Hiltner (see Baum, Hiltner, Johnson, and Sandage 1959). A schematic diagram of this device is shown in Figure 11 and a photograph is shown in Figure 12. This photometer, which uses dichroic filters to separate the several filter bands, is quite successful in B and V, but satisfactory filters for U are not yet available. One possible serious disadvantage of the simultaneous measurement

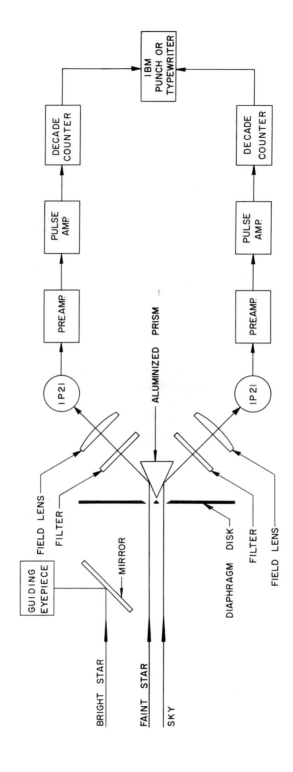

FIG. 9.—The schematic diagram of a two-channel photoelectric photometer

FIG. 10.—The complete two-channel photoelectric photometer. Spacers for use with an $f/32$ telescope beam are shown between the filter box and the refrigeration boxes. Photograph by the W. L. Richards Company.

171

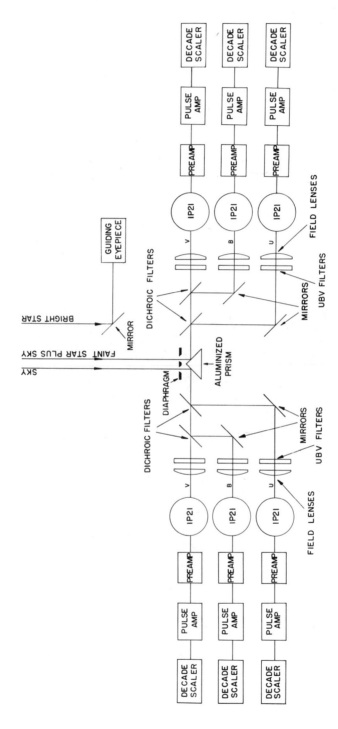

Fig. 11.—The schematic diagram of Hiltner's six-channel photometer

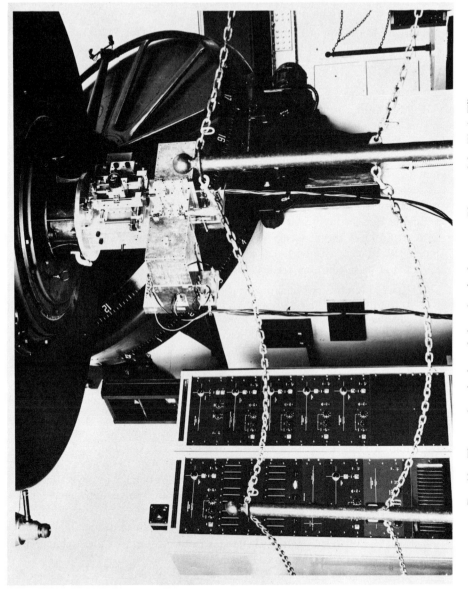

Fig. 12.—The complete six-channel photoelectric photometer. Photograph by W. A. Hiltner

of all three filter bands is due to the use of dichroic filters. These filters, by their nature, do not have exactly the same spectral pass-band characteristics as the standard U, B, V filters (Johnson and Morgan 1951), and there may be some difficulties in transformation to the U, B, V system. This point is of particular importance in this application, since the very faint stars for which the photometer is most useful are often quite different in their spectral-energy curves from the bright stars on which the U, B, V system was calibrated.[1]

§ 5. PULSE-COUNTING TECHNIQUES

Pulse-counting techniques have received some application in astronomical photoelectric photometers (Blitzstein 1953; Linnell 1953; Baum 1955; Johnson 1958). Rather than describe these individual applications in detail, however (the reader is referred to the above references), we shall compare pulse-counting methods with the more conventional d.c. methods and recommend, for those astronomers who wish to construct a pulse-counting photometer, sources of satisfactory electronic equipment.

In the earlier stages of the development of pulse-counting apparatus for astronomical use, there was overenthusiasm in regard to the advantages of the method when compared with d.c. methods. Some of the earlier anticipated advantages of pulse-counting are listed below (Blitzstein 1953):

1. Exact integration of fluctuating light source.
2. Direct digital registration.
3. Relative freedom from drift problems.
4. Discrimination against dark emission.
5. Insensitivity to leakage currents.
6. Ultimately higher speed (good observation in one second).

These anticipated advantages have now largely vanished because of technical developments and understanding of the two techniques. The following comments, however, can be made:

1. Exact integration of fluctuating light-sources may be obtained by a capacitor-charging integrator and d.c. amplifier (see Gardiner and Johnson 1955; Weitbrecht 1957).

2. Direct digital registration of d.c. signals can be obtained by several methods of analogue-to-digital conversion. Devices for this purpose are now commercially available.

3. There are no significant drift problems in either pulse or d.c. methods, provided that the apparatus is properly designed and constructed. The amplifier of Figure 5 has shown itself to be essentially drift-free.

4. Discrimination against dark emission can be obtained in pulse methods only with the rejection of a significant fraction of the primary photoelectrons.

---

[1] [It is now the opinion of some observers that the photometry of extremely faint objects should be done with a multicolor instrument, in which the spectral regions are isolated with prismatic dispersion.—EDITOR.]

There is no discrimination against dark current from the cathode, only against dark current from the dynodes of the photomultiplier. As Whitford (1953) has pointed out, the presence of the sky background usually renders such discrimination valueless.

5. Insensitivity to leakage currents is good. This can be important with some phototubes, but experience has shown that photomultipliers satisfactory for d.c. use can easily be selected. Most 1P21's are quite satisfactory for d.c. operation, so far as leakage is concerned.

6. The sixth point, ultimately higher speed, is illusory. Direct-current methods can be made to operate much faster than astronomers have any use for. The limit is imposed in both methods by the statistics of the photoelectrons. The height distribution of the output pulses from a photomultiplier is such as to cause an increase in the noise level of the d.c. signal above that predicted by the theoretical "shot effect." This increase is small, probably about 15 per cent (see Lombard and Martin 1961), and it may be minimized by raising the cathode-to-first-dynode voltage of the phototube as high as possible under the existing circumstances. For example, if one operates a 1P21 with 200–250 volts between the cathode and first dynode, the added noise in d.c. operation is less than 10 per cent. The objective is to make the multiplication of the first dynode as high as possible, thereby reducing the statistical fluctuations in the multiplication to a minimum.

Thus most of the supposed advantages of the pulse-counting method over d.c. methods do not exist, and those that do may not be of much importance in many applications. There is, however, one further advantage of the pulse method which has not yet been mentioned here. If we adjust the pulse amplifiers so that virtually all the pulses from the photomultiplier are counted, the resultant count is almost completely independent of small changes in the phototubes. The reason is that when all the pulses are counted, their total is independent of pulse size. On the other hand, the output of a d.c. amplifier is dependent on both the size and the frequency of the pulses. This advantage may be important in a multichannel photometer, where it is essential that the ratios of the outputs of the two channels remain constant to a very high degree (cf. Johnson 1958).

While many of the supposed advantages of pulse-counting methods are illusory, the original disadvantages remain. Principal among these are complexity and non-linearity for the brighter stars. This latter point is a very serious one, since appreciable non-linearity of response can—and does in practical cases—set in for stars that for many purposes are relatively faint. For example, the author's two-channel pulse-counting photometer (Johnson 1958) cannot be used to measure stars brighter than about the eleventh magnitude with the 82-inch telescope.

The original enthusiasm for pulse-counting methods can no longer be maintained; nevertheless, there are undoubtedly applications for which this method

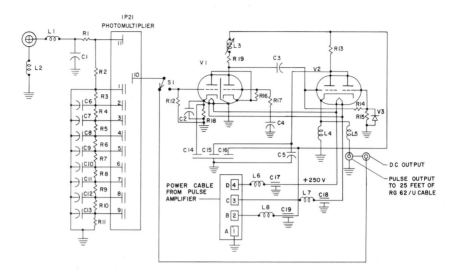

Fig. 13.—The schematic circuit diagram of the pulse preamplifier and 1P21 voltage divider. The parts are as follows:

Resistors ($\frac{1}{2}$ watt, 10 per cent tolerance unless otherwise specified):

R1—10 K ohms	R11—30 K ohms, 1 watt, 1 per cent
R2—200 K ohms, 1 watt, 1 per cent	R12—270 K ohms
R3—100 K ohms, 1 watt, 1 per cent	R13—10 K ohms, 5 watts
R4—100 K ohms, 1 watt, 1 per cent	R14—470 ohms
R5—100 K ohms, 1 watt, 1 per cent	R15—100 K ohms
R6—100 K ohms, 1 watt, 1 per cent	R16—1 meg. ohms
R7—100 K ohms, 1 watt, 1 per cent	R17—180 ohms
R8—100 K ohms, 1 watt, 1 per cent	R18—100 ohms
R9—100 K ohms, 1 watt, 1 per cent	R19—6.8 K ohms, 1 watt
R10—100 K ohms, 1 watt, 1 per cent	

Capacitors (400 v, 20 per cent tolerance unless otherwise specified):

C1—0.01 µf, 1000 volts, ceramic	C11—0.01 µf, 1000 volts, ceramic
C2—0.001 µf, mica	C12—0.01 µf, 1000 volts, ceramic
C3—0.001 µf, mica	C13—0.01 µf, 1000 volts, ceramic
C4—0.05 µf, paper	C14—20 µf, 25 volts
C5—0.01 µf, paper	C15—20 µf, 350 volts } Triple-section can-type electrolytic
C6—0.01 µf, 1000 volts, ceramic	C16—10 µf, 350 volts
C7—0.01 µf, 1000 volts, ceramis	C17—0.1 µf, feed-through, paper
C8—0.01 µf, 1000 volts, ceramic	C18—0.1 µf, feed-through, paper
C9—0.01 µf, 1000 volts, ceramic	C19—0.1 µf, feed-through, paper
C10—0.01 µf, 1000 volts, ceramic	

Inductances:

L1—2.5 mh	L5—2.3 µh
L2—2.5 mh	L6—18 µh, 1-amp capacity
L3—115–195 µh, variable	L7—18 µh, 1-amp capacity
L4—2.5 mh (total resistance = 150 ohms)	L8—10 mh

Tubes and diodes:

V1—6BQ7A	V3—1N54A
V2—6101	

Switches:

S1—one-pole double-throw, ceramic insulated, miniature rotary switch is the better. Several observers have found pulse-counting techniques convenient for observations of very faint stars (see Baum, Hiltner, Johnson, and Sandage 1959). One may find that the operation of a pulse-counting photometer in a telescope dome is affected significantly by the extraneous pulses caused by the operation of the slow-motion, dome, and other relays. In order to minimize these problems, it is necessary to use a well-shielded and filtered, relatively high-gain, preamplifier, whose circuit diagram is given in Figure 13. The diagram includes the filtered voltage divider for a 1P21.

REFERENCES

Baum, W. A.	1955	*Sky and Telescope*, **14**, 264 and 330.
	1957	*A.J.*, **62**, 6.
Baum, W. A., Hiltner, W. A., Johnson, H. L., and Sandage, A. R.	1959	*Ap. J.*, **130**, 749.
Blitzstein, W.	1953	*Astronomical Photoelectric Photometry*, ed. F. B. Wood (Washington: American Association for the Advancement of Science), p. 64.
Borgman, J.	1960	*B.A.N.*, **15**, 251.
Gardiner, A. J., and Johnson, H. L.	1955	*Rev. Sci. Instr.*, **26**, 1145.
Johnson, H. L.	1958	*Sky and Telescope*, **17**, 558.
Johnson, H. L., and Morgan, W. W.	1951	*Ap. J.*, **114**, 522.
Kron, G. E.	1958	*Pub. A.S.P.*, **70**, 285.
Linnell, A. P.	1953	*Astronomical Photoelectric Photometry*, ed. F. B. Wood (Washington: American Association for the Advancement of Science), p. 1.
Lombard, F. J., and Martin, F.	1961	*Rev. Sci. Instr.*, **32**, 200.
Weitbrecht, R. H.	1957	*Rev. Sci. Instr.*, **28**, 883.
Whitford, A. E.	1953	*Astronomical Photoelectric Photometry*, ed. F. B. Wood (Washington: American Association for the Advancement of Science), p. 126.

CHAPTER 8

Photoelectric Reductions

ROBERT H. HARDIE
Dyer Observatory, Vanderbilt University

§ 1. INTRODUCTION

THE photometric observer is customarily interested in the brightness of celestial objects as a function of certain parameters, such as wave length, time, or position in an image of a surface. As a rule, the dependence of brightness on wave length is an essential desideratum, although it may be ignored in some instances, as in the case of simply establishing a time variation in the brightness of an object.

The direct measures of brightness which are obtained in any photometric study are functions not only of the above-mentioned parameters but also of various other parameters related to the equipment which receives the light and to the atmosphere through which the light must pass. Even the interstellar space across which the light journeys may appreciably affect the brightness measures, as distinct from and in addition to, the customary inverse-square law. Therefore, the observer will generally attempt to treat his observed data in such a manner as to permit due allowance for all effects that are not directly related to the object being studied. To do this, he is obliged to consider with care all of these and to measure, control, or minimize their influence on the observed brightness data. Moreover, the precision of the adjusted data and the confidence to be placed in them will depend to a large degree on these factors.

In many instances it is possible to carry out useful photometric studies without necessarily accounting for each of the factors which govern the observed measures of brightness. This is the case when only relative measures among the stars are made, as in the case of medium-band width photometry. In contrast to this are narrow-band photometry or detailed spectrophotometry and, at the other extreme, broad-band width work like bolometry or radiometry, for which it may be desired to evaluate the results in absolute units. In the latter case various factors, such as the instrumental transmission and reflection characteristics, play a major role and have to be carefully allowed for, whereas in medium-band width work such factors customarily need little or no consideration in the reduction of data (although they are necessarily considered in the interpretation of the results).

In this chapter let us confine our attention to the problems encountered in medium-band width photoelectric photometry as practiced widely at the present time. The special problems related to narrow- and broad-band width studies, though of the utmost importance and interest, properly deserve independent treatment.

The light actively engaged in registering a response in a photometer will be characterized by a certain effective wave length and band width, and these are dependent on the transmission of optical parts—filters and windows—on the spectral sensitivity of the receiver, and on the energy distribution of the source (Strömgren 1937; Wesselink 1950; King 1952a). Customarily we take the term "medium-band width" to apply to photometry in which the ratio of the half-intensity band width to the effective wave length is of the order of 10–20 per cent. This will be seen to be consistent with such magnitude and color systems as the International photographic and visual and the more accurate Six-Color, C_1, (U, B, V), (P, V), and similar systems.

The reduction of data obtained in photometry of this kind consists primarily of two steps: (a) an adjustment for atmospheric extinction and (b) a transformation to a commonly used system of magnitudes and colors. Unfortunately, the latter step is sometimes omitted, particularly in variable-star studies when the work is published in arbitrary colors, thus rendering unavailable much valuable information.

§ 2. ATMOSPHERIC EXTINCTION

2.1. Extinction Law

It is a well-known fact that light suffers a loss in its course through the earth's atmosphere or in any other material. Consider an element of absorbing material of thickness δx which absorbs a fraction $\tau \delta x$ of a ray of intensity I. The amount of the loss is $I \tau \delta x$. Expressing this in differential form,

$$dI = -I \tau dx ,$$

and integrating through an entire path length x, we obtain

$$\log I = \log I_0 - \tau x ,$$

in which I_0 and I are the initial and final intensities, respectively. In magnitude form this becomes

$$m_0 = m - 2.5 \, \tau x$$
$$= m - kX . \tag{1}$$

It is convenient to specify the path length, X, in units of the air mass at the zenith of the observer, and the "extinction coefficient," k, is then seen to be a measure of the light-loss expressed in magnitudes for a star at the zenith. Thus the magnitude of a star observed by a fictitious observer just outside the atmosphere is readily deduced from the observed magnitude, provided that both k and X are known.

2.2. MEASUREMENT OF AIR MASS

The relative air mass, X, in units of the thickness at the zenith is given to a high degree of accuracy by the secant of the zenith distance, z (Schoenberg 1929). According to Bemporad's data as tabulated by Schoenberg (1929), the error introduced by the inaccuracy of sec z is only 0.005 air mass at $z = 60°$. Thus it is convenient to use sec z for the air mass except for extreme zenith distances, in which case slight corrections may be made to sec z to derive the true air mass, X. In Table 1 are tabulated smoothed correction terms which are to

TABLE 1
AIR-MASS CORRECTION TERMS

z	sec z	X	Correction	z	sec z	X	Correction
0°........	1.000	1.000	0.000	69°........	2.790	2.773	0.017
30........	1.155	1.154	.001	70........	2.924	2.904	.020
60........	2.000	1.995	.005	71........	3.072	3.049	.023
61........	2.063	2.057	.006	72........	3.236	3.209	.027
62........	2.130	2.123	.007	73........	3.420	3.388	.032
63........	2.203	2.196	.007	74........	3.628	3.588	.040
64........	2.281	2.273	.008	75........	3.864	3.816	.048
65........	2.366	2.356	.010	76........	4.134	4.075	.059
66........	2.459	2.448	.011	77........	4.445	4.372	.073
67........	2.559	2.546	.013	78........	4.810	4.716	.094
68........	2.670	2.655	0.015	79........	5.241	5.120	0.121

be subtracted from sec z values to obtain the appropriate air mass and which should be used for work of high precision in which any systematic errors are to be minimized. For more extreme values of zenith distance the observer is referred directly to Schoenberg's tables.

The value of sec z is readily determinable for any observation through the relation

$$\sec z = (\sin \phi \sin \delta + \cos \phi \cos \delta \cos h)^{-1}, \qquad (2a)$$

in which ϕ is the observer's latitude, while δ and h are the declination and hour angle of the star. While it is often convenient to use relation $(2a)$ to compute sec z as needed, there are other occasions when it is easier to use an extensive table giving sec z for a wide range of declinations and hour angles. A sample of such a table appears in Table 2. When it is desired to compute X, sec z is first found as above and then X may be determined by the formula

$$X = \sec z - 0.0018167 \, (\sec z - 1) - 0.002875 \, (\sec z - 1)^2$$

$$-0.0008083 \, (\sec z - 1)^3. \qquad (2b)$$

This polynomial approximation to Bemporad's values has been found to be useful for electronic computing-machine purposes and is adequate for all normal needs because it is accurate to better than $\frac{1}{10}$ per cent up to $X = 6.8$ and better than 1 per cent up to $X = 10$. It is doubtful indeed if Bemporad's tabulated values are trustworthy to such accuracy because of the variations in density, pressure, and other conditions in the atmosphere from those assumed in his work.

Several other means of determining sec z with ease are worthy of mention. An instrument designed to read the quantity directly and fastened to the telescope has been described by Pettit (1935), and a more refined version, ca-

TABLE 2

SAMPLE AIR-MASS TABLE FOR LATITUDE 36°

Hour Angle	$\delta = 28°$	$\delta = 26°$	$\delta = 24°$	$\delta = 22°$
0ʰ00ᵐ......	1.010	1.016	1.023	1.031
20........	1.013	1.018	1.025	1.034
40........	1.021	1.027	1.034	1.043
1 00........	1.035	1.042	1.050	1.059
10........	1.045	1.052	1.060	1.069
20........	1.056	1.063	1.071	1.081
30........	1.069	1.076	1.085	1.095
35........	1.076	1.083	1.092	1.102
40........	1.083	1.091	1.100	1.110
45........	1.091	1.099	1.108	1.119
50........	1.099	1.107	1.117	1.129
55........	1.108	1.117	1.127	1.138
2 00........	1.117	1.126	1.137	1.149
05........	1.127	1.137	1.148	1.160
10........	1.138	1.148	1.159	1.172
15........	1.149	1.159	1.171	1.184
20........	1.161	1.171	1.183	1.197
2 25........	1.173	1.184	1.197	1.211

pable of a higher accuracy, has been installed on the Ritchey-Chrétien reflector of the U.S. Naval Observatory (Hoag and Brown 1956).

A nomogram, which is useful in work not requiring the highest precision, may be constructed for any given latitude (see, for example, Lipka 1918 for details on the construction of a suitable nomogram.) Figure 1 is an example of a nomogram in which the left-hand scale has been slightly altered to read air mass in place of sec z. If drawn with care and with limited range, it can be used through most of its range with an error not exceeding $\frac{1}{2}$ per cent. Sometimes it is useful to plot up a family of curves, sec z or X versus hour angle, for particular values of declination, when a study of stars in a small area of sky is being made.

2.3. CONVENTIONAL MEASUREMENT OF EXTINCTION

To determine the extinction coefficient, k, we recall equation (1) and note that k is the slope of a straight line representing the graph of m versus X. Thus, under ideal conditions, k may be obtained from a plot of the measured magnitudes, m, of a single star versus air mass, X, suitable observations having been made at a number of zenith distances. Such an ideal plot is illustrated in Figure 2, a, from which m_0, as well as k, may be read. That such a figure would never be obtained in practice hardly needs pointing out. In the time interval during which a star moves through an appreciable range of air mass, the character of

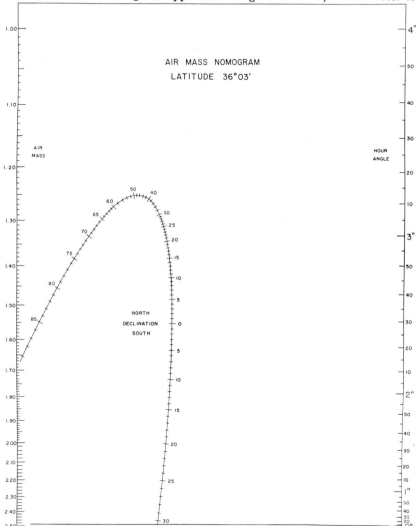

Fig. 1.—A nomogram of limited range for determining air mass. A straight line joining any hour angle (*right-hand scale*) and any declination (*curved scale*) will cut the left-hand scale at the corresponding value for air mass. A nomogram such as this can be constructed for observatories at any latitude, with any desired range in scales and, as in this illustration, can be made to read air mass instead of secant z.

the atmosphere may undergo substantial change. Moreover, it is often observed that even at a given instant the extinction in various parts of the sky is not uniform. Thus the actual observations will probably show some scatter, and the determined value of the coefficient will be more or less uncertain. However, if several independent determinations are made during a clear night, an average may be obtained for the night. It is usually found that a mean, based on a number of nights, is closer to the actual values than are the nightly averages themselves, particularly if the single nightly averages are based on relatively few extinction measures (Johnson and Morgan 1951; Hiltner 1956).

Considerable improvement in the accuracy of the extinction coefficient may be made, in principle, if measures over many nights are grouped together so that the constancy of the magnitude of any given star, as seen outside the earth's atmosphere, may be used as an additional condition in the determinations. The significance of this approach is illustrated graphically in Figure 2, *b*, in which a mean value of m_0 from determinations on two or more nights es-

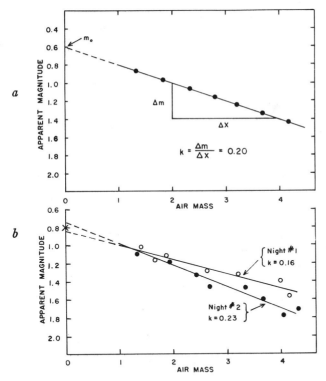

FIG. 2.—*a:* An idealized plot of observations in which the slope of the line provides the extinction coefficient, *k*. *b:* A plot of observed values to illustrate the effects of transparency changes in determining extinction values. Measures on several nights serve to give added weight by providing effectively an additional value at $X = 0$.

sentially adds another observed point at $X = 0$.[1] This requires, however, that the absolute sensitivity of the equipment remain constant (a condition hardly realizable with so many variable factors involved) or, alternatively, that some light-source of established constancy be used at all times to determine the sensitivity variation of the instrument. Many photoelectric observers use artificial references of radium paint, which, although substantially constant over intervals of 2–10 hours, seem to be inadequate for extended periods. Radioactive phosphors which use β-emitters are said to be more nearly constant, since the fluorescing compound is not subject to such intense breakdown as is the case with α-emitters. It is possible, then, that such artificial references may permit this improvement in extinction determination.

2.4. Extinction as a Function of Wave Length

That the atmosphere not only diminishes but also reddens the light passing through it is an everyday experience. It is evident that the longer wave lengths are not attenuated as much as the shorter ones. Various investigators have shown that there are three primary factors which cause extinction: (a) molecular absorption bands, (b) haze, which is fairly non-selective, and (c) scattering by molecules, which is roughly proportional to λ^{-4} (van de Hulst 1949, and other references found in his article). Figure 3 shows the wave-length dependence of extinction as determined by Abbott (1929) for good sky conditions at Mount Wilson, with additional determinations by Hiltner (1956) (with estimated effective wave lengths) for the best conditions at McDonald Observatory. As would be expected, the extinction is generally smaller and less erratic at high-altitude observatories, so that the data in Figure 3 would not be applicable for lower altitudes or poor sky conditions.

When working in a system of several bands at once, it is convenient to work in terms of a single magnitude and one or more color indices and to treat extinction in a differential manner for the color indices:

$$C_0 = C - k_c X , \qquad (3)$$

where C_0 and C are color indices for a star as seen outside and inside the atmosphere. It is clear that k_c is simply the difference between the corresponding magnitude coefficients. One advantage to this scheme is that the color coefficient, k_c, is measurable by the conventional method with higher accuracy than the magnitude coefficients of which it is the difference. There are apparently two reasons for this. In the first place, it appears that some of the variations in the magnitude coefficients are common to both (i.e., non-selective variation), and consequently k_c is less erratic. Second, the relative color sensitivity of the

[1] In much of the following discussion, graphical solutions will be used to illustrate methods of determining various parameters, and, for simplicity, these are treated as though derived from observations of single stars or single pairs of stars in some cases. It is hardly needful to add that an obvious substitution of a least-squares solution may often be useful and to stress that observations of many stars are always desirable to make the results secure.

equipment is apt to be more constant than the absolute sensitivity; therefore, it is possible to group the measures, from which k_c will be derived, over several nights of observations, using the condition that the stars' color indices, outside the atmosphere, are constant. (Such a method would also be available for the magnitude coefficient, it has been pointed out, if the absolute sensitivity of the equipment were constant or measurable.)

The conventional determination of the color extinction coefficient, k_c, is entirely analogous to that for the magnitude coefficient, k. A plot of the observed

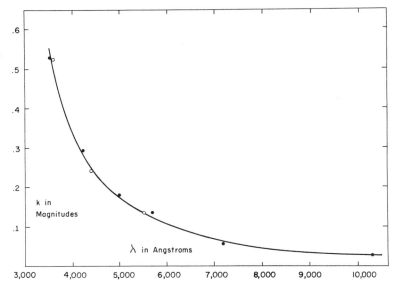

FIG. 3.—The variation of the extinction coefficient, k, with wave length, λ. The closed circles are for Mount Wilson (Abbott), and the open circles are for McDonald (Hiltner). The wave-length dependence is a function of sky conditions and altitude of the observatory, and the illustrated values are not to be considered as applicable to other locations.

color index, C, is made against air mass, X, for a single star measured at various zenith distances and on several nights. Figure 4 presents the method graphically.

2.5. EXTINCTION AS A FUNCTION OF COLOR INDEX

Since the light received in any photometric band is not monochromatic, the actual coefficients used are essentially those for a monochromatic beam at some predominant wave length (although not at the *effective* wave length) which is somewhat dependent on the stellar energy distribution. In the empirical determination of the coefficients for the various bands, then, it is to be noted that the values are dependent on the color index of the object (King 1952b, and further references contained in this paper). Generally it will be found possible to determine the manner in which the extinction varies with the color index of

different stars and to express the results, in the case of the magnitude coefficient, k, by a linear relation:

$$k = k' + k''C , \qquad (4)$$

where C is the color index for the star, uncorrected for extinction, k' is the magnitude extinction coefficient for a star of zero color index, and k'' is the increment
in the coefficient for a star of color index $C = 1.0$. In the case of the color coefficient, k_c, a similar situation is found if either or both of the bands used to
form a color index are subject to an appreciable change in the predominant
wave length according to the stellar energy distribution. As in the former case,
it is, in general, possible to define a linear relation:

$$k_c = k'_c + k''_c C , \qquad (5)$$

where k'_c is the color extinction coefficient for a star of zero color index, and the
correction term k''_c is the increment in the coefficient for a star of color index
$C = 1.0$. We shall refer to k' and k'_c as the "principal coefficients" and to k''
and k''_c as the "second-order coefficients" hereafter.

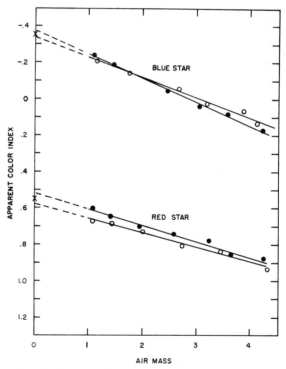

Fig. 4.—The color extinction coefficient dependence on the color index of the star. Measures
on several nights serve to give added weight by providing effectively an additional value at
$X = 0$.

In place of the color index inside the atmosphere, C, the extra-atmosphere value, C_0, is often used in these expressions in the second-order term thus:

$$k = k_1 + k_2 C_0, \tag{4a}$$

$$k_c = k_{c1} + k_{c2} C_0, \tag{5a}$$

where the coefficients are analogous to, but not identical with, those in equations (4) and (5). Although the matter is of little consequence in empirical work, expressions (4) and (5) are to be preferred to (4a) and (5a). The reason is that both the stellar energy distribution and the air mass affect the shape of the observed band of radiation and hence define an effective extinction coefficient. In using C_0, we assign a second-order color term to the extinction coefficient which depends only on the first of these two factors, while in using C we account to a better degree for both of them. Nevertheless, forms (4a) and (5a) are in more common usage, probably because it is thought that k_2 and k_{c2} are easier to determine than k'' and k_c''. That this is not necessarily the case will be shown presently. Neither of the two formulations of the second-order term rigorously describes the variation of extinction with color index. They are justified solely on the grounds that higher-order terms have not been measurable with present methods.

It is found that the second-order coefficient, k'', for the magnitude extinction is negligibly small or indeterminate for bands located in the yellow and red, as would be expected from the general shape of the curve in Figure 3 and from the relative absence of strong spectral features which affect the predominant wave length. In the blue region it commonly has a value in the range -0.02 to -0.04 (depending on band width) when the color index, C, has a scale and a zero point close to the International or $B - V$ system. Fortunately, it appears to be relatively constant compared with the principal coefficient, k'. Likewise the second-order coefficient, k_c'', for the color extinction is customarily small and not subject to much variation.

2.6. MEASUREMENT OF THE SECOND-ORDER COEFFICIENTS

In order to account for the second-order terms in equations (4) and (5), let us now modify equations (1) and (3) as follows:

$$m_0 = m - k'X - k''CX, \tag{6}$$

$$C_0 = C - k_c'X - k_c''CX$$
$$= C(1 - k''X) - k_c'X, \tag{7}$$

or, according to the alternative expressions (4a) and (5a),

$$m_0 = m - k_1 X - k_2 C_0 X, \tag{6a}$$

$$C_0 = C - k_{c1}X - k_{c2}C_0 X$$
$$= \frac{C - k_{c1}X}{1 + k_{c2}X}. \tag{7a}$$

To determine all the coefficients in relations (6) and (7), we may observe two stars (of widely differing color indices) close together in the sky through a number of different air masses. A close optical pair would be useful, since most physical pairs do not have sufficiently differing colors. If the two stars have substantially the same position, then differential measures of magnitude and color will behave according to these relations:

$$\Delta m_0 = \Delta m - k'' \Delta CX , \tag{8}$$

$$\Delta C_0 = \Delta C - k_c'' \Delta CX . \tag{9}$$

Therefore, plots of Δm versus (ΔCX) and of ΔC versus (ΔCX) will provide lines whose slopes are k'' and k_c''. Once good mean values of the second-order coefficients are obtained, the principal coefficients may be evaluated from the same observations from plots of $(m - k''CX)$ versus X and of $C(1 - k_c''X)$ versus X. For the alternative formulation as given by equations (6a) and (7a), the differential measures for a close pair of stars of suitable colors are given by

$$\Delta m_0 = \Delta m - k_2 \Delta C_0 X , \tag{8a}$$

$$\Delta C_0 = \frac{\Delta C}{(1 + k_{c2} X)} ,$$

or

$$\Delta C = \Delta C_0 + k_{c2} \Delta C_0 X . \tag{9a}$$

In this case ΔC is first plotted versus X; the best fitting straight line provides ΔC_0 as an intercept and $k_{c2} \Delta C_0$ as a slope from which quantities k_{c2} may readily be deduced. Then, in a plot of Δm versus $\Delta C_0 X$, the coefficient k_2 is found to be the slope of the appropriate straight line.

Upon considering these procedures, then, it is seen that the second-order coefficients are relatively easy to measure through a differential technique and that k'' and k_c'' are somewhat more directly obtainable than the alternatives, k_2 and k_{c2}.

2.7. Measurement of the Principal Extinction Coefficients through Standard Stars

In addition to the conventional methods reviewed above for determining extinction coefficients, there is another technique that is capable of higher speed and accuracy (Hardie 1959). It is supposed that the observer has already set up a consistent system of magnitudes and color indices, outside the atmosphere, for a network of reference stars or that he has successfully duplicated the color bands of an accurate standard system. (More will be said in a later section concerning such matching of bands.) It is also assumed that the second-order coefficients are known and that only the principal coefficients are being sought. This is quite a reasonable assumption, since variations in the second-order coefficients appear to be smaller than those in the principal coefficients in practice,

especially the magnitude coefficient, and since the role of the principal coefficients is more important in attaining over-all accuracy.

Let two known stars be observed, one near the zenith, the other through a
substantial air mass. To express the measures differentially, we may modify
equations (6) and (7) to these forms:

$$\Delta m_0 = \Delta(m - k''CX) - k'\Delta X, \tag{10}$$

$$\Delta C_0 = \Delta(C - k_c''CX) - k_c'\Delta X. \tag{11}$$

Therefore, from the measures on the two stars alone, in principle, it follows that

$$k' = \frac{\Delta(m - k''CX) - \Delta m_0}{\Delta X}, \tag{12}$$

$$k_c' = \frac{\Delta(C - k_c''CX) - \Delta C_0}{\Delta X}. \tag{13}$$

It is therefore apparent that within about 10 minutes of observing time the
principal extinction coefficients are determinable. It is of interest to inquire
into the sources of error inherent in this procedure. Apart from accidental
errors, which for bright stars may be about 0.01 mag., there will, in general, be
some residual errors in the known values of the extra-atmosphere magnitudes
and colors which may lead to systematically erroneous values. The obvious way
to minimize the influence of both kinds of error is to measure more than two
stars. In less than half an hour three high stars and three low stars may be
observed, and the errors should be reduced correspondingly. However, observing
more than about six stars may become undesirable, since the aim of the technique is to save time for other observations and to avoid the prime source of
error in the conventional method, viz., the change of transparency during the
measurement period. Typical accuracy achieved by this approach is about 2
per cent for k' and 3 per cent for k_c', which is markedly better than can be obtained by the conventional method, particularly in view of the economy in time
that is attained. It will be noted that the magnitude coefficient, k', is determined more securely than the color-index coefficient, k_c', contrary to the conventional results. Neither of the factors responsible for k_c' being customarily
better than k', which were discussed in § 2.4, are particularly relevant in the
faster method. In using the latter, time variations in extinction are essentially
eliminated, and the stability of the equipment is as trustworthy for the magnitude measures as it is for those of color index. Hence all the observed quantities
are measured with substantially the same precision, and therefore the color
indices, which are always dependent on the difference between two magnitudes,
should be found to be less accurate by a factor of $\sqrt{2}$ (Hardie 1959).

Besides the direct measure of the coefficients as outlined in equations (12)
and (13), an additional check on the extinction is possible from measures on

single stars, provided that a *constant* reference source of light is available. For this purpose let us consider a set of equations like (6) and (7) except for the inclusion of zero-point terms:

$$m_0 = m - k'X - k''CX + Z_m, \tag{6b}$$

$$C_0 = C - k'_c X - k''_c CX + Z_c. \tag{7b}$$

These terms allow for changes in the zero points of the inside-atmosphere system. (Additional discussion of their significance will be found in a subsequent section.) Once the principal extinction coefficients have been determined, say during the initial half-hour of observing, then the Z-terms are also known for that time.

A measure, m_r, on the constant reference source, made at the same time, will be equivalent to a stellar brightness $m_r + Z_m$. At any later time, if the sensitivity has changed somewhat, it may measure differently, say m'_r, since the zero-point term will have changed to Z'_m such that $m_r + Z_m = m'_r + Z'_m$. Hence it follows that, from a comparison of a standard star with the reference illumination at a later time in the night, the extinction may be evaluated for that instant:

$$k' = \frac{(m - k''CX) - m_0 + Z'_m}{X}$$

$$= \frac{(m - k''CX) - m_0 + Z_m + (m_r - m'_r)}{X}. \tag{14}$$

The standard star chosen may well be supplemented by another of different color, in order to minimize the effects of residual errors in their magnitudes, and these stars need not be in addition to those already on the program of observations but may be the standard comparison stars themselves.

Similarly, the principal color extinction coefficient, k'_c, is determinable from

$$k'_c = \frac{(C - k''_c CX) - C_0 + Z_c}{X}. \tag{15}$$

In this case it is generally safe to assume the constancy of the zero-point term, Z_c, during a night, or at least to assume a uniform drift between actual measures of it.

The usefulness of this supplementary procedure is dependent on the assumptions made relating to the dependability of the reference illumination, and confidence in this must be based on studies of its behavior. A prudent procedure would be to spend the initial and final half-hour periods of a night measuring the extinction according to equations (12) and (13), in order to check the behavior of the zero-point terms and to recalibrate the reference illumination, if necessary, to allow for any gradual change. To achieve the satisfactory use of these techniques requires careful attention to instrumental problems that are beyond the scope of this discussion. Nevertheless, the goal of achieving a dependable running account of extinction variation makes such attention worthwhile, or perhaps essential, when it is realized just how large the discrepancies between actual and mean extinction coefficients may be on some nights.

In summary, the extinction can be well determined in a brief period at the beginning and end of a night of observing. Normally the values will be considerably more dependable than those obtainable with the conventional methods, and the total time devoted to extinction determination may be conveniently small. No further observations of extinction stars need divert the observer from the principal task of measuring unknown stars. In addition, the measurement of a reference illumination of known dependability each time a pair of standard stars is observed may lead to the refinement of observing variations in extinction. For nights of excellent transparency and constancy, the advantage of the latter refinement consists primarily in obtaining a dependable check on the extinction with a small investment of time rather than any appreciable gain in accuracy. The chief virtue of the technique is to be found on nights of less constancy. However, it would be too much to expect it to render non-photometric nights useful!

§ 3. MAGNITUDE AND COLOR TRANSFORMATIONS

In medium-band width photometry the relative measures of magnitude and color index which result depend on the particular bands chosen. Each combination of telescope, filters, and light-receiver will develop and define its own set of magnitudes and colors, comprising the observer's "natural" system. Let us now turn to the problem of relating measures made in one system to those in another system.

3.1. STARS CONSIDERED AS IDEAL BLACK BODIES

The stars are known to radiate as black bodies to a first approximation (Stebbins and Whitford 1945). If they were indeed ideal black bodies, the radiation would be governed by the well-known Planck law:

$$E_\nu = \frac{8\pi h}{c^3} \frac{\nu^3}{e^{h\nu/kT} - 1},\qquad(16)$$

in which ν is the frequency of the radiation, c is the velocity of light, h is the Planck constant, k is the Boltzmann constant, T is the absolute temperature, and E_ν is the energy radiated per unit area per unit time per unit frequency interval. Typical energy-distribution curves are shown in Figure 5, a, in which the co-ordinates are $\log E_\nu$ and ν. It is seen that, for any given case, the curvature is slight. The slope of any curve is given by

$$\frac{d}{d\nu}(\log E_\nu) = \log e \frac{3(e^x - 1) - x e^x}{(e^x - 1)\nu},$$

where $x = h\nu/kT$. As an approximation, this may be written as follows:

$$\frac{d}{d\nu}(\log E_\nu) = \log e \left(\frac{3}{\nu} - \frac{h}{kT}\right) \qquad (17)$$

for any case in which $e^x \gg 1$. If it were not for the term $3/\nu$ in the right-hand expression, the slope would be constant for any given temperature within the limits of the approximation. But, since this contribution to the curvature is independent of T and is therefore common to all the curves in Figure 5, a, the effect may be eliminated by considering relative slopes.

Let us then consider curves of relative brightness, taking any arbitrary black-body temperature for comparison, say, $T = 6000°$ K. This procedure is particularly useful in the context of stellar photometry, since measures of stellar brightness and color index are always made relative to some standard stars.

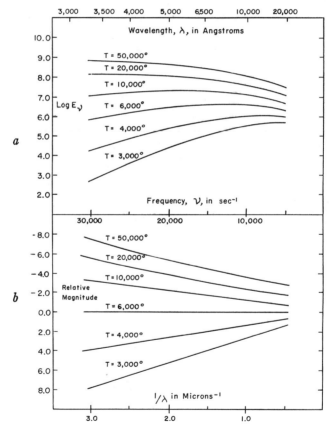

Fig. 5.—a: Black-body curves for various temperatures as a function of frequency. b: Black-body curves (relative to $T = 6000°$) showing their linear character when plotted against reciprocal wave length.

The resulting curves are shown in Figure 5, b, in which the co-ordinates are modified to magnitude and inverse wave length, $1/\lambda$. It is at once evident that the curves become virtual straight lines. The slope of any line is given approximately by

$$\frac{dm}{d(1/\lambda)} = 1.56 \left(\frac{1}{T} - \frac{1}{6000}\right). \tag{18}$$

The color index of a particular black body defined by measures at wave lengths λ_a and λ_b (in cm) is given by

$$C_{ab} = m_a - m_b = 1.56 \left(\frac{1}{T} - \frac{1}{6000}\right)\left(\frac{1}{\lambda_a} - \frac{1}{\lambda_b}\right) \tag{19}$$

when referred to a body having a temperature of 6000° K. The relative color index is merely the slope of the line multiplied by $(1/\lambda_a - 1/\lambda_b)$.

For ideal black bodies it is seen from the foregoing that color index measures on different natural systems are readily transformable through simple linear equations, provided that extremely long wave lengths and high temperatures are avoided. Thus any two color indices, C_1 and C_2, for the *same* black body but measured on slightly different scales could be related to a satisfactory precision by a relation of the form

$$C_2 = \mu C_1 + \zeta_c. \tag{20}$$

3.2. Deviations from Black-Body Characteristics

In the case of real stars, the departures from black-body behavior are primarily caused by absorption lines, bands, grosser absorption features, limb darkening, and related phenomena, and these are sufficient to impose limitations on the use of a linear relation like equation (20). It is not simply a matter of the necessity of a second-order term, which would suffice if the curves for actual stars departed from those of Figure 5, b, by a slight curvature. The discontinuities and spectral features preclude extremely high-precision conversion among color systems, a fact long recognized by photometric observers (Greaves 1950, 1952, 1955; Johnson 1952a; Morgan, Harris, and Johnson 1953).

Nevertheless, simple equations of the first and second degree may often suffice for adequate precision, provided that certain conditions are met. The three predominant of these are (1) that the color systems to be related be as similar as possible (whenever there is an element of choice) in regard to effective wave lengths and band widths; (2) that major spectral discontinuities, such as the Balmer jump, be excluded, or at least included only to a very similar degree in the corresponding bands of the two systems, as Baade (1938) pointed out regarding the inclusion of ultraviolet in the photographic magnitudes and as later emphasized by Johnson (1952a); and (3) that we do not require necessarily that one relation be found for stars of widely differing characteristics. It may well turn out, and usually does, that one transformation equation is found for main-sequence stars, another for yellow giants, another for reddened OB stars, and so forth (Morgan, Harris, and Johnson 1953). With these reservations, then, it is usually found that a transformation of form (20) may be used adequately for transforming color indices, while one of the following form will suffice for magnitudes:

$$m_2 = m_1 + \epsilon C_1 + \zeta_m. \tag{21}$$

Thus, if a sufficient number of stars were observed in common in two basically similar systems, the "scale" constants, ϵ and μ, and the "zero-point" constants, ζ_m and ζ_c, could be determined empirically.

3.3. INSTRUMENTAL SIGNIFICANCE OF THE SCALE AND ZERO-POINT CONSTANTS

A little reflection will tell us that if $\mu > 1$, then the color base line, $(1/\lambda_a - 1/\lambda_b)$, in the C_2 system is greater than that in the C_1 system and vice versa, while if $\epsilon > 0$, then the effective wave length of the m_2 magnitude system is to the blue side of that of the m_1 system. The significance of ζ_c and ζ_m depends on the particular reduction technique because of certain arbitrary steps which will appear in another section. However, if the (C_1, m_1) and (C_2, m_2) systems are made, say, by two different photocells on the same telescope with the same filters and amplifier and the reduction methods are identical, then, when $\zeta_c > 0$, the (C_2, m_2) photocell favors red light more than the (C_1, m_1) photocell, while if $\zeta_m > 0$, the (C_2, m_2) photocell produces a smaller current for a given star than does the other. The magnitude zero-point term, ζ_m, is usually regarded as the most troublesome parameter to measure or control, since it is at the mercy of sensitivity changes and can be measured adequately only when the extinction is accurately known. In working with stars in an existing accurate system, the problem is not difficult because the zero-point term can be well determined by the fast extinction method described earlier in § 2.7. However, in setting up a new system, the problem is more severe and requires, in addition to good extinction determination, reference stars near the pole which are available in all seasons (this is perhaps one of the few merits of the North Polar Sequence). An over-all check on the zero-point term and any possible variation in it with right ascension is available in the closing of the new system all around the sky. Nevertheless, any possible variations with declination are much more difficult to discover, and their elimination requires considerable care in the instrumentation.

3.4. MATCHING OF PHOTOMETRIC SYSTEMS

In order to insure that simple transformations of the type of equations (20) and (21) may be used for converting from an observer's natural system to some standard system with the least loss of precision, it is highly desirable to match the natural bands to those of the standard system. For this purpose, a large selection of filters and possibly of photocells is needed. Measures are made with various filters (approximating the known band widths and effective wave lengths) on stars having accurately known magnitudes and color indices until the best empirical fit is obtained. The preliminary selection is most conveniently made on visual binaries having widely differing color indices, so that extinction effects are minimized. While there are rather few such binaries with accurately known colors and magnitudes at the present time, it is to be hoped that further observations will correct this deficiency in the future (optical pairs would be adequate here just as in the case referred to in § 2.6). By a judicious empirical fit, it is possible to minimize the ϵ coefficient in the magnitude transformation (21), which applies to any color band, so that it is close to zero. The scale factor

TABLE 3

Approximate Magnitude Coefficients, ϵ_v, ϵ_b, ϵ_u

FILTER		1P21 No. 1		1P21 No. 2	
Type	Thickness (Mm)	Warm	Cold	Warm	Cold
GG5..............	2	−0.25	−0.30	−0.21	−0.25
GG7..............	2	− .16	− .20	− .10	− .16
GG11.............	2	− .12	− .17	− .07	− .11
GG14.............	2	− .07	− .11	− .02	− .07
OG4..............	2	− .03	− .06	+ .02	− .03
OG4..............	4	+ .04	+ .02	+ .07	+ .01
OG1..............	2	+ .12	+ .11	+ .16	+ .12
GG13+BG12........	2, 2	− .12	− .11	− .11	− .12
GG13+5543.........	2, 4	− .08	− .08	− .07	− .07
GG13+BG12........	2, 1	− .05	− .04	− .03	− .02
GG13+5543+5030....	2, 2, 2	− .01	.00	+ .03	+ .02
GG13+5543.........	2, 2	+ .03	+ .03	+ .07	+ .06
GG13+5030.........	2, 4	+ .10	+ .10	+ .13	+ .12
GG13+5030.........	2, 2	+ .16	+ .15	+ .20	+ .18
UG1..............	2	+ .01	.00	+ .01	+ .01
UG2..............	1	+ .02	+ .02	+ .02	+ .01
9863..............	2	+0.03	+0.02	+0.04	+0.03

μ, which applies to any color index, is made close to unity, of course, when the ϵ terms for each of the two bands are close to zero. The degree of duplication achievable may be seen from Table 3, in which are listed data pertaining to several combinations of photocells and filters in an attempt to match the bands of the Dyer Observatory photometer to those which define the U, B, V system. Although the matching of color bands in this way contributes much to precision, it must not be presumed to result in exact transformations, since it is primarily a control of the effective wave lengths rather than of the band widths. Thus there will, in general, remain second-order imperfections in the transformations. In addition to providing the best practical transformations, matched bands permit the use of existing standard system stars for quick and accurate extinction measures as described in § 2.7.

Mention may be made here concerning the specific problems of matching the U, B, V bands. It has been the experience of many observers that most 1P21 photocells do not have as much red sensitivity as that which originally defined this system; consequently, a filter which cuts somewhat to the red of the specified filter (Corning 3384; *see* Johnson 1955) is usually necessary to achieve a close match to the V magnitudes, and the resulting band width will therefore be narrower than the original V band. This is even more noticeable when using a refrigerated cell, since the far-red response of a cathode diminishes as the temperature is lowered (as do the thermal emission and the red leak through the ultraviolet filter). When the specified filters are used (Johnson 1955), the resulting bands will generally not be so close to the original ones as would be a matched set of bands.

3.5. Stability of Photometric Systems

During the course of time any natural system will change gradually, and occasional recalibration of the transformation coefficients will be desirable; a variation of a few per cent in the μ coefficients may be found over a few years, with corresponding small changes in the ϵ coefficients. Among other factors involved in such slow changes in system is the change in reflectivity, in a selective way, of the aluminum coating on reflectors and, in all probability, the migration of cesium within the photocells; this latter is much retarded by always keeping a cell cool.

The practice of refrigeration of photocells with dry ice is a very useful one. Not only is the thermal emission much diminished, but, equally important, the color system is stabilized for temperature effects. There is freedom from night-to-night, as well as seasonal, changes in the transformation constants which are found when the photocell is allowed to follow changes in the ambient temperature.

In some photocells there appears to exist a relation between the spectral response and the voltage between the cathode and first dynode; therefore, it is prudent to determine whether the transformation constants are a function of voltage. Fortunately, this phenomenon is absent or negligible for any of the cells of the 1P21 type which the writer has had occasion to use. However, in certain other types, particularly those having flat, semitransparent cathodes (the head-on types), there is a measurable effect. This behavior seems to be a consequence of the dependence of the primary electron focusing on the initial velocity distribution of the electrons, which is in turn dependent on the color of the incident light. Even in those cells showing this kind of phenomenon, the range of voltage required to change appreciably the ϵ and μ coefficients seems to be wider than any reasonably expected variation. On the other hand, the zero-point term, ζ_c, in the color equations varies considerably. This behavior would necessitate the normal requirement for using stabilized voltages not only on a short-term basis but also on a long-term basis—or at least some means of adjustment to the same voltage each night—whenever observations from several nights are combined, as in extinction determination. Naturally, the zero-point term, ζ_m, in the magnitude equation varies the most with voltage in any kind of photomultiplier.

Another effect, due to magnetic fields, occurs in some photocells and is particularly pronounced in the head-on types. Here again there is a tendency to alter the color system through peculiar focusing effects of the primary electrons. In the use of such photocells, thorough magnetic shielding is essential for stability in the resulting photometric system and for freedom from declination or hour-angle effects in either the scale factors or the zero-point terms.

In addition to those changes in system associated with photocell characteristics, there are others of independent cause. These may include changes in the optical parts of the telescope and photometer—changes in reflectivity, transmission, cleanliness, etc. The character of these may be of two different types—selective or non-selective. For the first kind, the scale factors and the zero-point terms all undergo changes because of slight alterations in effective wave length and therefore in the response of the light-receiver. For the second kind, the effective wave lengths remain the same, but the response of the instrument changes in one or more of the bands so that only the zero-point terms will reflect a change. As an example of the latter, let us suppose that one filter becomes dusty; the transmitted light is diminished, and the natural color index measures differently than formerly, but by the same amount for all stars. Therefore, ζ_c changes by a corresponding amount, leaving μ as it was.

Other forms of change of a temporary nature or dependent on position of the equipment are sometimes encountered. Such are sensitivity changes due to flexure of the dynode structure within a multiplier or to flexure in the optical mountings which may show up as declination or hour-angle effects, sensitivity differences across the image of a surface due to inadequate field-lens behavior, and many others. Clearly it is beyond the scope of this discussion to include consideration of these special problems. Suffice it to say that they must be minimized or controlled through careful instrumental design.

§ 4. PRACTICAL METHODS

Having reviewed in some detail the general aspects of the extinction and transformation problems, we turn now to a brief development of methods for the reduction of observations in practice. It will be convenient, for the sake of clarity, to work in terms of some specific system (we shall take the U, B, V system for this purpose), although no loss of generality follows therefrom.

4.1. WORKING EQUATIONS

Let d_v, d_b, and d_u be the observed readings for a given star in the visual, blue, and ultraviolet, respectively, with the sky corrections extracted (as well as any leaks in color bands), and let S_v, S_b, and S_u be the amplifier sensitivities used in the three colors, expressed in magnitudes which increase with sensitivity (with any arbitrary zero point). Then the observed magnitudes, on the natural system, expressed on a consistent scale of arbitrary zero point may be written as follows:

$$v = S_v - 2.5 \log d_v ,$$

$$b = S_b - 2.5 \log d_b ,$$

$$u = S_u - 2.5 \log d_u ,$$

whence follow the observed color indices:

$$b - v = (S_b - S_v) - 2.5 \ \log \left(\frac{d_b}{d_v}\right),$$

$$u - b = (S_u - S_b) - 2.5 \ \log \left(\frac{d_u}{d_b}\right).$$

TABLE 4

SAMPLE OF J_x AND G_x CRITICAL TABLE
(For $k_{bv}'' = -0.03$ and $k_{ub}'' = -0.01$)

X	J_x	X	G_x
1.000–1.016.....	1.030	1.000–1.049.....	1.010
1.017–1.049.....	1.031	1.050–1.149.....	1.011
1.050–1.083.....	1.032	1.150–1.249.....	1.012
1.084–1.116.....	1.033	1.250–1.349.....	1.013
1.117–1.149.....	1.034	1.350–1.449.....	1.014
1.150–1.183.....	1.035	1.450–1.549.....	1.015
1.184–1.216.....	1.036	1.550–1.649.....	1.016
1.217–1.249.....	1.037	1.650–1.749.....	1.017
1.250–1.283.....	1.038	1.750–1.849.....	1.018
1.284–1.316.....	1.039	1.850–1.949.....	1.019

Applying extinction terms to the observed quantities v, $b - v$, and $u - b$, we obtain the extra-atmosphere values, denoted by the zero subscripts:

$$v_0 = v - k_v X , \tag{22a}$$

$$(b - v)_0 = (b - v)J_x - k_{bv}' X , \tag{22b}$$

$$(u - b)_0 = (u - b)G_x - k_{ub}' X , \tag{22c}$$

where $J_x = (1 - k_{bv}''X)$ and $G_x = (1 - k_{ub}''X)$. The functions J_x and G_x are slowly varying functions of the air mass, X, and are conveniently tabulated in brief critical tables for intervals of X, as in the sample in Table 4. Note that no second-order extinction term is included in equation (22a) in accordance with the observed absence of any appreciable effect in the visual magnitudes.

Let the systemic transformations for any given group of stars be given by the following equations:

$$V = v_0 + \epsilon(B - V) + \zeta_v , \qquad (23a)$$

$$B - V = \mu(b - v)_0 + \zeta_{bv} , \qquad (23b)$$

$$U - B = \psi(u - b)_0 + \zeta_{ub} . \qquad (23c)$$

Then equations (22) and (23) combine into the following working equations:

$$V = v - k_v X + \epsilon(B - V) + \zeta_v , \qquad (24a)$$

$$B - V = \mu(b - v)J_x - \mu k'_{bv}X + \zeta_{bv} , \qquad (24b)$$

$$U - B = \psi(u - b)G_x - \psi k'_{ub}X + \zeta_{ub} . \qquad (24c)$$

There will be, as a rule, two kinds of observing programs: type A, designed to obtain unknown magnitudes and color indices for program stars, and type B, designed to determine the various parameters in equations (24). While the former will comprise the bulk of an observing program, it is convenient to include a few observations of the latter type to keep a running check on the system and the extinction. However, let us treat them as separate problems, and let us take up first a brief description of the reduction technique for type A observations.

4.2. Determination of Magnitudes and Color Indices

It is most convenient to start with the color index equations (since $B - V$ is needed in the V equation). It is assumed that ϵ, μ, ψ, J_x, G_x, and the extinction coefficients are known (their determination will be taken up presently). A critical table, similar to Table 4, but containing μJ_x and ψG_x, is useful here, and the modified extinction coefficients, $\mu k'_{bv}$ and $\psi k'_{ub}$ should be employed. The observed data for each star are put into equations (24). From the standard stars, to which frequent comparison has been made during observing, we may determine the zero-point terms, the only unknown quantities. With mean or interpolated values of these, all the terms in the right-hand members of the equations for the program stars are known from which the desired quantities are derived.

One reason for using the foregoing scheme in which the zero-point terms are taken as unknown but determinable is that some of the errors caused by incorrect extinction coefficients are diminished. If the extinction values used were exact and if the instrument were completely stable, the zero-point terms would be constant. However, since these conditions are seldom met with, the zero-point terms will appear somewhat variable as determined by the various standard stars. Apart from accidental errors, there usually is revealed a gradual trend in the zero-point terms, due in part to slow changes in extinction. Therefore, the use of interpolated values for each zero-point term for the program stars will diminish the errors due to inexact extinction terms, provided that the air mass is of the same order as that for the standard stars.

On the other hand, should the air masses cover a very wide range, this man-

ner of allowing for extinction variation may not be adequate. It is then necessary to measure the variation in extinction through the night, by means of the
refined method involving a constant light-source, already discussed, for the
best over-all accuracy.

4.3. Determination of Constants

We now turn to the evaluation of ϵ, μ, ψ, J_x, G_x, and all the k coefficients. In
principle, one could use observations of many standard stars and solve three
sets of many equations of type (24) by a least-squares technique to determine
all the unknown parameters. However, such a solution for all parameters at
once generally forces needless uncertainties and unrealistic variations into
those parameters that are substantially constant because of the much larger
and real variations in others. A better method is to reduce the number of unknowns in any given solution by separating the constant and variable parameters. In addition, independent evaluation of the various groups of unknowns
has the advantage that one can select a measuring technique that will maximize
the effects of the parameters being sought and minimize the effects of the others.
For instance, ϵ, μ, and ψ are best determined from stars having a wide range of
colors but located close together, preferably near the zenith. Conversely, the
principal extinction coefficients, k_v, k'_{bv}, and k'_{ub}, are best determined from stars
having a wide range of air mass but having similar colors. The second-order
extinction terms are best determined separately by a differential technique, as
was outlined earlier, by following close pairs of widely differing colors through
a wide range of X. (Their magnitudes and colors need not be known.) Differential measures of the components, in the natural system, will be governed by
these expressions (derived from eqs. [9] or [22b] and [22c]):

$$\Delta(b - v) = k''_{bv}\Delta(b - v)X + \Delta(b - v)_0 , \qquad (25a)$$

$$\Delta(u - b) = k''_{ub}\Delta(u - b)X + \Delta(u - b)_0 . \qquad (25b)$$

Therefore, a plot of $\Delta(b - v)$ versus $[X\Delta(b - v)]$ will reveal a line whose slope
is k''_{bv}, and similarly for k''_{ub}. Once determined, these coefficients need only occasional checks, as they do not appear to be subject to wide variation. (Hereafter we shall assume them known, and hence the J_x and G_x factors.)

While the above measures serve to determine the k'' coefficients, they may
also be used, if desired, to determine k_v, k'_{bv}, and k'_{ub} by the conventional method.
For the latter two, we make use of the k'' coefficients already determined to
remove the second-order color dependence and use equations (22b) and (22c)
rearranged as follows:

$$(b - v)J_x = k'_{bv}X + (b - v)_0 , \qquad (26a)$$

$$(u - b)G_x = k'_{ub}X + (u - b)_0 . \qquad (26b)$$

Therefore, a plot of $[(b - v)J_x]$ versus X will (if the transparency is constant)
reveal a line whose slope is k'_{bv}, and similarly for k'_{ub}. To make use of the faster

and more accurate technique for determining the principal extinction coefficients through the use of standard U, B, V stars, it is necessary to know the
scale factors ϵ, μ, and ψ. Therefore, it will be convenient to discuss their determination first and return at a later time to the derivation of equations suitable for the short extinction method.

We may choose one of a number of methods for determining the scale factors.
One obvious technique is to select as standard stars those in a cluster, to
minimize extinction effects, and to concentrate on an evaluation of ϵ, μ, and ψ.
In selecting clusters measured in the desired system, it is important to choose
those measured by the original equipment which defined the system and to
avoid those measured by different equipment which required transformations
of undetermined accuracy. For U, B, V calibration, several suitable clusters
with some variety among the stars are the Pleiades (Johnson and Morgan 1953),
the Hyades (Johnson and Knuckles 1955), and Praesepe (Johnson 1952b).

Since the measures are made differentially, the principal extinction coefficients have little influence, and approximate values for them will be adequate. Using equations (22), a set of values v_0, $(b - v)_0$, and $(u - b)_0$ can then
be determined which are satisfactory for the purpose at hand. Recalling equations (23), we see that if $(V - v_0)$ is plotted versus $(B - V)$ for each star, a
diagram such as Figure 6, a, will result; the slope of the best-fitted line is ϵ.
Likewise μ and ψ may be determined from plots of $(B - V)$ versus $(b - v)_0$
and of $(U - B)$ versus $(u - b)_0$. A more delicate determination of μ and ψ
results when the ordinates are $[(B - V) - (b - v)_0]$ and $[(U - B) - (u - b)_0]$,
as in Figure 6, b and c. The fact that the extinction coefficients may have been
inaccurate should hardly affect the values thus determined for ϵ, μ, and ψ; any
errors introduced by unaccounted-for variations in sky transparency would be
present, even though the mean coefficients were better known. However, the
zero-point terms will remain uncertain for this reason, but this uncertainty is
of little consequence here, since these terms are used only when measuring unknown stars, when extinction is under thorough control.

An evident extension of the above method of determining the constants ϵ,
μ, and ψ is to measure standard stars at any place in the sky. However, this requires a good determination of the principal extinction coefficients. A most useful list of stars for such purposes has been drawn up by Johnson and Harris
(1954), and it may be augmented by the local standards in several clusters,
including those already named, as well as by stars in the original list (Johnson
and Morgan 1953), which may have, however, larger accidental errors.

If the latter method is used, and if mean values are used for the principal
extinction coefficients, the resulting values of ϵ, μ, and ψ will be somewhat inexact because of real discrepancies between the actual and the mean values of
the extinction coefficients. Indeed, ϵ, μ, and ψ will depend on the mean extinction coefficients which are forced into the solution. More dependable results
may be obtained by using extinction values determined by the short extinction

method, together with a running check on possible extinction variations, through observing some convenient standard star and a constant light-source periodically. For this purpose, the extinction solutions described in the next paragraph are used with the approximation that $\epsilon = 0$, and $\mu = \psi = 1$, or other suitable preliminary values. On the basis of these, preliminary extinction coefficients and zero points can be found and used to keep a running account of extinction variation and thence to obtain intermediate values of the scale factors. A process of

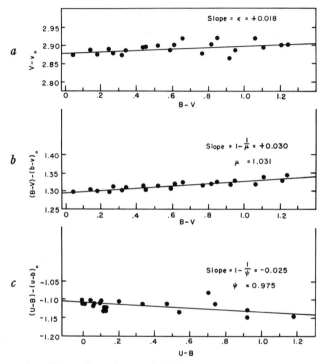

FIG. 6.—a, b, c: Observations of some of the Hyades stars to determine the scale factors, ϵ, μ, and ψ, respectively. (Each point represents only a single observation, and all observations, good and poor, are plotted.)

iteration then permits the observer to refine his evaluation of the extinction and zero-point data and to obtain the best values for the scale factors.

Once the scale factors are well known, it is a simple matter to measure the principal extinction coefficients by the short method. For the most reliable results, the matching of the natural to the standard system must be of a high order; in this case ϵ will be close to zero, while μ and ψ each will be close to unity.

Equations (12) and (13) may be rewritten, for the case in which equations (24) govern, as

$$k_v = \frac{\Delta v - \Delta V + \epsilon \Delta (B - V)}{\Delta X}, \qquad (27a)$$

$$k'_{bv} = \frac{\Delta\,[\mu J_x(\,b-v\,)] - \Delta(B-V\,)}{\mu\Delta X}\,, \tag{27b}$$

$$k'_{ub} = \frac{\Delta\,[\psi G_x(\,u-b\,)] - \Delta(\,U-B)}{\psi\Delta X}\,. \tag{27c}$$

These are given, it will be recalled, for differential measures between two standard stars having a substantial difference in air mass. In practice, when several high and several low stars are measured for greater confidence, the modifications to these expressions are obvious. A plot of $[v + \epsilon(B-V) - V]$ is made versus X, and k_v is the slope of the straight line best fitting the observed points. Likewise, plots of $[\mu(b-v)J_x - (B-V)]$ and of $[\psi(u-b)G_x - (U-B)]$ versus X provide graphical evaluations of $\mu k'_{bv}$ and $\psi k'_{ub}$.

Measurement of the extinction in this manner provides a good determination of the zero-point terms as well and makes possible the calibration of any constant source of light for further reference during the night, which in turn leads to the refinement of frequent rapid extinction measures on single standard stars.

§ 5. DIFFERENTIAL MEASURES

In the study of variable stars it is customary to select a comparison star so close to the variable star that their air masses are virtually identical. By so doing, it is frequently assumed that all the extinction effects are eliminated, although this is true only to a first approximation. Consideration of second-order terms may render possible work of a very high precision in which systematic errors may be kept smaller than one or two thousandths of a magnitude.

5. 1. CONCURRENT MAGNITUDES AND COLOR INDICES

Let us consider equations (24) as applied to both comparison and variable stars and express them in terms of differential magnitudes and color indices. Ignoring third-order terms, we may then write

$$\Delta V = \Delta v - k_v \Delta X + \epsilon\Delta(B-V)\,, \tag{28a}$$

$$\Delta(B-V) = \mu\Delta(b-v) - \mu k'_{bv}\Delta X - \mu k''_{bv}\Delta(b-v)\bar{X}\,, \tag{28b}$$

$$\Delta(U-B) = \psi\Delta(u-b) - \psi k'_{ub}\Delta X - \psi k''_{ub}\Delta(u-b)\bar{X}\,, \tag{28c}$$

in which the symbol Δ stands for the difference in the associated quantity for the two stars always taken in a consistent sense and $\bar{X}$ is the mean air mass for the two stars. Whether the correction terms are significant in any particular study will depend primarily on ΔX, $\Delta(b-v)$, and $\Delta(u-b)$. A useful formula for ΔX follows from differentiating formula (2a), given earlier for sec z, partially with respect to declination and hour angle:

$$\Delta X = (P \sin \bar{h} + Q \cos \bar{h} + R)\bar{X}^2\,,$$

where $P = (\Delta a \cos \phi \cos \bar{\delta})$, $Q = (\Delta\delta \cos \phi \sin \bar{\delta})$, $R = (-\Delta\delta \sin \phi \cos \bar{\delta})$, Δa is the difference in right ascension in radians, $\Delta\delta$ is the difference in declination in radians, and $\bar{h}$ is the mean hour angle (taken as positive eastward and negative westward). For any pair of stars the quantities P, Q, and R are constant and are readily computed; the differential air mass, ΔX, may then be determined and plotted as a function of hour angle.

The last term in the color equations (28b) and (28c) depends on both air mass and the observed differential color index. It will be noted that it adjusts the equation for any change in extinction which is due to a change in color index, a phenomenon observed in virtually all variable stars. In order to keep it conveniently small, or possibly insignificant, the observer may well abide by the old-fashioned rule of choosing comparison stars of color index close to the mean of the variable. In any case, the correction terms are easily determined and applied, and they convert the work into measures on a standard system.

5. 2. Separated Magnitudes and Color Indices

Since variable-star observers often observe in a single color at any given time and determine differential magnitudes rather than color indices, it will be appropriate to develop an alternative set of equations, although the method of § 5.1 is to be preferred and is simpler. Equations (22) may be converted to the following forms if third-order terms are neglected:

$$\Delta v_0 = \Delta v - k_v \Delta X , \tag{29a}$$

$$\Delta b_0 = \Delta b \bar{J}_x + \Delta v k''_{bv} \bar{X} - k_b \Delta X , \tag{29b}$$

$$\Delta u_0 = \Delta u \bar{G}_x + \Delta b (k''_{ub} - k''_{bv}) \bar{X} + \Delta v k''_{bv} \bar{X} - k_u \Delta X , \tag{29c}$$

where $k_b = (k'_{bv} + k_v)$, $k_u = (k'_{ub} + k_b)$, while $\bar{X}$, $\bar{J}_x$, and $\bar{G}_x$ are mean values for the two stars.

In these equations the first term in each right-hand member is the principal one, those following being correction terms, generally of the order of a few hundredths of a magnitude at most. As a rule, the correction terms containing ΔX are sufficiently small to neglect. In the remaining correction terms, the quantities Δv and Δb are supposed to be simultaneous measures through the same air mass as the principal measurement. Since these are not available, they may be replaced by Δv_0 and Δb_0, taken from mean light-curves at the same phases, with negligible loss of accuracy. Thus the Δv_0 data must be completed and used to reduce the Δb_0 data, and both are needed to reduce the Δu_0 data.

The differential magnitudes thus derived are in the natural system, and they may be converted to the standard system through the following equations (which are readily derived from eqs. [23]):

$$\Delta V = (1 - \epsilon\mu)\Delta v_0 + \epsilon\mu\Delta b_0 , \tag{30a}$$

$$\Delta B = (\mu + \epsilon\mu)\Delta b_0 + (1 - \mu - \epsilon\mu)\Delta v_0 , \tag{30b}$$

$$\Delta U = \psi\Delta u_0 + (\mu + \epsilon\mu - \psi)\Delta b_0 + (1 - \mu - \epsilon\mu)\Delta v_0 . \tag{30c}$$

In practice, it is most convenient to correct the observed data for extinction and to convert to the standard system in a single step without having to pass through the natural system. Moreover, it would be most convenient to arrange for the coefficients of the principal terms to be independent of air mass and to incorporate all the effects of the latter into the small correction terms. To achieve this goal, preliminary plots of the observed quantities Δv, Δb, and Δu, entirely uncorrected, are made versus phase. From these, mean values of $\Delta(b - v)$ and $\Delta(u - b)$ are deduced and plotted in a similar fashion. Then the following equations permit the final results to be computed; they result from combining equations (29) and (30) and neglecting terms containing $\epsilon\Delta X$, $(1 - \mu)\Delta X$, and $(1 - \psi)\Delta X$ as factors:

$$\Delta V = (1 - \epsilon\mu)\Delta v + \epsilon\mu\Delta b - k_v\Delta X - \epsilon\mu k_{bv}''\Delta(b - v) \, \bar{X}, \tag{31a}$$

$$\Delta B = (\mu + \epsilon\mu)\Delta b + (1 - \mu - \epsilon\mu)\Delta v - (\mu + \epsilon\mu)k_{bv}''\bar{X}\Delta(b - v) - k_b\Delta X, \tag{31b}$$

$$\Delta U = \psi\Delta u + (\mu + \epsilon\mu - \psi)\Delta b + (1 - \mu - \epsilon\mu)\Delta v$$
$$- (\mu + \epsilon\mu)k_{bv}''\bar{X}\Delta (b - v) - \psi k_{ub}''\bar{X}\Delta(u - b) - k_u\Delta X. \tag{31c}$$

In each instance, the first term involves the actual observed quantity, while the remaining terms employ estimated values of the unobserved quantities at the appropriate phases, under the assumption that these are adequate for this purpose. Under normal circumstances, the effects of such assumptions and of the approximations noted earlier will seldom be as large as 0.002 mag., well below customary observational errors. In many cases, some of the correction terms are negligible.

§ 6. TIME-SAVING ARTIFICES

In addition to several time-saving techniques which have been mentioned earlier (an air-mass meter, an air-mass nomogram, various tabulated parameters, and a short method of determining extinction), there remain others deserving of attention. Probably many more ingenious devices or techniques exist than can be included here, since each observer will have his own favorite short cuts and still other techniques await development.

For observers of variable stars, an efficient time-saver is a decimal-day clock, reading in Julian days such as one described by Blitzstein, Thorpe, and Wood (1951). Any heliocentric correction appropriate to the star and the date may be put into a clock of this sort. (These corrections are tabulated by Prager 1932.) It is apparent that a time read from this clock saves many time-consuming steps and possible mistakes in going from date, hours, and minutes to heliocentric Julian date. Another valuable aid to the variable-star observer is the set of tables and nomograms made by Merrill (1953) for computing eclipsing star parameters.

For observers using strip-chart recorders, such as the Speedomax or Brown instruments, a specially constructed scale, illustrated in Figure 7, speeds up the measurement of the deflections. The original of the sample illustrated was made to read 0 mag. for a full-scale reading, and 2.5 mag. for a 10 per cent reading. When ruled to a large scale and carefully copied onto a photographic plate of the appropriate size, readings to $\frac{1}{10}$ per cent of full scale are possible, which is fully commensurate with other reading methods. The long index line is placed through the center of gravity of the star-plus-sky deflection, and the scale is read at the sky deflection point (usually a smoother or noiseless deflection for bright-star work). Since it reads directly in magnitudes, this scale eliminates two chart readings, a subtraction, and a reference to a magnitude or log table.

Another useful instrumental device which expedites the reductions is an amplifier having sensitivity steps of precise multiples of $\frac{1}{2}$ mag. through its entire range. This characteristic eliminates the need for bothersome calibration corrections.

Undoubtedly the greatest gain in speed may be had through the use of electronic computing devices. A description of a photometer which includes a

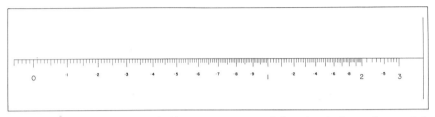

FIG. 7.—A magnitude scale to facilitate measurements of photoelectric observations carried out on a strip-chart recorder.

digitizer and a card-punching device has been made by Hall (1956). If photometrists follow instrumental developments in related fields, they may well use automatic observing procedures in the near future, as it appears technically feasible to operate multichannel photometers, measuring several spectral bands at once in conjunction with data-handling equipment that can record automatically all the measures, the amplifier sensitivities, the hour angle, declination, date, time, and any other relevant data on punched-cards or tape.

§ 7. CONCLUDING REMARKS

Since all the procedures used in photoelectric photometry are relative, it cannot be stressed too strongly that frequent periodic observations are required of known comparison stars. Ideally, each observation of an unknown star ought to be preceded and followed by one on a reference star for the highest precision. In practice, this condition may be relaxed to observing the reference stars every half-hour or hour, depending on the observer's experience with his local sky conditions. It is important to observe reference stars with greater and lesser values of X and with bluer and redder color indices than those being studied, so that interpolative and not extrapolative methods can be used. In cases of extreme air mass which occasionally arise in the study of stars at very low altitude and where no suitable reference stars may be found other than at higher declinations, the observing program ought to be planned to measure the stars at equal altitudes. In this manner, inaccuracies in extinction values will have the least effect.

Although the discussion heretofore has been in the context of photoelectric photometry, it applies to photographic photometry as well. In recent years there has perhaps been some tendency to overestimate the value of photoelectric work at the expense of photographic methods. While it is true that the photoelectric technique is potentially capable of higher accuracy per unit time, inadequate attention to basic observational and instrumental problems has occasionally led to work of a poorer quality than is expected. On the other hand, there are noted examples of excellent photographic photometry (see, for example, Haffner and Heckmann 1937 and Haffner 1940; Stoy and Cousins 1953; Stock and Wehlau 1956, to mention only a few), and no doubt the high quality is due to painstaking attention to the numerous details that good photometry warrants.

In gathering together the material for this chapter the author has benefited from the experience of many photoelectric observers, and it is a pleasure to record his gratitude to them for sharing it so freely. In particular, he is grateful to Dr. D. L. Harris for many valuable discussions.

REFERENCES

Abbott, C. G.	1929	*The Sun* (New York: Appleton & Co.), p. 297.
Baade, W.	1938	*Trans. I.A.U.*, **6**, 216.
Blitzstein, W., Thorpe, J. K., and Wood, F. B.	1951	*Sky and Telescope*, **10**, 226.
Greaves, W. M. H.	1950	*Trans. I.A.U.*, **7**, 268.
	1952	*Ibid.*, **8**, 355.
	1955	*Ibid.*, **9**, 338.
Haffner, H.	1940	*Göttingen Veröff.*, No. 67.
Haffner, H., and Heckmann, O.	1937	*Göttingen Veröff.*, No. 55.
	1940	*Ibid.*, No. 66.
Hall, J. S.	1956	Reported in *A.J.*, **61**, 349.
Hardie, R. H.	1959	*Ap. J.*, **130**, 663.
Hiltner, W. A.	1956	*Ap. J. Suppl.*, **2**, 389.
Hoag, A. A., and Brown, T. W.	1956	*Pub. A.S.P.*, **68**, 457.
Hulst, H. C. van de	1949	*The Atmospheres of the Earth and Planets*, ed. G. P. Kuiper (Chicago: University of Chicago Press), chap. 3.

JOHNSON, H. L.   1952a   *Ap. J.*, **116**, 272.
      1952b   *Ibid.*, p. 640.
      1955   *Ann. d'ap.*, **18**, 292.

JOHNSON, H. L., and
  HARRIS, D. L.   1954   *Ap. J.*, **120**, 196.

JOHNSON, H. L., and
  KNUCKLES, C. F.   1955   *Ap. J.*, **122**, 209.

JOHNSON, H. L., and
  MORGAN, W. W.   1951   *Ap. J.*, **114**, 522.
      1953   *Ibid.*, **117**, 313.

KING, I.   1952a   *Ap. J.*, **115**, 580.
      1952b   *A.J.*, **57**, 253.

LIPKA, J.   1918   *Graphical and Mechanical Computation* (1st ed.; New York: John Wiley & Sons), chap. 5, Art. 57.

MERRILL, J. E.   1953   *Princeton Contr.*, Nos. 23 and 24.

MORGAN, W. W.,
  HARRIS, D. L., and
  JOHNSON, H. L.   1953   *Ap. J.*, **118**, 92.

PETTIT, E.   1935   *Ap. J.*, **81**, 17.

PRAGER, R.   1932   *Kleinere Veröff. Berlin-Babelsberg*, **3**, No. 12.

SCHOENBERG, E.   1929   *Hdb. d. Ap.* (Berlin: Julius Springer), **2**, 268.

STEBBINS, J., and
  WHITFORD, A. E.   1945   *Ap. J.*, **102**, 318.

STOCK, J., and
  WEHLAU, W. H.   1956   *A.J.*, **61**, 80.

STOY, R. H., and
  COUSINS, A. W. J.   1953   *Cape Mimeogram*, No. 3.

STRÖMGREN, B.   1937   *Handbuch der Experimentalphysik* (Leipzig: Akademische Verlagsgesellschaft), **26**, 392.

WESSELINK, A. J.   1950   Reported by W. M. H. GREAVES in *Trans. I.A.U.*, **7**, 269.

CHAPTER 9

An Application of an Electronic Calculator to Photoelectric Reductions

STEWART SHARPLESS

U.S. Naval Observatory, Washington

§ 1. INTRODUCTION

THE application of electronic calculators to the reduction of photoelectric observations now makes it possible to reduce an observation in considerably less time than is required to obtain it. A dozen nights' observations, once they are in proper input form, can be reduced by a medium-speed electronic calculator in a few hours. An additional advantage of this means of reduction, as compared with hand reduction on a desk calculator, is that small computational errors are eliminated.

The IBM 650 Magnetic Drum Data Processing Machine is particularly applicable to this problem. Data are fed into the machine in decimal form on punched cards. The use of punched-card input, as compared with other types of input, has the advantage that each datum is quickly accessible to the operator for examination and correction if necessary. The machine itself is simple to operate, external controls are few, and the computation is controlled by simple instructions.

The purpose of this chapter is to enable an observer having a partial knowledge of the IBM 650 *Manual of Operation* to reduce his own observations on this machine. The following section contains a description of the operation of the IBM 650. Section 3 contains a discussion of a simple photoelectric reduction program, and certain principles of programing are thereby illustrated. This program can be copied and used for the reduction of three-color photoelectric observations of the type which are now commonly being made.

209

§ 2. THE IBM 650

2.1. INPUT-OUTPUT

The IBM 650 is a stored program calculator, i.e., the instructions which the machine is to perform are stored in coded form in the machine's memory. Numerical data on which the machine is to operate are stored in the same way. Once the program has been read into the machine and the input data are made available to it, the computations can be made to proceed automatically.

Information can be read into and out of the machine by means of punched cards. Each card contains 80 columns, each of which may contain a punch indicating a digit 0 through 9. For the purposes of this chapter, the card will be divided into eight "words," each word consisting of ten digits and a sign. The sign is punched in the area over the tenth column of each word. The *word*, as defined here, is the basic unit of information on the punched card and within the machine. A sample card is shown in Figure 1.

The input-output unit of the machine allows the information on punched cards to be read into the memory of the machine; likewise, the results of a computation can be punched onto cards from the memory. The reading and punching of cards are controlled by the stored program and proceed automatically.

2.2. MEMORY

The magnetic-drum memory of the IBM 650 contains either 1000 or 2000 storage locations, each of which can contain one word. These storage locations are numbered from 0000 to 1999, in the case of the 2000-word storage. These four-digit numbers are called "addresses." In order to place a word in the memory or to remove a word from the memory, the address of the storage location must be specified in the program. A word is retained in a storage location until a new word is stored there, in which case the old one is automatically erased. The storage locations are arranged in bands of fifty around the magnetic drum. Thus the 2000-word storage contains forty such bands.

2.3. ARITHMETICAL UNITS

Arithmetical operations are performed in the upper and lower accumulators. These are analogous to the registers of a mechanical desk computer. The upper and lower accumulators can accommodate ten digits each and a single algebraic sign. A third register, called the "distributor," can contain ten digits and a sign, i.e., one word. All words entering or leaving the accumulator from or to the storage must pass through the distributor and are retained there until the next such operation. The upper and lower accumulators and the distributor can be referred to in the programing by the addresses 8003, 8002, and 8001, respectively.

2.4. CONTROL CONSOLE

The control console provides manual access to the memory. A word can be set up on switches and manually read into the memory, or a word can be read

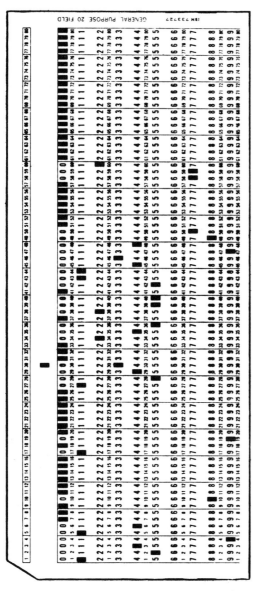

FIG. 1.—An IBM card containing the following information: Star designation = HD 154914; night no. = 8; HA = 1^h09^m0; $\delta = -15°43'$; b, y gain = 245; u gain = 255; $u = 51.1$; $b = 43.9$; $v = 48.7$; standard source = 77.2.

out of the memory, accumulator, or distributor and exhibited on display lights. An instruction set up on the console switches can be referred to in the programing by the address 8000.

2.5. INSTRUCTIONS

A program consists of a series of instructions, stored in the memory, to be carried out sequentially by the machine. Each instruction consists of a numerical code in the form of a ten-digit word.

The first two digits of an instruction are called the "operation code." This instructs the machine as to which arithmetical operation to perform. Some of the most frequently used operation codes are listed in Table 1. The reader is referred to the IBM 650 *Manual of Operation* for a complete discussion of the operation codes.

TABLE 1

COMMONLY USED OPERATION CODES

Code	Operation	Code	Operation
70.....	Read a card	20.....	Store lower accumulator in memory
71.....	Punch a card	19.....	Multiply
69.....	Load distributor	14.....	Divide
24.....	Store distributor	44.....	Branch on non-zero in upper accumulator
10.....	Add to upper accumulator		
15.....	Add to lower accumulator	46.....	Branch on minus sign of accumulator
11.....	Subtract from upper accumulator		
16.....	Subtract from lower accumulator	30.....	Shift right
60.....	Reset and add to upper accumulator	35.....	Shift left
65.....	Reset and add to lower accumulator	31.....	Shift right and round
21.....	Store upper accumulator in memory		

The third through the sixth digits of an instruction are called the "data address." This is usually the address of the word in the memory on which the operation is to be performed. Exceptions to this are as follows: (1) shift instructions, in which the data address specifies the number of places in the accumulator that the contents of the accumulator are to be shifted; (2) branch instructions, in which the machine will go either to the data address or to the instruction address for the next instruction, according to a certain contingency, such as the sign of the accumulator; and (3) read or punch instructions which can have for a data address any address in the fifty-location band to or from which the reading or punching is to be done. Each band contains ten locations into which data from a card can be read and ten other locations from which data on the drum can be punched. In each case, however, only the first eight locations are used when the card is divided into eight words.

The seventh through the tenth digits of an instruction are called the "instruction address." This is the address of the next instruction to be executed.

As an example of a simple series of instructions, the first few instructions from the program contained in Table 2 are given below. The number at the left corresponds to the running number in the left-hand column of Table 2 and serves as an identification for reference purposes within this chapter. This is followed by the address of the instruction and the instruction itself. After each instruction, a verbal explanation of it is given, and the contents of the accumulator are shown. The data from Figure 1 are used.

1   0250   70 0251 0301

Read the eight words of data from a card into consecutive locations 0251 through 0258; go to location 0301 for the next instruction.

Accumulator: 0000000000 0000000000+

2   0301   60 0252 0307

Reset the accumulator to zero and add to the upper accumulator the contents of location 0252; go to location 0307 for the next instruction.

Accumulator: 0000001090 0000000000+

3   0307   30 0003 0265

Shift the contents of the accumulator three places to the right; go to location 0265 for the next instruction.

Accumulator: 0000000001 0900000000+

4   0265   21 0252 0305

Store the contents of the upper accumulator in location 0252; go to location 0305 for the next instruction.

Accumulator: 0000000001 0900000000+

5   0305   11 8003 0263

Subtract from the upper accumulator the contents of the upper accumulator; go to location 0263 for the next instruction.

Accumulator: 0000000000 0900000000+

The purpose of these operations is to separate the hours from the minutes of the hour angle preparatory to expressing the hour angle as a decimal of 24 hours.

2.6. SUBROUTINES

A certain type of computation may be done several times in the course of a program, e.g., the quantity $-2.5 \log x$ is computed four times in the course of the photometric program: for the two colors, the magnitude, and the standard light-source. The instructions for computing $-2.5 \log x$ need not appear explicitly four times in the program, however. Instead, this series of instructions is set apart, in a consecutive series of locations in the memory and called a "subroutine." The subroutine may be entered from the main course of the program whenever $-2.5 \log x$ is needed in the computation. In each case, however, a special "link" instruction must be provided to return the course of the computation to the proper point in the main program.

TABLE 2

A PHOTOELECTRIC REDUCTION PROGRAM

No.	Location	Instruction	No.	Location	Instruction	No.	Location	Instruction
1	0250	70 0251 0301	26	0378	69 0304 0099	51	0406	69 0257 0310
2	0301	60 0252 0307	27	0304	20 0005 0264	52	0310	24 0283 0336
3	0307	30 0003 0265	28	0264	65 0253 0358	53	0336	69 0258 0361
4	0265	21 0252 0305	29	0358	69 0261 0098	54	0361	24 0284 0287
5	0305	11 8003 0263	30	0261	20 0012 0315	55	0287	69 0256 0309
6	0263	35 0003 0271	31	0315	65 0252 0408	56	0309	24 0258 0411
7	0271	19 0274 0295	32	0408	69 0311 0098	57	0411	65 0255 0359
8	0295	35 0004 0355	33	0311	20 0013 0266	58	0359	35 0004 0419
9	0355	10 0252 0357	34	0266	60 0012 0267	59	0419	21 0255 0458
10	0357	35 0006 0321	35	0267	19 0013 0333	60	0458	11 8003 0415
11	0321	19 0324 0345	36	0333	16 8002 0505	61	0415	35 0003 0273
12	0345	31 0003 0405	37	0505	19 0243 0463	62	0273	21 0256 0409
13	0405	20 0252 0455	38	0463	30 0001 0371	63	0409	11 8003 0417
14	0455	60 0253 0407	39	0371	21 0014 0317	64	0417	35 0003 0375
15	0407	30 0002 0363	40	0317	60 0005 0365	65	0375	21 0257 0360
16	0363	21 0253 0306	41	0365	19 0242 0513	66	0360	69 0251 0354
17	0306	11 8001 0413	42	0513	30 0002 0421	67	0354	24 0277 0330
18	0413	35 0002 0269	43	0421	10 0014 0369	68	0330	69 0253 0456
19	0269	19 0274 0395	44	0369	21 0014 0367	69	0456	24 0278 0381
20	0395	35 0005 0457	45	0367	65 0270 0275	70	0381	24 0252 0506
21	0457	10 0253 0507	46	0275	64 0014 0325	71	0506	69 0254 0508
22	0507	35 0005 0319	47	0325	31 0001 0331	72	0508	24 0279 0332
23	0319	19 0272 0293	48	0331	35 0004 0291	73	0332	24 0253 0459
24	0293	31 0002 0351	49	0291	20 0253 0356	74	0459	60 0258 0314
25	0351	20 0253 0378	50	0356	21 0252 0406	75	0314	69 0467 0100

TABLE 2 - Continued

No.	Location	Instruction	
76	0467	20 0258	0461
77	0461	65 0256	0511
78	0511	35 0004	0471
79	0471	64 0257	0517
80	0517	31 0001	0323
81	0323	20 0259	0262
82	0262	65 0255	0509
83	0509	35 0004	0469
84	0469	64 0256	0268
85	0268	31 0001	0425
86	0425	60 8002	0383
87	0383	69 0386	0100
88	0386	20 0282	0335
89	0335	60 0259	0364
90	0364	69 0318	0100
91	0318	20 0281	0334
92	0334	60 0257	0312
93	0312	69 0465	0100
94	0465	16 0258	0414
95	0414	20 0280	0433
96	0433	60 0254	0410
97	0410	30 0003	0519
98	0519	20 0254	0460
99	0460	16 8002	0320
100	0320	35 0003	0329

No.	Location	Instruction	
101	0329	69 0382	0156
102	0382	20 0259	0362
103	0362	60 0280	0385
104	0385	10 0259	0464
105	0464	21 0280	0483
106	0483	60 0254	0510
107	0510	44 0514	0515
108	0514	30 0003	0373
109	0373	69 0276	0156
110	0276	16 0259	0316
111	0316	15 0282	0337
112	0337	20 0282	0515
113	0515	60 0281	0435
114	0435	11 0240	0445
115	0445	46 0298	0299
116	0299	19 0241	0412
117	0412	31 0003	0423
118	0423	15 0282	0387
119	0387	20 0282	0298
120	0298	69 0280	0533
121	0533	24 0254	0462
122	0462	69 0281	0384
123	0384	24 0255	0512
124	0512	69 0282	0485
125	0485	24 0256	0366

No.	Location	Instruction	
126	0366	69 0283	0436
127	0436	24 0257	0416
128	0416	69 0284	0437
129	0437	24 0258	0466
130	0466	60 0278	0434
131	0434	19 0230	0401
132	0401	31 0006	0368
133	0368	20 0011	0516
134	0516	60 0280	0535
135	0535	11 0011	0418
136	0418	21 0280	0484
137	0484	21 0254	0468
138	0468	60 0278	0534
139	0534	19 0231	0451
140	0451	31 0006	0518
141	0518	20 0011	0370
142	0370	60 0278	0486
143	0486	19 0232	0303
144	0303	31 0006	0420
145	0420	20 0012	0470
146	0470	60 0473	0327
147	0327	10 0012	0520
148	0520	21 0012	0521
149	0521	65 0281	0536
150	0536	16 0011	0322

TABLE 2 - Continued

No.	Location	Instruction	No.	Location	Instruction	No.	Location	Instruction
151	0322	35 0004 0487	176	0474	20 0011 0524	201	0340	19 0237 0427
152	0487	64 0012 0523	177	0524	65 0234 0339	202	0427	31 0003 0390
153	0523	31 0001 0379	178	0339	35 0003 0297	203	0390	15 0236 0341
154	0379	20 0281 0537	179	0297	15 0011 0475	204	0341	15 0280 0492
155	0537	20 0255 0372	180	0475	20 0011 0525	205	0492	35 0001 0440
156	0372	60 0278 0288	181	0525	60 0328 0389	206	0440	20 0011 0477
157	0288	19 0233 0353	182	0389	11 0244 0349	207	0477	60 0380 0490
158	0353	31 0006 0422	183	0328	31 0006 0350	208	0380	31 0004 0391
159	0422	20 0012 0472	184	0349	21 0012 0326	209	0490	11 0244 0449
160	0472	60 0282 0338	185	0326	65 0011 0012	210	0449	21 0012 0527
161	0338	11 0012 0522	186	0350	20 0281 0439	211	0527	65 0011 0012
162	0522	21 0262 0388	187	0439	60 0256 0489	212	0391	20 0280 0540
163	0388	21 0256 0374	188	0489	19 0239 0376	213	0540	69 0252 0428
164	0374	71 0277 0250	189	0376	20 0011 0426	214	0428	24 0278 0481
165	0300	70 0251 0501	190	0426	65 0238 0343	215	0481	69 0253 0478
166	0501	60 0251 0432	191	0343	35 0003 0352	216	0478	24 0279 0482
167	0432	21 0277 0431	192	0352	15 0011 0476	217	0482	69 0257 0479
168	0431	35 0008 0495	193	0476	20 0011 0526	218	0479	24 0283 0491
169	0495	30 0004 0302	194	0526	60 0429 0539	219	0491	69 0258 0430
170	0302	10 0424 8003	195	0429	31 0006 0545	220	0430	24 0284 0441
171	0424	60 0183 0438	196	0539	11 0244 0399	221	0441	71 0277 0300
172	0438	10 0254 0488	197	0399	21 0012 0377	222	0274	00 0000 1667
173	0488	21 0280 0538	198	0377	65 0011 0012	223	0324	00 0041 6667
174	0538	60 0255 0289	199	0545	20 0282 0290	224	0272	00 0002 7777
175	0289	19 0235 0474	200	0290	60 0281 0340	225	0270	01 0000 0000

TABLE 2 - Continued

No.	Location	Instruction	No.	Location	Instruction	No.	Location	Instruction
226	0473	00 0000 1000	251	0160	10 0180 8003	276	0128	60 0012 0114
227	0156	24 0049 0157	252	0180	15 0220 0161	277	0114	10 0121 0129
228	0157	20 0011 0164	253	0161	15 0011 0049	278	0129	21 0013 0130
229	0177	20 0012 0165	254	0100	24 0049 0102	279	0130	11 0133 0137
230	0165	16 8002 0173	255	0102	11 0105 0109	280	0133	00 0000 2000
231	0173	30 0001 0179	256	0105	00 0000 3000	281	0137	30 0005 0149
232	0164	30 0005 0177	257	0109	46 0112 0116	282	0149	64 0013 0131
233	0179	20 0013 0166	258	0112	10 0105 0110	283	0131	20 0014 0132
234	0166	16 8002 0175	259	0110	11 0113 0117	284	0132	60 0014 0134
235	0175	30 0001 0181	260	0113	00 0030 0300	285	0134	19 0014 0135
236	0181	20 0014 0167	261	0117	46 0120 0124	286	0135	31 0005 0150
237	0167	60 0014 0169	262	0124	10 0113 0118	287	0150	60 8002 0136
238	0169	30 0005 0182	263	0118	20 0011 0114	288	0136	19 0014 0138
239	0182	10 0158 8003	264	0120	10 0113 0119	289	0138	35 0005 0151
240	0158	15 0200 0163	265	0119	35 0001 0125	290	0151	21 0015 0139
241	0163	15 0011 0168	266	0125	21 0012 0115	291	0139	60 0014 0140
242	0168	20 0011 0170	267	0115	66 0121 0127	292	0140	19 0143 0144
243	0170	60 0013 0171	268	0121	00 0000 1000	293	0143	00 0008 6304
244	0171	30 0005 0183	269	0127	20 0011 0122	294	0144	31 0005 0107
245	0183	10 0159 8003	270	0122	60 0012 0114	295	0107	20 0013 0141
246	0159	15 0210 0174	271	0116	10 0105 0111	296	0141	60 0015 0142
247	0174	15 0011 0172	272	0111	30 0001 0106	297	0142	19 0145 0146
248	0172	15 0011 0176	273	0106	21 0012 0123	298	0145	00 0003 6415
249	0176	20 0012 0178	274	0123	60 0121 0126	299	0146	31 0005 0147
250	0178	30 0005 0160	275	0126	21 0011 0128	300	0147	15 0013 0148

TABLE 2 - Concluded

No.	Location	Instruction	No.	Location	Instruction	No.	Location	Instruction
301	0148	20 0015 0101	326	0097	21 0011 0066	351	0093	15 0096 0055
302	0101	65 0011 0152	327	0066	19 8001 0050	352	0051	49 9999 9999
303	0152	35 0002 0103	328	0050	31 0010 0058	353	0065	99 9999 9999
304	0103	15 0015 0104	329	0058	20 0021 0075	354	0096	25 0000 0000
305	0104	20 0015 0153	330	0075	60 0078 0089	355	0082	15 7079 6318
306	0153	61 0108 0154	331	0089	19 0021 0052	356	0080	06 4596 3711
307	0108	00 0002 5000	332	0052	31 0010 0059	357	0070	00 7968 9679
308	0154	19 0015 0155	333	0059	16 0064 0069	358	0064	00 0467 3766
309	0155	31 0006 0049	334	0069	60 8002 0077	359	0078	00 0015 1484
310	0099	24 0049 0055	335	0077	19 0021 0053			
311	0055	10 8002 0063	336	0053	31 0010 0067			
312	0063	10 8001 0071	337	0067	15 0070 0079			
313	0071	47 0074 0076	338	0079	60 8002 0090			
314	0076	10 8003 0083	339	0090	19 0021 0054			
315	0083	47 0086 0088	340	0054	31 0010 0072			
316	0088	60 8003 0097	341	0072	16 0080 0094			
317	0086	66 8002 0095	342	0094	60 8002 0056			
318	0095	15 0051 0055	343	0056	19 0021 0060			
319	0074	10 8003 0081	344	0060	31 0010 0073			
320	0081	47 0084 0087	345	0073	15 0082 0091			
321	0087	61 8003 0097	346	0091	60 8002 0057			
322	0084	65 8002 0092	347	0057	19 0011 0068			
323	0092	46 0061 0062	348	0068	31 0010 0049			
324	0062	16 0065 0055	349	0098	24 0049 0085			
325	0061	15 0065 0055	350	0085	67 8002 0093			

218

2.7. Alteration of Instructions

Both instructions and data are stored in the memory as ten-digit words. Thus arithmetical operations may be performed on the instructions themselves in order to generate new instructions. This can reduce considerably the amount of programing that must be done, especially when the computation involves iterative processes. Examples of this and other principles described above will appear in the following section.

§ 3. A SAMPLE PROGRAM

3.1. Input

The program contained in Table 2 is intended for general use in the reduction of three-color photoelectric observations. It is simple to use and sufficiently flexible that alterations or additions can be made to fit individual circumstances.

The punched-card input can be prepared in several ways. First, the data can be hand-punched from measured recorder charts. This is the most time-consuming method, but the over-all increase in efficiency as compared with hand reduction is still great. Second, the recorder charts can be measured by means of a hand-operated measuring device which digitizes the measures and actuates an IBM punch. Third, a programing device can be incorporated into the photometer itself such that, in connection with an integrator, digitizer, and IBM punch, the observation is recorded on a punched card directly at the time of observation. Such a device has been developed and described by Hoag (1957).

The input required by the program in Table 2 is described in detail below:

Word 1:	xxxxxxxxxx
Word 2:	000000x^{h}xx^{m}x
Word 3:	000000xx°xx$'$
Word 4:	000xxx0xxx
Word 5:	0xx.xxx.xxx.x
Word 6:	0000000xx.x
Word 7:	free
Word 8:	free

Word 1: The first eight digits are reserved for the star designation. No provision is made for the inclusion of an algebraic sign in the designation. The last two columns contain a night number (01 through 15). This is needed for the application of systematic night corrections to the magnitudes. If no systematic night corrections are made, these columns should contain zeros.

Word 2: This contains, as indicated above, the hour angle of the object at the time of observation.

Word 3: The declination of the object. If the declination is negative, the sign is indicated by an overpunch in column 30.

Word 4: The first three columns contain zeros. The next three contain the usual numerical code to indicate the gain settings of the amplifier for the blue and yellow deflections. If the amplifier contains only two gain adjustments, the first of these three columns should be zero. The seventh column is always zero, and the last three columns contain the gain settings for the ultraviolet deflection. If the same gain was used for the ultraviolet as for the blue and yellow deflections, these three columns should contain zeros.

Word 5: The first column is zero. The next nine columns contain, respectively, the ultraviolet, blue, and yellow deflections: u, b, and v. It is assumed here that the effects of sky have been removed in the process of reading the recorder chart.

Word 6: The first seven columns are zero. The last three contain the deflection on the standard source. If no standard source is used in connection with the observations, these three columns should contain zeros.

Words 7 and 8: These may contain any additional information which the observer wishes to record. This information will be retained by the machine and punched out with the intermediate and final results. If data in these two words have a minus sign associated with them, this should be punched over the tenth digit of the word, as in the case of a negative declination. All columns not otherwise filled should contain zeros.

3.2. OUTPUT

The first output of the program of Table 2 will be the instrumental colors and magnitudes corrected for extinction, and will have the following form:

Word 1:   (same as Word 1 of input)
Word 2:   000x.xx0000   air mass
Word 3:   (same as Word 4 of input)
Word 4:   00000xx.xxx   instrumental yellow magnitude
Word 5:   000000x.xxx   instrumental blue-yellow color
Word 6:   000000x.xxx   instrumental ultraviolet color
Words 7 and 8:   (same as Words 7 and 8 of input)

This output can be tabulated and examined by the operator in order to determine the systematic night corrections and coefficients for the transformation to a standard system and to correct errors due to errors in input.

These corrections and coefficients, once determined, can be read into the machine as described below, and the magnitudes and colors on the standard system will be computed and punched. The output of the first part of the program serves as the new input. The final output will have the same form as the previous output except that the instrumental colors and magnitudes will be replaced by the colors and magnitudes transformed to the standard system.

The program of Table 2 may be punched in connection with the standard IBM 650 loading routine (see IBM 650 *Manual of Operation*) and used, along with the precepts given here, to reduce three-color photoelectric observations. The running number at the left is for reference purposes within this chapter and need not be punched. In what follows, the program in Table 2 will be described, and portions of it will be used to illustrate some of the programing methods.

3.3. LOCATIONS UTILIZED

The following locations in the memory are used in the program:

0000 to 0049	temporary storage
0050 to 0099	sine-cosine subroutines
0100 to 0155	$-2.5 \log x$ subroutine
0156 to 0183	gain lookup subroutine
0184 to 0199	systematic night corrections to the magnitudes
0200 to 0244	instrumental constants
0250 to 0499	photoelectric reduction program

Reading and punching are done to and from the 0250 band.

3.4. AIR MASS

The first part of the program computes the air mass according to the formula:

$$A M = \sec z = \frac{1}{\sin \phi \sin \delta + \cos \phi \cos \delta \cos H A} ,$$

where ϕ is the latitude of the observer. Instructions 1 through 13 and 14 through 25, respectively, transform δ and HA into decimals of a circle as required for entrance into the subroutines which compute the sine and cosine. When instruction 25 has been carried out, δ, as a decimal of a circle, is contained in the lower accumulator, and the following instructions are carried out:

$$
\begin{array}{llll}
26 & 0378 & 69\ 0304\ 0099 \\
(27 & 0304 & 20\ 0011\ 0264)
\end{array}
$$

Load the distributor with the contents of 0304 (the link instruction shown in parentheses) and go to location 0099 for the next instruction. Location 0099 contains the first instruction of the sine subroutine. This causes the link instruction to be stored at location 0049, and subsequent instructions compute sin δ. When the last instruction of the sine subroutine has been carried out, sin δ is in the lower accumulator, and the machine is referred by the subroutine to location 0049 for the next instruction. This is the link instruction previously stored there:

$$20\ 0011\ 0264$$

which instructs the machine to store the lower accumulator (i.e., sin δ) in the temporary location 0011 and go to location 0264 for the next instruction in the main course of the program. Cos δ and cos HA are computed in a similar manner. Terms are combined in instructions 34 through 44, and in instruction 44 cos z is stored in temporary location 0014. Instructions 45 through 49 compute the reciprocal of cos z and store it in location 0253.

3.5. Raw Colors and Magnitudes

Instructions 50 through 73 rearrange the data in the memory so that the raw colors and magnitudes are stored in both read and punch locations. Thus, by means of a slight alteration of the program, the raw data can be punched out preparatory to an extinction solution. This output can then be used as input for the next part of the program. The quotients b/y and u/b are then computed by means of instructions 74 through 95, and the $-2.5 \log x$ subroutine is entered to compute raw colors and magnitudes. The $-2.5 \log x$ subroutine is based on the following expansion (Hastings *et al.* 1955):

$$\log_{10} x = C_1 \left(\frac{x-1}{x+1}\right) + C_3 \left(\frac{x-1}{x+1}\right)^3 ,$$

where

$$C_1 = 0.86304, \qquad C_3 = 0.36415 .$$

$$\text{Maximum error} = \pm 0.0005 \qquad \text{for} \qquad \frac{1}{\sqrt{10}} \le x \le \sqrt{10} .$$

This approximation does not provide for a sufficiently wide range in x; therefore, the range is extended by a factor of 10 each way, i.e., the machine tests whether $x > 3$. If so, it computes $\log x/10$ and adds 1.000 to the logarithm. If $x < 0.3$, it computes $\log 10x$ and subtracts 1.000 from the logarithm.

3.6. Gain Corrections

Corrections for amplifier gain are made by means of instructions 96 through 112. The b, y gain code and the u gain code are separated, and the gain lookup subroutine is entered to obtain the Δm corresponding to the b, y gain code. The three digits of the gain code are first separated by means of shift and store instructions. The first is stored in location 0014, the second in 0013, and the third in 0012. These digits will be referred to, respectively, as A, B, and C. The values of Δm corresponding to the values of A, B, and C have previously been read into the memory, along with other instrumental constants, in the following locations:

$$\Delta m \text{ for } A = 0 \quad \text{in location } 0200$$
$$\Delta m \text{ for } A = 1 \quad \text{in location } 0201$$
$$\text{etc.}$$
$$\Delta m \text{ for } B = 0 \quad \text{in location } 0210$$
$$\text{etc.}$$
$$\Delta m \text{ for } C = 0 \quad \text{in location } 0220$$
$$\text{etc.}$$

Thus ten locations have been reserved for each set of calibrations, although not all of them need be filled. The following will illustrate the lookup process: code A

has been stored in location 0014, and for the purposes of this example we will let $A = 3$. The contents of location 0014 thus is

$$3000000000+$$

Beginning with instruction 237, we have

$$237 \quad 0167 \quad 60\ 0014\ 0169$$

Reset and add into the upper accumulator the contents of location 0014; go to location 0169 for the next instruction.

$$238 \quad 0169 \quad 30\ 0005\ 0182$$

Shift the contents of the accumulator right five places; go to location 0182 for the next instruction. The contents of the upper accumulator now is

$$0000030000+$$

The next instruction is

$$239 \quad 0182 \quad 10\ 0158\ 8003$$
$$(240 \quad 0158 \quad 15\ 0200\ 0163)$$

Add to the upper accumulator the contents of location 0158 (in parentheses) and go to the upper accumulator for the next instruction.

The contents of the upper accumulator at this point is the sum of the gain code and the instruction in location 0158, i.e.,

$$15\ 0203\ 0163$$

Add to the lower accumulator the contents of location 0203; go to location 0163 for the next instruction.

The content of location 0203, however, is the value of Δm corresponding to the gain code $A = 3$. This is stored in a temporary location until the values of Δm corresponding to B and C are obtained, and the three are then added together to form the gain correction. If the amplifier has two, rather than three, gain controls, the first digit of the gain code will be zero, and the corresponding value of Δm, as obtained by the above lookup procedure, will be zero and have no effect on the result.

If the ultraviolet gain code is different from zero, the corresponding value of Δm is obtained in the same way. The difference between $\Delta m_{b,y}$ and Δm_u is then applied to the raw ultraviolet color.

3.7 INFRARED LEAK

The infrared leak of the ultraviolet filter, if it exists, is expressed in magnitudes in the following form:

$$L = A(C_{y_0} - B) \quad \text{for} \quad C_{y_0} > B,$$
$$L = 0 \quad\quad\quad\quad \text{for} \quad C_{y_0} < B,$$

where C_{y_0} is the raw blue-yellow color.

The coefficients A and B are stored in locations 0241 and 0240, respectively.

The difference $C_{y_0} - B$ is formed in the upper accumulator by instructions 113 and 114. The sign of $(C_{y_0} - B)$ is tested in the next instruction:

115   0445   46 0298 0299

Branch on minus, i.e., if the sign of the accumulator is minus, go to location 0298 for the next instruction; if it is plus, go to location 0299 for the next instruction.

If, when the branch instruction is performed, the sign of the accumulator is plus, then $C_{y_0} > B$, and the quantity L is computed and applied to the raw ultraviolet color. The next instruction, after this correction has been made, is in location 0298. If, when the branch instruction is performed, the sign of the accumulator is minus, then $C_{y_0} < B$, and the program goes directly to location 0298 for the next instruction, thus bypassing the instructions for computing L.

3.8. CORRECTION FOR EXTINCTION

Instructions 130 through 163 apply the extinction corrections to the instrumental colors and magnitudes according to the following formulae (Johnson and Morgan 1951; Sharpless 1952, 1954):

$$m_y = m_{y_0} - Q \sec z ,$$

$$C_y = \frac{C_{y_0} - k_1 \sec z}{1 + k_2 \sec z} ,$$

$$C_u = C_{u_0} - k_u \sec z .$$

The next instruction, 164, causes the instrumental colors and magnitudes to be punched, as described earlier.

3.9. TRANSFORMATION TO THE STANDARD SYSTEM

When the systematic night corrections and transformation coefficients have been determined, they may be read into the appropriate memory locations, and the final part of the computation can then be performed. The previous output cards are used as input, and the computation is begun with the instruction at location 0300.

The transformation to the standard system has the following form:

$$B - V = A + BC_y ,$$
$$V = C + m_y + D(B - V) ,$$
$$U - B = E + FC_u ,$$

in the case of a transformation to the U, B, V system. Transformation can, of course, be made to any other photometric system for which the above linear equations are valid. The results will be rounded to either two or three decimals, depending on the constant stored at location 0244.

3.10. Operating Precepts

The following precepts must be followed if the program in Table 2 is to be used successfully:

1. Use standard 8–10-digit wiring panel.
2. Set overflow switch to "sense."
3. Clear drum to zero.
4. Load instructions into the machine by means of the standard IBM loading routine, using any of the storage bands from 0550 through 1950.

3.11. Arrangement of Instrumental Constants

Systematic night corrections:

Location	Form of Word	Explanation
0184	0000000000	Must be zero
0185	0000000.xxx	S_1
.	.	.
0199	.	S_{15}

Gain calibration corresponding to first digit of gain code:

0200	00000xx.xxx	$\Delta m(A = 0)$
0201	00000xx.xxx	$\Delta m(A = 1)$
.	.	.
0209	00000xx.xxx	$\Delta m(A = 9)$

Gain calibration corresponding to second digit of gain code:

0210	00000xx.xxx	$\Delta m(B = 0)$
0211	00000xx.xxx	$\Delta m(B = 1)$
.	.	.
0219	00000xx.xxx	$\Delta m(B = 9)$

Gain calibration corresponding to third digit of gain code:

0220	00000xx.xxx	$\Delta m(C = 0)$
0221	00000xx.xxx	$\Delta m(C = 1)$
.	.	.
0229	00000xx.xxx	$\Delta m(C = 9)$

Extinction coefficients:

0230	0000000.xxx	Q
0231	0000000.xxx	k_1
0232	0000000.xxx	k_2
0233	0000000.xxx	k_u

Transformation coefficients:

0234	000000x.xxx	A
0235	000000x.xxx	B
0236	000000x.xxx	C

0237	000000x.xxx	D
0238	000000x.xxx	E
0239	000000x.xxx	F

Infrared leak:

0240	0000000.xxx	B
0241	0000000.xxx	A

Latitude of observer:

0242	00.xxxxx000	$\sin \phi$
0243	00.xxxxx000	$\cos \phi$

Number of decimals desired in final colors and magnitude:

0244	00000x0000	2 or 3

3.12. ALTERATIONS OF PROGRAM

The program given here may be considered as the nucleus for a more elaborate program designed by a particular observer to fit his particular needs. An extinction solution may be inserted between instructions 129 and 130. If this is done, the resulting coefficients should be stored in the locations specified here, so that subsequent portions of the program given here can be used. The extinction coefficients have purposely been assigned to punchout locations so that, if an extinction solution is inserted, the coefficients can be punched for examination and still be in the proper locations for use in the next portion of the program.

The program, as it appears here, can most logically be used in two steps. The standard star observations should be processed first. The systematic night corrections and transformation coefficients can be determined and placed in the appropriate locations in the memory. The observations of the program stars can then be processed. For these observations, the intermediate punchout of instrumental colors and magnitudes is not necessary, and this punching can be bypassed by reading in the following instructions after the program has been stored:

0388	21 0256 0501
0441	71 0277 0250

With these additional instructions, the computation of colors and magnitudes on the standard system can be accomplished in one operation by using the raw data as input.

All memory locations having addresses greater than 0549 are not used in this program and are thus available to the operator for any additional instructions he may wish to add. In order to facilitate the alteration of this program, a flow diagram is given in Figure 2. This shows the logical flow of the program and the corresponding instruction numbers.

The program given here has been optimized, i.e., storage locations of the

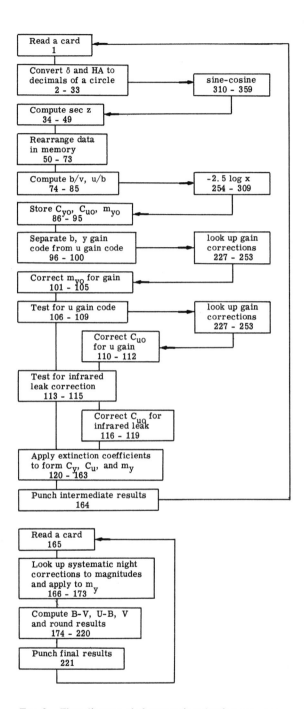

FIG. 2.—Flow diagram of photometric reduction program

instructions have been assigned such that the computation is carried out by the machine in a near-minimum number of rotations of the magnetic drum. This was accomplished by means of the Numerically Operated Symbolic-Ortho-Assembly-Program (NO SOAP) devised by Drs. G. M. Clemence, R. L. Duncombe, and Paul Herget. Approximately four hundred drum revolutions are necessary for the reduction of one observation. Thus the computations proceed at the rate of about thirty observations per minute.

The author is indebted to Dr. R. L. Duncombe for permission to reproduce here the sine-cosine subroutines devised by him and to Mrs. J. S. Duncombe for assistance in optimizing the program.

REFERENCES

HASTINGS, C., JR.,
  HAYWARD, J. T., and
  WONG, J. P., JR.   1955   *Approximations for Digital Computers* (Princeton, N.J.: Princeton University Press).
HOAG, A. A.   1957   See *A.J.*, **62**, 248.
JOHNSON, H. L., and
  MORGAN, W. W.   1951   *Ap. J.*, **114**, 522.
SHARPLESS, S.   1952   *Ap. J.*, **116**, 251.
                            1954   *Ibid.*, **119**, 200.

CHAPTER **10**

Polarization Measurements

W. A. HILTNER
Yerkes Observatory, University of Chicago

§ 1. INTRODUCTION

Dᴜʀɪɴɢ the past decade the measurement of polarization has become increasingly important in stellar astronomy. The earlier observations of polarized radiation were primarily in the general field of reflection nebulae—extended objects in which polarization may be introduced by scattering. However, polarization measurements of stellar radiation today are usually made because of their ability to establish the presence and nature of magnetic fields, either the general field of the galaxy or extragalactic nebulae or more restricted fields, such as that found in the Crab Nebula or in M87. Since all the applications in stellar astronomy have been either photographic or photoelectric in nature, we shall restrict our attention to these methods. This is not to imply that the visual methods are necessarily obsolete and inaccurate, for, in the hands of experts, when sufficient light is available, visual techniques can give accuracies to one or two parts per thousand.

Fully to describe a beam of polarized light, four parameters must be evaluated. The parameters, originally set down by Stokes, are

$$I = I_l + I_r , \qquad\qquad U = I \cos 2\beta \sin 2\chi ,$$
$$Q = I \cos 2\beta \cos 2\chi , \qquad\qquad V = I \sin 2\beta ,$$

where β is the angle whose tangent is the ratio of the axes of the ellipse traced by the end-point of the electric vector; χ is the angle between the major axis of the ellipse and the x-axis of the observer's co-ordinate system, where z is the direction of propagation; and I_l and I_r are the intensities at right angles. However, for partially plane-polarized light with I_{max} the intensity in the plane of vibration and I_{min} the intensity at right angles, the parameters become

$$I = I_{max} + I_{min}, \qquad\qquad U = (I_{max} - I_{min}) \sin 2\theta ,$$
$$Q = (I_{max} - I_{min}) \cos 2\theta, \qquad V = 0 ,$$

where θ is the angle measured from the plane of vibration.

TABLE 1

ANALYSIS OF POLARIZED RADIATION

With Analyzer There Is No Intensity Maximum

If λ/4 plate in front of analyzer gives no maximum		The light is natural
If λ/4 plate in front of analyzer gives a maximum and	If one position of analyzer gives zero intensity, the light is circularly polarized	
	If no position gives zero intensity, the light is partly circularly polarized and partly unpolarized	

With Analyzer There Is an Intensity Maximum

If one position gives zero intensity			The light is plane-polarized
If no position gives zero intensity and	If λ/4 plate in front with zero axis parallel to maximum intensity gives	Zero intensity with analyzer	The light is elliptically polarized
		No zero intensity and	If the same analyzer setting gives maximum intensity, the light is partly plane-polarized
			If some other analyzer setting gives maximum intensity, the light is partly elliptically polarized

Since I is essentially the magnitude, a polarization observation of an astronomical object reduces to that of measuring I_{max} relative to I_{min} and the position angle of I_{max}, the plane of vibration. Except in unusual cases, the magnitude I can be measured more conveniently along with the color of the object.

The classical definition of the *amount of polarization* is

$$\text{per cent polarization} = \frac{I_{max} - I_{min}}{I_{max} + I_{min}} 100 \, ,$$

with the plane of polarization referred to the magnetic vector. However, in the field of stellar astronomy the amount of polarization is usually expressed in magnitudes:

$$P_{mag} = 2.5 \log \frac{I_{max}}{I_{min}} \, ,$$

and the plane as the plane of vibration of the electric vector. The complete systematic analysis of radiation for polarization is given in Table 1.

§ 2. PHOTOGRAPHIC METHODS

The photographic process lends itself to the measurement of polarization in a manner not significantly different from that found in the observation of photographic magnitudes and colors. The photographic emulsion, with its integration ability and high resolution (many image points), has its greatest application in survey programs where only moderate accuracy is acceptable. Its accuracy may often be borderline or too low, so that even survey programs are of limited value. This is especially true for surveys of stellar polarization where the amount of polarization is usually less than 0.05 mag. However, in other programs it has provided useful material.

The simplest and most direct photographic method for measuring polarized radiation consists of a series of direct photographs taken through an analyzer, such as Polaroid. The analyzer is rotated through the same angle, say 30° or 45°, between exposures. The series of photographs thus obtained are processed together. With assumptions regarding the uniformity of the emulsion and its development and exposure, the plates can be analyzed for polarized radiation. The Crab Nebula shown in Figure 1 is an excellent example in which this technique has yielded significant results because of the relatively high polarization—up to 1.44 mag. The technique is plagued, however, with large systematic errors that may lead to false polarization. The principal error probably arises in non-uniformity in sky or fog background on the various plates.

The accuracy of the photographic process in polarization measurements can be greatly enhanced by simultaneous photographs through birefringent crystals or prisms made from these crystals. With the natural crystal or prisms, two images of an object can be photographed simultaneously in which the planes of vibration are perpendicular. Figure 2 illustrates the point. In this simple case a

Wollaston prism is placed in front of the focal plane at a distance sufficient to separate the two images properly. The Wollaston prism or Wollaston prism plus photographic emulsion is rotated by a constant amount (again say 30°–45°) between exposures, so that the relationship between the difference in magnitude of the pair and the position angle can be established. The calibration of the emulsion must be impressed on the plate by an auxiliary source, such as the

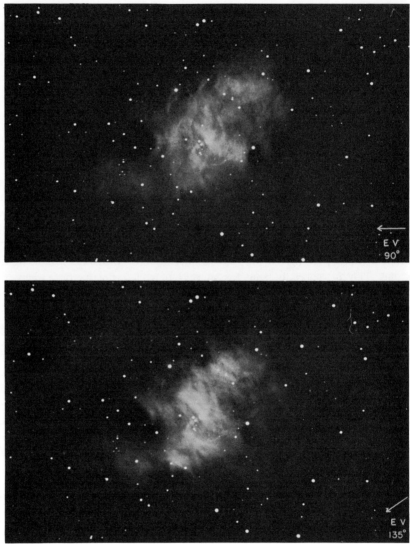

Fig. 1.—Two exposures of the Crab Nebula. The analyzer (Polaroid) was rotated through 45° between exposures. Taken with the 200-inch Hale reflector by W. Baade.

spot photometer discussed in chapter 4. The remaining photographic techniques to be discussed are only modifications of this basic instrument. Also it will be seen thàt all two-cell photoelectric polarimeters are essentially equivalent to this basic instrument in which the photographic emulsion is replaced by photocathodes.

Öhman (1941) has introduced several modifications of the two-image polarimeter. Figure 3 illustrates the instrument that he developed to observe the moon, M31, and other extended objects for polarized radiation. It is essentially a spectrograph in which the typical 60° prism or grating is replaced by a Wollaston prism and the slit system is a multiple one, in which the closed spaces be-

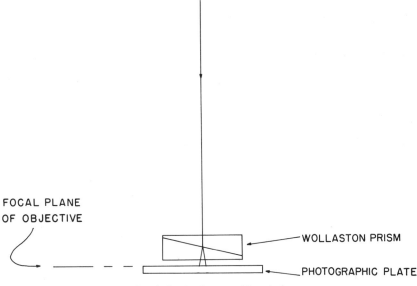

FOCAL PLANE
OF OBJECTIVE

WOLLASTON PRISM

PHOTOGRAPHIC PLATE

FIG. 2.—A simple photographic polarimeter

tween the individual slits are equal to, or greater than, the open spaces. The angle of the prism and the material from which it is made are so chosen that the two images from a single opening occupy parallel strips at the focal plane of the camera.

A second modification introduced by Öhman (1947) produces four images, one pair corresponding to a particular color and the other pair to another color. In this instrument two Wollaston prisms are used, separated by a quartz plate. This quartz plate is cut perpendicular to its axis. Hence rotatory dispersion is introduced. This instrument can provide immediate measurements of any variation of polarization with wave length.

If the quartz plate between these two Wollaston prisms is cut parallel to the axis and of sufficient thickness, four images will be produced, all with the same spectral distribution. However, since the quartz plate has split the light into two perpendicular components, the relative intensities of the two pairs can be adjusted by a rotation of the quartz plate. By this technique, a calibration of the emulsion is obtained, in addition to simultaneous images.

A still further modification of the two-image instrument is the replacement of the multi-slit with a multi-aperture one in two dimensions with the aperture diameters equal to, or smaller than, their separation. This arrangement permits

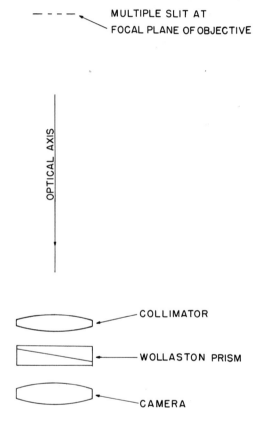

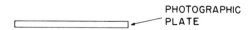

Fig. 3.—A multi-slit polarimeter developed by Öhman

rotation of the Wollaston prism on the optical axis for analysis at any position angle. This type of slit is especially useful for more accurate surveys of extended objects, such as the Crab Nebula, than are possible with direct single exposures through an analyzer.

The accuracy of photographic polarization observations is not significantly different from that of other photographic photometry—of the order of a few hundredths of a magnitude. The observer must be continuously on guard for instrumental systematic errors.

§ 3. PHOTOELECTRIC METHODS

The photoelectric techniques used for measuring polarization of starlight fall into two general classes. In the direct-current method, the radiation is observed for a long period of time, say 10–30 seconds, after which the analyzer is shifted to another position angle. The second group is often referred to as the "flicker technique," in which the analyzer is rotated rapidly on the optical axis. Either method can employ one or two cells, depending on whether perpendicular planes of vibration are observed simultaneously. Whether one technique or the other is used depends strongly on the type of observation to be made, the equipment available, and the individual experience of the observer.

3.1. SINGLE-CELL INSTRUMENTS

The simplest method is one in which an analyzer, such as Polaroid, is placed in the optical path in an ordinary photoelectric photometer. It is desirable that the analyzer be followed by a depolarizer,[1] since the photocathode may be sensitive to the plane of vibration.[2] The intensity of the radiation is then observed at discrete settings of the analyzer. This is normally done by the rotation of the entire instrument. If the object is polarized or there are systematic errors in either the photometer or the telescope, a cos 2θ-curve will result, with the amplitude a measure of the polarization and the plane of vibration corresponding to the position angle of maximum intensity. To maximize the accuracy, the analyzer is normally provided with a second rotation in addition to the rotation of the whole instrument. This second rotation is exactly 90°. This permits an intensity measurement of the perpendicular plane, immediately followed by a measurement with the analyzer in its original position. This arrangement reduces the opportunity for extinction variation during an exposure at any discrete position angle. Systematic errors must, as always, be carefully and fully evaluated. The most direct method of evaluating these errors, of course, is to

---

[1] A depolarizer (Lyot, 1929) consists of two quartz plates cut parallel to the optical axis, one twice the thickness of the other, and cemented together with the optical axis rotated by 45°. For narrow spectral regions, such as those isolated by interference filters, the depolarizer should be made of calcite instead of quartz. A monochromatic depolarizer has been discussed by Billings (1951).

[2] Caution must be exercised even with the "end-on" photomultipliers, where radiation can strike the inclined photosensitive dynodes.

observe objects similar but with no known polarization. Observations of a sufficiently large number of nearby stars will permit reasonable evaluation of the systematic errors. The accuracy with an instrument of this type for bright stars, where scintillation is the primary source of noise, is superior to that of photoelectric magnitude and color observations, since there is no extinction correction—that is, the extinction coefficient is the same for all planes of vibration. For fainter stars the accuracy is limited by the shot noise in the photocathode current.

A simple flicker method for the detection of polarized radiation need consist of only a rapidly rotating analyzer in front of a photocell, the output of which is amplified by an a.c. amplifier. However, for the instrument to become a working one, one or more additions must be introduced (see Öhman 1949). The above instrument would indicate only that polarized radiation was present, assuming, of course, that no systematic errors were present. Some method of calibration, for both amount and position angle of the electric vector, must be introduced. In principle, both can be obtained by a thin glass plate placed in the optical path ahead of the analyzer. This glass plate can be tilted and, at the same time, rotated on the optical axis to any position angle. With the proper tilt and position angle, any polarization in the stellar radiation can be canceled. The position angle of the electric vector is then read directly from the position angle of the glass plate, and the amount of polarization can be obtained from the tilt with the help of Fresnel's formulae. In practice, however, other techniques are more efficient in the use of telescope time.

A polarimeter developed by Hall and Mikesell (1950) is an excellent example of the type of instrument under discussion. It is illustrated in Figure 4. With the help of this figure, the modes of operation will be described. In mode G, the collimated light is passed through the rotating Glan-Thomson prism after traversing a strain-free glass disk. This prism is similar to the more common Nicol prism, but the faces are cut perpendicular to the optical path, to prevent deviation of the beam. If the star is polarized, the photocell output will vary as $\cos 2\theta$, where θ is the angle through which the prism has rotated beyond maximum intensity. This output is rectified by a phased rectifier whose phase is advanced by 360° during a period of 2 minutes. Thus the d.c. output of the amplifier varies as $\cos 2\theta$ with a period of 2 minutes. The phase of the curve will be a function of the position angle of the plane of vibration.

In mode D a quartz depolarizer is substituted for the glass disk in mode G. The glass disk (strain-free fused quartz may be preferable) was used in mode G, in order to retain similar optical paths for both modes. The radiation in mode D operation is therefore depolarized. Hence, if there are no spurious polarizations, the amplifier output will be zero. Consequently, a horizontal line (with noise, of course) will be drawn in the 2-minute cycle.

In mode DT, the depolarized radiation must pass through the tilted cover glass. This introduces a known amount of polarization, from which the amount of polarization in the starlight can be determined.

In addition, the sky is observed when needed under mode G.

The reduction of the observations is more or less obvious. The curves obtained with modes G and DT are corrected for any spurious polarization observed with mode D, and mode G is further corrected for any (moonlit) sky-background polarization. A comparison of the corrected modes G and DT will give both the amount of polarization and its plane of vibration.

In principle, the d.c. and the a.c. or flicker methods should give essentially the same accuracy.[3] The principal noise for the brighter stars will be caused by scintillation and by shot noise of the photocathode current for the fainter ones, from either the stellar or the sky radiation. Errors resulting from variations in

[3] The choice of 30 cycles per second for the above instrument was not a favorable one since the scintillation noise is near a maximum at this frequency (Mikesell, Hoag, and Hall, 1951).

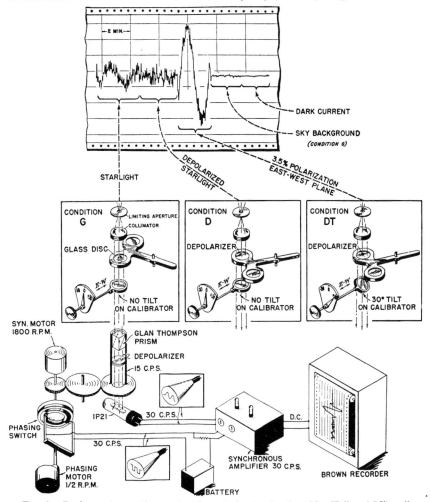

FIG. 4.—Design and operation modes of a polarimeter developed by Hall and Mikesell

extinction because of the rapidity with which all planes of vibration are compared have less opportunity to affect the a.c. methods. However, a significant analysis of the published data is not possible because of the difference in climatic conditions under which the observations were obtained. The published data obtained with the a.c. method (see Hall and Mikesell 1950) have a random error that is a function of the amount of polarization, whereas the d.c. method has a smaller error and is constant with the amount of polarization. The apparent contradiction may be a consequence of a difference in climatic conditions (eastern seaboard versus the Southwest) and a possible difference in effective integration times (see Hiltner 1951).

3.2. Two-Cell Instruments

The theoretical accuracy for a photometric observation should be a function of the total amount of radiation available for that observation, or

$$\text{m.e.} = \frac{[(n_s + n_*)\epsilon l + n_* \epsilon l]^{1/2}}{n_* \epsilon l}$$

$$= \frac{1}{n_*} \left(\frac{2n_s + n_*}{\epsilon l} \right)^{1/2},$$

where m.e. is the mean error, n_s the number of photons from the sky per unit time, n_* the number of photons from the star per unit time, ϵ the effective[4] efficiency of the photocathode, and l the duration of the observation. If the sky radiation may be neglected, the above equation reduces to

$$\text{m.e.} = \left(\frac{1}{n_* \epsilon l} \right)^{1/2}.$$

To illustrate, a tenth-magnitude star in a 10-inch telescope gives approximately 2×10^3 photoelectrons per second or 10^3 for any one plane of vibration. Therefore, if an accuracy of 0.001 mag. is desired for any one plane of vibration, an integration time of 1000 seconds is required. This assumes no sky background. To define the amount and the position angle of the polarization, the ratios of perpendicular planes of vibration are measured for at least two position angles.[5] Thus the observing time will be in excess of 1 hour. The same observing time is needed for a fifteenth-magnitude star with a 100-inch telescope. The observing time can be reduced by a factor of 2 with the introduction of two cells for simultaneous observations of perpendicular planes of vibration. There are other advantages in addition to the reduction in observing time for a specific observation: guiding errors on irregular extended objects and variations in atmospheric extinction and sky brightness are eliminated.

However, the principal advantage of the two-cell instrument is not in the

[4] Product of the photocathode and the photoelectron collection efficiency of the photomultiplier.

[5] In practice, with a d.c. system, observations are taken at from 5 to 12 discrete position angles differing by either 30° or 45°.

reduction of the observing time but in the increased accuracy when the accuracy is limited by scintillation noise. With an instrument with only one
photocell and assuming no scintillation noise, the theoretical accuracy for a
7.5-mag. star with a 100-inch telescope is 0.001 mag/sec, or 0.0001 mag. in 100
seconds. But the accuracy obtained in practice is more nearly 0.002 mag. The
principal source of this discrepancy is obvious. The above theoretical accuracy
was computed from the statistics of the photocathode current, whereas the
observed accuracy is limited by scintillation noise. Fortunately, scintillation
noise is coherent for all planes of vibration—in other words, the noise pattern
is the same. Since a polarization measurement is a ratio, it follows that this
scintillation noise can be eliminated by measuring the output ratio of the two
photocells. In theory, then, the accuracy will be limited by the shot noise only.

The two-cell photoelectric polarimeter is basically the photographic one with
the photographic emulsion replaced by two photocells. Without exception, a
Wollaston prism is used for the analyzer. As with the single-cell instrument, the
two-cell polarimeter can be so designed that the photocell outputs can be
measured with either a d.c. or an a.c. amplifier.

Although it has not been discussed for this purpose, there appears no reason
why the two-cell polarimeter described by Lyot (1948) and modified by Dollfus
(1958) should not give an internal accuracy limited only by shot noise. The
principle of the Lyot-Dollfus polarimeter is shown in Figure 5. A pair of half-
wave plates is mounted on a circular glass plate with such orientation that the
plane of vibration is rotated through 90° on passing from one half-wave plate
to the other. This combination is mounted and rotated so that the beam under
analysis must periodically pass through one half-wave plate and then the other.
The speed of rotation is 20 rpm. When the half-wave plates are rotated, either
cell experiences a variable light-intensity if the beam is polarized. The difference
in the outputs of the two cells is amplified and subsequently rectified with a
phased detector. To make a measurement of a star, for example, two observations are made with different settings of the compensator both in tilt and in
position angle. The true value of the polarization is then interpolated from these
two observations. Dollfus (1958) has reported accuracies up to one part in 10^5 in
the laboratory.

An instrument designed especially for the elimination of scintillation noise
is shown in Figure 6 (Hiltner 1951). The whole instrument can be rotated about
the optical axis. Thus observations at position angle with intervals of 30° or 45°
can be made to which a cos 2θ-curve can be fitted by least squares. A difference
amplifier is used to measure the difference of the two outputs instead of their
ratio. This is permitted because the measured polarizations are small and hence
the ratio is always near 1. A circuit for a difference amplifier is given in Figure 7.
The amplifier is followed (when desired) by a voltage to frequency converter
and scaler or by a current integrator similar to that described by Gardiner and
Johnson (1955). A complete instrument is illustrated in Figure 8.

For faint stars, where shot noise predominates, it may be more convenient

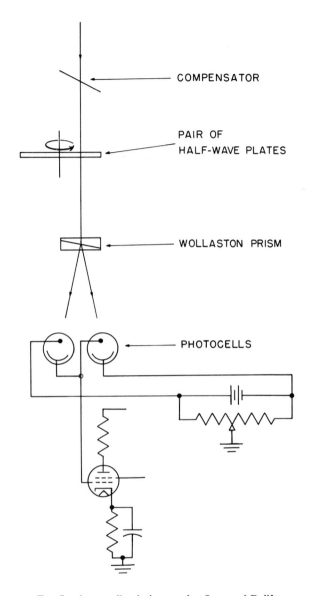

COMPENSATOR

PAIR OF
HALF-WAVE PLATES

WOLLASTON PRISM

PHOTOCELLS

FIG. 5.—A two-cell polarimeter after Lyot and Dollfus

to use either two independent scalers for photon counting or two independent amplifiers followed by either two current integrators or two voltage to frequency converters and scalers. In either case, the remaining scintillation noise and variations in atmospheric extinction are eliminated.

Figure 9 illustrates the ability of such an instrument greatly to reduce the scintillation noise. The observations of two stars are given. The left tracing for either star shows the scintillation noise. The right tracing of either star shows the remaining noise when the scintillation noise is reduced.

An observation of a star for polarization is shown in Figure 10, along with a

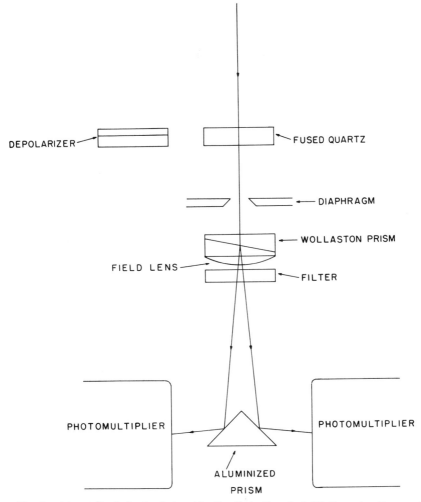

DEPOLARIZER

FUSED QUARTZ

DIAPHRAGM

WOLLASTON PRISM

FIELD LENS

FILTER

PHOTOMULTIPLIER

PHOTOMULTIPLIER

ALUMINIZED
PRISM

FIG. 6.—A two-cell polarimeter designed for the elimination of scintillation noise. Care must be exercised in dust removal from the optics and in the selection of photomultipliers with similar photocathode sensitivity patterns.

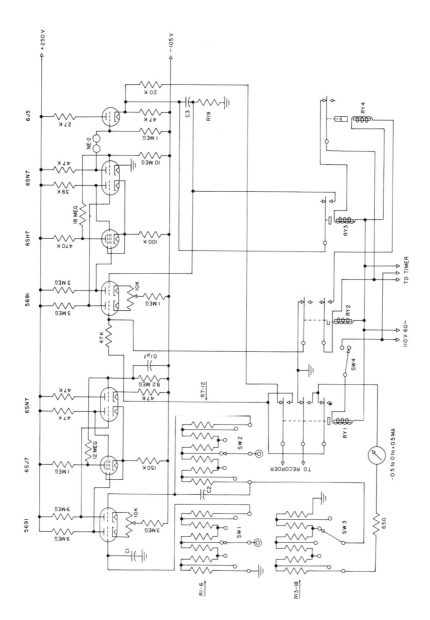

FIG. 7.—Circuit for the difference amplifier and integrator used at the Yerkes Observatory. *R1–6* and *R7–12* are two sets of dividers with a total series resistance of 100 megohms. *R13–18* is also a series divider that gives half-magnitudes. C_1 and C_2 are adjusted to give equal time constants of about 1 second to either input circuit. *RY4* is a hydraulic relay that remains closed for an adjustable length of time after the coil is de-excited. *SW4* selects whether the amplifier or the amplifier plus integrator is used.

FIG. 8.—A two-cell polarimeter designed to eliminate scintillation noise. The upper section is an offset guiding mechanism. The instrument below the guider is rotatable on the optical axis on precision preloaded large-diameter ball bearing.

243

laboratory source (without scintillation noise) of the same intensity as the star. Although the stellar tracings are short, it is apparent that scintillation noise is essentially eliminated. The observed internal accuracy for a fourth-magnitude star in the 82-inch reflector of the McDonald Observatory is approximately 0.0001 mag. for a 2-minute observation.

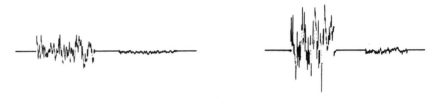

FIG. 9.—Performance of a two-cell polarimeter for the elimination of scintillation noise

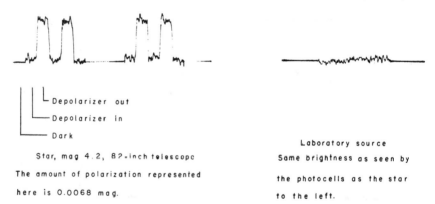

FIG. 10.—Observation of a star with a two-cell polarimeter. Note that the laboratory source shows the same noise as the stellar one. It is only shot noise.

This differential technique has now been applied to the polarization of the 75-cm galactic radiation (van de Hulst 1961). Evidence for a general galactic magnetic field was obtained, in complete support of the optical polarization data.

§ 4. CONCLUSION

With the internal accuracy now possible with a two-cell instrument, the systematic errors become of primary importance. Although raw polarization measurements are easier than any other photometric problem in astronomy, the elimination of systematic errors is probably one of the more difficult. Magnitude and color observations are all relative, that is, relative to a group of standard stars that were assigned definite magnitudes and colors. Polarization measurements, on the other hand, must be absolute. A standard star for polarization measurements can also be used, but the amount of polarization must be rigorously established to the desired accuracy. Since all photoelectric polarimeters have their own calibration devices, either by a compensator (thin cover glass) or in the amplifier, the most useful standard would be one with *no* polarization. It is not permissible to assume that the nearer stars, such as τ Ceti ($\pi = 0.297$) or ϵ Eri ($\pi = 0.303$), have no interstellar polarization. On the assumption that the ratio of interstellar polarization to distance is 0.1 mag/kpc (this is not to imply that the relationship of interstellar polarization to distance is a fixed quantity), the polarization of these two stars may be several ten-thousandths of a magnitude—significantly larger than the instrumental accuracy.

At the present time, there are two possible solutions to the elimination of systematic errors—one statistical and the other absolute. The former requires the observation of many nearby stars and proceeds on the assumption that, on the average, the net polarization is zero. The latter follows that discussed by Behr (1960), that is, the construction of a precision telescope that is rotatable on its optical axis. It is evident that the predominant systematic error is telescopic in origin. For example, the systematic error of the 82-inch McDonald reflector in November, 1960, was about 0.0060 mag. The exact value (significant to 0.0001 mag.), of course, cannot be determined.

In the measurement of polarization, it is prudent to assume, first, that any newly observed unique polarization is false and then to proceed on this assumption with further observations (with all reasonable modifications in the instrumental arrangement) until the authenticity of the polarization is established beyond reasonable doubt. A "first" observation that gives zero polarization is the only reliable "first" one.

The preparation of this chapter was supported in part by the United States Air Force under Contract No. AF 19(604)4955.

REFERENCES

BEHR, A.	1960	*Lowell Bull.*, **4**, 292.
BILLINGS, BRUCE H.	1951	*J.O.S.A.*, **41**, 966.
DOLLFUS, A.	1958	*C.R.*, **246**, 2345.
GARDINER, A. J., and		
JOHNSON, H. L.	1955	*Rev. Sci. Instr.*, **26**, 1145.
HALL, JOHN S., and		
MIKESELL, A. H.	1950	*Pub. U.S. Naval Obs.*, **17**, 1.

HILTNER, W. A.   1951   *Observatory*, **71**, 234.
HULST, H. C. VAN DE   1961   *Versl. Afd. Natuurk., Kon. Ned. Akad. Wetensch.,*
                                    Amsterdam, **70**, 23.
LYOT, B.   1929   *Ann. Obs. Paris* (Meudon), **8**, 102.
                            1948   *C.R.*, **226**, 137.
MIKESELL, A. H.,
  HOAG, A. A., and
  HALL, JOHN S.   1951   *J.O.S.A.*, **41**, 689.
ÖHMAN, Y.   1941   *Stockholm Obs. Ann.*, Vol. **13**, No. 11.
                           1947   *Ibid.*, Vol. **15**, No. 2.
                           1949   *Ibid.*, No. 8.

CHAPTER **11**

The Reduction of Astronomical Polarization Measurements

P. J. TREANOR*

Yerkes Observatory, University of Chicago

§ 1. INTRODUCTION

THE reduction processes involved in the determination of polarization have much in common with those involved in other fields of astronomical photometry and to that extent might not seem to require special treatment. Indeed, certain techniques of punched-card and electronic computing now used in general photometry were first applied in the field of polarization (Hall and Hoag 1958). To the extent that polarization determinations involve only measurements of small intensity differences in the same source, they are less dependent on extinction corrections and easier to reduce. Polarization measurements do, however, possess certain characteristic problems which warrant an explicit account of reduction techniques.

First, it has been pointed out in chapter 10 that polarization measurements are absolute in character. The results of multicolor photometry of their nature carry a built-in instrumental characteristic, which does not impair their usefulness. Even if the filter system used differs from an accepted standard, a relative calibration can be set up by reference to standard stars, which preserves the relative usefulness of the system. The case is quite different for polarization measures, since an absolute physical measurement of polarization and position angle is required, and a measure is all but useless even for purposes of comparison with other observations made with the same equipment, until the instrumental characteristics have been removed.

Second, the significant quantities in a polarization measurement usually depend on smaller differences in magnitude than do those in multicolor photometry. Differences of a few thousandths of a magnitude are important, and much smaller differences may still be significant. In the Pleiades cluster, for

* Now at the Vatican Observatory.

247

example, the characteristic polarization for the majority of the members does not exceed 0.01 mag. Errors of two- or three-thousandths of a magnitude of instrumental origin may distort the measured position angle quite severely, and the instrumental polarization may much exceed this amount in unfavorable cases. In general, the polarization in stars of higher galactic latitudes and of the nearby stars is also very small. These stars, in principle, can provide the least ambiguous information on the nature of the polarizing particles and the structure of their galactic distribution. Moreover, they include many relatively bright stars, for which it is possible to obtain a consistency of the order of 1–2 $\times$ 10^{-4} mag. by the methods of seeing-compensated polarimetry described in chapter 10. This fact raises the investigation of accidental errors and instrumental corrections to one of prime importance for the future of polarization measurements.

Furthermore, the problem of high accuracy is not confined to measurements of small polarizations. Determination of wave-length dependence, even of highly polarized stars, devolves on measurements involving differences of a few thousandths of a magnitude. In this context, scale errors and the wave-length dependence of the instrumental corrections become vitally important. The present unsatisfactory state of the measurements of highly polarized stars may be gauged from the fact that measures of HD 183143, a highly polarized, relatively bright, and much measured star, range from $0^{m}126$ to $0^{m}147$. Finally, polarization measurements are currently made by the several methods described in chapter 10—a situation which contrasts strongly with the highly standardized procedures of multicolor photometry. Since, however, the purpose of this chapter is to highlight basic features of reduction, it will not be necessary to consider the differences in detail and problems of programing peculiar to each method; for these, reference must be made to the individual research papers. For the sake of definiteness, a description will be given of the reduction process applied to measurements made in the double-channel polarimeter and difference amplifier described in the preceding chapter.

§ 2. OBSERVATIONAL PROCEDURE

After the star has been centered in the diaphragm with the depolarizer in position and the polarimeter head (which carries all the optical components) at an (arbitrary) initial setting θ, a deflection is obtained with one amplifier. The second amplifier is switched in and its gain increased until a balance is obtained (on a zero-centered recorder). Balance is checked again after the gain of both amplifiers is increased to give a large equivalent base line, R. At this stage, the second amplifier is switched off, and gain on the first amplifier is reduced by known gain steps to give a deflection, r, from which the base line R can be calculated.

The star is now observed as indicated in chapter 10. A reference intensity, D_1, is recorded with the depolarizer in position. The quartz compensator, Q, is inserted in place of the depolarizer, and a reading, Q_1, follows. The reading D_1 is then repeated. Next the polarimeter head is rotated, anticlockwise, through 30° (or 45°), and readings of Q and D are made in the same way, and so on through 360° at 30° (or 45°) intervals. The observations are concluded by a repetition of the base-line determination. From each set of three readings a quantity

$$f_i = \frac{Q - \bar{D}}{R} \qquad (1)$$

is determined, where $\bar{D}$ is the mean of the two readings of D.

§ 3. DERIVATION OF THE LEAST-SQUARES SOLUTION

The problem is now to derive the best value of the polarization, p (measured in magnitudes), and position angle, ϕ, from the twelve values of f_i. The intensity due to the electric vector of starlight in a plane making an angle θ to the meridian, measured eastward from the north point, is

$$I_\theta = I_{\min}[1 + \cos^2 (\theta_i - \phi)], \qquad (2)$$

where ϕ is the position angle of the polarization (measured eastward from the north point and, by convention, increased by 180° where necessary to secure a positive value between 0° and 180°). Denote the percentage polarization defined in chapter 10 by p_0. Then

$$p = 2.1717 \left(p_0 + \frac{p_0^3}{3} + \frac{p_0^5}{5} + \cdots \right), \qquad p^2 < 1 \quad (3)$$

(see Hall 1958 for the derivation of this expression). By a simple transformation of equation (2),

$$I_{\theta i} = I_0[1 + p_0 \cos 2(\theta_i - \phi)], \qquad (4)$$

where I_0 is the mean intensity. The quantity I_θ corresponds to the intensity of the ray transmitted in one of the images, formed by the Wollaston prism, having an electric vector with position angle θ. The intensity in the other image will be

$$I'_{\theta i} = I_0[1 - p_0 \cos 2(\theta_i - \phi)]. \qquad (5)$$

The difference-current deflection at any setting of the polarimeter, expressed as a fraction of the deflection corresponding to I_0, will be

$$f_i = 2p_0 \cos 2(\theta_i - \phi) = 2p_0 \cos 2\theta_i \cos 2\phi + 2p_0 \sin 2\theta_i \sin 2\phi. \quad (6)$$

Denoting

$$A = 2p_0 \sin 2\phi, \qquad B = 2p_0 \cos 2\phi, \qquad (7)$$

we obtain normal equations for a least-squares solution of A and B:

$$\Sigma(\sin^2 2\theta_i) A + \Sigma(\sin 2\theta_i \cos 2\theta_i) B = \Sigma(f_i \sin 2\theta_i),$$
$$\Sigma(\sin 2\theta_i \cos \theta_i) A + \Sigma(\cos^2 2\theta_i) B = \Sigma(f_i \cos 2\theta_i), \qquad (8)$$

and hence by equations (7) we may derive p_0 and ϕ. However, we may further use the fact that readings are made at equal intervals, in this case 30°, both to simplify the computation and to eliminate certain systematic errors. We number the f_i's from 1 to 12 in order of increasing position angle (measured eastward from the north point) and form the sums

$$F_1 = (f_1 + f_7 - f_4 - f_{10}) ,$$
$$F_2 = (f_3 + f_9 - f_6 - f_{12}) , \tag{9}$$
$$F_3 = (f_5 + f_{11} - f_2 - f_8) .$$

Solving equations (7) and (8) for this particular case, we obtain

$$p_0 = \tfrac{1}{12}(F_1^2 + F_2^2 + F_3^2 - F_1 F_2 - F_2 F_3 - F_3 F_1)^{1/2} . \tag{10}[1]$$

This expression is symmetrical in F and is therefore an optimal solution. Moreover, since from the symmetry of this situation $f_1 = - f_4$, etc., this form of solution automatically removes small-scale asymmetries associated with sign or due to a displaced reference level D.

The expression for ϕ obtained from the least-squares solution does not have these properties. To determine ϕ, therefore, it is preferable to use the value of p_0 determined by equation (10), in equation (6). Each of 12 observational equations then yields a value of $\cos 2(\theta_i - \phi)$ of the form

$$\cos \psi_i = \cos 2 (\theta_i - \phi) = \frac{f_i}{2 p_0}. \tag{11}$$

The trivial ambiguity is solved by listing the alternative values of $(\theta - \phi)$ and accepting those which increase by 30°.

Alternatively and more expeditiously, we may use the symmetry of the situation to deduce the three equations

$$\frac{F_1}{8 p_0} = \cos 2 (\theta_1 - \phi),$$

$$\frac{F_2}{8 p_0} = \cos 2 (\theta_1 + 60° - \phi), \tag{12}$$

$$\frac{F_3}{8 p_0} = \cos 2 (\theta_1 + 120° - \phi).$$

Each of these three equations yields independently a pair of values of $\psi = 2(\theta_1 - \phi)$ of which only the three nearly equal values are accepted. Differentiating equations (11), we obtain

$$d\psi = \frac{d f}{2 p_0 \sin \psi_i}.$$

[1] I am indebted to a suggestion of Dr. Ivan King for this particular solution.

The error in ψ_i, which is carried over into the individual values of ψ_1 and ϕ, is therefore proportional to cosec ψ_i, and the corresponding statistical weight of each value of ϕ is $\sin^2 \psi_i$. Hence, finally,

$$2(\theta_1 - \phi) = \frac{\Sigma \psi_1 \sin^2 \psi_i}{\Sigma \sin^2 \psi_i}. \tag{13}$$

The value of θ_i must be determined by reference to a star of known position angle or from the geometry of the instrumentation. Equation (13) then serves to determine ϕ.

From the following worked example it will be seen that the form of reduction described can be carried through quite quickly.

Example—14 Cep, Oct. 25, 1960 (McDonald 82-inch reflector), $R = 402.0$.

Position	$Q - \bar{D}$	$f = (Q - \bar{D})/R$	Position	$Q - \bar{D}$	$f = (Q - \bar{D})/R$
1 (0°)	+ 8.8	+0.0219	7 (180°)	+ 8.0	+0.0199
2 (30°)	+13.1	+ .0326	8 (210°)	+13.0	+ .0323
3 (60°)	+ 4.8	+ .0119	9 (240°)	+ 4.8	+ .0119
4 (90°)	− 8.0	− .0199	10 (270°)	− 8.0	− .0199
5 (120°)	−13.3	− .0331	11 (300°)	−12.7	− .0316
6 (150°)	− 4.6	−0.0114	12 (330°)	− 4.4	−0.0109

$$F_1 = (f_1 + f_7 - f_4 - f_{10}) = +0.0816,$$
$$F_2 = (f_3 + f_9 - f_6 - f_{12}) = +0.0461,$$
$$F_3 = (f_5 + f_{11} - f_2 - f_8) = -0.1297.$$

$$F_1^2 = +0.00666, \qquad F_1 F_2 = +0.00376,$$
$$F_2^2 = +0.00213, \qquad F_2 F_3 = -0.00597,$$
$$F_3^2 = +0.01680, \qquad F_3 F_1 = -0.01058,$$
$$\Sigma F_i^2 = +0.02559, \qquad \Sigma F_i F_j = -0.01279,$$

$$p_0 = \tfrac{1}{12}[(\Sigma F_i^2 - \Sigma F_i F_j)]^{1/2} = 0.01633,$$
$$p = 2.1717 p_0 = 0.0355 \text{ mag.}$$

$$F_1/8p_0 = \cos 2(\theta_1 - \phi) \qquad = +0.6246;$$
$$F_2/8p_0 = \cos 2(\theta_1 - \phi + 60°) \quad = +0.3529;$$
$$F_3/8p_0 = \cos 2(\theta_1 - \phi + 120°) \quad = -0.9920;$$

$$2(\theta_1 - \phi) \qquad\qquad = 51°.3 \text{ or } 308°.7,$$
$$2(\theta_1 - \phi + 60°) \quad = 69°.3 \text{ or } 290°.7,$$
$$2(\theta_1 - \phi + 120°) = 172°.8 \text{ or } 187°.2.$$

Deduced $2(\theta_1-\phi)$	$w_i = \sin^2(\theta_1-\phi)$	$w_i(\theta_1-\phi)$
308°7............	0.6100	94°05
309.3............	0.8754	135.38
307.2............	0.0160	2.45
	$\Sigma w_i = 1.5014$	$\Sigma w_i(\theta_1-\phi) = 231.88$

Hence

$$\langle\,(\,\theta_1-\phi\,)\,\rangle = \frac{\Sigma w_i(\,\theta_1-\phi\,)}{\Sigma w_i} = 154°4\ .$$

From similar measures of HD 183143, of assumed position angle 179°0, we derived $\theta_1 = 33°9$. Hence, for 14 Cep, $\phi = -120°5$. In accordance with the convention that the plane of vibration is identified by a positive position angle less than 180°0, we finally have

$$p = 0^{m}0355, \qquad \phi = +59°5\ .$$

§ 4. SOURCES OF ERROR

4.1. ACCIDENTAL ERRORS

The standard deviation of $\bar{\psi}$ and hence of $2\bar{\phi}$ is

$$\sigma = \frac{[\Sigma(\psi_i-\psi)^2 \sin^2\psi_i]^{1/2}}{\Sigma \sin^2\psi_i}\ . \tag{14}$$

The accidental errors in f may be obtained by further analysis of the solutions. However, for most purposes, we may use the approximate expression

$$dp_0 = \frac{df}{2}, \qquad d\bar{\phi} = \frac{df}{4\,p_0}(\text{radians})\ . \tag{15}$$

The latter expression indicates how, for values of p_0 near the lower limit of detection, the value of ϕ becomes quite untrustworthy. The value of this lower limit is, of course, dependent on the brightness of the star, the telescope aperture, and the cell sensitivity, as well as on the amount of polarization. A particular characteristic of the difference-amplifier arrangement is the elimination of scintillation noise. This compensation ceases to be significant at low light-levels, when the shot noise in the cells predominates, and hence the random errors increase rather rapidly at the onset of shot noise. Even with fairly bright stars, shot noise may predominate with narrow-band filters or in unfavorable spectral regions.

4.2. SYSTEMATIC ERRORS

The main sources of systematic error, in order of increasing importance, are due to imperfections in the depolarizer, alignment errors, and instrumental polarization in the telescope. Errors in the Lyot-type depolarizers have been analyzed by Billings (1951). He shows that the fractional depolarization failure may be represented by

$$\frac{dp}{p} = \frac{5}{3}\frac{dx}{x},$$

(16)

where dx is the linear error in thickness of a compensator where the thinner plate has a thickness x. In a well-made depolarizer, this source of error should be negligible. Billings also showed experimentally that the alignment of the axes of the two depolarizer plates at 45° was very important, a misalignment of 5° introducing a 30 per cent depolarization failure. This can also be predicted analytically from an expansion of Lyot's analysis (Lyot 1929). In the presence of a small alignment error, ϵ, the ratio of beam intensities will be a function of the direction of the polarization of the incident beam. Maximum failure results in a ratio of beam intensities given by

$$r = \frac{1 + \sin 2\epsilon}{1 - \sin 2\epsilon}.$$

(17)

Finally, the depolarizing action depends on the band width of the incident light. We have found it possible to use quartz depolarizers with interference filters of 200 A band width, but in this case a depolarization failure varying from 1 to 1.5 per cent between 4000 and 6000 A is already present, and for this a correction must be made. It is probable that calcite depolarizers can be used successfully with considerably narrower band passes, but it is important that their efficiency be carefully studied. Billings (1951) has considered the question of strictly monochromatic depolarizers.

4.3. ALIGNMENT ERRORS

The double-channel type of polarimeter requires careful alignment, to bring the optical axis of the telescope into coincidence with the axis of rotation of the polarimeter. If this is not achieved, the center of the images of the telescope aperture will describe a small circle on each photocathode as the polarimeter head is rotated, and, on account of the differing sensitivity of different areas of the photocathodes, the balance will be lost in a way that is also a function of wave length, and the base-line measurement will become inapplicable. This variation is accentuated by the fact that the image on the photocell contains a central hole corresponding to the shadow of the Cassegrain mirror. This unfortunately blocks out what may often be the most uniform area of the photocathode. Perfect alignment is by no means easy to achieve. While it is desirable to have precise control of this adjustment, it is even more important that the rather heavy photometer head should be free from flexure, so that the adjustment remains permanent. However, when a fair alignment is achieved, the errors arising from misalignment are fairly small and tend to be eliminated by the procedure of measuring through 360°.

An instrumental effect which may be confused with alignment error may arise from the sensitivity of the anode current of some photomultipliers to the earth's magnetic field. For example, according to the published data for RCA 7102 tubes, the effect amounts to a decrease of the order of 1 per cent for a field of ±0.2 gauss parallel to the dynode-cage axis. The effect may be diminished by increasing the potential between the cathode and the first dynode and by magnetic shielding. The coaxial arrangement of the cells in the polarimeter at Yerkes Observatory (in addition to magnetic shields) tends to eliminate loss of balance due to this effect, leaving only small scale-errors, the effect of which is diminished by the process of measurement through 360°.

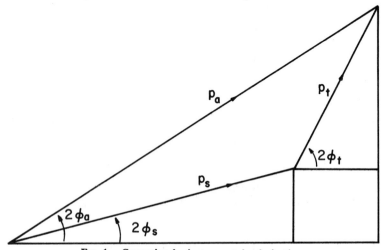

FIG. 1.—Correction for instrumental polarization

4.4. INSTRUMENTAL POLARIZATION

It will normally be adequate to assume that instrumental polarization is produced predominantly by variations in the reflection coefficients in and perpendicular to the planes of incidence of the rays on the telescope mirrors. It has been suggested that phase changes may also occur, producing a depolarizing effect. If this happens, it must usually be relatively small. The writer has investigated phase changes near normal incidence with a phase-change polarimeter, using badly tarnished front-surfaced aluminum mirrors, and finds no evidence of phase changes exceeding 5° in phase angle except in highly localized regions, where obvious major blemishes occur. On the other hand, instrumental plane polarization of the order of 0^m04 has been observed just prior to re-aluminizing (Behr 1960). If we restrict consideration to this latter effect, we may consider that the polarization effects in the starlight and the telescope are simply vectorially additive. Under these conditions, the telescope polarization may be determined by methods suggested in the preceding chapter. We denote the telescope polarization by $p_t \phi_t$; the true polarization of the starlight by $p_s \phi_s$, and the apparent polarization by $p_a \phi_a$. The relation between these quantities is shown in Figure 1, and from this we deduce

$$p_a \cos 2\phi_a = p_s \cos 2\phi_s + p_t \cos 2\phi_t,$$

$$p_a \sin 2\phi_a = p_s \sin 2\phi_s + p_t \sin 2\phi_t.$$

Hence

$$\tan 2\phi_s = \frac{p_a \sin 2\phi_a - p_t \sin 2\phi_t}{p_a \cos 2\phi_a - p_t \cos 2\phi_t}, \tag{18}$$

$$p_s^2 = (p_a \cos 2\phi_a - p_t \cos 2\phi_t)^2 + (p_a \sin 2\phi_a - p_t \sin 2\phi_t)^2. \tag{19}$$

To derive the appropriate value of ϕ_s from $\tan \phi_s$, the geometry of the vector diagram must be consulted.

The most insidious feature of the error due to instrumental polarization is that it distorts position angles of stars with polarization of the same order of magnitude in a way that is a complicated function of their true polarization and position angle so as, for example, completely to mask the presence of aligned polarization in a cluster. In a recently aluminized Cassegrain mirror system, the effect may amount to less than 0^m001. It is liable to have a wave-length dependence, which may affect measures in stars of different color temperatures or measures of variable stars and may predominate in measurements of wavelength dependence of interstellar polarization.

A comprehensive study of the errors associated with polarization measurements by the differential method will be found in an important paper by Behr (1956), and reference should be made to this for a more extensive treatment of some of the topics of this chapter.

The preparation of this chapter has been supported by the United States Air Force with contract No. AF 19(604)-4955.

REFERENCES

BEHR, ALFRED	1956	*Göttingen Obs. Pub.*, No. 114.
	1960	*Lowell Obs. Bull.*, **4**, No. 105, 292.
BILLINGS, B. H.	1951	*J. Opt. Soc. America*, **41**, 966.
HALL, J. S.	1958	*Pub. U.S. Naval Obs.*, **17**, Part 6, 275.
HALL, JOHN S., and		
HOAG, ARTHUR A.	1958	*The Present and Future of the Telescope of Moderate Size*, ed. F. B. WOOD (Philadelphia: University of Pennsylvania Press), p. 87.
LYOT, B.	1929	*Ann. Obs. astr. phys. de Paris* (Meudon), **8**, 102 (Fasc. 1–2).

CHAPTER 12

Instrumentation for Infrared Astrophysics

JOHN STRONG AND FREDERIC R. STAUFFER

The Johns Hopkins University

§ 1. INTRODUCTION

THIS chapter is concerned with applications of modern infrared detectors to astrophysical problems, especially to problems opened up by balloon and satellite astronomical observing stations. Observations from a balloon or satellite station are important to astrophysics on three counts: they are free from the major part of infrared absorption by atmospheric water vapor and carbon dioxide; the angular resolving power with a telescope is not limited by atmospheric seeing but rather by diffraction or by aberration; and daylight observation of stars and planets is possible because of freedom from sky radiations, particularly in the red and infrared. This last feature affords the possibility of using the sun as a sighting reference point in the sky for acquisition and rough tracking.

Freedom from infrared absorption permits determination of the amounts of water vapor and carbon dioxide in planetary atmospheres by the radiations they reflect to us. Also, infrared solar and stellar emission spectra may be studied, such as will define both the over-all envelope of emission, as it is influenced by hydrogen absorption, etc., and details of spectra due to absorption by molecules and atoms.

Use of a balloon gondola as a vehicle for high-altitude infrared astrophysical observations contrasts interestingly with the recent successful use of rocket vehicles for ultraviolet observations. Infrared detectors are sluggish in contrast with the detectors that can be used in rocket observations to measure actinic ultraviolet radiations. The balloon gondola is therefore peculiarly adapted to infrared observations because it can remain at peak altitude for a long time. Also the altitudes obtainable by means of a balloon gondola are sufficient to transcend substantially all the infrared atmospheric absorption, while the superior altitude of rockets is necessary to transcend ultraviolet atmospheric absorption.

Telescopes that can be carried aloft by balloons will have smaller apertures than the largest at surface observatories. The attendant inferiority of light-gathering power is not so serious a limitation as it might seem; this is because modern infrared detectors are two orders of magnitude more sensitive than the thermopiles that were formerly used to measure the infrared spectra of stars. Not only are balloon telescopes attractive because they can measure the envelope of stellar emission in regions in which our atmosphere is opaque; but they can also determine emissions in spectral regions where the atmosphere is partially opaque without the uncertainties of extrapolation. Table 1 shows the esti-

TABLE 1

SIGNAL-TO-NOISE RATIO FOR BRIGHT STARS

Star and Type	Bolometric Magnitude	Approx. Temp. (° K)	Star Const. (watt/cm²)	Signal-to-Noise Ratio for 10^{-11}-Watt ENI and 500-Cm² Equiv. Area for 1.0 Total Radiation
Betelgeuse M0	−1.38	3000	5.4×10^{-12}	27
Antares M0	−1.07	3000	4.1	20
Aldebaran K5	−1.00	4400	3.8	19
Arcturus K0	−0.96	5000	1.5	7
Capella G0	+0.14	6000	1.3	6
Vega A0	+0.14	11000	4.2	21
Sirius A0	−1.6	11000	6.6	33

mated emission of several of the brighter stars. The expected available signal-to-noise ratio for detector response to one-tenth of the total emission is indicated in that table. Spectral bands that decimate the total flux are shown in Figure 1.

Figure 2 shows a balloon observatory—a telescope and spectrometer mounted in a balloon gondola. Figure 3 shows the optical system of the spectrometer. This telescope and spectrometer and the optical principles involved are described below. Figure 4 illustrates a procedure using multiple narrow slits in our spectrometer. This procedure is advantageous when band absorption is being used for chemical analysis of planetary atmospheres. It was suggested by W. S. Benedict (1958) to enhance the signal-to-noise values for the weak reflected radiations from Mars. Fourteen slits were arranged to correspond to the fourteen strongest lines or groups of lines in the 1.13-μ water-vapor band. These fourteen lines were scanned back and forth together, each across its assigned absorption line. The variation in aggregate response indicates penetrated water vapor with a tenfold signal-to-noise advantage over the use of a single slit and with very little sacrifice of water-vapor sensitivity, corresponding to a resolving power of 1–2 cm⁻¹. Figure 4 shows the band as resolved by scanning a single slit of our spectrometer across it, and the location of the fourteen slits as determined by scanning them across the 1.129-μ emission mercury line. The response of our spectrometer to the radiation from Mars, when these fourteen lines were located in the spectrum at wave lengths adjacent to the 1.13-μ band, was characterized by a signal-to-noise ratio between 5 and 10. This response was obtained with the radiation collected by our 16-inch balloon telescope stopped to 12-inch aperture. The detector here was a chilled

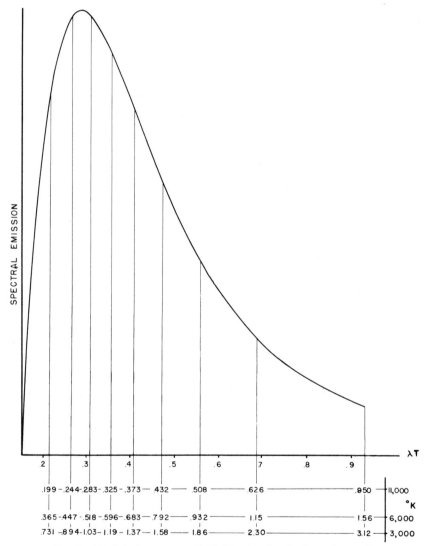

Fɪɢ. 1.—Black-body spectrum divided into ten bands of equal strength

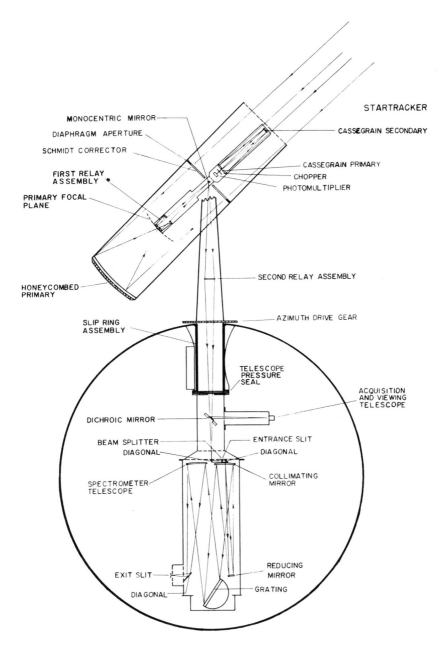

STARTRACKER

MONOCENTRIC MIRROR

DIAPHRAGM APERTURE

SCHMIDT CORRECTOR

FIRST RELAY ASSEMBLY

PRIMARY FOCAL PLANE

HONEYCOMBED PRIMARY

CASSEGRAIN SECONDARY

CASSEGRAIN PRIMARY

CHOPPER

PHOTOMULTIPLIER

SECOND RELAY ASSEMBLY

SLIP RING ASSEMBLY

AZIMUTH DRIVE GEAR

TELESCOPE PRESSURE SEAL

ACQUISITION AND VIEWING TELESCOPE

DICHROIC MIRROR

BEAM SPLITTER

DIAGONAL

ENTRANCE SLIT

DIAGONAL

SPECTROMETER TELESCOPE

COLLIMATING MIRROR

EXIT SLIT

REDUCING MIRROR

DIAGONAL

GRATING

FIG. 2.—Telescope and spectrometer

(dry-ice) S-1 photomultiplier tube. Unfortunately, the balloon flight to carry this spectrometer to high altitude above the absorption by water vapor in our atmosphere, in order to determine the amount of water vapor in the atmosphere of the planet Mars, scheduled for November, 1958, was not made.[1]

[1] The balloon observatory was successfully launched November 28, 1959, with the result that water vapor in the atmosphere of Venus, above her reflecting cloud layer, was detected. The measurements are to be repeated, in several unmanned flights in 1962, to confirm this result and measure the dependence of water vapor absorption on phase, near dichotomy.

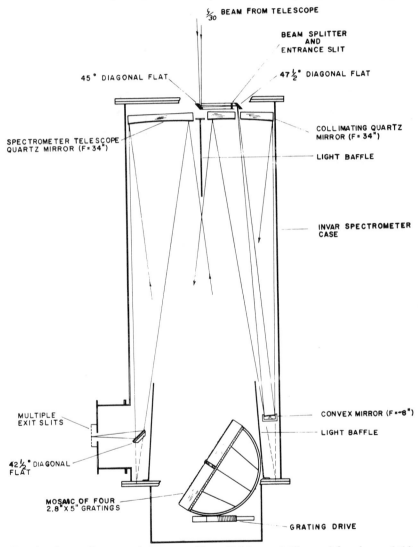

FIG. 3.—Czerny-Turner optical system. *Note added in proof:* The resolving power of this spectrometer has been improved by almost an order of magnitude with a corrector lens in the entrance beam. It will be described in a forthcoming publication.

The manned Johns Hopkins balloon observatory and its spectrometer are shown diagrammatically in Figure 2. The telescope is of the Schmidt type, with a primary mirror of 16-inch diameter. This mirror is stopped by the usual corrector plate of 12-inch aperture.

The telescope is adapted to mount on a relatively light balloon gondola. It is suited for this use because it gives a stable image of the light collected from an astronomical object by the heavy (16-inch) mirror. The problem of precise aiming of a heavy telescope tube with its heavy spherical mirror and corrector plate, when mounted on a relatively light gondola, as in the present instance, is a severe one. Here we trade this problem for an easier problem, namely, that of aiming a low-moment-of-inertia telescope component that carries a relay optical system. Then the aiming of the heavy telescope tube at an astronomical

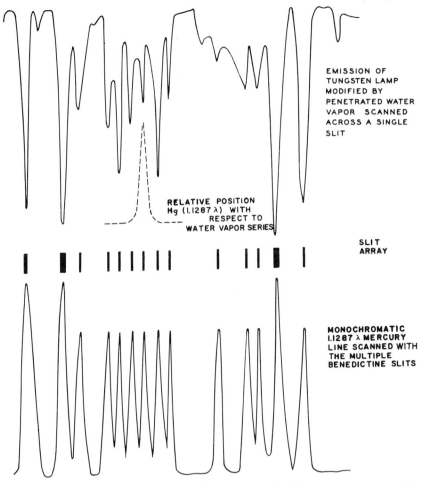

EMISSION OF
TUNGSTEN LAMP
MODIFIED BY
PENETRATED WATER
VAPOR SCANNED
ACROSS A SINGLE
SLIT

RELATIVE POSITION
Hg (1.1287 λ) WITH
RESPECT TO
WATER VAPOR SERIES

SLIT
ARRAY

MONOCHROMATIC
1.1287 λ MERCURY
LINE SCANNED WITH
THE MULTIPLE
BENEDICTINE SLITS

FIG. 4.—Scan over the water spectrum with a single exit slit (*above*), and scan over a single mercury line with multiple exit slits (*below*).

object, say the planet Mars, becomes easy; it is only required to aim the heavy tube to within a few degrees. This low aiming requirement arises because the low-moment-of-inertia component carrying the relay optical system can stabilize the image of Mars to a precision of a few seconds of arc.

The heavy telescope is mounted with its altitude and azimuth axes passing through the center of curvature of its spherical mirror. The low-moment-of-inertia, servo-controlled optical system relays the collected radiations to that center, called the "monocenter," to form an image of an astronomical object there. This relay system transforms the aperture $f/1.5$ of the primary mirror to $f/20$ at the monocenter. In our system an auxiliary mirror located at the mono-center directs the radiations focused there to a second relay system, which transforms the aperture from $f/20$ to $f/30$. This second relay system focuses the relayed radiations on the entrance slit of the spectrometer with an over-all magnification of 20.

The light-relay system is precisely controlled by means of a star tracker. For acquisition, this relay system must be aimed toward the object studied, such as Venus, Mars, or one of the brighter stars, to within $\frac{1}{2}°$. Then, as long as the heavy main alt-azimuth mounted component is directed toward the desired object to within $\pm 3°$, the star tracker will control the light-relay system so as to yield a stable image (to a few seconds of arc). In the rough tracking to $\pm 3°$, the star tracker requires a tracking-rate demand not in excess of $0°.1/\text{sec}$.

Astronomy of the stars and planets can be made a daytime profession by taking advantage of the darkness of the daytime sky at 80,000 feet, or higher. Here we use the sun, now available, as a sighting reference. Once acquired, with the help of the sun, an astronomical object can be tracked by the relay system, servo-controlled, while the sun is further used for rough tracking the main telescope—all in daytime. Here the photocell in the star tracker servomechanism may be controlled by light from the tracked object, passed through a red filter in order further to suppress the background sky. The arrangement that we have developed to use the sun as the object of acquisition and for rough tracking is composed of a small acquisition telescope attached parallel to the axis of the main component. This acquisition telescope is rotated about its optical axis by clockwork (at a rate appropriate to the occasion), and in front of its objective an attachment deviates the line of sight by a bias angle that is equal to the great-circle angle from sun to desired object (which will be substantially constant for Venus during observation). The clock-controlled roll angle, and also the bias angle can be trimmed during flight to correct for variations of latitude and local time due to the travel of the balloon (and for relative changes of hour angle or declination during that same time, if these are significant). Thus the problem of acquisition and rough tracking of a daytime planet or star is traded for an easier problem—that of acquisition and rough tracking of the sun. The acquisition and tracking may be effected either manually from a manned balloon observatory or automatically from an unmanned balloon observatory.

§ 2. ENERGY-LIMITED SPECTRAL RESOLVING POWER

In astrophysics the limitation set by the small angular diameter of astronomical objects is usually severe. When the entrance slit of a spectroscopic instrument is narrower than the astronomical images that are formed on it (see chap. 2), collected energy is wasted. Avoidance of this loss by making the slit wider is achieved at the expense of spectral resolution unless a longer focal-length collimator with larger prism or grating is used.

In contrast, the effective entrance aperture of a Fabry-Perot interferometer-type spectrometer, because its dispersion can exceed that of a grating, can be large enough to use all the collected radiations simultaneously. However, a compensating inefficiency in the Fabry-Perot spectrometer arises because it wastes time as the astronomical body is scanned along the length of the wide slit of an auxiliary spectrograph, such as is necessary to separate the different free spectral ranges of the interferometer.

Neither waste is encountered in the case of some new interferometric methods of astronomical spectroscopy that are now being developed (Strong and Vanasse 1958, 1959, 1960; Vanasse, Strong, and Loewenstein 1959; Loewenstein 1960, 1961). These new methods divide the light from an astronomical object into two beams which are recombined on the detector; and the detector response is recorded as the phase difference between the coherent light in these two beams is increased. The record of detector response versus phase difference is called an "interferogram." The desired spectrum is then determined by means of a Fourier transform of the interferogram. These new techniques, now in development, can only be mentioned here. Below we contrast the energy limitation of spectroscopic resolving power in the laboratory with that in the observatory.

Resolving power is said to be energy-limited when it is not limited by diffraction or aberration but rather by an inadequate flux of energy or by a too insensitive detector. This limitation exists when the entrance and exit slits cannot be set narrow enough to enjoy the resolving power that diffraction, or freedom from aberration, would afford, but when the slits must be kept wide because light-sources are not bright enough or because detectors are not sufficiently sensitive. It is presumed, in the laboratory, that the entrance slit can be illuminated, no matter how wide it may be. To evaluate the limitation when the slit can be filled, let us calculate the energy that is available at the detector of a prism or grating spectrometer.

For simplicity (Strong 1958) we consider the focal lengths of the collimator and telescope as being equal. We let S represent the useful projected area of the grating or prism with its over-all transmission factor T, including the blaze of the grating or the transmission of the prism; s represents the area of the entrance slit and also the area of an equal exit slit. We calculate the flux emergent from this exit slit when the entrance slit is filled with light from a source of spectral brightness, B_λ. If B_λ is expressed in watts per unit area per steradian of solid angle per unit spectral band pass, then the emergent flux available to the detector can be expressed simply as follows:

$$F = B_\lambda \frac{S}{f^2} sT\Delta\lambda \text{ watts}.$$

In order to calculate the spectral bands pass, $\Delta\lambda$, when it is determined by the exit and entrance slit widths, e and x, and by the dispersion of the instrument, rather than by diffraction or aberration, we introduce a symbol to represent the ratio of the slit length l to the focal length f, called the "L-number" ($L = l/f$). If x represents the slit width, then

$$\Delta\lambda = \frac{d\lambda}{da}\left(\Delta a = \frac{x}{f}\right), \qquad s = l \cdot x = Lf\left(f\frac{da}{d\lambda}\Delta\lambda\right).$$

And when the minimum operable flux on the detector is F^*, by eliminating the slit area s and solving for $\Delta\lambda$, we get

$$\Delta\lambda = \sqrt{\left[\frac{F^*}{B_\lambda L(da/d\lambda)ST}\right]}.$$

Although this is an oversimplified equation, it is very useful for designing balanced laboratory equipment, say to determine absorption spectra. It tells us that, to make $\Delta\lambda$ small, we should use large dispersion; we should choose a sensitive detector (with F^* small); we should choose as bright a source as possible (making B_λ large); we should choose an optical arrangement that can use a long slit (making L large); we should choose a large prism or grating and large mirrors or lenses (to make S large); and, finally, T should be as great as possible. Because the dispersion $(da/d\lambda)$ for a conventional grating is some tenfold greater than for a conventional prism (except in the case of a quartz prism worked in the ultraviolet), we would expect the resolving power of a grating spectrometer under energy-limited conditions to be about threefold better than that of a prism. In the laboratory we use a carbon arc to get large B_λ. We obtain a large L by the use of the Ebert-type optical arrangement (Fastie 1952, 1953). Large gratings are made possible by thermal evaporation. And T is improved by proper blazing of the grating grooves.

When we extend our considerations to the observatory, we see that the situation is different—it is seldom possible to fill the entrance slit of a spectrometer with the image of an astrophysical source (except in the case of the sun and moon).

In Figure 5 we show a spectrometer at a and telescope of focal length f_0 at b, both diagrammatically. As shown at c, let δ be the angular diameter of a circle that circumscribes all the radiation collected in the image of an astronomical body on the entrance slit of a spectrometer. If the ratio of the entrance slit width e (of a conventional spectrometer representing a spectral band pass $\Delta\lambda$), to angular diameter of our circle is

$$\rho = \frac{e}{f_0\delta},$$

this ratio determines the fraction ϵ of the collected light which the spectrometer uses. This fraction ϵ, for a uniformly illuminated image, is expressed by

$$\epsilon = \frac{2\psi + \sin 2\psi}{\pi} \qquad \text{where} \qquad \psi = \sin^{-1} \rho \ .$$

If the focal length of the collimator optics and the telescope optics of our spectrometer are unequal—say represented by f_c and f_t—then they each subtend the band pass $\Delta\lambda$, when

$$\Delta\lambda = \frac{e}{f_c(da/d\lambda)} = \frac{x}{f_t(d\beta/d\lambda)} \ .$$

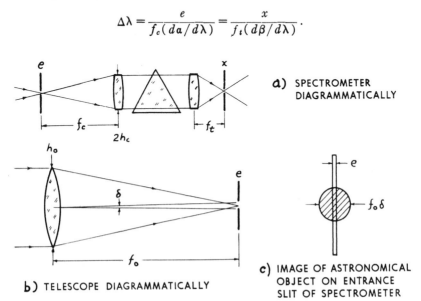

a) SPECTROMETER DIAGRAMMATICALLY

b) TELESCOPE DIAGRAMMATICALLY

c) IMAGE OF ASTRONOMICAL OBJECT ON ENTRANCE SLIT OF SPECTROMETER

Fig. 5.—Symbols involved in matching a spectrometer and a telescope

Here $(da/d\lambda)$ and $(d\beta/d\lambda)$, the angular dispersions of the spectrometer, are obtained by partial differentiation of,

$$k\lambda = a(\sin \alpha + \sin \beta) \ .$$

From these derivatives we may express the relationship between $\Delta\lambda$ and ρ as follows:

$$\rho = \frac{f_c}{f_0\delta}\left(\frac{da}{d\lambda}\right)\Delta\lambda = \frac{h_c}{h_0\delta}\left(\frac{da}{d\lambda}\right)\Delta\lambda \ ,$$

where h_c is the radius of the round-aperture collimator lens or mirror and h_0 is the radius of the round-aperture telescope primary.

If h_0 is fixed, in the expression above, in order to keep ρ fixed so that the fraction of the collected light that is used is maintained at an acceptable level, then we must have, from the above, $h_c(da/d\lambda)\Delta\lambda = $ constant. To reduce $\Delta\lambda$, it is apparent that a large grating or a mosaic of smaller gratings will be required or that a grating of greater dispersion will be required. But a small **grating** with a large dispersion can substitute for a large grating with a smaller dispersion only when the blazing of the small grating, worked at larger angles, is equally efficient.

The use of a spectrometer with a telescope is less than optimum if it does not accept and use all the radiation collected by the telescope. It is sometimes possible to rearrange the collected flux on the spectrometer slit by means of an image-slicer. The flux, naturally distributed over a circular area, is redistributed over a long, narrow, rectangular area that is sufficiently narrow to pass through a slit narrower than the original circular image diameter. Such redistribution of flux cannot, of course, be accomplished by means of a cylindrical lens, since it is a requirement of the Abbé sine relation, or of thermodynamics, that a dimension of an aberration-free image cannot be decreased without correspondingly increasing the solid angle of the cone of rays that produces it. However, thermodynamics does not forbid rearrangement of the flux in an equal area of different shape.

Our expressions tell us that the ratio f_c/f_0, not the actual values of f_c and f_0, is significant here. Accordingly, we may increase both these focal lengths until f_0 advantageously produces an enlarged image on a correspondingly widened entrance slit. Such an enlarged image is also advantageous if an image slicer is used because the correspondingly larger slicer will be easier to construct and adjust.

It must not be overlooked that diffraction may play a role in determining the over-all transmission, T, of an astrophysical spectrograph, as has been described by Moore (1904). Diffraction enters and produces a loss of light when the entrance slit produces a diffraction pattern that is not completely circumscribed by the rim of the collimator mirror, or when

$$\frac{\lambda}{e} \leq \frac{h_c}{f_c}.$$

If we write $f_c(da/d\lambda)\Delta\lambda$ for e, we get a more understandable condition on this energy limitation of the resolving power. When this condition is not met, we get a loss of efficiency due to the diffraction of radiation outside the edge of the spectrometer collimator. This energy limitation yields a resolving power limit:

$$R_e = \frac{\lambda}{\Delta\lambda} < h_c \left(\frac{da}{d\lambda}\right).$$

This limitation and the diffraction-limited resolving power, arising from the requirement to keep the radiation diffraction by the aperture edge of the spectrometer telescope between the slit jaws, are substantially equivalent. If $e = x$ and $(da/d\lambda) = (d\beta/d\lambda)$, then the ordinary diffraction-limited resolving power is also the same:

$$R_d = \frac{\lambda}{\Delta\lambda} = \frac{\lambda}{(\lambda/h_c)/(da/d\lambda)} = h_c \left(\frac{da}{d\lambda}\right).$$

These equations show us, for example, that double-passing a grating, or going to a higher order, or otherwise increasing the effective angular dispersion will mitigate the limitation on both R_e and R_d. On the other hand, increasing the diameter of a grating, by making a mosaic of component gratings that are not phased together, will mitigate only the limitation on R_e.

In contrast with the laboratory, where the merit of a grating or prism spectrometer is determined by the product of efficiency and dispersion, in the observatory it is not necessary that the dispersion be greater than that required to make $\rho = 1.0$.

These simple considerations show the significant parameters and their interrelationship—particularizing elaborations are obvious. We shall illustrate the application of these parameters to one particular astronomical design problem—that of a spectrometer suited for use above the earth's infrared absorbing atmosphere in a balloon gondola.

§ 3. APPLICATION OF DESIGN PARAMETERS

The diameter of the magnified image of Mars at the entrance slit of the spectrometer was 0.9 mm in November, 1958. In the beginning of our program to study Mars we had planned to have the entrance slit 0.3 mm wide; and, in order not to waste the collected light, we constructed an image-slicer to go in front of the entrance slit and dissect this 0.9-mm diameter image of Mars into three slices, each 0.3 mm wide. The pressure of time did not allow us to use the image-slicer; actually, the entrance slit was 0.6 mm wide, giving an efficiency of $\epsilon = 0.78$—that is, 78 per cent of the collected light focused in the stable image on the entrance slit was passed by that slit. With this slit width, the focal length of the collimator and the grating dispersion yielded a resolving power between 1 and 2 waves per centimeter. The effective focal length of the collimator was 14 feet. It was a two-mirror Cassegrain-type collimator yielding an $f/30$ beam of radiation of 5.6 inches in cross-section. This collimated radiation fell on a mosaic of four unphased diffraction gratings (7500 lines per inch) whose projected area was a square 5.6 inches on a side. The dispersed beams emerging from the mosaic were imaged on an exit-slit plane by a telescope of $f/6$ aperture, thus giving monochromatic images of the entrance slit reduced fivefold. The radiations were incident and reflected at the mosaic at an angle of $7°$ to the axis of symmetry of the spectrometer. The aberration arising from this angle off-axis swelled the monochromatic images of the entrance slit to 0.08 mm—contrasted with 0.12 mm, the geometrical size of our 0.6-mm entrance slit when reduced fivefold.

We used multiple slits—14 exit slits in the exit-slit plane. These slits extended over about 10 mm of spectrum. A field lens behind them converged the radiations they passed onto a condenser lens, and thence onto the 3-mm sensitive area of the detector photocathode, with a final $f/2$ aperture.

To summarize, we used a 12-inch-aperture Schmidt telescope, in order to collect sufficient flux from the radiations of Mars. The image of this $f/1.5$ telescope was magnified twenty fold, in order to make the entrance slit wide and to facilitate the use of an image-slicer there. The $f/30$ beam emerging through the entrance slit required a collimator of sufficiently great effective focal length to give the desired spectral resolution. The $f/30$ beam and this focal length yielded a beam diameter requiring a mosaic of four diffraction gratings, with a projected square area 5.6 inches on a side, in order to accept all the monochromatic radiation in the $f/30$ beam. After changing the aperture ratio from $f/1.5$ to $f/30$ for illumination of the mosaic, it was again transformed to a high aperture beam ($f/2$), in order to be contained by the small area of the detector.

§ 4. INFRARED DETECTORS—GENERAL

A discussion of infrared detectors implies an eventual comparison among them. Although no completely satisfactory standard of comparison exists because of differences in the method of operation of the detectors and in the nature of the task to be performed by them, certain concepts descriptive of both spectral and time responses, when properly evaluated with due regard for electronic and mechanical considerations, do lend themselves reasonably well to the problem of detector comparison and evaluation.

The term *responsivity* carries the meaning of detector output for unit radiation signal input. Ordinarily, responsivity is expressed in the units output voltage per watt of input radiation. Responsivity does not take into account the electronic or physical parameters of the cell. Since detector noise is not considered, responsivity alone does not allow determination of the minimum detectable signal capability.

Noise equivalent power (NEP) provides a measure of the minimum detectable signal capability. It is the incident power required to provide a root-mean-square (r.m.s.) voltage output equal to the r.m.s. cell noise voltage or a signal-to-noise ratio of unity. In considering detector noise it is necessary to specify the chopping frequency and electronic band width, since the noise is dependent on these parameters. Furthermore, the chopping frequency is usually chosen so that the detector's time constant does not limit the response to the impressed signal. The time constant is defined as the time required for the detector to rise to within $1 - 1/e$ of steady-state response after illumination or fall to within $1/e$ of steady-state response after termination of illumination. In much of the engineering literature, the details of the dependence of responsivity on wave length is ignored—NEP is conventionally measured in engineering with the total emission from a 500° K black-body source. The NEP thus determined is known as the "black-body NEP."

Detectivity (D) is defined as the reciprocal of NEP, or the quotient of responsivity divided by the r.m.s. noise voltage output of the cell, and is inversely proportional to the square root of the cell area for area-effect detectors. While it is implied that detectivity may thus be increased by decreasing detector area, the shape of the detector surface is important—a very long and narrow surface is not always equivalent to a square one of the same area.

The term D^* is defined as

$$D^* = \frac{\sqrt{\text{Area}}}{NEP} = D\sqrt{\text{Area}} .$$

In cases where the detectivity D is proportional to the inverse square root of cell area, D^* is independent of area. The curves shown in Figure 6 are plotted in terms of D^* and wave length.

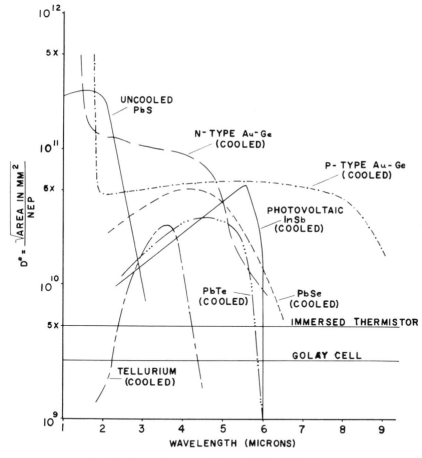

Fig. 6.—Spectral response of several infrared detectors

§ 5. DETECTOR CLASSIFICATION

A natural classification of infrared radiation detectors divides them into three categories according to the mechanism of operation—thermal, photoconductive, and photovoltaic physical processes.

Thermal detectors are characterized by (1) non-selective wave-length response, (2) relatively long time constant, (3) significantly lower sensitivity than many photoconductors in the near infrared, and (4) freedom from cooling requirements.

The photoconductive element is a poor electrical conductor whose electrical resistance decreases on illumination with infrared radiation. Cell resistances vary from 10^5 to 10^8 ohms for the different photoconductive materials. Some photoconductors show sensitivity at room temperature, but in all cases maximum sensitivity is obtained at reduced temperatures. The inconvenience of cooling is more than compensated for by the resulting superior sensitivities and extended spectral response.

Photoconductive detectors are characterized by (1) spectrally selective response, (2) short time constants, (3) very high sensitivity, and (4) coolant usually required to yield desired sensitivity and time constant. Photoconductors developed recently have significantly extended the region of spectral response; and, in the future, photoconductors useful in the infrared to perhaps 100 μ may be expected.

The photovoltaic elements develop a voltage difference across their terminals upon illumination with infrared radiation. They are generally inferior to photoconductor elements. In some cases this is because of a basic inferiority. In others it is because of lack of development. The photovoltaic effect in indium antimonide has been rather thoroughly investigated, and photovoltaic indium antimonide cells are currently available. Photovoltaic sensors are characterized by (1) spectral response similar to that of photoconductive sensors, (2) short time constant, (3) moderately good sensitivity, (4) increase in sensitivity and cell resistance with reduction in temperature, (5) low impedance, and (6) low noise level.

§ 6. NOISE

All radiation detectors are ultimately limited in minimum detectable power and minimum detectable change in power by noise inherent in the detector itself. A thorough treatment of detector noise has been given by Jones (1953). The following résumé epitomizes the role that electrical noise plays in infrared spectroscopy.

Internal-thermal or Johnson noise (Johnson 1928) depends on electrical resistance, absolute temperature, and the band width of the electrical detection circuitry in the manner given by the Nyquist formula:

$$N = \sqrt{(4 kTR\Delta f)}.$$

Here k = Boltzmann's constant, T = absolute temperature, R = electrical resistance, and Δf = band width. Johnson noise is the limiting noise for thermal detectors (excluding the Golay cell). It is usually not advantageous to work at low temperatures to decrease Johnson noise in thermal detectors because of increased detector time constant.

Shot noise results from the particle nature of electricity. As with Johnson noise, it depends on the band width of the electrical detection circuitry. It also depends on the average current through the detector. This noise was first treated by Schottky (1918) and is expressed analytically by Schottky's formula, as follows:

$$\langle i_f^2 \rangle = 2\, ei_0\Delta f \ .$$

Here $\langle i_f^2 \rangle$ = mean-square value of fluctuating current through the detector, e = charge on the electron, i_0 = average current through the detector, and Δf = band width.

The Nyquist formula for Johnson noise shows it to be independent of frequency; this noise is present when no impressed current is flowing through a detector element. An extra frequency-dependent noise often becomes important with semiconductor detectors, particularly at low frequencies. This current noise is characterized at low frequencies by a noise power per unit band width approximately inversely proportional to the modulation frequency of the radiation signal. The current noise is accordingly sometimes referred to as "$1/f$ noise." Among infrared photoconductive detectors, current noise frequently sets a low-frequency working limit.

Thermal fluctuations produce so-called temperature noise. This noise arises from the statistical nature of thermal equilibrium (Jones 1953). The equilibrium temperature of a detector fluctuates about a mean value because of the statistical interchange of energy between the detector and its surroundings. The mean-square value of this temperature fluctuation is

$$\langle \Delta T^2 \rangle = \frac{kT^2}{c},$$

where ΔT = detector temperature fluctuation from its mean temperature, k = Boltzmann's constant, T = absolute temperature of detector and surround, and c = heat capacity of the detector.

§ 7. COOLING

Thermal detectors are usually not cooled, and some of the photoconductors, notably lead sulfide, may be operated cooled or uncooled. Lead sulfide, if cooled, is usually operated at dry-ice temperature. Additional cooling to liquid nitrogen, although more inconvenient, yields increased sensitivity, but with attendant disadvantages of longer time constant and higher cell impedance.

Coolant is required for most other photoconductors. They should be cooled to at least the temperature of liquid nitrogen. Lead selenide and lead telluride cells require temperatures in this region, and gold-doped germanium cells must be worked at 90° K or even lower if good sensitivity is to be achieved. The time constants of all these cells at liquid nitrogen temperature are quite small. In the case of gold-doped germanium the time constant for impurity response is of the order of 0.2 microsecond. Cooling below 90° K increases sensitivity still further in tellurium and gold-doped germanium photoconductive cells. Zinc-doped germanium requires liquid neon as a coolant.

Several manufacturers have made closed-loop cooling systems available. These utilize the Joule-Thomson effect as the basis for operation. The problems encountered with these liquid coolant systems include inadequate drying for the nitrogen gas and contamination by oil in the pumping process. These problems are being, and to some extent have been, solved. However, an open system in which a reservoir of liquid coolant is provided, with provision for proper feeding, is currently most satisfactory. The use of dry ice (usually powdered) is limited to the lead sulfide detectors. New types of cooling systems, based on the Peltier effect, are being developed. Such devices may find full use as supplemental subsystems in the near future.

Some cells, notably positive carrier (P-type) gold-doped germanium, show increased sensitivity at temperatures lower than that of liquid nitrogen. However, a condition may be reached where further temperature reduction is not profitable because photons from the detector's surround excite the sensitive element and provide a dominant noise that increases with decreasing temperature. If the sensitive element could be shielded from all such stray radiation from the surround, with the shield itself at or near the temperature of the sensing element, additional sensitivity would be gained.

As long as a detector housing and, more particularly, the detector window are cooled below ambient temperature, there is a very real danger of water-vapor condensation on the window. If adequate ventilation does not prevent such condensation, then heating of the window, although more complicated, can be resorted to.

Some detectors exhibit a marked degradation in operating characteristics after exposure to intense radiation. This phenomenon is called *blinding*. Such cell damage depends on the intensity and duration of the incident energy. Short of producing a permanent damage, the effect is generally followed by a slow recovery to near-initial conditions—complete return to original characteristics may require extremely long periods of time. This blinding may be controlled sometimes by spectral filtering. Automatically inserted shutters during the time of irradiation have also been successfully employed.

Among the photoconductors showing little or no blinding effects, indium antimonide and P-type gold-doped germanium are perhaps most notable. Although the germanium is susceptible to damage by gamma radiation, both immediate and long-term effects have not been clearly evaluated. There is indication of immediate recovery after removal of the gamma radiation.

§ 8. THERMAL DETECTORS

We now consider characteristics of the various infrared detectors. Yates's (1958) treatment is referred to for a detailed treatment of thermopiles. Here it will suffice to point out that the time constant of a thermocouple is long, of the order of 0.1 second, providing a major limitation to its use. Sensitivities are about 5×10^{-11} watt NEP for a 1-cycle band width. The resistance of thermocouples is of the order of ohms, or tens of ohms, so that impedance-matching transformers are necessary to match them to electronic amplifier inputs.

The thermistor bolometer is a strip of semiconductor with attached metallic electrodes. The semiconductor is a metallic oxide or sulfide ribbon characterized by a high rate of change of electrical resistance with temperature. The sensitive ribbons of this material may be suspended in air, gas, or vacuum; but in many modern applications they are attached to heat sinks. Those so attached are known as "backed thermistor bolometers." The unbacked thermistors are slow in response and tend to be fragile and susceptible to microphonic noise. The backed bolometers are much faster, more rugged, free from microphonics, relatively insensitive to shock and vibrations, and can withstand exposure to wide temperature ranges. Electrical impedances are such as to work into electronic amplifiers well without impedance-matching transformers. The spectral response of thermistors is flat except as it may be dominated by spectral characteristics of window or coating materials. Thermistors are used out to 40-μ wave length. Thermistor bolometer sensitivities as low as 4×10^{-11} watt NEP have been reproducibly made (DeWaard and Wormser 1958). Time constants of about 800 microseconds have been measured, although the fastest thermistors are not the most sensitive. DeWaard and Wormser report 6.4 millisecond time constant with 3.9×10^{-11} watt sensitivity for a 0.1×0.1-mm copper-backed thermistor, and an 800-microsecond time constant with 1.3×10^{-9} watt NEP for a 0.5×0.5-mm type E sapphire-backed element. The band width in both cases was 10 c/s. The limiting noise in thermistors is Johnson noise, with an additional small contribution of current noise.

Thermistor bolometers have the useful characteristic that they lend themselves easily to arbitrary detector configurations and sizes. Detector mosaics composed of 100 individual elements have been made, and patterns with an even larger number of component elements are reasonable. The requirement of uniformity of characteristics and spacing among all members of the mosaic has led to the new technique of printed linear arrays (DeWaard and Wormser 1958), with uniformity within each such assembly held to within a few per cent for all characteristics. Figure 7 shows one such bolometer array with 24 elements. Although the use of mosaics requires multichannel amplification, mosaics may be adaptable to astrophysical problems.

Optical immersion of a thermistor in a lens system of high index of refraction affords increased illumination by the factor N^4, where N is the index of refraction of the lens. Consequently, there is an N^2 gain because of the fact that a detector of smaller area may be used. Spectral selectivity arises because of the selectivity of the refractive element. Reflection losses due to high index of refraction may be minimized by antireflection coatings, although again spectral selectivity will result.

The characteristics of thermistor bolometers are summarized in Figure 6 and Table 2. A complete treatment of the subject has been prepared by DeWaard and Wormser (1958).

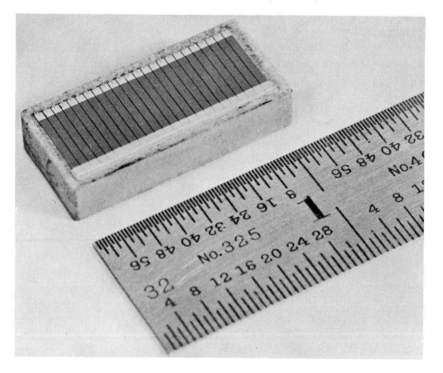

FIG. 7.—Twenty-four-element bolometer array. (Courtesy of Barnes Engineering, Stamford, Conn.)

The Golay cell (Zahl and Golay 1946; Golay 1947, 1949) is a pneumatic radiation detector. Its sensitivity is comparable to that of thermistor bolometers. Detection arises from absorption of radiation by a very thin membrane that seals one end of a gas-filled chamber. The change in temperature of the membrane produces a change in temperature of the gas in contact with it. This temperature change, in turn, results in a change in volume of the gas and its container to deflect a flexible membrane over a connected auxiliary chamber which acts as a flexible mirror. The membrane heating is measured by light that is reflected from the flexible mirror and focused on a photocell. The flexible-mirror membrane lies in a cavity protected by a glass window.

The transmission of the metallic absorbing film for the detected radiations is selected to be about 35 per cent. Although this represents less than 50 per cent absorption in a single pass through the membrane, it is compensated for by absorption of radiation on a second pass, when radiation is reflected by the back wall of the absorbing chamber. The advantage of this thin-film mechanism for absorption lies in its non-selective wave-length response—out to $\lambda = 1000\ \mu$.

The detectivity of the Golay cell is limited by temperature noise; in time response the detector is limited to about 10–50 milliseconds. It serves quite well for laboratory purposes at room temperatures, but it is less rugged under shock and vibration conditions than bolometers.

TABLE 2

INFRARED DETECTORS

Detector	Spectral Response (Microns)	Time Constant (Seconds)	$D^* = (Area)^{1/2}/NEP$ (Mm/Watt)	Approximate Detector Size Limits†
Thermocouple....	Non-selective	10^{-3}–10^{-2}	1×10^{10}	0.1–5 mm
Thermistor bolometer..........	Non-selective	8×10^{-4}–8×10^{-3}	7×10^9	0.1 mm–1 cm
Golay cell........	Non-selective	10^{-2}	Sensitivity about equivalent to bolometer	3.2-mm diam. standard
Lead sulfide (uncooled)........	1–3.5‡	10^{-4}–10^{-3}	3×10^{11}	0.2 mm–1 cm
Lead selenide.....	1–6†	2.5×10^{-5}–10^{-4}	6×10^{10}	0.2 mm–1 cm
Lead telluride....	1–5.5‡	5×10^{-6}–5×10^{-4}	4×10^{10}	0.2 mm–1 cm
Indium antimonide (photovoltaic)...........	1–5.5‡	10^{-6}	6×10^{10}	0.5–6 mm diam.
N-type gold-doped germanium.....	1–5‡	5×10^{-5}–10^{-3}	10^{10}	0.5–4 mm diam.
P-type gold-doped germanium.....	{1–1.8‡ {1.8–9	2×10^{-6} 2×10^{-7}	7×10^{11}} 7×10^{10}}	0.2 mm–1 cm
Tellurium........	2–4.5	10^{-4}	3.5×10^{10}	....

† Limits are set by practical considerations, such as matching, noise, cooling capabilities, etc.

‡ Response below 1 μ not considered.

§9. PHOTOCONDUCTIVE AND PHOTOVOLTAIC DETECTORS

Lead sulfide cells have been the most widely used photoconductors for infrared detection. These cells may be made either by chemical deposition or by vacuum evaporation of the sulfide onto an insulating (usually glass) substrate. They are the most sensitive photoconductors available for the 1–3.5 or 4-μ region, their peak sensitivity (when cooled) being unmatched by any photoconductor in any other spectral region.

At room temperature the NEP for lead sulfide cells is of the order of 10^{-12} watt at 90 c/s chopping speed, 3 c/s band width, and 1 mm² area. Time constants at room temperatures range from 100 to 1000 microseconds. Cooling increases the sensitivity. At liquid nitrogen temperatures, NEP's of 7.7×10^{-14} watt have been reported (Levy 1958). Also, cooling increases the long-wave-length response. However, the time constant at low temperatures increases with increased sensitivity. The fact that the product of time constant and sensitivity is nearly a constant was suggested in 1951 by E. D. McAlister (see Jones 1953).

The resistance of lead sulfide cells is of the order of 10^5–10^6 ohms at room temperatures, with increased resistance at reduced temperatures. Some resistance anomalies appear between liquid nitrogen (90° K) and dry-ice temperatures. The limiting noise for lead sulfide is current noise.

Lead telluride cells are responsive over the 1–6-μ region, with peak sensitivity about 4.5 μ. They are operated at a temperature of 90° K (liquid nitrogen). Under standard measuring conditions the NEP has a representative value of 3×10^{-11} watt, cell area normalized to 1 mm². Time constants range from 50 to 500 microseconds.

The resistance of lead telluride cells is substantially greater than for lead sulfide, so that the problem of impedance matching to a preamplifier becomes more difficult. Because of this high impedance, electrical leads from a lead telluride cell housing to the preamplifier should be as short as possible and provided with proper shielding, to avoid stray electrical pickup. Provisions for avoiding electrical leakage because of condensed water vapor are also important.

Lead telluride has been widely used for spectroscopic purposes. The sensitive surface can be arranged in various shapes and sizes to match the shape of the spectrometer output.

With the longer-wave-length response of lead telluride, it becomes necessary to consider spurious photoresponse to room-temperature radiation falling on the detector from its surround (as contrasted to thermal noise induced by radiation from the surround).

In recent years lead selenide cells have been extensively developed. The long-wave-length response has been extended slightly beyond the telluride region. When operated at 90° K, the sensitivity of a selenide cell is approximately that of lead telluride. The time constant for cooled cells ranges between 25 and 100 microseconds. Although cooled operation is generally preferred, lead selenide can be operated at room temperature, with a reduction in time constant, spectral response, and sensitivity.

Mosaics of lead selenide detector elements have been made quite successfully. The use of mosaics of any type requires due consideration to element matching. Additional cooling capacity is required with photoconductive mosaics.

The element tellurium, in single-crystal form, is one of the most recent photoconductive cells to join the family of infrared detectors. Investigation of single-crystal tellurium photoconductors was begun in 1957 by the Infrared Laboratory of the University of Michigan Research Institute (Suits and Rice 1958).

At liquid nitrogen temperature, the NEP of tellurium detectors is of the order of 10^{-10} watt. The peak NEP is about 10^{-11} watt at 3.5 μ, with an unusually sharp rise and fall on either side of the peak response (see Fig. 6). The resistance of typical tellurium cells falls within or near the 500–2000-ohm range. Present cells are current-noise-limited. The bias current can be adjusted, as with P-type gold-doped germanium, to assure detector-noise-limited operation. Sensitivity continues to increase with decreasing temperature, even below 90° K. Proper radiation shielding is necessary.

A peaked detector response, as tellurium manifests, that could be trimmed easily with filters to yield a narrow-band response, should yield an excellent detector for scanning star fields, say from a balloon or satellite station, to determine the relative magnitudes of stellar emission for narrow infrared bands.

As for indium antimonide, there are basically two kinds of cells: the junction-type photovoltaic detector, operated at liquid nitrogen temperature, and the photoelectromagnetic detector (PEM), with a capability of operating at room temperature and with a slightly extended spectral response. The latter exhibits less sensitivity by several orders of magnitude than does the junction type.

One outstanding feature of indium antimonide is the low impedance it offers. Cell resistance usually falls between 100 and 1000 ohms, as compared with the megohm or greater resistance for most photoconductive cells. The low impedance permits direct transformer coupling, and the severe pickup problems with high-impedance cells are avoided. Except for possible physical damage to the cell, intense radiation has no effect on indium antimonide cells.

The photovoltaic indium antimonide, referred to previously, has a rather slow and steady increase in sensitivity, with increasing wave length, to its peak response at 5.5 μ. At this point the NEP is about 10^{-10} watt for a sensitive surface area of 4 mm². The sensitivity drops very sharply after 5.5 μ, with several orders of magnitude less response at 6 μ. It is stable under small temperature fluctuations. Actual measurements of the time constant seem to be lacking, but the time constant is known to be less than 1 microsecond. It is current-noise-limited.

During 1957 and 1958 considerable progress has been made in the development of P-type gold-doped germanium. While reported characteristics vary considerably, the values used here are typical of the cells developed by the Westinghouse Research Laboratories. Gold-doped germanium (P-type) exhibits both an intrinsic and an impurity response. The intrinsic response drops very sharply at about 1.8 μ, with the impurity response continuing nearly uniform until about 8 μ, where a slow fall-off occurs. The useful spectral response region is generally considered to extend somewhat beyond 9 μ. The NEP in the impurity region under standard measuring conditions is about 2×10^{-11} watt for germanium element volumes of $0.2 \times 0.2 \times 1$ cm³. The NEP in the intrinsic region peaks at an order of magnitude smaller than that given for the impurity region. The intrinsic response has a time constant of 2 or 3 microseconds, while for the impurity response it is 0.2 microsecond.

The gold-doped germanium cells must be operated at least as cold as liquid nitrogen. These cells are insensitive at room temperatures. Sensitivity increases at reduced temperatures and is still increasing below 90° K. Increased sensitivity may be had by using the temperature of liquid neon. A constant temperature must be maintained, since temperature fluctuations cause significant changes in sensitivity. Proper shielding from surrounding radiation is important. Radiation shields, surrounding the germanium, must be maintained at temperatures nearly as low as that of the detector itself, with only a small aperture of sufficient size to admit the desired radiation.

Cell noise increases linearly with bias current over a very wide current range. Signal output also increases linearly over the same range with increase of current. The signal-to-noise ratio is therefore constant over this current range. This is significant because no degradation in signal-to-noise ratio is encountered by increasing bias current to such a value as will assure cell-noise limitation for the over-all system, a condition that should ideally always exist. The tellurium cells described above share this property.

Negative carrier (N-type) gold-doped germanium is more restricted in spectral response than its P-type counterpart. The long-wave-length response is limited to about 6 μ. It is slightly more sensitive than the P-type impurity response up to 5 μ, with decreasing sensitivity beyond that wave length. Below 2.4 μ a long time constant of about 10 milliseconds is observed, representing a contribution from the intrinsic response. At longer wave lengths the time constant is less than 50 microseconds. The detector is operated at liquid nitrogen temperature, with cell impedance ranging between 2 and 10 megohms.

A recent report by Levenstein et al. (1957), of Syracuse University, presents a fine theoretical treatment of response in lead telluride, N-type, and P-type gold-doped germanium cells. This report gives, in addition, experimental results on these three cells.

Zinc-doped germanium is one of the most recent of the germanium family and very likely will become one of the best detectors. Experimental models have been made for laboratory evaluation, but the inevitable period of complete development lies ahead. The characteristics of zinc-doped germanium appear to be similar to those for gold-doped germanium, except that the spectral response extends as far as 40 μ. Liquid neon coolant is required and may present some restriction to widespread use. Little information is presently available on this detector, but its promise for spectroscopy in the intermediate infrared region exceeds that of any other photoconductor.

Antimony-doped germanium is still in the research stage. However, there is indication of response to radiation out to 120 μ.

The problem of selecting an infrared detector is similar to determining whether a knife is better than a spoon. The knife is better for carving but falls short of the merits of the spoon for enjoying soup. The application and conditions under which the detector is to operate, together with the detector characteristics, must determine the "best" detector in every case.

§ 10. A LOOK TO THE FUTURE

A look at some of the possibilities for the future concludes this brief survey of infrared detectors. Thermistor bolometer developments are aimed, in part, toward the great potentiality offered by multielement detectors. Mosaics of thermistor elements have been successfully made. The complete solution of the switching problem seems inevitable, so that storage of signal and sequential use of only one amplifier, rather than a multiplicity of amplifiers, will be feasible. In particular, switching at extremely low signal levels may prove feasible with further development of solid-state commutators. These developments will have important applications in astrophysics from balloon and satellite stations.

For surveying a two-dimensional radiation field, the gain in over-all detectivity by using an array of detectors, rather than scanning with a single element, may be substantial. Hence the use of thermistor bolometer mosaics with astronomical telescopes will permit infrared exploration of sections of the sky with extraordinary sensitivity.

Similar mosaic potentialities are anticipated for tellurium and gold-doped germanium. In both materials a multielement cell could be made from a single crystal. While surely some questions must be answered—for example, the elimination of "cross-talk"—the increased resolution and system sensitivity will be significant.

Finally, it must be noted that as long as a photon possesses sufficient energy to disturb electronic equilibrium within a receiving device, detection of that photon is possible in principle. This being the case, it is clear that the future of infrared detectors does not necessarily lie with any of the basic processes that have made present detectors possible.

REFERENCES

BENEDICT, W. S.	1958	Private communication.
DEWAARD, R., and		
WORMSER, E.	1958	*Thermistor Infrared Detectors*, Part I (Stamford, Conn.: Barnes Engineering Co.).
FASTIE, W. G.	1952	*J. Opt. Soc. America*, **42**, 641.
	1953	*Ibid.*, **43**, 1174.
GOLAY, M.	1947	*Rev. Sci. Instr.*, **18**, 357.
	1949	*Ibid.*, **20**, 816.
JOHNSON, J. B.	1928	*Phys. Rev.*, **32**, 97.
JONES, R. C.	1953	*Advances in Electronics*, ed. L. MARTON (New York: Academic Press, Inc.), Vol. **5**, chap. 1.
LEVENSTEIN, H., BEYEN, W., BRATT, P., DAVIS, H., JOHNSON, L., and MACRAE, A.	1957	*Germanium and Lead Telluride Infrared Detectors: Final Report* (Syracuse: Solid State Laboratory, Syracuse University).
LEVY, G.	1958	"Infrared System Design," *Electrical Design News*, May.

LOEWENSTEIN, E. V.   1960   *J. Opt. Soc. America*, **50**, 1163.
                           1961   *Ibid.*, **51**, 108.
MOORE, J. H.   1904   *Lick Obs. Bull.*, **3**, 42.
SCHOTTKY, W.   1918   *Ann. d. Phys.*, **57**, 541.
STRONG, JOHN   1958   *Concepts of Classical Optics* (San Francisco: W. H.
                                   Freeman & Co.), p. 240.

STRONG, JOHN, and
   VANASSE, G.   1958   *J. de phys. et radium*, **19**, 192.
                           1959   *J. Opt. Soc. America*, **49**, 844.
                           1960   *Ibid.*, **50**, 113.
SUITS, G., and RICE, P.   1958   "A Single-Crystal Photoconductive Tellurium
                                   Detector," University of Michigan Engineering
                                   Research Institute (Report 2144-240-T).
VANASSE, G. A.,   1959   *J. Opt. Soc. America*, **49**, 309.
   STRONG, JOHN, and
   LOEWENSTEIN, E. V.
YATES, H. W.   1958   In JOHN STRONG, *Concepts of Classical Optics* (San
                                   Francisco: W. H. Freeman & Co.), Appendix I.
ZAHL, H., and GOLAY, M.   1946   *Rev. Sci. Instr.*, **17**, 511.

CHAPTER 13

Direct Recording of Stellar Spectra

A. D. CODE AND WILLIAM C. LILLER

Washburn Observatory, University of Wisconsin, and Harvard College Observatory

§ 1. INTRODUCTION

MODERN astrophysics owes much of its empirical basis to the analysis of stellar spectra. As our knowledge has expanded, theory has called for more precise measurements of stellar energy distributions and line profiles. It is only natural, therefore, that one should turn to photoelectric techniques which have proved so successful in wide-band photometry. Historically, the direct recording of stellar spectra had its origin in the extension of wide-band photometry to more precisely defined band passes. Probably the first to use a photocell to scan stellar spectra was J. S. Hall (1936). His equipment consisted of a 24-inch refractor equipped with a wire objective grating giving a dispersion of 483 A per millimeter in the first order. A pair of 1-mm slits was moved in synchronization across the two first-order images and the light recombined and measured with a CsO-Ag photocell.

§ 2. GENERAL PRINCIPLES

The direct recording of spectra implies the use of a physical detector yielding an electrical signal in the output that bears a functional relationship to the incident radiation flux. One of the primary advantages of photoemissive detectors is the linear relation that exists between the number of incident photons and the electrical output over a very large dynamic range. In its simplest form the photoelectric spectrophotometer consists of a photosensitive detector placed behind an analyzing slit, which is scanned across the spectrum. In comparing photoelectric with photographic techniques, the high quantum efficiency and linearity of the photocathode must be balanced against its inability to record more than one "picture element," or slit width, at a time. For single, equal band widths the photoelectric method is several hundred times more efficient; thus approximately 100 picture elements can be scanned in the time taken to record the information photographically. That is, for N picture elements, as long as

$$\epsilon_{pe} > N\epsilon_{pg} \tag{1}$$

in a given time interval, the photoelectric method is more efficient. The quantities ϵ_{pe} and ϵ_{pg} are the quantum efficiencies of the photocathode and the photographic plate, respectively. For obtaining line profiles of a narrow line, the photoelectric method might be much more efficient, but to obtain a high-resolution spectrum over a broad-wave-length region the photographic method would be more efficient. Higher precision, however, is obtained in the photo-electric method by increasing the exposure time, while the photographic ac-curacy is limited by the finite number of photographic grains and requires broadening of the spectrum. An output in the form of an electrical signal pro-vides considerably more flexibility in processing the data and is a necessity for remote operation of a system such as that required for observations from space vehicles.

By the use of various physical detectors, spectral regions not accessible to the photographic plate are made available. Indeed, a black heat-sensitive detector, such as a thermocouple, responds throughout the entire electromagnetic spec-trum. Bolometric devices of this type, however, have poorer signal-to-noise ratios and hence higher threshold detection than selective receivers. The infrared, solid-state devices, such as the doped germanium detectors, open up new possibilities in the spectral region from 8 to 14 μ, while solar blind detectors are under development for the vacuum ultraviolet. The RbTe photomultiplier, for example, has a peak response near 2000 A and is relatively insensitive long-ward of 3000 A. In the usual spectral windows delineated by the terrestrial atmospheric absorption, the CsSb (S4) photocathode and the trialkali tube have proved most satisfactory in the region from 3000 to 6000 A and 7000 A, respec-tively. Selected tubes of these types have been found with quantum efficiencies greater than 0.30. Probably the CsO-Ag (S1) photocathode is still the best choice in the region from 7000 to 11,000 A, although a Ge phototransistor cooled to liquid nitrogen temperatures is competitive and extends the spectral range to 18,000 A. The PbS photoconductive cell is most satisfactory for observations in the 2.2 μ atmospheric window.

The minimum detectable signal is set by the particular astronomical applica-tion, as well as by the nature of the detector. The statistical fluctuation of the incoming photons establishes the ultimate limitation; however, in some ap-plications the noise from the sky background or thermal environment may over-ride photon noise. An instrument is regarded as perfect when the instrumental noise is smaller than these external noise sources. Indeed, the blue-sensitive photomultipliers and associated electronics are nearly ideal in this sense. For moderate- or high-resolution spectrophotometry in the 3000–6000 A region the system is photon-limited, while for low-resolution observations on faint stars or galaxies it is sky-limited. As the observations are extended toward the red and infrared, the thermal radiation from the immediate environment of the detector becomes dominant. Since this thermal noise is independent of the astronomical source, it may be regarded as coherent throughout the spectra to be scanned, and various differential or multiplexing schemes have been developed to improve the signal-to-noise ratio of infrared spectrophotometers. Photon- or sky-limited operation may be improved, however, only by increasing the number of detectors, the quantum efficiency, or the observing time. The mean-square fluctuation of incident photons is given by Boson statistics, for which

$$\langle q_\nu^2 \rangle = \bar{q}_\nu \left(1 + \frac{\bar{q}_\nu}{N} \right), \tag{2}$$

where $\bar{q}_\nu$ is the mean number of quanta in the spectral interval $d\nu$ and N is the number of cells in phase space between ν and $\nu + d\nu$. The first term on the right of equation (2) corresponds to the classical fluctuations of particles or shot noise. The last term on the right is a wave phenomenon corresponding to the interference of waves. The wave noise is important in the radio region and is the basis of the Hanbury Brown–Twiss stellar interferometer. For high frequencies or low temperatures—namely, where Wien's law is a good approximation to a Planck distribution—the second term on the right is small for the spectral resolutions generally attainable, and the fluctuations become Maxwellian. In the following treatment we shall regard photon noise as classical fluctuations.

Consider, first, the signal-to-noise ratio of an ideal shot-limited photon-counting device. The number of recordable events will be

$$n = \frac{1}{4}\pi \ D^2 \epsilon_\lambda \tau_\lambda q_\lambda \Delta\lambda \cdot t , \tag{3}$$

where D is the telescope aperture, t is the exposure time, $\Delta\lambda$ is the spectral band pass, and ϵ_λ, τ_λ, and q_λ are the quantum efficiency, optical transmission, and number of incident photons per second per square centimeter per unit wavelength interval, respectively, at a wave length λ. The signal-to-noise ratio, therefore, is

$$\frac{S}{N} = \sqrt{n} = \tfrac{1}{2} D \sqrt{(\pi \epsilon_\lambda \tau_\lambda q_\lambda \Delta\lambda \cdot t)}. \tag{4}$$

Here we see, as expected, that detection may be improved by increasing the telescope aperture, detector quantum efficiency, or optical efficiency. This is the maximum signal-to-noise ratio achievable with a single picture-element device. No improvement is to be expected by the application of techniques that simultaneously measure more than one band pass with a single detector, such as may be achieved by multiplexing or interferometer Fourier transform techniques. This may be seen by considering a system that measures simultaneously a band pass, B, for a time, T, and derives spectral information on many $\Delta\lambda$'s simultaneously. The signal-to-noise ratio, then, is

$$\frac{S}{N} = \frac{\tfrac{1}{4}\pi \ D^2 \epsilon_\lambda \tau_\lambda q_\lambda \Delta\lambda T}{\sqrt{\tfrac{1}{4}\pi \ D^2 \epsilon_\lambda \tau_\lambda q_\lambda B T}} \tag{5}$$

or

$$\frac{S}{N} = \tfrac{1}{2} D \sqrt{(\pi \epsilon_\lambda \tau_\lambda q_\lambda \Delta \lambda)} \sqrt{\frac{\Delta \lambda T}{B}} , \qquad (6)$$

but the total exposure time T is related to the exposures on individual picture elements, t, by

$$T = \frac{B}{\Delta \lambda} t . \qquad (7)$$

Thus equation (6) becomes identical with equation (4). This has been demonstrated more rigorously for one particular type of interferometer spectrometer by Kahn (1959).

On the basis of equation (4), the limiting magnitude set by the photon noise may be derived. The visual magnitude of a star corresponds to the monochromatic flux at λ 5465 and is therefore given by

$$V = -2.5 \log q_{5465} + \text{constant} . \qquad (8)$$

For a star of apparent magnitude $V = 0.00$, the monochromatic flux at the effective wave length of the V filter is 3.8×10^{-9} erg cm^{-2} sec^{-1} A^{-1} or 6.45×10^3 quanta in^{-2} sec^{-1} A^{-1} (Code 1960). If the telescope aperture is measured in inches, the time in seconds, and the band width in angstroms, the constant occurring in equation (8) has the value 9.52. On substituting equation (4) for q_λ in equation (8), we find

$$V = 9.24 + 5 \log D + 2.5 \log \Delta \lambda \cdot t + 5 \log \sigma + 2.5 \log \epsilon_\lambda \tau_\lambda , \qquad (9)$$

where σ is the fractional accuracy desired or the reciprocal of the signal-to-noise ratio. In practice it is possible to select tubes with $\epsilon_\lambda \approx 0.2$ and design optical systems with total transmission (atmospheric and instrumental) of 0.1; thus, for a 100-inch telescope and a 1 per cent accuracy, equation (9) becomes

$$V = 5.0 + 2.5 \log \Delta \lambda \cdot t . \qquad (10)$$

Thus, for example, with a 10 A band pass and a 180-second exposure, one could measure a 13-mag. object to a 1 per cent accuracy; however, only 200 A would be measurable in 1 hour of total exposure. On the other hand, a line profile over a range of 10 A could be measured for a 5.0-mag. star with a resolution of 0.1 A with a total exposure time of 100 seconds.

In practice, a photon-counting system falls short of the results described by equation (9) because some counts are missed by the selection of the discriminator level used to reject the thermal emission of the photocathode. More efficient optical systems can be designed, however, and the results expressed by equation (10) are realizable. If the current is measured with a d.c. amplifier, the effective exposure time is one-half that of a perfect photon counter (Whitford 1953), which corresponds to a loss of approximately 0.7 mag. In general, the rate of scan should be such that a single picture element is scanned no faster than approximately five times the instrumental time constant. A higher scan rate will reduce the effective spectral resolution. The extrapolation of equation (9) to large band passes and long exposure times is not justified, since then the sky background increases the noise. For an entrance aperture corresponding to 100 square seconds of arc, the sky background corresponds to a 16-mag. star, and for a 100-inch telescope there are approximately 16 photons per second from the sky. For sky-limited operation, where the photon flux from the sky background, Q_λ, dominates the stellar flux, the signal-to-noise ratio expressed by equation (4) is reduced by the factor $\sqrt{(q_\lambda/Q_\lambda)}$.

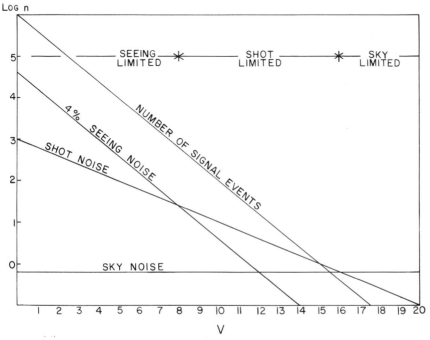

FIG. 1.—Graph of the signal and various noise sources as a function of apparent magnitude.

The above considerations applied to a single picture-element device. It is obvious that the use of several photomultipliers will increase the efficiency of the system. For a system of N detectors, the signal-to-noise ratio will be increased by a factor of $\sqrt{N}$. The logical extension of this is to employ an image tube. There is, however, a further advantage to the use of multipicture-element spectrophotometers. This is the possibility of rejecting coherent noise. One of the major sources of such noise is stellar scintillation. Indeed, for bright stars, seeing fluctuations represent the dominant noise. If, for example, the observing program required the measurement of a particular spectral line, a simple two-detector unit, with one photomultiplier centered on the line and the other on a neighboring part of the continuum, would provide a means of doubling the effective exposure time while at the same time rejecting the fluctuations due to seeing. There are a variety of electronic techniques to implement this procedure.

Figure 1 shows a plot of the signal and various noise sources as a function of apparent magnitude. It is based on the case considered in formulating equation (10) for a 100-inch telescope with a 1 A band pass and 1-second exposure and assumes that the seeing fluctuations are 4 per cent of the signal. The sky noise is computed on the basis of an entrance aperture of 100 square seconds of arc; the magnitude is the visual magnitude, and log n refers to the number of recorded events. Down to 8.0 mag., seeing is the dominant noise source; the statistical fluctuation of the signal photons dominates to about 16.0 mag., at which point the sky noise takes over. To these noise sources should be added the system noise, which, for a good refrigerated photomultiplier and associated electronics, should be comparable with the sky noise.

In the discussion that follows we shall first examine the application of these techniques to low- and moderate-resolution spectrophotometry, which is generally feasible with an entrance slit or aperture that admits the entire seeing tremor disk. In the final section we shall consider high-resolution applications, where the use of a slit alone reduces the total transmission and increases the effect of seeing noise greatly.

§ 3. LOW-RESOLUTION SPECTROPHOTOMETRY

In this section we shall describe instrumentation intended primarily for measurement of continuous energy distributions or integrated line intensities. Scanners for securing detailed line shapes will be discussed in the next section. The spectral band passes are, in general, greater than 1 A but seldom more than 100 A. Entrance apertures admit the light from all or nearly all of an entire star image and frequently are large enough to include all the radiation from small nebulosities, star clusters, or galaxies.

Following an initial discussion of the instrumental specifications required to give the desired results, we shall describe some specific systems, including a brief discussion of the advantages of each system.

3.1. DESIGN CONSIDERATIONS

Let us first limit our discussion to a system in which a continuous scan of wave length is provided by the rotation of a diffraction grating. Here, then, the sum of the angles of incidence and dispersion is

$$\alpha + \beta = C \text{ , a constant ,} \tag{11}$$

and the grating equation becomes

$$\frac{m\lambda}{d} = \sin \alpha \pm \sin (C - \alpha) = A \sin \alpha \pm B \cos \alpha , \tag{12}$$

where

$$A = 1 - \cos C , \qquad B = \sin C ,$$

and the other quantities have their usual meaning. If we set α close to zero, then

$$\lambda \simeq \frac{d}{m}(A\alpha + B),\qquad(13)$$

so that λ is linearly related to α as long as the grating is rotated through a small angle. We obtain a similar result by setting $\beta \simeq 0$. One usually wishes to have a spectrophotometer that will accept all the light from an image with angular diameter $\Delta\theta$ and yet have available a certain minimum band pass $\Delta\lambda$. Therefore, it is necessary that the dispersion of the system, $\Delta\lambda/\Delta x$, be great enough to allow the use of an exit slot[1] with a width at least as large as the diameter of the image, Δs (as it would appear in monochromatic light), at the exit slot. If the telescope has a focal length F_{tel}, then

$$\Delta s = \Delta\theta \cdot F_{\text{tel}} \left(\frac{F_{\text{cam}}}{F_{\text{coll}}} \right),\qquad(14)$$

where the quantity within the parentheses is the ratio of focal lengths of the spectrometer camera and collimator. Differentiating λ with respect to α and dividing by the camera focal length give the linear dispersion of the system:

$$\frac{\Delta\lambda}{\Delta x} = \frac{A\,d}{m F_{\text{cam}}}.\qquad(15)$$

If Δx is set equal to Δs, then the minimum usable value of the band pass, or spectral purity, is

$$\Delta\lambda_{\text{min}} = \frac{A\,d\Delta\theta}{m}\frac{F_{\text{tel}}}{F_{\text{coll}}}.\qquad(16)$$

Since the focal ratios of the telescope and collimator are always nearly equal, as are the diameters of the collimator and grating,

$$\frac{\Delta\lambda_{\text{min}}}{\Delta\theta} = \frac{A\,d}{m}\left(\frac{D_{\text{gr}}}{D_{\text{tel}}} \right),\qquad(17)$$

where the D's are the diameters of the grating and the telescope. It is clear, then, that one should incorporate in his design the largest possible grating, and it should be so positioned that it is normal to either the incident (or dispersed) beam near the middle of the desired wave-length range. It should be noted that these results do not necessarily pertain to concave gratings.

Now that excellent, but inexpensive, replica gratings are available in a wide variety, these are to be preferred, in general, to prisms, whose dispersions are non-linear and which must be made of fused quartz or other similar material if the ultraviolet is to be recorded. Only the occasional inconvenience of overlapping orders is disadvantageous in the use of diffraction gratings.

---

[1] Throughout this section we shall frequently refer to the rectangular apertures of a spectrophotometer as *slots*. This term, suggested first by A. E. Whitford, distinguishes it from the familiar spectrograph *slit*, which has a much narrower width.

Before describing some specific low-resolution photoelectric scanners, a few words should be added concerning the advantages of single- and multichannel low-resolution spectrophotometers. The simplest form of recording the intensity as a function of wave length is to scan with a single slot the spectrum of the program object and to precede and follow this scan with similar observations of a standard star or other source. One must rely upon, among other things, the predictability of the photomultiplier response, the amplifier gain, and particularly the atmospheric transmission. Attempts have been made by several workers to reduce the reliance on these factors by measuring at the same time neighboring pass bands or the integrated light from the object. One method is to use a rotating prism or mirror which alternately flashes the two channels on a single photocell followed by a tuned a.c. amplifying system. Another technique is to use two photomultipliers and two amplifiers and to measure the ratio of the signals by replacing the reference voltage source of the recorder with the output of the reference channel. The advantages of the two systems become particularly apparent in the more cloud-bound parts of the world.

3.2. One-Channel Spectrometers

The earliest photoelectric spectrometers were adaptations of existing laboratory or photographic instruments. Mention has already been made of Hall (1936), who combined an objective grating and the refractors at both the Sproul Observatory and Amherst College, to scan the spectra of a number of stars from 4500 to 10,300 A. The scanning slot averaged about 485 A over the region. Kuiper, Wilson, and Cashman (1947) used a two-prism spectrometer to observe the infrared spectra of planets and a few stars (see also Kuiper 1952). Code (1952) replaced the plateholder of a one-prism spectrograph attached to the Mount Wilson 60-inch reflector with a moving-slit arrangement, behind which was a photomultiplier. MacRae (1953) and Liller and Aller (1954) scanned spectra formed by the objective prisms of the Case and Michigan Schmidt telescopes. The latter technique has been continued by others (see, for example, Bonsack and Stock 1957) and was recently employed quite successfully by Stecher and Milligan at the Goddard Space Flight Center of the National Aeronautics and Space Administration when they flew several objective reflection grating spectrophotometers to an altitude of about 120 miles in an Aerobee-Hi rocket and obtained scans of stellar spectra down to a wave length of 1700 A. The scanning by this instrument, which was designed by Blakney, Murty, Hochgraf, and Staudenmaier of the Institute of Optics, Rochester (Fig. 2), was accomplished simply by taking full advantage of the in-flight rotation of the rocket (see Fig. 3, a). The spectrophotometer used a paraboloid of 23-cm focal length and a mosaic grating of either 500 lines/mm (66 A/mm dispersion between λ 1700 and λ 4000) or 600 lines/mm (53 A/mm between λ 1255 and λ 3000). Both 50 and 100 A slots were used.

Further developments by Whitford and Code have resulted in the versatile instrument mounted at the Cassegrainian focus ($f/13.6$) of the 36-inch reflector of the University of Wisconsin Pine Bluff Observatory (Fig. 4). In one housing are mounted a spectrograph, a direct photoelectric photometer, and a spectrophotometer. The latter instrument has for its collimator an inverted Cassegrainian system, which in a small volume provides a large-diameter bundle of collimated radiation (see Fig. 3, *d*). A 4-inch diameter grating with 600 l/mm blazed for 5000 A in the second order and a second Cassegrainian system bring to the final focus a spectrum of high spectral purity ($D_{tel}/D_{gr} = 9$) and convenient dispersion (10 A/mm, second order).

Liller (1957) has chosen to work at the Newtonian foci of the Mount Wilson

FIG. 2.—Photograph of one of the objective-grating spectrophotometers designed by Blakney, Murty, Hochgraf, and Staudenmaier of the Institute of Optics, University of Rochester, and used in an Aerobee-Hi rocket by Stecher and Milligan, of the National Aeronautics and Space Administration.

100-inch and the University of Michigan Curtis Schmidt telescopes, so that a large-diameter collimated beam is provided with a simpler Newtonian system (Fig. 3, *b*). A 2-inch-diameter, 600 lines/mm grating with a 5000 A blaze in the second order, a second Newtonian system, and infrared- and blue-sensitive photomultipliers complete the spectrophotometer.

Oke (1960, Oke & Greenstein, 1961) prefers the *f*/16 Cassegrainian focus of the 100-inch telescope and has used an Ebert-Fastie optical system (Fastie 1952)

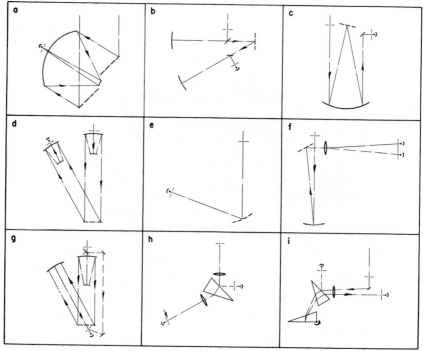

FIG. 3.—Schematic diagram of the optical systems of representative spectrophotometers. In all the diagrams, the light enters from the top. Gratings are indicated by heavy dashed lines; the reference or monitored beams are shown as light dashed lines. See text for detailed comments.

of 32-inch focal length in a scanner designed originally by Code. This combination with a 600 lines mm grating working in the second order gives a convenient 10 A/mm dispersion at the exit slot (Fig. 3, *c*).

Recently Liller has designed and constructed an extremely compact *f*/5 spectrophotometer (Fig. 5) which employs only one optical component: a concave grating (Fig. 3, *e*). Reasoning that each reflection or transmission reduces the efficiency of the instrument by about 10 per cent or 0.1 mag., he has adopted the Seya-Namioka system (see Namioka 1961) to put the number of optical components at an absolute minimum. This instrument is intended for and is

Fig. 4.—Photograph of the combination spectrograph–direct photometer-scanning spectrophotometer designed by Whitford and Code and mounted at the Cassegrain focus of the 36-inch reflector of the Pine Bluff Observatory, University of Wisconsin.

limited to use primarily in the wave-length range 3000–7000 A, since the off-axis aberrations ruin the spectral purity at greater wave lengths (see Fig. 5).

An interesting scanner of moderately high resolution has been described by Dimov (1960). Using a grating spectrograph with a dispersion of 25 A/mm, he scans 110 A of a spectrum with a moving exit slot 2.5 A wide. As the slot moves, a large number (49) of capacitors are switched in, one at a time. In this way the signal from the photomultiplier at a large number of points in the spectrum is stored. Additional scans add to the individual charges until a sufficient number of sweeps is made. Each scan takes 25 seconds; as many as 15 scans are made during one observation. The stored charges are then recorded, the capacitors discharged, and the instrument is ready for the next observation.

Of an entirely different nature is the scanner which Hinteregger (1961) has used to obtain ultraviolet spectra of the sun from rockets. This instrument is a grazing incidence type and has no optical component other than a 2-meter-radius concave grating. Scanning is achieved by moving a slit along the Rowland circle; a stationary photomultiplier with a large cathode mounted behind the slit completes the instrument. The slit moves continuously on a flexible steel tape, while the electron showers released by photons are counted during successive 0.1-second intervals. Ten seconds are required to scan from λ 250 to λ 1300 with a slit measuring several angstroms in width.

3.3. MULTICHANNEL SPECTROPHOTOMETERS

Making the best of the weather conditions in Britain, Griffin and Redman (1960) and Griffin (1961) have employed two-channel scanners with the Cambridge 36-inch reflector. The first of these is designed around an Ebert-Fastie system with a 36-inch focal length and is used at the $f/18$ coudé focus. A grating provides the dispersion, which amounts to 18.4 A/mm in the first order. In the work which they describe, Griffin and Redman chose to improve the spectral purity by passing the starlight first through a 2-inch, 3 A slot. At the focus of the original spectrometer, a chopping device permitted a single photomultiplier to measure in turn the radiation from each of three pass bands averaging about 50 A wide. The central band was positioned on the spectral feature of interest; the other two bands were placed approximately symmetrically on either side of the principal band. However, the inefficiency caused by the requirement that the observations be three times as long as if the counts ran simultaneously and the introduction of noise occasioned by the frequent switching convinced Griffin and Redman to use, in an improved design, three photomultipliers, one behind each exit slot. An auxiliary lamp allowed calibration of the three channels, as was found necessary, every 10 or 15 minutes. Satisfactory observations made during extremely hazy nights (zenith extinction 2.5 mag.) attest to the success of their system.

The second spectrophotometer constructed at Cambridge (Griffin 1961) has for its collimator a 6-inch $f/18$ mirror and for its camera a 7-inch doublet lens of 103-inch focal length (see Fig. 3, f). A grating provides the dispersion, which

FIG. 5.—Photograph of the scanner (top removed) designed by Liller for use at the Newtonian focus of the 61-inch reflector at the Agassiz Station Observatory of Harvard University.

amounts to 5 A/mm in the first order. The remainder of the system is similar to the scanner described above, except that only two photomultipliers are used, one behind the central slot and one behind (optically) the two reference pass bands. The width of the entrance slots used in Griffin's work is 2 sec. of arc or 0.8 A; the exit slots range in width from 11 to 34 A.

Several workers have successfully used prism-compensating spectrophotometers. For example, Guérin (1959) monitors the output of a photomultiplier located behind a 44 A (at 4300 A) slot with that from a second photocell, which measures the white light reflected off the quartz-prism face. The prism and the quartz collimator and camera lenses remain stationary and provide a 210 A/mm (at 4300 A) dispersion; a moving exit slot produces the spectral scan (see Fig. 3, *h*). This instrument has been used very successfully at the Observatoire de Haute-Provence.

Dobronravin and Nikonov (1955), at the Crimean Astrophysical Observatory, use a similar instrument, the main differences resulting from their decision to scan in wave length by rotating the prism. A thin, uncoated glass plate located just behind the camera lens diverts a small portion of the dispersed but unfocused radiation to the monitoring photomultiplier. 15 A (at Hγ) of the spectrum, whose dispersion is 40 A/mm, illuminate the analyzing photomultiplier.

A high-resolution spectrophotometer ingeniously combining the advantages of the two-prism spectrophotometers described above has been described by Geake and Wilcock (1956). A single doublet lens of 25-cm focal length serves as both collimator and camera (see Fig. 3, *i*). A fixed flint-glass prism reflects a portion of the white light into the monitoring photocell, while the dispersed light passes into a second prism whose back face is silvered. The light then returns through the system and through the exit slit, behind which is the analyzing photomultiplier. Scans over a wide range of wave lengths are achieved by rotating the silvered prism (and leaving undisturbed the light-path to the monitoring photocell), while a scan over no more than a few angstroms can be made by tilting a plane-parallel glass plate just in front of the exit slit. The dispersion produced is 25 A/mm (at Hγ), and bilateral slits allow the use of a wide range of pass bands. The maximum spectral purity is in the vicinity of 0.5 A.

In the United States, Tull at the University of Michigan designed a spectrophotometer (see Fig. 6) which has an inverted Cassegrainian system as a collimator, a 4-inch, 600 lines/mm grating as the dispersing component, and a 4-inch, *f*/2.7 paraboloid as a camera (see Fig. 3, *g*). A chopping mirror mounted behind the entrance slot allows light to enter the scanner for one third of the time. During the next third of a cycle, the light passes undispersed via a second optical system onto the cathode of the single photomultiplier. For the last third of a cycle, no radiation reaches the photocell. These signals are then fed into an a.c. amplification system which produces the ratio of the intensities of the two light-beams on a pen-and-ink recorder.

FIG. 6.—Photograph of the spectrophotometer (top removed) designed by Tull and mounted at the Cassegrain focus of the 24-inch reflector at the Portage Lake Observatory, University of Michigan.

At Kitt Peak National Observatory, Meinel and Golson (1959) constructed a low-resolution scanning ratio spectrophotometer, which has been applied to the problem of spectral classification.

§ 4. HIGH-RESOLUTION SPECTROPHOTOMETRY

We now shift our attention to that group of instruments that scan spectra photoelectrically with resolving powers generally over 10,000. As a rule, these spectrophotometers are more specialized than the lower-resolution instruments described in Section 2 because of the high dispersion needed at the exit slit. Furthermore, as the entrance slit is narrowed, large fluctuations in the signal are introduced because of variations in the seeing tremor disk. It follows from equation (17) that the larger the ratio of collimator aperture to telescope aperture, the higher the spectral purity that can be obtained for a given angular slit size. It is unlikely, however, that seeing will permit an entrance slit smaller than about 3 seconds of arc or that a large telescope optical system yielding a resolution much better than 1 A is practical, if this slit width is to define the purity. Thus a slit instrument usually requires some form of seeing compensation.

In general, one of three techniques has been applied to effect compensation. The first method is to scan the spectra with one detector and monitor a fixed spectral region with a second detector. The electrical outputs are then combined to yield the intensity ratio. The second scheme utilizes the monitor signal to adjust either the light-flux or the photomultiplier gains to give a constant response for the monitor signal. The third technique involves setting one detector on a picture element of interest and integrating, while a second detector integrates the output from a standard monitoring picture element. The two counts are recorded, and the signal detector is moved to the next picture element.

The earliest of the high-resolution photometers described by Hiltner and Code (1950) employed the first of the techniques sketched above. The measurements were made at the coudé focus of the McDonald 82-inch reflector. The spectrograph was an autocollimating prism instrument with a linear dispersion of 3 A/mm at 4400 A. The plateholder was replaced by a moving slit and photomultiplier, and a compensating beam was taken to the monitoring cell by a plane-parallel flat inserted in the dispersed beam. The slide wire of a self-balancing Brown recorder potentiometer was used to obtain the ratio of the scanning-cell output to the monitoring cell. This method is illustrated in Figure 7, a. A modification of this approach has been employed at Mount Wilson Observatory.

The second method, in which the light-flux or gain is controlled, has been employed in a number of commercial spectrophotometers in one form or another and by several astronomers (Walraven 1953; Bradford 1956). The method is sketched in Figure 7, b.

Rogerson, Spitzer, and Bahng (1959) have used the counting technique with the Mount Wilson 100-inch coudé spectrograph. The technique was first outlined by Dunham (1956) and is shown in Figure 7, c.

It is difficult to put down a formula which will enable one to calculate at what rate a spectrum should be scanned. In a sky having no time variations of transparency and with perfect equipment, the rule is simply that the longer one observes, the higher the final accuracy. In practice, however, it is always advisable to make a spectral scan in the quickest possible time, so that the observation can be compared with a standard source before any uncontrollable change takes place in the instrumental or environmental characteristics. Usually three factors limit the minimum time in which a spectral scan can be made: the number of photon-released electrons per unit time, the short-time variations in atmospheric transparency (scintillation), and the time constant of the instrument. The combined result of these factors is that one finds that about a 20-second deflection or exposure is required to make a single good-quality observation of a moderately bright star with a conventional direct photoelectric photometer. Carrying this rule of thumb over to scanning spectrophotometers, one would conclude that, to obtain a good point-to-point determination of the shape of a continuous spectrum or line profile, the scan rate should be no greater

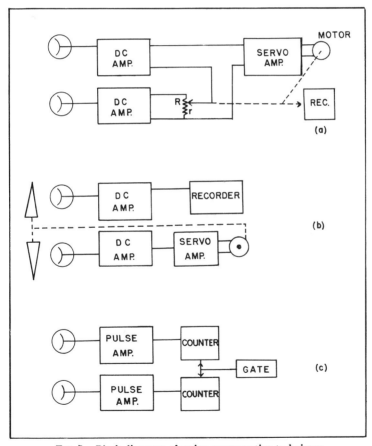

FIG. 7.—Block diagrams of seeing-compensation techniques

than one spectral band width per 20 seconds. However, when a continuum is relatively free from lines or if a line profile is broad, one has the advantage of interpolation. Thus, with a 10 A slot, one might be able to scan at a rate of 300 A/minute rather than at 30 A/minute, as suggested above. If, however, response-curves and energy distributions combine to make a deflection change rapidly and if the time constant of the equipment is large, distorted wave-length scans might result. Consider, for example, a wave-length scan during which the signal changes by 10 per cent in a 10 A interval, as measured with a very small time constant. If the time constant is raised to a value of 1 second, then at least 2.3 seconds should elapse before a 10 A slot moves on to the adjoining 10 A interval, since in 2.3 seconds the signal would reach to within 10 per cent of its time value or, in our example, to within 1 per cent of the correct value. The corresponding scan speed is 260 A/minute.

The minimum usable value of the spectral band pass is set by the spectral purity available. However, for faint sources, a very narrow band pass may result in a weak signal with very long integration times required. Considerations of the value of the information acquired per unit time, constancy of atmospheric and instrumental characteristics, etc., may then dictate going to wider band passes. There are, of course, dangers involved in spectrophotometry when the analyzing slits are large compared with the detailed spectral features. Not only is it difficult to locate the true continuum, but it is even possible to have dips in a scan occur where really there is a local maximum or emission line. This latter possibility is discussed clearly and more fully by Wilson et al. (1954).

Numerous scanning spectrographs have been developed for solar research. Probably the finest existing instrument of this type is the one in operation at the McMath-Hulbert Observatory of the University of Michigan. Lines separated by only 0.009 A can be distinguished on photoelectric scans. The 6 × 8-inch grating having 15,000 lines/mm and a collimator 50 feet in focal length and camera mirrors are all mounted inside a single, large, evacuated chamber. To work at 3000 A wave length, one uses the ninth order, which produces a dispersion of 14.58 mm/A. A full description of this instrument appears elsewhere (McMath 1956).

One of the most promising instruments for future stellar spectroscopy is the tunable Fabry-Perot étalon. The fundamental relations that apply to the étalon have been discussed by Chabbal (1953). An instrument designed at Bellevue by Chabbal et al., using the simultaneous sweeping property of a grating Fabry-Perot combination (Hirschberg and Kadesch 1958) is currently in operation for solar observations at the University of Wisconsin. The instrument is capable of a resolving power of approximately 10^6 in absorption and much greater in emission with very low scattered light and is shown in Figure 8. This type of instrument is particularly attractiv   for stellar observations because the resolution is not defined by an entrance slit and therefore the seeing difficulties are substantially solved, while Jacquinot has shown that the efficiency of the étalon

FIG. 8.—Photograph of the Fabry-Perot spectrograph of the University of Wisconsin Physics Department. The instrument is used with a 12-inch solar telescope in Madison, Wisconsin.

is greater than that of prisms or gratings. Geake, Ring, and Woolf (1959) have employed a Fabry-Perot interferometer in combination with a spectrograph to obtain spectra of stellar and nebular objects. For the same transmission, they obtained 32 A resolution with the spectrograph alone and 1 A resolution with the combination spectrograph plus Fabry-Perot.

Several of the scanners described in the preceding section are capable of relatively high-resolution work, particularly the multichannel instruments.

A number of high-dispersion spectrophotometers are planned for satellite instruments. Among these are the solar instruments under construction at Harvard University (see Liller 1961), at the University of Colorado (see Rense, Stuart, and Todd 1961), and by the National Aeronautics and Space Administration (see Goldberg 1961). Stellar instruments are being developed at Princeton (see Spitzer and Rogerson 1961) and by the National Aeronautics and Space Administration (see Davis 1961).

While we can look forward to the increasing use of image tubes in spectroscopy, it is realistic to believe that accurate spectrophotometry will still demand techniques similar to those described above for some time to come.

REFERENCES

BONSACK, W. K., and STOCK, J.	1957	*Ap. J.*, **126**, 99.
BRADFORD, W. R.	1956	*Astronomical Optics* (New York: Interscience Publishers), p. 244.
CHABBAL, R.	1953	*J. Rech. cent. nat. rech. sci.*, **24**, 138.
CODE, A. D.	1952	*Observatory*, **72**, 201.
	1960	*Stars and Stellar Systems*, ed. G. P. KUIPER and B. M. MIDDLEHURST (Chicago: University of Chicago Press), Vol. **6**, chap. 2, p. 50.
DAVIS, R. J.	1961	*Colloque International d'Astrophysique Communications* (Liége: Institut d'Astrophysique), No. 10, 25.
DIMOV, N. A.	1960	*Russ. A.J.*, **37**, 464.
DOBRONRAVIN, P. P., and NIKONOV, V. B.	1955	*Izvest. Krymsk Ap. Obs.*, **13**, 32.
DUNHAM, T.	1956	*Vistas in Astronomy*, ed. A. BEER (New York: Pergamon Press), **2**, 1268.
FASTIE, W. G.	1952	*J. Opt. Soc. America*, **42**, 641.
GEAKE, J. E., RING, J., and WOOLF, N. J.	1959	*M.N.*, **119**, 616.
GEAKE, J. E., and WILCOCK, W. L.	1956	*M.N.*, **116**, 561.
GOLDBERG, L.	1961	*Colloque International d'Astrophysique Communications* (Liége: Institut d'Astrophysique), No. 10, 30.
GRIFFIN, R. F.	1961	*M.N.*, **122**, 181.
GRIFFIN, R. F., and REDMAN, R. O.	1960	*M.N.*, **120**, 287.
GUÉRIN, P.	1959	*Ann. d'ap.*, **22**, 611.

HALL, J. S.   1936   *Ap. J.*, **84**, 369.
                                     1941   *Ap. J.*, **94**, 71.
HILTNER, W. A., and
  CODE, A. D.   1950   *J. Opt. Soc. America*, **40**, 149.
HINTEREGGER, H. E.   1961   *Space Astrophysics*, ed. W. LILLER (New York:
                                             McGraw-Hill Book Co., Inc.), p. 34.
HIRSCHBERG, J. G., and
  KADESCH, R. R.   1958   *J. Opt. Soc. America*, **48**, 177.
KAHN, F. D.   1959   *Ap. J.*, **129**, 518.
KUIPER, G. P.   1952   *Atmospheres of the Earth and Planets*, ed. G. P.
                                             KUIPER (Chicago: University of Chicago
                                             Press), chap. 12.
KUIPER, G. P.,
  WILSON, W., and
  CASHMAN, R. J.   1947   *Ap. J.*, **106**, 243.
LILLER, W.   1957   *Pub. A.S.P.*, **69**, 511.
                                     1961   *Colloque International d'Astrophysique Communi-
                                             cations* (Liége: Institut d'Astrophysique), No.
                                             10, 94.
LILLER, W., and
  ALLER, L. H.   1954   *Ap. J.*, **120**, 48.
McMATH, R. R.   1956   *Ap. J.*, **123**, 1.
MACRAE, D. A.   1953   *Astr. J.*, **58**, 43.
MEINEL, A. B., and
  GOLSON, J. C.   1959   *Pub. A.S.P.*, **71**, 445.
NAMIOKA, T.   1961   *Space Astrophysics*, ed. W. LILLER (New York:
                                             McGraw-Hill Book Co., Inc.), p. 228.
OKE, J. B.   1960   *Ap. J.*, **131**, 358.
OKE, J. B., and
  GREENSTEIN, J. L.   1961   *Ap. J.*, **133**, 349.
RENSE, W. A., STUART,
  F. E., and TODD, E. P.   1961   *Colloque International d'Astrophysique Communi-
                                             cation* (Liége: Institut d'Astrophysique), No.
                                             10, 89.
ROGERSON, J. B.,
  SPITZER, L., and
  BAHNG, J. D.   1959   *Ap. J.*, **130**, 991.
SPITZER, L., and
  ROGERSON, J. B.   1961   *Colloque International d'Astrophysique Communi-
                                             cations* (Liége: Institut d'Astrophysique), No.
                                             10, 886.
WALRAVEN, T.   1953   *Astronomical Photoelectric Photometry*, ed. F. B.
                                             WOOD (Washington: American Association for
                                             the Advancement of Science), p. 114.
WHITFORD, A. E.   1953   *Astronomical Photoelectric Photometry*, ed. F. B.
                                             WOOD (Washington: American Association for
                                             the Advancement of Science), p. 126.
WILSON N. L., TOUSEY,
  R., PURCELL, J. D., and
  JOHNSON, F. S.   1954   *Ap. J.*, **119**, 590.

CHAPTER 14

Image Detection by Television Signal Generation

J. D. McGEE

Imperial College of Science and Technology, London University

§ 1. INTRODUCTION

AFTER a relatively short period of development, the electronic television camera has equaled and surpassed the photographic cinematograph camera in sensitivity. It seems pertinent to inquire, therefore, whether or not such a television camera could be applied as the image-detecting instrument in an astronomical telescope. Several attempts have been made to use commercial television pickup tubes for astronomical observations but with limited success, probably mainly because the television camera tube is designed to reproduce 25 or 30 pictures per second and will not operate properly at the very long time-exposures that the astronomer usually requires and for which the photographic plate is very convenient. Also the image definition that is satisfactory for entertainment television is well below the standard required for most scientific purposes and especially astronomical photography. Again, fidelity of geometrical reproduction is very much inferior to that of a direct photograph. When one adds to these defects the disadvantages of cost and technical complexity, it is perhaps not surprising that television has not been adopted by astronomers.

All existing television camera tubes depend for their operation on the photoelectric effect, and their ultimate sensitivity will be determined by the random fluctuations, or "shot noise," associated with this quantized process of conversion of light into electricity. However, no existing camera has reached, and most are still very far from, this limit, and a great deal of work remains to be done to reach it. Also little has been done to develop cameras for long time-exposure operations, so common in photography, which would be of fundamental importance in astronomy.

It might be asked: Why bother with apparatus as complex as a television camera channel when, as appears from chapter 16, image intensifiers of one type or another enable single photoelectrons to be detected individually? There appear to be four reasons for this: (1) The charge-integrating target of certain television signal-generating tubes can be made to store far more "bits" of information than a light-sensitive photographic plate of the same area. (2) The picture information is converted to electrical quantities which can be measured accurately without the intervention of a photographic plate. (3) There are occasions when it is desirable to be able to transmit the picture information to a distant receiving station, either over cable or radio link, and this can be done only when it is in the form of a television signal. This is already important in satellite astronomy and is likely to become more important in the near future. (4) The amount of information recorded on photographic plates is becoming so vast that the conventional methods for extracting the essential facts from it are becoming overwhelmed. Hence automatic methods are being considered for doing this. They usually involve some method of electronic scanning and evaluation of the photographs, with the information stored in a suitably coded form. It is clear that, in principle at least, it is not necessary to go through the process of recording the photograph at all. All the essential information could be obtained by scanning the original image. Hence this is another, even if long-term, reason for developing the television image-detecting methods.

There are many observations in astronomy which are most readily carried out by conventional photography because there is adequate light and image contrast available to give satisfactory records in reasonable exposure times. It is very unlikely that the use of photographic methods in these cases will be displaced by photoelectronic methods because of the relative simplicity of the former and the permanent record that results. However, there are several cases in which photoelectronic methods may offer considerable advantages. These are as follows:

1. *Very faint images.*—If they are such that the exposure time becomes excessive, it will be very useful to be able to reduce this by a factor of about 100. This may be done by image intensifiers in many instances, but there are possible conditions, such as when a telescope is sent aloft in a balloon or satellite, where it would be a great advantage for the picture to be converted to signals that could be relayed by radio to a convenient base. The limit of sensitivity in this case should be identical with that of an image intensifier.

2. *Bright, variable objects.*—In this case the object, such as a planet, may be quite bright but is distorted by atmospheric turbulence to such a degree that even fairly short-exposure photographs are severely blurred. The maximum possible sensitivity would enable the minimum exposure time to be used, which would reduce blurring. This also could be achieved with an image intensifier. However, the television system would be required for remote operation, and it also allows for selective contrast control, which can be very useful in examining special features of an image.

3. *Low-contrast images.*—This is one of the most serious limitations to the use of big telescopes, since the very faint objects that are being observed at extreme range are only slightly brighter than the more or less uniform background caused by sky illumination.

The amount of light collected in a star image is proportional to the area of the aperture of the telescope (D^2), while the brightness of the background is proportional to the square of the relative aperture $(D/F)^2$. Thus, as the telescope diameter is made larger in order to collect more light from faint stars, the relative aperture D/F must be kept reasonably small, otherwise the focal length becomes excessive. The brightness of the sky has been measured by Baum (1955) to correspond to the light-flux from a twenty-second magnitude star spread over 1 square second of arc, which is about the area covered by a star image in a big telescope under average seeing conditions. Now the time required to expose a film due to background alone will depend on $(D/F)^2$, and this is about $\frac{1}{2}$ hour when using $f/3.3$ and Eastman-Kodak 103a-O emulsion. If the diameter of the telescope is increased, keeping D/F constant, fainter and fainter stars will be detectable against the sky background until the light-flux in

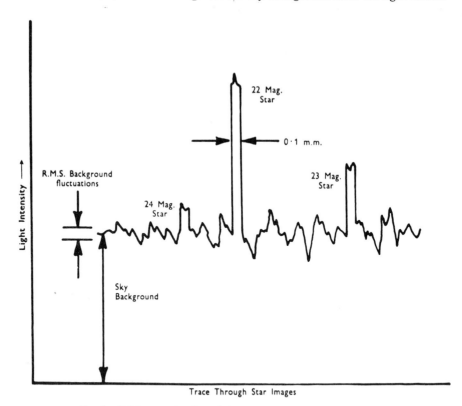

Fig. 1.—Brightness plot through images of stars and sky background

a star image, covering about 1 square second of arc, is comparable with the flux over the same area from the sky background. For the biggest telescope in use, the 200-inch Hale telescope, this situation is reached for stars of about twenty-second magnitude; this is illustrated in Figure 1. Here the ordinates represent a trace through the sky background superimposed on stars of twenty-second, twenty-third, and twenty-fourth magnitude. The mean amplitude of the twenty-second magnitude star is equal to the mean background amplitude. However, both these quantities are subject to statistical fluctuations. While the twenty-second magnitude star is quite certainly recognizable from the random background fluctuations and the twenty-third magnitude star can be distinguished without much doubt, the signal from the twenty-fourth magnitude star may readily be confused with a noise pulse.

In this representation of the recording of a light-image, the signal amplitude is proportional to the number of recorded photons, provided that each is recorded with equal clarity, while the r.m.s. fluctuation is proportional to the square root of this number. Thus the more photons that are recorded, the greater will be the ratio of the recorded signal to the r.m.s. fluctuations of the background. Thus, in recording a light-image, it is important that as many photons as possible should be effective in producing a recordable event, that each event should be recorded with equal amplitude or clarity, and that as many of these events as possible must be integrated in the record.

The problem of detecting an optical image reduces to that of recording as large a proportion as possible of the photons arriving in the image as recognizable events, such as developable grains of silver halide in a photographic emulsion or recorded charges on a charge-storage target. Not all incident photons produce a recognizable event, but the percentage that do is known as the "quantum efficiency" (γ) of the process. The emission of photons and photoelectrons and the activation of silver halide grains follow a Poisson distribution, and hence an average number N will have a standard deviation associated with it of magnitude $\sqrt{N}$. This fluctuation in a nominally uniform distribution of events sets a limitation to the accuracy with which contrast in the image can be detected.

If we consider a small square area of such an image with sides of length h upon which the density of photon flux is $\rho/\text{cm}^2/\text{sec}$, the number N of incident photons in time t will be

$$N = \rho h^2 t . \tag{1}$$

The standard deviation from this value is $\sqrt{N} = \sqrt{(\rho h^2 t)}$. Considering now a second area with incident photon flux ρ', the number N' falling on an equal area is

$$N' = \rho' h^2 t , \tag{2}$$

and the standard deviation is $\sqrt{N'} = \sqrt{(\rho' h^2 t)}$.

It is required that the brightness difference $(N - N')$ should be detectable in the presence of the statistical fluctuations of N and N', which combine to give an average difference $(N - N')$ equal to $\sqrt{(N + N')}$. To insure detection, we assume $(N - N')$ to be greater than $\sqrt{(N + N')}$ by a factor of K, known as the "coefficient of certainty." Hence

$$(N - N')_{\min} = K\sqrt{(N + N')} . \tag{3}$$

Therefore, the minimum picture contrast detectable will be

$$C_{\min} = \frac{(N - N')_{\min}}{N} = \frac{K\sqrt{(N + N')}}{N} \cong K\sqrt{\frac{(2)}{(N)}} . \tag{4}$$

Since $(N - N')_{\min}$ is small, therefore $N \cong N'$. If the probability of a photon's being detected or recorded is γ, then

$$C_{\min} = \frac{K}{h}\sqrt{\left(\frac{2}{\rho\gamma t}\right)} . \tag{5}$$

Thus the minimum contrast detectable is directly proportional to the required coefficient of certainty of detection and inversely proportional to the square root of the number of recorded photons per unit area ($\rho\gamma t$) and to the linear dimensions of the detail to be detected.

In evaluating this recorded image, noise may be added, which will reduce the minimum detectable contrast. This noise may arise from the first stage of a signal amplifier or from the noise carried by a scanning beam. In all practical television camera tubes it is one form or the other of this instrument noise that limits sensitivity.

§ 2. EXISTING TELEVISION CAMERA TUBES

To appreciate the limitations of the existing commercial television tubes for the purposes of astronomical observations and the possibilities of developing tubes more suitable for these purposes, it is worthwhile to consider briefly the mechanism of operation and the resulting characteristics of the three types of tube at present in use. These are the Image Orthicon, the C.P.S. Emitron (or Orthicon), and the Vidicon.

2.1. The C.P.S. Emitron

The C.P.S. Emitron (McGee 1950) is similar in principle of operation to the earlier, and now obsolete, Orthicon (Rose and Iams 1939) but has been so greatly improved in important features that it is the only tube of this type that we need consider.

The tube and its immediately associated driving circuits are shown in Figure 2. The glass envelope, *1*, has an electron gun, *2*, mounted axially at one end, which projects a beam of electrons toward a target, *7*, which is mounted on the inner surface of a flat end-window, *6*. This target is a thin sheet of glass about 0.01 cm thick and 3.5 × 4.5 cm in area. It is coated on the surface facing the end-window, *6*, with a highly transparent, conducting coating—the signal plate—

from which a lead passes through the tube wall to earth through the signal resistance, *9*, of the head amplifier. On the free surface of the target is formed a mosaic of minute, transparent, square elements, *7*, of suitable photosensitive material. These square elements are separated and well insulated from one another by strips of clean insulating surface.

The light of the optical image, formed, for example, by the lens, *10*, passes through the end-window, the signal plate, the dielectric, and the photosensitive mosaic elements, from the free surface of which it liberates photoelectrons.

The electron beam is projected by the electron gun, *2*, from a thermionic cathode at earth potential along the axis of the tube, in space maintained at a uniform potential of about 200 volts by a conductive coating, *3*, on the tube walls. The beam is focused by the axial magnetic field, H_a, produced by the solenoid, *11*, to form an image of the limiting aperture of the electron gun on the

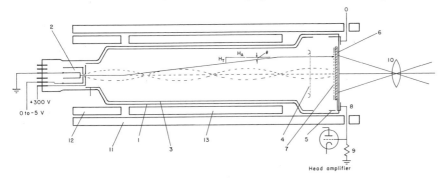

FIG. 2.—The C.P.S. Emitron

mosaic, *7*. It passes through the fine metal mesh, *4*, which is held at approximately the potential of the wall electrode, *3*, and from the mesh to the mosaic the beam is decelerated, since, in the absence of light falling on the target, the mosaic tends to take up earth potential—the same as that of the cathode of the electron gun. Hence, in the equilibrium condition, the beam electrons approach the mosaic surface with very small energy, and only if·the mosaic has by some means lost negative charges can any beam electrons land to compensate for them. The unaccepted beam electrons are reflected and return along approximately the same path to the electron gun.

It will be clear that under these conditions there is a strong electric field between the mesh, *4*, and the mosaic, *7*, which effectively removes any electrons released from the mosaic. Hence, when an optical image is projected onto the mosaic, photoelectrons liberated in strict proportionality at any point to the image intensity are accelerated away from the mosaic and collected on the tube walls. Thus positive charges, corresponding accurately in distribution and magnitude to the light in the optical image, are built up on the mosaic surface. This may be termed a "charge image," and it can be integrated on the mosaic over various lengths of time, provided that the resistivity of the material of the target dielectric is sufficiently high to reduce electrical leakage, either through the dielectric or across its surface between mosaic elements, to a negligible amount.

The electron beam is scanned across the mosaic in a raster of about 500 lines by two pairs of saddle-coils, of which one pair, *13*, is shown. These produce transverse magnetic fields, H_t, at right angles to the tube axis and to one another. The complete raster of about 500 lines is scanned 25 times per second in Europe and 30 times per second in the United States. In between scans, positive charges are built up on the mosaic elements because of loss of photoelectrons, and at each passage of the scanning beam over a picture point the integrated charges are discharged in about 2×10^{-7} second. This discharge from a mosaic element produces an induced current to earth through the signal resistance, *9*, which is accurately proportional at each point to the integrated light-flux on that picture point during the previous frame period ($\frac{1}{25}$ or $\frac{1}{30}$ sec). This picture signal current is superimposed on an opposite and, on the average, equal current flowing in the opposite direction, owing to the steady loss of photoelectrons from the photosensitive mosaic. If the image illumination does not change during a frame period, this charging current will be constant. However, changes in total image illumination will produce proportional changes in this current, which will be superimposed, as unwanted interference, on the picture signal.

From the dimensions of the glass dielectric of the target ($3.5 \times 4.5 \times 0.01$ cm) and assuming the dielectric constant k to be 6, we see that the capacitance of the mosaic to the signal plate is $\sim$750 $\mu\mu$f, or about 3.75×10^{-3} $\mu\mu$f per picture point if we have 2×10^5 picture points per picture frame. Hence a rise of 4 volts in potential of a picture point will result from a charge of 1.5×10^{-14} coulomb or $\sim$10^5 electron charges. If such a charged element is discharged in the time taken to scan one picture point (2×10^{-7} sec), we obtain a signal current of $\sim$0.75 $\times 10^{-7}$ amp.

It is found in practice that if the areas of the mosaic corresponding to the peak white areas of the image rise to a potential greater than about 4 volts, then both the focus and the direction of travel of the approaching low-velocity electron beam are distorted. This sets one limit to the operation of such a tube. Also it is found that the beam current that can be landed on such a target from an electron gun which produces a focused spot about 0.01 cm in diameter and so drives it down to cathode potential is about 10^{-7} amp. Hence the capacitance and, therefore, the thickness of the target are determined. If the target capacitance is too large, the integrated charges will not be discharged in one scan, and serious frame-to-frame lag will appear. If the capacitance is too small, the potential rises on the mosaic necessary to give adequate signal/noise ratio will be such that loss of definition and image distortion are incurred.

The shot noise associated with a signal current i_s is given by

$$\langle i_n^2 \rangle = 2ei_s f, \tag{6}$$

where f is the band width over which the noise is observed and in this case may be 3 Mc/s. Evaluating i_n for the values $i_s = 10^{-7}$ amp and $f = 3$ Mc/s, $i_n = 3 \times 10^{-10}$ amp. The noise generated in the first stage of the head amplifier (James 1952) is given by the expression

$$\langle i_n^2 \rangle = 4\,kTf \left(\frac{1}{R} + \tfrac{4}{3}\pi^2 f^2 C^2 R_n \right), \tag{7}$$

where k is Boltzmann's constant, T is the absolute temperature, C is the input capacity of the amplifier, R is the signal resistance, and R_n is the equivalent noise resistance of the first value.

Again evaluating $\langle i_n \rangle$ for such practical values of the components as $C = 30\ \mu\mu f$, $R = 10^6\ \Omega$, $R_n = 100\ \Omega$, $f = 3$ Mc/s, we arrive at a value of $\langle i_n \rangle \simeq 10^{-9}$ amp. Hence the noise generated in the head amplifier is considerably greater than the noise inherent in the signal current. Moreover, the amplifier noise appears of equal amplitude, superimposed on all levels of signal, whereas the noise inherent in the signal current is a maximum in the peak white signals and zero in the black areas. Hence the amplifier contributes substantially all the noise appearing in a reproduced picture and sets the limit to the sensitivity of the tube.

The color-response curves showing the quantum efficiency of the photosensitive mosaics of the types formerly used in this type of tube (i.e., Sb-Cs, or S-11 and Ag-Bi-Cs, or S-10) are illustrated in Figure 3. An effective sensitivity of 25 μA/L is then to be regarded as good, since the mosaic cannot cover more than about 60 per cent of the actual image area. Hence a peak white illumination of $\sim$0.02 L/ft² on the mosaic or $\simeq$0.4 L/ft² illumination on a white object in a scene using an objective lens of about $f/2$ gave a signal/noise ratio of 100/1 or 40 db. This is a good-quality picture in which the amplifier noise is hardly noticeable even in the dark areas of the picture.

In the signal-generating tubes used in the early days of electronic television—iconoscope, Emitron, Super-Emitron, etc.—serious spurious signals were developed, and the reproduced picture was only an approximation to the original. However, the C.P.S. Emitron develops substantially no spurious signals; absolute black level in the picture is reproduced at constant signal level, and the signal at any point is very accurately proportional to the product of the illumination in the image at that point integrated over the previous frame period and the photosensitivity of the mosaic at the point where that part of the image falls. Thus the device is capable of giving accurate quantitative light-measurements in the form of an electrical signal.

The resolution of this device depends on the beam focus, the mosaic structure, and the band width of the amplifier used. In practice, 5-line pairs/mm can be resolved with 100 per cent modulation and 10-line pairs/mm with 30–50 per cent modulation, given an amplifier of adequate band width.

If greater image resolution is required, it becomes necessary to reduce the area of the focused spot of the scanning electron beam, yet to retain the same effective beam current, since the mosaic must be discharged at the same rate. If this is done, then the reduction in area of the spot is compensated for by its greater speed of travel across the mosaic, and hence the signal current remains constant. However, it is necessary to provide a signal amplifier with a greater band width, since the band width is proportional to the square of the number of scanned lines. Thus to raise the number of lines from the present British standard of 405 to the European standard of 625 requires a band-width increase by a factor of $\sim(625/405)^2$ or ~ 2.5 times. From equation (7) we see that the r.m.s. amplifier noise current increases as the $\frac{3}{2}$ power of the band width, or, in this case, by $(2.5)^{3/2}$, or about four times, to about 4×10^{-9} amp. On the other hand, the shot noise inherent in the signal current increases only as the $\frac{1}{2}$ power of the band width and hence in this case will increase to only about 5×10^{-10} amp.

The area of the photosensitive mosaic of this tube (3.5 × 4.5 cm) is rather larger than that of the unvignetted image at the prime focus of the 200-inch Hale telescope, and the area of one picture point using a 405-line raster is approximately the same as that of a star image under good seeing conditions, i.e., 0.1 mm. Hence, as a first approximation, we may consider the practicability of reproducing such an image.

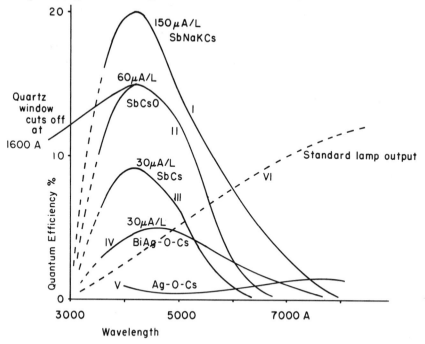

Fig. 3.—Quantum efficiency-curves for principal photocathodes and relative energy output from standard lamp.

As we have seen, in reproducing such an image at 25 frames/sec, we require approximately 10^5 electron charges per picture point to give a signal/noise ratio of 40 db. Now the light received from a twenty-second magnitude star at ground level is 10^{-18} L/in², and hence the light collected by the 200-inch telescope in the image of a twenty-second magnitude star is $\pi \times 10^{-14}$ L. Thus in Figure 1 the uniform background may be taken as $\pi \times 10^{-10}$ L/cm², with twenty-second magnitude star images superimposed over an area of 10^{-4} cm² of an equal additional illumination.

The sensitivity of photoelectric devices is measured in terms of current yield per lumen from an agreed source of light, which is a tungsten-filament lamp operated at 2875° K (or 2870° K in the United States). The variation of light-energy radiated with wave length is shown as the dotted curve *VI* in Figure 3, from which it is clear that this source radiates light which has a much greater proportion of red to blue than has white light, such as average starlight. As most photoelectric surfaces that would be used for the detection of visible light have a strong concentration of their sensitivity in the blue end of the spectrum (again see Fig. 3), the actual current yield per lumen of white light will be between twice and four times that as measured by a standard source. Hence photo-cathodes of the Sb-Cs-O, Sb-Cs, or Bi-Ag-Cs type (curves *II*, *III*, and *IV*, Fig. 3) may have effective sensitivities to white light of between 100 and 200 µA/L. In a photosensitive mosaic this would be reduced to between 60 and 120 µA/L. If we assume 100 µA/L as a reasonable value, then the number of photoelectrons produced by the image of a twenty-second magnitude star per picture point per second $= (\pi \times 10^{-14} \times 10^{-4})/(1.6 \times 10^{-19}) = 20$ electrons/sec/picture point. Hence for this image to charge a mosaic picture point to a level that will result in a signal/noise ratio of 40 db on discharge will require integration for $\sim 10^5/20 = 5000$ seconds. However, a signal/noise ratio of 40 db, or 100/1 ratio of signal amplitude to r.m.s. noise, is probably an unnecessarily large coefficient of certainty. It is probable that if we assume a value of 20 db, the signal of a star will very seldom be simulated by a noise pulse. Hence an exposure time of 500 seconds, or 8 minutes, should give a record in which the star images are clearly distinguishable from amplifier noise, and the ratio of star signal to shot noise of the signal due to the sky background is an order of magnitude larger still. The exposure time required to obtain clear discrimination between a twenty-second magnitude star and sky background using the 200-inch telescope and the best photographic plates is ~ 30 minutes. Hence this television tube seems to be rather more sensitive than this film.

Another factor that must be considered is the thermal electron emission from such a photosensitive mosaic surface that will produce a uniform distribution of charge on the mosaic which will use up storage capacity and contribute to noise. The thermal emission from the commonly used photocathode surfaces is not known with great reliability. That from an Ag-O-Cs (S-1) photocathode (curve *V*, Fig. 3) is large, probably $\sim 10^{-10}$ amp/cm², but from an Sb-Cs cathode it is very much less. It has been quoted as 10^{-13} amp/cm² (Sommer 1947), but this appears to be much too high, and a more realistic figure would be 10^{-15} amp/cm², while in some cases it must be one or even two orders of magnitude smaller than this.

If we assume a dark current of 10^{-15} amp/cm², then the emission from a photosensitive mosaic will be

$$\frac{10^{-15} \times 3.5 \times 4.5}{1.6 \times 10^{-19}} \text{ electrons per second}$$

or

$$\frac{10^{-15} \times 3.5 \times 4.5}{1.6 \times 10^{-19} \times 2 \times 10^{5}} = 0.5 \text{ electrons per second per picture point} .$$

Thus the contribution of the thermal electron emission is probably less than 2.5 per cent of that due to the uniform sky background, and it may be considerably less. Hence it should not appreciably limit the efficiency of operation of such a device.

The effect of thermal emission may be a little more serious if the more red-sensitive photocathode of the Bi-Ag-Cs type S-10 is used, since this has a distinctly higher dark current. However, it appears likely that the more recently developed trialkali cathode (Sommer 1955) will be used because of its greater quantum efficiency (see curve I, Fig. 3). It appears that, in spite of its greater quantum efficiency, especially in the red and infrared, its dark current is not greater than that of the Sb-Cs (or S-9) cathode. If the Ag-AgO-Cs photocathode (curve V, Fig. 3) is used for the purpose of achieving high infrared sensitivity, the thermal current will be serious at room temperature. To achieve the best results, it will be necessary to cool this cathode, and at the temperature of $-80°$ C the dark current is reduced by a factor of $\sim 10^3$ compared with that at room temperature.

These data suggest that a television signal-generating tube of this type would be at least as efficient as, or possibly more efficient by a useful factor than, the photographic plates normally used for recording faint optical images. However, in practice this tube is not satisfactory, because the insulation of the storage target is not adequate to retain the electrical charges for the times required to integrate a useful charge. The glass dielectric (see p. 308) is made of a glass with a specific resistivity of $\sim 10^{14}$ Ω-cm. That is, the total resistance between the mosaic elements and the signal plate is

$$R \cong \frac{10^{14}}{1500} \; \Omega .$$

The total capacitance of the mosaic elements to the signal plate is $C \sim 750 \; \mu\mu f$. Hence the time constant, τ, of this condenser is ~ 50 seconds. Now it will be clear that the mosaic can integrate effectively only for a period much less than τ—say 5 seconds. This is very much shorter than the time required (500 sec) to integrate sufficient charge to give a reliable discrimination of twenty-second-magnitude stars from amplifier noise.

Another defect of this type of tube for the purpose of charge integration is the fact that leakage of charge may take place across the mosaic surface. The efficiency of this insulation is a compromise with photosensitivity. In the case of commercial television tubes, this is adjusted to give the maximum photosensitivity with adequate insulation to insure that no substantial electrical leakage takes place from element to element in one picture-frame period, 0.04 second. However, this is quite inadequate when the charges must be integrated for many minutes. The trouble in this case, of course, is not loss of charge but loss of image definition. In the normal way of operating such tubes, the adequate mosaic insulation can be achieved only at the expense of photosensitivity.

To sum up: such a television signal-generating tube would probably give useful results but for the following defects: (1) low insulation of mosaic elements from signal plate; (2) low insulation of mosaic elements from one another; (3) rather low capacitance of mosaic elements to signal plate.

2.2. Improved C.P.S. Emitron

Recently an improved version of the C.P.S. Emitron has been produced by E.M.I. Electronics Ltd., which has two important new features. (1) The mosaic potential is completely stabilized by a fine metal mesh stretched close to and in front of the mosaic and held at 10–15 volts positive. Though this is very important in normal television operation, it is probably not very important in our application, although some cases may occur where it may be necessary to observe faint objects in the presence of very much brighter objects. (2) The photosensitive mosaic is the trialkali (S-20) type (Sb-Na-K-Cs) (curve I in Fig. 3). This not only gives something like three times the effective sensitivity but, by some unexplained mechanism, also results in exceptionally high insulation between mosaic elements.

Thus it occurred to the author that, starting with such a tube, a very useful performance might be attained by cooling the target and hence increasing both dielectric and surface insulation. By the same process, any residual dark current would be reduced by a large factor and a gain of sensitivity as compared with the old type of tube by a factor of 3 would correspondingly reduce the required integration times.

Experiments carried out by Randall (1960) in the author's laboratories showed that, by cooling the tube until the target reached about $-50°$ C, the resistivity of the glass of the dielectric could be increased to about 10^{18} Ω-cm, and hence the time constant of the mosaic capacitance was increased to $\sim 5 \times 10^5$ seconds.

The cooling also increased the insulation between mosaic elements so that it became practicable to integrate for times greater than an hour without losing either charge or definition. The procedure adopted is as follows:

1. The operation of the tube is checked on a fixed test image to insure adjustment of focus, alignment, beam current, etc.

2. The optical test image is removed and all residual charge scanned off the mosaic. The electron beam is then suppressed by biasing the control grid negative.

3. The cathode heater current is reduced until the cathode emits no light capable of liberating electrons from the mosaic.

4. The focus and scanning currents may be cut off to reduce heat dissipation in the environment of the tube, which is cooled, for example, by blowing refrigerated dry air through the tube housing in the direction from the target end to the electron-gun end.

5. The static voltages applied to all electrodes are maintained so that photoelectrons liberated from the mosaic are effectively removed to the wall electrode or mesh.

6. The image to be detected is now projected onto the mosaic, and charge integration is continued until a charge has been accumulated which, on "reading off," will give an adequate signal/noise ratio. The times required for integration must be found by trial and error.

7. The tube and camera are then brought back to operating conditions. The focus and scan currents, etc., are switched on and adjusted.

8. With the control grid of the electron-gun biased to suppress the beam current and the stabilizing mesh (immediately in front of the mosaic) biased to suppress photoemission, the temperature of the cathode is raised, in a few seconds, to its normal operating level.

9. The stabilizing mesh is switched to its normal operating potential, and, in as short a time thereafter as practicable, the electron beam is turned up to its normal value.

10. The scanning beam discharges the mosaic to produce a picture signal. Substantially all the integrated charges should be discharged in one complete frame scan. The picture produced is displayed on a high quality C.R.T. display monitor, which may be photographed. The signals may also be recorded on magnetic tape for reproduction and measurement as required.

This procedure was carried out successfully, and it was shown that integration for about 1 hour could be achieved without apparent loss of signal or image definition. In fact, there was little difference between the image quality reproduced under normal television conditions and that reproduced when the image brightness was reduced by a factor of 10^5 and the exposure increased by the same factor. Thus there is no departure from reciprocity. Photographic exposures made under the same conditions showed pronounced reciprocity failure, and the television camera tube was several times faster than direct photography using the best available photographic emulsions, even when conventional, high-speed scanning of the tube was used to reproduce the image and the quality of the image was limited by amplifier noise. Had slow scanning been used to read out the charge image, better definition and/or signal/noise ratio could have been achieved.

The main reason why this project was abandoned was because of an irregular spurious background that appeared strongly on the reproduced picture when the tube was operated at low temperature. It was known that signal-generating tubes of this type were prone to produce a very irregular signal in uniformly illuminated areas of the mosaic when the surface insulation of the latter was very high (E.M.I. Electronics Ltd., private communication). This is due to slight variations in the insulation and/or size of the mosaic elements which vary the coplanar biasing effect of the insulating spaces between the mosaic elements. This modulates the amount of charge that a mosaic element can accumulate and hence the signal amplitude that is reproduced. Thus a uniformly illuminated area of the image is reproduced with an irregular, mottled brightness. If

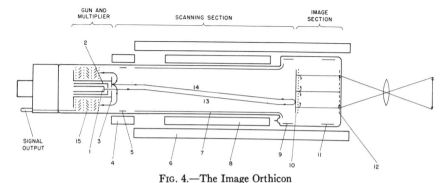

Fig. 4.—The Image Orthicon

the fairly uniform sky background, illustrated in Figure 1, is reproduced with such irregularity, it will obviously make the detection of faint stars against such a background very difficult indeed.

Mainly because of this difficulty, work on this method of image recording with this particular tube was discontinued. It also became clear that any such signal-generating device would need to be free from similar spurious signal defects if it were to be useful in astronomical observations.

2.3. The Image Orthicon

The camera tube that we must consider next is the Image Orthicon, since it is widely used in television; it is a very sensitive tube, it has been used in some experimental astronomical observations, and it incorporates some important television techniques.

The tube is illustrated in Figure 4. The glass envelope has an electron gun sealed into it axially at one end, and a beam of electrons, *13*, is produced from the cathode, *1*, modulated by the electrode, *2*, accelerated to about 200 ev and limited to a cross-section of about 0.002 inch by the electrode, *3*. The beam is focused by the axial field produced by the solenoid, 6 (the beam diameter may then be about 0.003 inch in diameter), and scanned by transverse magnetic fields produced by saw-tooth wave-form currents in the coils, 8, as in the case of the tube described in the last section.

The electron beam scans the target, 10, and stabilizes the scanned surface to the potential of the cathode of the electron gun. The unaccepted electrons return along the path, 14, nearly the same as that followed by the outward-bound beam, 13, but diverge from it slightly and land on the electrode, 3, slightly out of focus. The surface of 3 is a good emitter of secondary electrons, and the secondaries liberated by the return beam are attracted to the first stage of the electron multiplier, 15. They are directed to this electrode by the electrode 5 held at a potential negative to 3. After passing through several stages of electron multiplication, throughout which the signal/noise ratio decreases very little, the greatly multiplied beam is collected by the output electrode and passes into the signal amplifier. However, the output signal current is much larger than the amplifier noise current, and hence the output signal/noise ratio is little less than that inherent in the beam returning from the target.

The charge-storage target, 10, is quite different from that described in the previous section. It consists of a very thin sheet of slightly conducting glass 2–3 μ thick, about 1.25 inches in diameter, stretched and mounted on a metal ring to which is also attached a stretched metal mesh having 500–750 meshes/inch and a shadow ratio of about 40 per cent. The mesh is mounted parallel to, and at a distance of about 0.002 inch from, the glass. It is the capacitance formed by this mesh and the glass film that forms the charge-storage capacitance. The effective area of the target is about 5 cm², and hence it has a capacitance of $\sim$50 $\mu\mu$f. This is smaller by a factor of $\sim$15 than that of the C.P.S. Emitron target and is an important parameter in the operation of the tube, especially for storage of large charges.

The light of the optical image is focused by a lens onto a transparent conducting photocathode, 12, formed on the inner surface of the flat end-window of the tube. The photoelectrons liberated from it by the light are accelerated by an electric field between the cathode and the target and focused by the extension of the axial magnetic field of the solenoid, 6, to form an electron image on the target, 10. Rather more than 50 per cent of these incident electrons pass through the metal mesh and land on the glass diaphragm, which is a fairly good secondary-electron emitter. Each primary electron, having an energy of $\sim$ 500 ev, will liberate about 5 secondary electrons, most of which are captured by the mesh, which is held approximately 2 volts positive relative to the glass surface. Thus, although maximum photoelectric efficiency is obtained from the continuous photocathode (as compared with $\sim$60 per cent from a mosaic), an almost equal loss is suffered by interception of photoelectrons by the mesh. The shot noise carried by that part of this stream of photoelectrons that actually contributes to the charging of the mosaic sets one limit to the tube sensitivity.

Each photoelectron that reaches the glass surface produces perhaps 5 secondary electrons, which contribute to build up the charges integrated on the capacitance formed by the glass surface and metal mesh. This process results in those points on the glass being charged positively, and in proportion to the brightness of the image in the areas to which they correspond. At least, this is approximately true until the potential of the glass surface approaches that of the mesh, and over this range the charges integrated on the storage target are fairly accurately proportional to the light.

When the potential of the glass surface approaches that of the adjacent metal mesh, the field accelerating the secondary electrons toward the mesh decreases, then vanishes, and finally may reverse. This is because the secondary electrons have appreciable initial energies and so are able to penetrate through the mesh. They then find themselves in a reverse field, which accelerates them back toward the mesh, on which some may land, but others pass through and land on adjacent areas of the glass target, charging it negatively. This area may correspond to a completely dark area of the picture, and hence these electrons spreading from a bright area will depress the potential of this area below that corresponding to absolute black in the picture signal. Thus a bright area is surrounded by a dark halo.

The signal characteristic of this tube is fairly linear for small signals while the potential of the glass is below that of the mesh, but, as the light intensity is raised and the potential of large areas of the glass target approaches that of the mesh, a different signal-production regime is set up. The secondary electrons now spread fairly widely across the mosaic, leaving their point of origin positive and driving their point of landing negative. It follows that a dynamic equilibrium will be set up in which those areas of the target receiving most photoelectrons and corresponding to bright areas of the image will be more positive than those corresponding to darker areas of the image. When these areas are restored to cathode potential by the scanning beam, a picture signal is generated, but it is far from being proportional to the brightness of the image at the point to which it corresponds.

It is the combination of these two modes of signal generation, which often coexist on neighboring areas of the target, that gives the Image Orthicon its special characteristics as a television camera tube. The second of these modes is important in television broadcasting but is of limited interest in circumstances where the tube is required to give a quantitative signal output as a measure of the light-input. For this purpose we must work in the first mode, where the glass surface potential is below that of the mesh and the integrated charges on the glass and hence the modulation of the scanning beam are proportional to the integrated light-input at each point over the previous frame period.

The positive charges induce equal and like free charges on the other surface of the glass plate, which are discharged by the scanning beam at each transit, thus modulating the beam that returns to the multiplier so that it is at a minimum at points corresponding to peak white illumination. At the same time a potential difference is established across the glass diaphragm which is equalized by current leakage through the slightly conducting glass. Substantially all this charge equalization must take place within the television picture-frame period of 0.04 second, otherwise a serious time lag results which produces blurring of moving objects. To avoid this undesirable feature in television operation, the characteristiç of the glass of the diaphragm must be such that the time constant τ of the capacitor formed by opposite surfaces of area A of the sheet of glass of thickness d must be very much less than the television picture-frame period. Or $\tau \ll 0.04$ second. But

$$\tau = CR = \frac{KAB}{4\pi d}\frac{\rho d}{A} = \frac{K\rho B}{4\pi},$$

where K is the dielectric constant and ρ is the specific resistance of the glass and B is a constant. If $K = 5$ and $\rho = 5 \times 10^{10}$ Ω-cm, then $\tau = 0.02$ second. This requirement is met by the lime-soda glass used at a correct operating temperature, $\sim 40°$ C. At a temperature less than $35°$ C, the target shows image lag when operated at standard rates (25 or 30 frames per second). However, this rapid repetition rate, as implied previously, is of little astronomical interest. When the target is cooled, the time constant τ increases from 15 seconds at $-50°$ C to 300 seconds at $-75°$ C (see Livingston 1957). The tube functions properly at these lowered temperatures and correspondingly long exposure times. With the development of thin film targets (see § 2.4), the glass ones can now be considered obsolete for most astronomical purposes.

The considerations that determine the signal/noise ratio are more complex than in the case of the C.P.S. Emitron. The first item to consider is the charge-storage target. This is of the order of 50 $\mu\mu$f capacitance, and hence it will be charged to 2 volts by ~ 3000 electrons/picture point. However, this represents complete saturation—a state in which no more secondary electrons can be collected by the metal mesh—and hence results in departure from linear relationship between image intensity and integrated electric charge. Hence, for reasonable proportionality, we may allow accumulation of about 2000 electrons/picture point, but these in turn will have been produced by no more than ~ 400 primary photoelectrons. Hence the mean deviation in such a charge is $\not< \sqrt{400}$, and the signal/r.m.s. noise is $\not> 400/\sqrt{400} = 20$. This noise is a maximum in the peak white areas and zero in absolutely black areas and hence is not so serious as noise that appears equally in both white and black areas, as, for example, amplifier noise.

If the stored charges are now used to modulate the scanning beam, the most efficient performance would be achieved if the beam could be fully modulated, i.e., completely absorbed by the target in peak white areas. This is impossible, and in practice a beam modulation of greater than 20 per cent is difficult to achieve; probably 10 per cent is a representative value. Hence the scanning beam i_B must be $\sim$10 times the signal current i_s, or

$$i_B = 10 i_s = \frac{10 \times 2000 \times 1.6 \times 10^{-19}}{2 \times 10^{-7}}$$

$$= 1.6 \times 10^{-8} \text{ amp} .$$

Now the peak white signal current is 1.6×10^{-9} amp, and the shot noise carried by the scanning beam i_B will be a maximum in the black areas of the picture and will be given by

$$\langle i_n^2 \rangle = 2 \, ei_B f$$

$$= 2 \, (1.6 \times 10^{-19}) \, (1.6 \times 10^{-8}) \, (3 \times 10^6)$$

if f is equal to 3 megacycles per second. Therefore,

$$\langle i_n \rangle = 1.24 \times 10^{-10} \text{ amp}$$

or

$$\frac{i_s}{\langle i_n \rangle} = \frac{1.6 \times 10^{-9}}{1.24 \times 10^{-10}} \cong 13 .$$

Hence the noise from this source not only is greater than that due to the fluctuations of the charges stored on the target but appears at its maximum in the black areas of the picture, where it is most obvious and objectionable. The noise from these two sources adds together in the return beam, which passes into the electron multiplier, in which it is multiplied by a factor of at least 10^3. It is the important characteristic of such electron multipliers that a modulated electron stream can be multiplied by very large factors without decreasing the signal/noise ratio of the electron current by more than a small amount, generally of the order of 10 per cent. Thus the output signal current ($\sim 10^{-6}$ amp) is far greater than the noise current of the thermionic value amplifier into which the signal passes, and the amplifier noise contributes very little to the total noise of the output signal.

It should be noted that the noise associated with the signals from the Image Orthicon is "white noise," i.e., it is uniformly distributed in energy throughout the frequency spectrum. Thus there are considerable low-frequency components of this noise which appear as long horizontal "dashes" in the reproduced picture. By contrast, the noise produced by the amplifier used in conjunction with the C.P.S. Emitron or Vidicon is mainly concentrated on the high-frequency ranges and appears as dots of short duration. For normal observing purposes and for the same signal/r.m.s. noise ratio, the white noise is more disturbing than the peaked-amplifier, high-frequency noise, and it has been estimated (Schade 1948) that comparable picture quality is reached when this is 5–10 db greater for the electron-multiplier output device than for those with peaked-amplifier output.

It was noted above that the r.m.s. noise current from this tube is proportional to the square root of the frequency band ($f^{1/2}$) required. On the other hand, it was noted that the r.m.s. noise of a peaked-response wide-band signal amplifier is proportional to $f^{3/2}$. Hence this type of tube, with electron-multiplier output, gains in sensitivity relative to those in which the main signal amplification takes place in a thermionic amplifier as the required band width increases— that is, as the number of picture points scanned per second increases.

Under the television standards of the United Kingdom (405 lines, 25 frames/ sec) this camera tube will give an adequate, though noisy, picture with a photo-cathode illumination of $\sim$0.01 L/ft² and appreciably greater depth of focus than the C.P.S. Emitron, since its effective photocathode area is smaller. If the television standards are increased to those of Europe (625 lines, 25 frames/sec), the Image Orthicon becomes relatively more efficient than the C.P.S. Emitron; but if the total time of scanning a raster can be reduced, then the situation is reversed, since the band width (f) is reduced. Thus, as in possible astronomical applications the time of scanning the charged mosaic can be lengthened almost at will, the type of tube with amplifier output (C.P.S. Emitron or Vidicon) can be as efficient as or more efficient than the Image Orthicon (Theile 1960).

This tube is not satisfactory for long time-exposure television, since the lime-soda glass target on which the charge image is stored has a relatively low transverse insulation. Hence charges will leak across its surface appreciably in little more than a television frame period. In the original design of Image Orthicon, this feature was inherent because the tube would operate only when there was reasonable charge conduction from one surface of the glass target to the other. Even with the thinnest glass targets that could be made ($\sim$2.5 μ thick), the transverse charge leakage was just adequate to give acceptable picture definition. That is, the leakage became appreciable in $>$0.04 second, and it appeared that the tube could not be used for charge integration for any useful time duration.

2.4. MODIFIED IMAGE ORTHICON

More recently (Day, Hannam, and Wargo 1958) a modified tube has been developed in which the glass diaphragm of the charge-storage tube is replaced by a much thinner film of magnesium oxide, $\sim$500 Å thick, but of much higher resistivity, and a trialkali photocathode (S-20) is incorporated. This film appears to have a higher resistivity parallel to, than normal to, its surface. The latter is low enough to insure an adequately short discharge time-constant for television operation and because of the high transverse resistivity the spread of charges over the film is greatly reduced. This is claimed to result in improved image resolution in normal television operation. Also, because of the high efficiency of the magnesium oxide as a secondary-electron emitter, the multiplication of the primary photoelectrons at the target surface is appreciably greater than for glass. This need not necessarily be an advantage because it may result in too few primary photoelectrons being able completely to charge the target capacitance. Then the shot noise in the stored charges could become the dominant source of noise instead of the noise of the scanning beam, as at present.

Another advantage claimed for the magnesium oxide target is that, since the transfer of charge is by electron conduction, there is little deterioration in the performance of the target, such as occurs in the glass target, where the conduction is by sodium ions, resulting in loss of sodium and change in the quality of the glass.

Recently reported experiments by DeWitt (1961), using an Image Orthicon of this type (General Electric Co. type Z-5396), have given very promising results. It is necessary to cool the tube to achieve adequate target insulation, but, when this is done, integration for some tens of minutes is claimed without image deterioration.

Slow read-out is used and found to be very advantageous, not so much because it gives any improvement in signal/noise ratio but for the incidental advantages—for example, more complete target discharge with smaller, better-focused beams; easier recording of the generated signals on magnetic tape or by photography of a cathode-ray display tube; easier scanning of a raster with a large number of lines, etc.

Presumably because of the small target capacitance, charge integration is allowed to go on for only a few minutes, and the target is then scanned, and the integrated charge image is "read out" and recorded. This procedure is repeated several times on the same subject, and the several reproductions are recorded—superimposed, say, on the same photographic plate. The wanted signals add directly, but the random noise partially cancels out, giving an improvement in signal/noise after n added recordings by a factor $\sqrt{n}$.

DeWitt has made comparisons between the speed of recording of test patterns by this image orthicon used as an integrating device and typical photographic emulsions—Eastman Kodak types 103a-O and 103a-U, the former with blue light and the latter with red.

For equal detectability of star images, the exposure for the emulsion was 1 minute, while that for the tube was 1/112 minute, a gain by a factor of 112. For a plate exposure of 600 minutes, the relative gain was by a factor of 450, of which a factor of 4 times was due to reciprocity failure, which affects the plate but not the tube. Using red light and 103a-U plates, the gain was about the same for 1-minute exposures, but 900 times for the longer exposures.

The resolution of the photographic emulsion is limited to about 40 lp/mm, but that of the television tube to 10 and under optimized conditions as much as 16 lp/mm (Livingston, private communication), and, for a realistic appraisal of the relative efficiencies, it is necessary to divide the above factors of gain in speed by the square of the relative resolutions, i.e., by 16×. This reduces the large gain factors to a less attractive value of 15× at the relatively high levels of image brightness, but it is still a very impressive factor (30✕ to 60✕) at the low light-levels where reciprocity failure is seriously reducing the efficiency of the photographic emulsions.

The mechanism of charge and discharge of the storage target of this image orthicon shows some peculiarities, according to DeWitt, and is apparently not yet fully understood. It seems possible that it may not have a strictly linear signal versus light characteristic. It would appear also that its most probable use is for straight image intensification such as might equally well be done by an image intensifier. Because of the small storage capacitance of the target, it does not seem well suited to the problem of detecting faint images superimposed on a bright sky background.

2.5. The Intensifier Orthicon

It is, in principle, possible to combine an image intensifier as the first section of a television signal-generating tube, so that a brighter image is incident upon the first photocathode. This has been done by the Radio Corporation of America, resulting in the Intensifier Orthicon (Morton and Reudy 1960).

A diagram of a two-stage Intensifier Orthicon is shown in Figure 5. This comprises, in essentials, a two-stage image intensifier such as that described by Stoudenheimer (1960), built onto the front of a conventional Image Orthicon with the output phosphor screen of the former in close proximity to the photocathode of the latter. Each stage of the cascade image intensifier operating at ~10 kv should give a gain of ~10✕. Thus for each photoelectron that leaves the primary photocathode, about 100 should leave the last cathode and arrive on the target, where each will produce ~5 secondary electrons from the target. Therefore, the charge-storage target can be fully charged and peak white picture signal produced with a primary optical image intensity of one-hundredth that required by the conventional Image Orthicon. It must be pointed out that each primary photoelectron produces ~500 electron charges on the storage target if all its daughter electrons reach the target. However, about 40 per cent of these, on the average, must be intercepted by the target mesh, and, since the disk of confusion of each group of daughter electrons, as they arrive on the target, must be ~50 μ, it will cover several mesh apertures, and hence about 60 per cent of these electrons will reach the glass target, and about 300 electron charges will be deposited. It follows that fully to charge the storage target to the knee of the characteristic curve will require only about 10 primary photoelectrons. The resulting signal/noise ratio is determined mainly by the random fluctuations in this small number and will be ≯ $\sqrt{10}$, regardless of any subsequent amplification. Increasing the light-intensity in the image will result in the tube operating above the knee of the characteristic curve, where the signal ceases to be proportional to the incident illumination.

A signal/noise ratio of ~3 is very unsatisfactory and would result in the details of a 400-line picture being largely obscured. It is probably better to

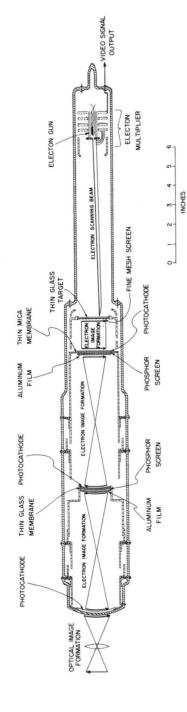

VIDEO SIGNAL OUTPUT

ELECTON GUN

ELECTRON MULTIPLIER

INCHES

0 1 2 3 4 5 6

ELECTRON SCANNING BEAM

FINE MESH SCREEN

PHOTOCATHODE

THIN GLASS TARGET

THIN MICA MEMBRANE

ALUMINUM FILM

PHOSPHOR SCREEN

ELECTRON IMAGE FORMATION

PHOTOCATHODE

THIN GLASS MEMBRANE

PHOTOCATHODE

ELECTRON IMAGE FORMATION

PHOSPHOR SCREEN

ALUMINUM FILM

ELECTRON IMAGE FORMATION

OPTICAL IMAGE FORMATION

Fig. 5.—The Intensifier Orthicon

limit the picture detail to say 100 lines and a correspondingly smaller band width, in which case the number of primary electrons per picture point would increase by a factor of 16 and the signal/noise ratio by a factor of 4.

2.6. The Vidicon

The Vidicon (Weimer, Forgue, and Goodrich 1950) has much in common with the C.P.S. Emitron except that a photoconductive target is used, and it is to this that it owes its special characteristics.

The tube with its associated operating circuits is shown in Figure 6. For reasons that will become clear later, the tube can be made smaller than those described above. It is usually about 1 inch in diameter and 6 inches long. A simple electron gun with cathode, *13*, modulator, *14*, and accelerator, *15*,

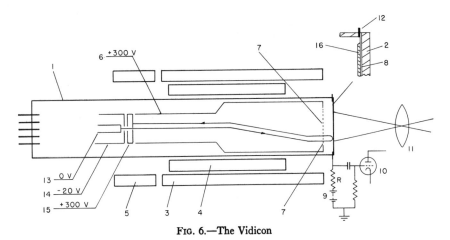

Fig. 6.—The Vidicon

projects a beam of electrons along the axis of the tube, *1*. This beam is focused by the field of the solenoid, *3*, aligned by the coils, *5*, and scanned by the fields produced by the coils, *4*. The beam travels in field-free space as far as the mesh, *7*, attached to the end of the metal cylinder, *6*. The end wall of the tube is a flat glass plate, *2*, which has, on its inner surface, a conducting, transparent coating which is the signal plate and is connected conductively through the ring, *12*, to the signal resistance, R, and through the capacitor to the grid of the first valve, *10*, of the preamplifier.

On the conducting signal plate, *8*, is formed a thin layer of photoconductive material, such as amorphous selenium or antimony trisulfide. In fact, the latter in a special spongy form is now generally used. This layer is about 1 μ thick, so that light of the image formed on it by the lens, *11*, penetrates substantially through it and lowers its resistance. When no light falls on the photoconductive layer, its resistance is high, and its front surface will be maintained at the potential of the cathode of the electron gun by the scanning electron beam, as in the tubes described above. But the signal plate, *8*, on the other side of the photo-conductive layer is maintained at a positive potential of 10–40 volts by the potential source, *9*, and the top of the signal resistance, *R*, is connected to the grid of the first valve, *10*, through a capacitor, so that the signal plate potential can be adjusted without altering the operating potential of the valve grid. Thus a potential difference of 10–40 volts will be maintained across the photoconduc-tive layer, causing a small positive current that is steadily discharged by beam of electrons reaching the free surface of the layer. Clearly, this steady dark current will depend on the potential difference that is maintained across the layer and it must be both small compared with the signal current and uniform from place to place on the mosaic, otherwise it will contribute noise and shading signal.

With this type of tube an electron multiplier is not used, and the signal cur-rent from the signal plate passes directly to the first stage of a preamplifier. For a 400-line picture and 3 Mc/s band-width amplifier, an r.m.s. amplifier noise current of $\sim 10^{-9}$ amp is the best normally realized, and the signal current re-quired to give peak white signal with a signal/noise ratio of 40 db is $\sim 10^{-7}$ amp. It is clear that the dark current should not be greater than 10^{-9} amp with 10 volts applied across the layer. Hence its resistance must be $\sim 10^{10}$ Ω, and, since its area is ~ 1.2 cm^2 and its thickness ~ 1 μ, its resistivity in the dark must be $\sim 10^{14}$ Ω-cm. This must drop to $\sim 10^{12}$ Ω-cm when illuminated to give a signal current of $\sim 10^{-7}$ amp.

For efficient operation, the image light must pass right through the photo-conductive dielectric layer, and for this it is found that the thickness cannot exceed ~ 1 μ. The material generally used (SbS$_3$) has a high S.I.C. (~ 8), but in the cellular form in which it is used this is reduced to near unity. Hence the capacitance per unit area of this target is larger by a factor of ~ 30 than that of, e.g., the C.P.S. Emitron and 500 times that of an Image Orthicon. Now, for a given accumulated charge, the voltage rise and hence the efficiency of current acceptance from the scanning beam decrease as the capacitance in-creases. Thus the area of the photoconductive target must be reduced considera-bly compared with, for example, that of the C.P.S. Emitron, in order to main-tain a comparable capacitance per picture point and so be able to achieve a satisfactory discharge rate or signal current. Thus the area is, of necessity, kept to $\sim 9.5 \times 12.5$ mm. This raises the further problem of achieving adequate beam focus to give 400-line resolution, or better, over such a small area. In fact, the achievement of this is assisted by the small area, since it becomes possible to use a stronger axial magnetic field and still scan the target at the line fre-quency. Both these changes result in better beam focus.

The net result of these design compromises is that the tube is small and re-quires only small, and comparatively light, focus and scanning coils. Good reso-lution of > 500 lines is achieved, as well as a peak white signal current of well over 10^{-7} amp, if adequate image intensity can be used. This gives a peak white signal/noise ratio of >40 db, and hence considerable top frequency boost, or "aperture correction," can be used in the amplifiers to give 100 per cent modulation at 500 lines or ~15 lp/mm resolution in the target plane, without undue amplifier noise appearing in the picture.

The best photoconductive material available at present for the dielectric has a response time that is appreciably greater than the television picture-frame period. Thus there is some lag from one picture frame to the next, and this, in fact, constitutes the main limitation to the tube sensitivity. This lag can become objectionable in normal televising of scenes of movement if more than 5 per cent of the signal properly belonging to one frame is held over until the next. This may be due to two different causes: first, the scanning beam may be unable to discharge all the charges built up on the mosaic either because of lack of beam current or because the target has a too high capacity; second, the photoconductivity excited in the dielectric layer may persist and hence allow charging current to flow for more than one frame period. In the Vidicon, the latter is the main cause of lag. Now the percentage decay of the induced photoconductivity in a given time—say a television frame period—is greater, the greater the average illumination on the dielectric. Hence the lag effect is less for brighter incident images, and, as the target illumination is reduced, it becomes more objectionable. In fact, in the present Vidicon tube it is the incidence of unacceptable lag that sets a practical limit to the sensitivity of the tube, since this becomes objectionable for moving objects before the signal/noise ratio becomes unacceptably low. Thus for general television purposes a target illumination of 1 L/ft^2 is required; but if the scene is stationary, so that lag does not matter, then the light can be reduced to much less than this, say ~0.1 L/ft^2, when amplifier noise begins to be objectionable.

The picture signal produced by this tube is not strictly proportional to the incident light integrated over the previous frame period, as in the C.P.S. Emitron or the early part of the characteristic of the Image Orthicon. It has a gamma of ~0.7. Again there is no charging signal current superimposed on the wanted signal current, as in the C.P.S. Emitron. Certainly, charge passes from the signal plate to the free surface of the target, but this charge does not leave the target as a whole, and hence no compensating charge flows to the signal plate through the signal resistor. This has the important advantage that the light-image that is being detected can be intermittent, or varying in intensity, without interfering with the picture signal.

The photoconductive charging current will be approximately proportional to the bias voltage across the dielectric, and hence the greater this bias, the greater the sensitivity. Unfortunately, the dark current also increases with bias voltage and relatively more rapidly than the photocurrent, and it tends to increase non-uniformly across the target. Hence there is, in practice, an optimum value for the bias voltage above which more sensitivity can be achieved only at the expense of deterioration of picture quality.

Thus the Vidicon is a tube that is suitable for a small, light, low power-consumption television camera channel which is widely used for industrial television purposes, though it is not widely used in entertainment television services because it is not so sensitive (without lag) as the C.P.S. Emitron or Image Orthicon. It would probably be the most suitable television camera for use in a space vehicle to relay back to earth pictures of the earth, moon, or other bright heavenly bodies.

For normal astronomical observations it does not appear to be very suitable. It is not sensitive enough to compete with the other television cameras for short-exposure work. For long-exposure work the bias voltage across a semi-conducting dielectric results in a slow charging of the target surface which can be negligible, say ∼1 per cent of the signal current during one normal frame period. However, this would mean that in 100 frame periods, or 4 seconds, the integrated dark current would have charged the target to full capacity. Moreover, it is very difficult to make the dielectric free from minute fissures and pin-holes through which excessive leakage can take place and give rise to very non-uniform background.

2.7. Summary of Existing Television Camera Tubes

It seems from the foregoing review that existing television camera tubes are not likely to be of much direct use in normal astronomical observing, with the exception of the new and improved Image Orthicon, which shows some promise of giving a useful gain as an image intensifier. However, in this field it must compete with the various image intensifiers that are being developed and seem likely to give better results with much simpler apparatus.

There are a few possible applications, such as the relaying back to a ground station of a picture from an observation balloon or satellite, in which a simple television camera channel would be essential. For this purpose a Vidicon camera would seem to be the most suitable at present. However, in time it will be required to detect and relay to earth television pictures of very faint astronomical pictures from telescopes in earth satellites. For this purpose the most efficient, charge-storage signal-generating tubes will be necessary.

§ 3. ULTIMATE-SENSITIVITY TELEVISION CAMERA TUBES

The ultimate sensitivity will be reached when all photoelectrons liberated by the light of the optical image from the most efficient photocathode can be recorded as definite, identical marks on the recorded or reproduced picture. At the same time, the image definition and geometrical accuracy must be preserved with maximum fidelity. No existing television camera has reached, or even approached, this limit of perfection. However, the intensifier orthicon briefly described above is directed to this goal but still seems to be some distance away.

The method followed in the author's laboratory to achieve the ultimate sensitivity is to couple optically a highly efficient image intensifier with a conventional television camera tube. Each of these vacuum tubes is difficult to manu-fracture, and it is considered to be an unwarranted complication to attempt to manufacture both within the same vacuum envelope.

Image intensifiers now exist (Wilcock, Emberson, and Weekley 1960; McGee 1961) in which a light gain of $> 10^5$ can be achieved. That is, if the pri-mary photocathode has a quantum efficiency of ~ 10 per cent, each primary photoelectron after multiplication results in 10^6 photons being liberated from the output phosphor screen. Of this burst of photons, ~ 10 per cent can be focused optically onto the photosensitive surface of a pickup tube (in the experiment considered, a C.P.S. Emitron), where they will liberate $\sim 10^4$ elec-trons. This, as has been noted above, will give a signal ten times above the r.m.s. noise. Hence in this case the television picture signal is limited only by the shot noise of the photoemission of the image intensifier. Further work is being done to improve the resolution, field diameter, and gain of the image intensifier which should lead to the limit of performance stipulated above. Such a system might be used for observing relatively bright, but rapidly varying, objects, such as planets. The image intensifier can be used as a very high-speed shutter, and hence television pictures, each corresponding to a very short ex-posure, could be recorded.

Another possible use for such a system is for observing an object against a uniform bright background. This situation is illustrated in Figure 1, and it is obvious that if an image intensifier alone were used to produce an intensified image of such a picture, the detectability of the star image would be greatly re-duced by the bright, extensive background. If this picture is now converted faithfully to a television picture signal, it is then quite simple to cut off, in the amplifier circuits, all the signal below any desired level. Thus the star-image signal alone, without any bright background, could be displayed on the tele-vision screen. In this way, faint objects could be much more clearly displayed and observed. It seems that such a system could be employed with advantage in tracking faint satellites across the sky.

§ 4. CONCLUSION

It appears that television signal-generating devices are still of limited use to the working astronomer, but there are indications that useful devices are not far away, and, with the intensive work going on in this field, it should not be long before more become available. In the meantime, it is felt that many astronomers would like to understand the operation of these tubes in more detail.

While image intensifiers are likely to be very effective rivals in the field of earth-bound astronomy, it seems inevitable that the television signal-generating device must come into its own in the future in astronomical observations from satellites. This alone warrants an attempt to appreciate their advantages and limitations.

REFERENCES

Baum, W. A.	1955	*Trans. I.A.U.*, **9,** 686.
Day, H. R., Hannam, H. J., and Wargo, P.	1958	*Proc. Image Intensifier Symposium,* U.S.A.E.R.D.L., Fort Belvoir, October, p. 163.
DeWitt, J. H.	1961	*Trans. I.A.U. 11,* Subcommission 9a, in press.
James, I. J. P.	1952	*Proc. I.E.E.*, **99,** Part III A, No. 20, 796.
Livingston, W.	1957	*Pub. A.S.P.*, **69,** 390.
McGee, J. D.	1950	*Proc. I.E.E.*, **97,** Part III, 377.
	1961	*Photoelectronic Image Intensifiers* (Reports on Progress in Physics, No. 24 [London: The Physical Society]).
Morton, G. A., and Reudy, J. E.	1960	*Advances in Electronics*, ed. J. D. McGee and W. L. Wilcock (New York and London: Academic Press), **12,** 184.
Randall, R. P.	1960	*Advances in Electronics*, ed. J. D. McGee and W. L. Wilcock (New York and London: Academic Press), **12,** 219.
Rose, A., and Iams, H.	1939	*Proc. I.R.E.*, **27,** 547.
Schade, O. H.	1948	*R.C.A. Rev.*, Vol. **9.**
Sommer, A. H.	1947	*Photoelectric Tubes* (London: Methuen & Co.), p. 95.
	1955	*Rev. Sci. Instr.*, **26,** 725.
Stoudenheimer, R. G.	1960	*Advances in Electronics*, ed. J. D. McGee and W. L. Wilcock (New York and London: Academic Press), **12,** 41.
Theile, R.	1960	*Advances in Electronics*, ed. J. D. McGee and W. L. Wilcock (New York and London: Academic Press), **12,** 277.
Weimer, P. K., Forgue, S. V., and Goodrich, R. R.	1950	*Electronics*, **23,** 70.
Wilcock, W. L., Emberson, D. L., and Weekley, B.	1960	*Nature*, **185,** 370.

CHAPTER 15

Application of the Image Orthicon to Spectroscopy

W. C. LIVINGSTON

Kitt Peak National Observatory

§ 1. INTRODUCTION

In the previous chapter, Professor McGee has listed those characteristics peculiar to signal-generating tubes which justify the use of this relatively complex genus of image tube. Some observations have been made with the image orthicon which we think illustrate all the properties that McGee has mentioned except that of remote communication. In particular, the signal-generating feature of an image orthicon (hereafter referred to as "orthicon") permits (1) the recording of the spectrum directly in the form of a plot of intensity versus wave length; (2) the information capacity of the orthicon to be extended through external storage; (3) the signal-to-noise ratio to be optimized by filtering, taking into account the frequency content of the desired spectral features; and (4) small wave-length shifts, in this case due to the Zeeman effect, to be clarified by the method of profile display. An effort has been made to investigate features in these observations and obtain data of astrophysical interest. Of course, these measurements are exploratory rather than definitive.

§ 2. DIRECT-INTENSITY RECORDING OF SPECTRA

The light-transfer characteristics of an orthicon depend mainly on the spacing between the target membrane, which is glass or a thin film of MgO, and the target mesh. If this spacing is 0.001 inch, the tube exhibits a gamma of unity over a light-range of about 30 (latitude = 1.5). Tubes with a wider spacing will have a reduced latitude. For example, the Z-5396, with a spacing of about 0.080 inch, has a latitude of less than 1.0. A limit to the closeness of the spacing is set by mechanical deflections produced by electrostatic forces. A spacing of 0.001

inch is used in such glass-target tubes as the RCA 7513 and 6474 or the EEV P-809 and P-817.

In order to obtain a correct exposure over the wide range of light-levels encountered in astronomical spectroscopy, the target must have a time-independent storage characteristic. This suggests an MgO target. A target-mesh spacing of 10 mils has been the minimum achieved with MgO targets, owing to their extreme thinness. As the spacing is further reduced, the target may be deflected, touch the mesh, and be destroyed. However, the 10-mil limit refers to the standard 1.2-inch-diameter target. The nature of a spectrum image suggests that a narrow strip target with an area of 0.1×1.2 inches will permit a spacing of 1 mil even with an MgO film. Such a tube is currently under development. The method of using the orthicon for spectrum studies is explained as follows:

The usual television raster consists of a repetitive array of "horizontal" lines stacked "vertically" one above the other. Now project a spectrum onto the photocathode so that the dispersion axis is vertical. Restrict the band width of the signal amplifier from d.c. to about the horizontal-line frequency. Further, match the size of the horizontal-line deflection to the width and position of the spectrum. The scanning beam of the orthicon then assumes, in effect, a fan shape, which is analogous to the analyzing slit of the familiar spectrophotometer. Then the current output of the orthicon, within the bounds of its latitude, accurately indicates intensity as a function of wave length.

With one exception—a stellar observation—records were made with an orthicon camera attached to the 75-foot spectrograph of the Mount Wilson 150-foot solar tower. A Babcock grating, blazed for the fifth-order green, gave a linear dispersion of 11 mm/A in the fifth order. The usable area of the photocathode was about 33 mm, which was equivalent to 3 A. Since the Doppler half-width of a solar line is about 0.1 A and the resolution of the orthicon about 0.01 A at this scale, line profiles could be studied.

The orthicon used had a glass target, a spacing of 1 mil, and an S-10 photocathode (RCA6474). Sufficient light was not available to permit optimum slit widths in the green (5250 A). Furthermore, in the red (6500 A), a still wider slit was unavoidable in order to retain a good signal-to-noise ratio. The amplifier band width was about 7.5 kc.

In the case of the stellar observation, an orthicon with MgO target and a 10-mil spacing was employed (GE ZL-7802). A prism spectrograph of the Ebert type with a dispersion of 100 A/mm at 4300 A was attached to the 36-inch reflector of Kitt Peak National Observatory.

The Utrecht *Photometric Atlas of the Solar Spectrum* (Minnaert, Mulders, and Houtgast 1940) represents first-quality photographic photometry. It happens that the material for this atlas was gathered with the same Mount Wilson equipment as that used for the orthicon observations, but with a different grating. It is thus interesting to compare the Utrecht *Atlas* profiles with the orthicon profiles. An inspection of Figure 1 indicates that the profiles are comparable,

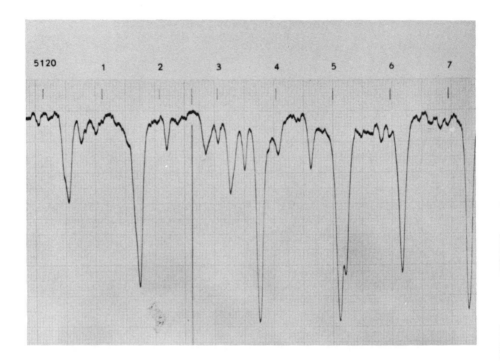

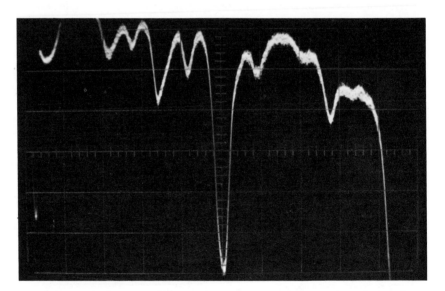

FIG. 1.—Comparison between a Utrecht *Atlas* line profile and image orthicon line profile. Data: Disk λ 5123. RCA6474. Exposure: 1 second (i.e., an integration of 15 scans, each of $\frac{1}{15}$-second exposure, for a total exposure of 1 second). Slit: 10 × 2 seconds of arc. Filter: Wratten No. 61 (30 per cent transmission).

although detailed differences are evident. The orthicon scan displays less resolution. This was caused by the wide slit width.

Although it is not particularly clear from this illustration, experience has shown that the orthicon is relatively free of the equivalent of small specks and defects common to the photographic emulsion. However, the orthicon photo-cathode has some non-uniformity over its surface. It has been found that the variation in sensitivity is always gradual, at least for the S-10 surface. In an exacting photometric study such variations can easily be taken into account.

The λ 5123 line of neutral iron has a Landé g-factor equal to zero and hence shows no splitting in a magnetic field. This line is therefore useful for examining velocity fields, temperature, and other physical parameters in the presence of strong magnetic fields found in sunspots. Figure 2 contains scans centered on this line and with the slit on the disk (a and b) and in the spot (c). In order to compensate for the reduced light in the spot, the amplifier gain was increased so that the apparent strength of the line in the spot was about the same as on the disk.

The half-width of a line can be a temperature indicator. If a continuum can be drawn as shown in Figure 2, one obtains a half-width of 0.13 and 0.11 A for the disk and spot, respectively. Assuming a disk temperature of 5700°, then, by the relation

$$\frac{\Delta\lambda \text{ disk}}{\Delta\lambda \text{ spot}} = \sqrt{\left(\frac{T \text{ disk}}{T \text{ spot}}\right)},$$

one obtains a temperature of 4100° in the spot.

Astronomical seeing causes the intensity of the spectrum to fluctuate when the spectrograph slit is near an image discontinuity, such as a sunspot or a star. In the case of the sunspot, the true spot spectrum is thus altered by photo-spheric light. The orthicon uniquely allows one to select the purest spot spec-trum. At 15 exposures per second, a 10-second exposure forms an envelope of 150 scans. The upper edge of the envelope, which shows faint peaks, contains a maximum of photospheric light. This is the unwanted profile. The bottom edge, which is produced by the dark spot, then forms the purest spot spectrum ob-tainable under these conditions.

In the case of the star the spectrum changes only in intensity. Figure 3, b, illustrates fluctuations that occur in 1/7 second. Ideally, the three scans should be added together to obtain the best signal-to-noise ratio.

Figure 4 is a series of records which illustrate some of the problems con-nected with spot spectra. Scattered light from the photosphere, seeing, magnetic effects, and the increased number of unidentified lines, probably molecular, complicate any study. Figure 3 describes how we were able, by use of the orthi-con, to eliminate the dilution of spectral purity due to seeing.

Figure 4, b, suggests the complexity and percentage of unidentified lines. Note that the strength of the line at λ 5251.17, tentatively identified as gado-

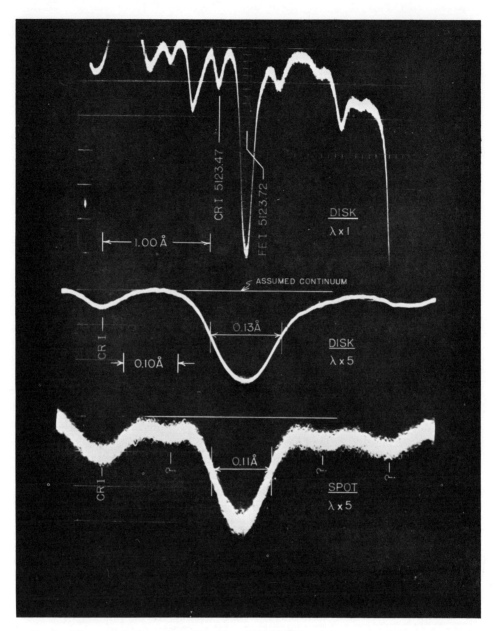

Fig. 2.—The magnetically unaffected line Fe I λ 5123.72, disk and spot compared. Data: *a*, solar disk λ 5123; *b*, solar disk λ 5123 × 5 (i.e., wave-length scale expanded five times on display oscilloscope); *c*, solar sunspot λ 5123 × 5. Exposure: 15 scans of $\frac{1}{15}$ second each. Slit: 10 × 2 seconds of arc. Filter: Wratten No. 61.

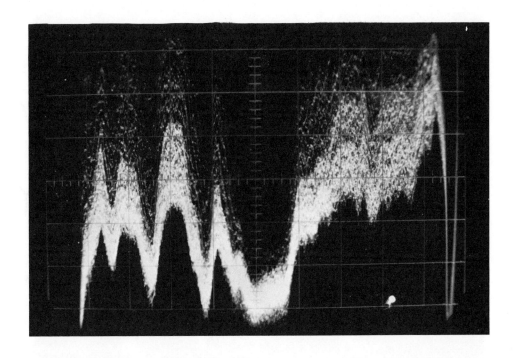

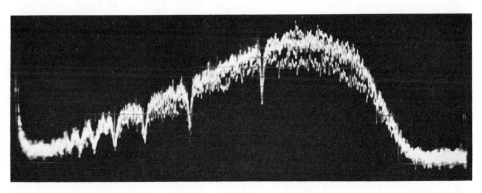

FIG. 3.—The effect of seeing: *a*, near a sunspot; *b*, a stellar spectrum. Data: *a*, λ 4861.33, RCA6474. Exposure: 150 scans of $\frac{1}{15}$ second each. Slit: 5 × 2 seconds of arc. Data: *b*, Star 109 Vir (A0 V, $m_v = 3.8$), GE 7802. Exposure: 3 scans of $\frac{2}{15}$ second each. Telescope 36-inch. Dispersion: prismatic, 100 A/mm at 4300 A.

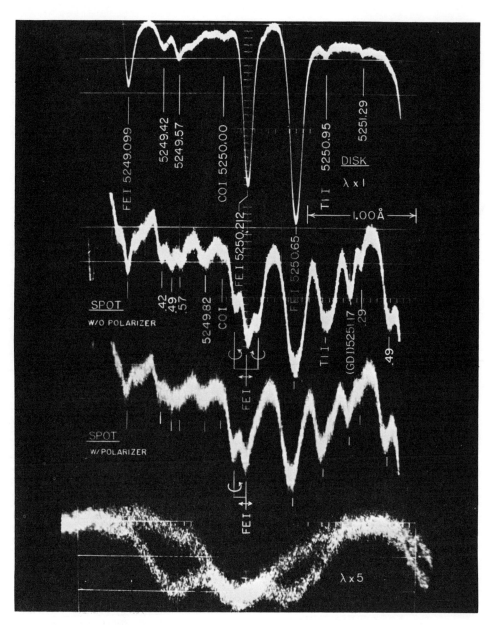

FIG. 4.—The magnetically sensitive line Fe I λ 5250.212, disk and spot compared. Data: *a*, disk λ 5250; *b*, spot without polarizer; *c*, spot with polarizer; *d*, spot with polarizer × 5. Slit: 10 × 2 seconds of arc. Exposure: 15 scans of $\frac{1}{15}$ second each. Filter: Wratten No. 61.

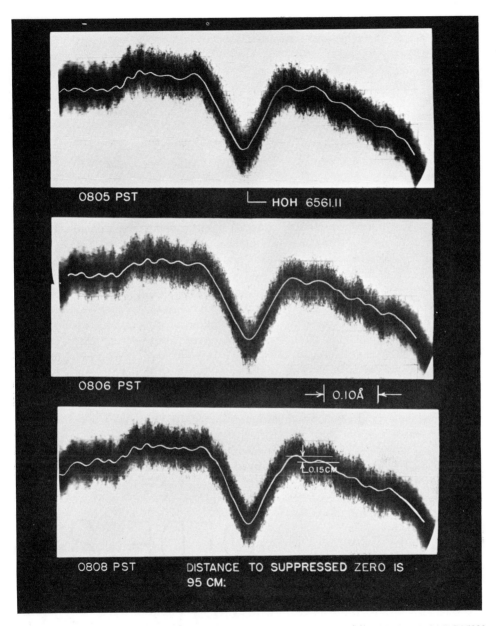

Fig. 5.—Search for deuterium in the sun; phosphor storage. Data: λ 6561.11 (4th order). RCA5820 (same as RCA6474 except that it has a 2.5-mil target-mesh spacing). Exposure: 150 scans of $\frac{1}{15}$ second each. Slit: 10 × 3 seconds of arc. *a*, 0805 P.S.T.; *b*, 0806 P.S.T.; *c*, 0808 P.S.T., September 15, 1958.

linium, is strong in the spot but not detectable on the disk. If a circular polarizer is inserted in the light-beam, one Zeeman component can be suppressed. This helps to simplify the analysis (Fig. 4, c). Ordinarily, the profile of a single Zeeman component cannot be resolved. By making a double exposure and rotating the polarizer appropriately, the profile can be displayed as in Figure 4, d.

The raw Zeeman splitting in Figure 4, d, is 0.21 A (or $2\Delta\lambda$). Taking blending into account increases the splitting to 0.28 A. From the formula

$$\Delta\lambda = 4.7(10^{-5}) gH\lambda^2 ,$$

a field strength of 3700 gauss is calculated. The value found visually by other means was 3500 gauss.

Kinman (1956) has made a careful photometric investigation of the blue wing of $^1H\alpha$, in an attempt to detect $^2H\alpha$, deuterium. He concludes that a weak line of equivalent width 1.1 mA might be undetectable by photographic photometry.

We have studied this same spectral region with the orthicon (Fig. 5). A maximum signal-to-noise ratio was obtained by opening the slit excessively wide. The wide slit resulted in a triangular profile for the λ 6561.11 water-vapor line. The orthicon beam noise, seeing effects, and possible intrinsic variations in the spectrum combine to produce an envelope of noise. Three separate records, each of 150 scans, were made. If we trace these envelopes by eye-estimate, many features common to all three may be detected. The particular feature just to the right of the water-vapor line has an equivalent width of about 0.28 mA. If we consider this to be the limit of detectability, the precision of the observation is better than 0.1 per cent of the continuum.

An accuracy of 0.1 per cent is at least as good as the best photoelectric spectrophotometry and about ten times better than can be done photographically (for example, examine this same spectral region in the Utrecht *Atlas*).

The technique employed here is termed "phosphor integration" and has been studied by Lawson and Uhlenbeck (1950) in connection with the detection of faint radar signals. A much more efficient integration of the orthicon signals can be done numerically by a special-purpose digital computer. Such methods as are regularly used in radio astronomy should permit an accuracy of 0.01 per cent to be achieved.

§3. CONCLUSION

An orthicon with a "close-spaced target" has sufficient latitude for the direct-intensity recording of high-dispersion spectra. Quantitative measurements can be made. The quality of the single-scan records is at present comparable with good photographic photometry. Considerable improvement can be expected in the orthicon technique, while photographic photometry is already perfected.

The dynamic display of line profiles by the orthicon enables the observer to judge better the degradation of spectral purity caused by seeing-produced image extursions. Change of line profile as a function of time, position of slit, and Doppler and Zeeman effects is also clarified.

If external storage of the orthicon signal is used, the signal-to-noise ratio increases. The simple process of phosphor integration yields a relative accuracy equal to that of photoelectric spectrophotometry. Digital integration should increase this accuracy by a further factor of 10 for an exposure time of a few minutes. This will permit the detection of Fraunhofer lines with a central depth about 0.02 per cent of the continuum.

REFERENCES

KINMAN, T. D.   1956   *M.N.*, **116**, 77.
LAWSON, J. L., and
  UHLENBECK, G. E.   1950   *Threshold Signals* (New York: McGraw-Hill Book
                                   Co., Inc.).
MINNAERT, M.,
  MULDERS, G. F. W.,
  and HOUTGAST, J.   1940   *Photometric Atlas of the Solar Spectrum* (Amster-
                                   dam: D. SCHNABEL, KAMPERT, and HELM).

CHAPTER 16

Image Converters for Astronomical Photography

W. A. HILTNER

Yerkes Observatory, University of Chicago

§ 1. INTRODUCTION

THE basis for interest by astronomers in image converters stems almost entirely from the relative quantum efficiency of photographic emulsions and photocathodes. Photographic emulsions have a sensitivity or efficiency of the order of about 0.16 per cent (Webb 1948), while good photocathodes give efficiencies of from 10 to 20 per cent—nearly 100 times greater than emulsions.

In classical photography the only energy available for emulsion exposure is, of course, that of the photon, about 3 ev for a 4000 A photon. However, if this energy can be used for the liberation of an electron from a photocathode, this electron can be imaged and given an energy many orders of magnitude greater than that of the original photon. Assume an efficiency of 10 per cent for the photocathode and a practical working potential for the image tube of 30 kv. Therefore, the energy amplification is 10^3. If this greater energy is used for the exposure of an electron-sensitive emulsion, several developable grains will be exposed for each electron. Therefore, the gain, assuming no significant loss in resolution, will be in the ratio of the quantum efficiency of the photocathode and the light-sensitive emulsion.

Other receivers may be used for detecting the accelerated electrons. The electrons may strike a phosphor, where the image may be inspected visually or photographed. Also, the electrons may be used for further amplification, either by secondary electron emission or by a phosphor-photocathode sandwich. In either case the final picture is usually displayed on a phosphor.

The following outline will assist in the classification of image tubes:

340

Single stage (no internal amplification)
  1. Phosphor target
     a) Optical coupling to emulsion by lens system
     b) Optical coupling by contact
  2. Emulsion target
     a) Photocathode preserved by refrigeration of photocathode and emulsion
     b) Photocathode preserved by thin film

Multistage (internal amplification)
  1. Amplification by phosphor-photocathode sandwich (cascaded image converter)
  2. Amplification by secondary emission
     a) Weiss electron multiplier
     b) Transmission electron multiplier
     c) Channel electron multiplier

All the tubes in this classification will be discussed except those with either Weiss or channel electron multipliers. The usefulness of the former is limited by low gain, scattered light, and low resolution. The channel electron multiplier, by its very nature, has low resolution and, consequently, is probably of little interest to astronomers at the present time.

§ 2. ELECTRON OPTICS FOR IMAGE CONVERTERS

The photoelectrons may be focused on the target by either electrostatic or magnetic lenses. An image converter with a magnetic focusing system may consist of a flat photocathode and a flat target (anode), with a homogeneous electrostatic field between these two electrodes. The homogeneous electrostatic field is generally approximated by impressing a linear potential increase between photocathode and target (anode) onto the cylindrical tube wall by means of conductive rings or a conductive spiral. The homogeneous magnetic field may be approximated with a solenoid or a permanent magnet.

An electrostatic triode system—the one more generally used for image converters—may consist of a spherical photocathode, a cylindrical focus electrode, and a spherical pierced anode (see Fig. 10). The image-plane curvature of a magnetic system is, in principle, smaller than that of an electrostatic system. This results in improved peripheral resolution in the former. For strictly homogeneous electric and magnetic fields, the image plane for a magnetic system is flat. However, the image-plane curvature for the electrostatic system can be reduced by adjusting the strength of the negative aperture lens formed by the pierced spherical anode (Niklas 1961) and by utilizing a focus electrode of large diameter compared with the effective photocathode diameter. Within certain limitations, a satisfactory image-plane curvature can be obtained with an electrostatic system.

On the assumption that the target is of sufficient resolving power (not the case for settled phosphors), the resolution limitations of a single-stage image converter are mainly of an electron-optical nature. If space-charge effects in the elementary beam (the electron density is extremely low) and chromatic aberrations (caused by variations in exit velocity of the photoelectrons) are neglected, the paraxial resolution is limited in both systems by astigmatism. In the magnetic system the astigmatism is caused either by beam deflection from stray magnetic fields or by asymmetrical radial components of the electrostatic field. Therefore, strict parallelism between the superimposed magnetic and electrostatic fields must be maintained to avoid astigmatic distortion. For the electrostatic system, proper mechanical alignment of the components is a necessary condition.

§ 3. CONDITIONS FOR APPLICATION TO ASTRONOMY

For an image tube to be useful for astronomical research, certain conditions must be met. These conditions will be discussed in some detail.

3.1. RESOLUTION

The resolution of the typical fast photographic emulsion is approximately 50 line pairs (one black and one white line) per millimeter. If the resolution of the image tube is different from the emulsion with which it is compared, the observed gain in speed must be multiplied by

$$\left(\frac{R_I}{R_p}\right)^2,$$

where R_I is the resolution of the image converter in lines per millimeter and R_p is the resolution of the light-sensitive emulsion in the same units. This ratio states that when the rates of blackening per unit area for two detectors are measured, the true gain in speed is not this quantity but the product of this quantity and the ratio of the picture-element areas. This gives a *figure of merit* for the tube. It is assumed that the images from image converters are ultimately recorded on a photographic emulsion. However, under circumstances where information can be extracted from the image, regardless of the amount of information recorded, the critical factor may then be the number of resolvable elements in the picture frame.

3.2. BACKGROUND

The greatest application of image converters to astronomical research will probably be in the detection and measurement of faint images. This detection must often take place in the presence of sky background (see chap. 1). Since background in the image converter may be equated to additional sky background, it is important that the detector's contribution be negligible. There are three primary sources of background in image converters—thermionic emission, ionization of residual gases, and field emission between tube components.

The thermionic emission from either a cesium antimonide (S11) or a trialkali photocathode (S20) at room temperature is negligible when used for direct photography. However, when extraordinarily low backgrounds are required or when cesium oxide on silver (S1) photocathodes are used, modest refrigeration with solid CO_2, for example, may be necessary.

Residual gases in image converters can be ionized by electron collision. The positive ions are accelerated toward the photocathode and, on impact, give rise to secondary electrons. These secondary electrons are accelerated toward the output of the tube. These electrons, then, contribute, of course, to the background. Since the ions are approximately focused on the electron-optical axis on collision with the photocathode, the background will then also be concentrated on the optical axis. This gives rise to the so-called ion spot. If the pressure within the tube is less than 10^{-6} mm Hg, the background from ionization of the residual gases will be negligible.

Field emission between tube components is doubtless the most important contributor to the background. The probability of field emission increases both with the number of tube components acting as possible sources of field emission and with the magnitude of the potential gradient between those components. The gap or gaps between components consist normally of uncoated glass surfaces. When the photocathode is processed, alkali metal vapors may be adsorbed on the glass surfaces. This leads to relatively high local potential gradients that cause field emission. Photoelectrons are released from the cathode by fluorescence induced by this field emission.

3.3. PHOTOCATHODE SIZE

Image converters have been made with a variety of photocathode sizes. Electrostatic image converters with cathodes over 22 cm in diameter and magnetically focused tubes with cathodes as large as 8 cm have been routinely manufactured. In the future, photocathodes with such large diameters will be useful for direct photography and some applications in spectroscopy. However, at the present time, photocathodes of 2.5-cm diameter are more customary. This diameter (with adequate resolution) is sufficient for low-dispersion spectroscopy and limited direct photography.

3.4. QUANTUM EFFICIENCY

As discussed above, the interest in image converters for astronomical research is related to the high efficiency of photocathodes relative to photographic emulsions; consequently, photocathodes of high efficiency are needed. The better S11 and S20 photocathodes have efficiencies of 10–20 per cent. Although the infrared-sensitive S1 photocathode has an efficiency of less than 1 per cent, it is nevertheless useful for the 7000–11,000 A region. The available emulsions for this spectral region are even slower in proportion to the low photocathode quantum efficiencies.

Not only are high quantum efficiencies of the photocathode required, the target must likewise be efficient. The target must record the photoelectrons so that the noise in the image is principally the shot noise of the photocathode current. In other words, the detector must be essentially capable of recording or displaying individual electrons from the photocathode. On the other hand, the information capacity of the recording target must not be consumed excessively by individual photon events.

3.5. Information Capacity

Whether or not an image against a background can be detected depends on whether there is sufficient information in the image to make its presence apparent against the statistical fluctuations of the background (see chap. 1). In a direct photograph of a star field, the faintest stars must be detected against a bright (although moonless) sky. For a star to be detected, its signal must be larger by some factor a than the root-mean-square noise of the sky. If the receiver is linear, the signal will increase as the first power of the integration (exposure) time and the r.m.s. noise of the sky as the square root. Obviously, long integration times are desirable. However, the receiver may have a limited information capacity, such as a photographic emulsion. After saturation begins, any additional information will not only be lost but will subtract from the information already accumulated. As an example, exposures of unfiltered Kodak 103a-O emulsions with an $f/3.5$ camera are limited to about 30 minutes on a moonless night. Therefore, larger storage capacity (that is, smaller emulsion grain) than the emulsions now employed is needed if we are to detect fainter stars (or spectral lines at the same dispersion and resolution) than those observed with present-day equipment.

§ 4. SINGLE-STAGE TUBES WITH PHOSPHOR TARGET

The simplest of all image converters and the first to be developed consists of a photocathode, electron lens, and phosphor in an evacuated envelope (see Fig. 1). The tube received its name "image converter" from its ability to detect an object in one spectral region and display its image in another. For example, the photocathode may be sensitive in the infrared, but the phosphor radiates blue light when excited by the accelerated photoelectrons.

4.1. Lens Coupling to Emulsion

The phosphor in the simple image converter or tube may be coupled to a light-sensitive emulsion by lenses, for example, two $f/1.5$ lenses face to face. However, this arrangement is ineffective for the observation of faint sources because of its low over-all effective light-amplification and loss in resolution. The effective gain in the visible spectral region is approximately 1. Tubes of this design have had extensive applications in clinical fluoroscopy. For X-ray fluoroscopy, the tubes have photocathodes not less than 15 cm in diameter, but the electron optics reduce the image so that the output phosphor is about 2.5 cm in diameter. The phosphor is then inspected by a low-power microscope.

4.2. Contact Coupling to Emulsion

The effective gain of the simple image tube can be enhanced by more efficient coupling of the emulsion to the phosphor. Instead of lenses, the emulsion may be placed in contact with the window that supports the phosphor, as shown in Figure 2. The emulsion is pressed against the mica window by either mechanical or atmospheric pressure. An emulsion medium may be used to aid the optical contact. The resolution is dependent on (1) the original resolution of the electron lens, (2) the structure of the phosphor, (3) the thickness of the supporting window, (4) the resolution capabilities of the recording photographic emulsion, and (5) the contact quality of emulsion and window. If a is the image size for the electron lens and phosphor combination, t the distance from phosphor sur-

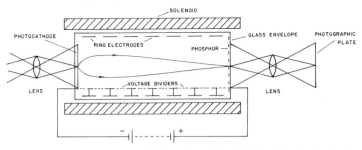

Fig. 1.—A simple image converter for image intensification. In this tube the electrons from the photocathode are focused on the phosphor by uniform electric and magnetic fields.

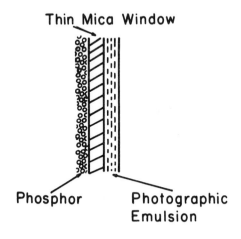

Fig. 2.—The structure of the output window of a mica-window image converter. The mica is about 10 μ thick.

face to the emulsion, and b the emulsion grain size, the resulting image size will be given approximately by

$$A = a + b + 2 \frac{t}{\tan a},$$

where a is the critical internal angle. For a equal to 15, b equal to 10, and t equal to 10 μ, A equals approximately 45 μ, since a is near 45°. However, resolutions up to 30 line pairs per millimeter have been reported. Tubes of this design have been constructed in Russia, in England at the Imperial College, and in the United States by International Telephone and Telegraph.

The electrostatically focused tubes described by Krassovsky (1958) at the Tenth General Assembly of the I.A.U. had a working field of 10 mm and a resolution of 50 μ. The accelerating potential was 10–20 kv. The reported background was sufficiently low that exposures up to 10 hours in duration were possible before the background became detectable. Tubes with three different photocathodes have been tested at the Sternberg Institute (see Shcheglov 1960; Volkov, Yesipov, and Shcheglov 1959; Yesipov 1960): (1) cesium oxide on silver, sensitive in the infrared; (2) bismuth-cesium or multialkali, sensitive in the blue and red-near-infrared; and (3) cesium antimonide, sensitive in the blue. Gains of several orders of magnitude, 50–100 and 20 to 30 times, respectively, have been reported for these tubes. These gains are probably "rate-of-blackening" gains and may not have been corrected for loss in resolution.

McGee and Wheeler (1960) at the Imperial College in London have made magnetically focused image tubes with a mica window 2.5 cm in diameter and 12 μ thick (see also Zacharov and Dowden 1960). With cesium antimonide photocathodes of 30–40 μA/L, the rate of blackening gain is about 50 at 30 kv. Since the resolution is 30 line pairs per mm, the effective gain or figure of merit should be approximately 10–15.

The earlier thin mica-window image tubes manufactured by the International Telephone and Telegraph Laboratories were electrostatically focused. Tubes with cesium oxide on silver and cesium antimonide photocathodes have been tested extensively at the Lowell Observatory (see Baum et al. 1955–1961). The mica windows were 14 mm in diameter and 12 μ thick. Paraxial resolution was 26 line pairs per mm. Exposure times of 1 hour with little spurious background were possible with the cesium oxide on silver photocathodes when cooled with dry ice. The rate of blackening gains of 30 (in the blue) to 500 (in the far infrared) were observed. Since the resolution of the blue-sensitive emulsions is greater than the image tube by a factor of 2, the gain of 30 must be corrected for this loss in resolution.

Recently the I.T.T. Laboratories produced a magnetically focused image with a mica-window output. The window is 40 mm long and 3 mm wide for spectroscopic applications (Hall 1961). The field of good focus is about 35 mm long.

§ 5. SINGLE-STAGE TUBE WITH EMULSION TARGET

If the accelerated photoelectron is permitted to strike a photographic emulsion in an image tube instead of a phosphor, several grains in the emulsion become exposed. The number, of course, is a function of the electron energy. Such a tube was proposed several decades ago by Lallemand (1936). Under normal conditions an emulsion and a photocathode in the same vacuum envelope are incompatible. The gas evolved by the emulsion reacts chemically with the cesium in the photocathode. The lifetime of the photocathode is of the order

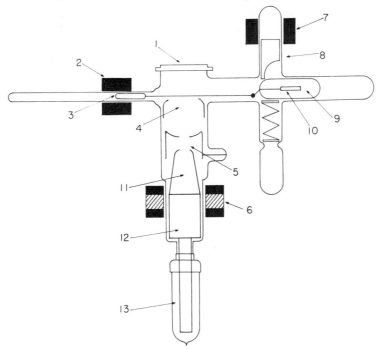

FIG. 3.—Schematic diagram of Lallemand's "electronic camera"

of milliseconds. However, this difficulty has been partially or completely overcome by either of two techniques. First, the evolution of gas from the emulsion, as well as the rate of chemical reaction at the photocathode, can be reduced by lowered emulsion and photocathode temperatures. Second, the photocathode can be separated from the emulsion by a gas-tight, electron-transparent window. The two methods will be discussed in some detail.

5.1. THE LALLEMAND "ELECTRONIC CAMERA"

The first technique was proposed by Lallemand (1936) and has now been developed to perfection (see Lallemand 1960; Lallemand, Duchesne, and Wlerick 1960). Figure 3 is a schematic drawing that illustrates the principle. The preparations necessary for placing the equipment in operation are as follows: The optical glass window *1* is removed. First, the magazine *12* that holds eight plates with electron-sensitive emulsions is inserted. This is followed with the electron lenses *4, 5,* and *11,* which must be correctly positioned. The photocathode *10,* in its separate container *9,* is then placed in a side arm. The tube is now ready for evacuation after the window *1* is replaced and sealed vacuum-tight. Figure 4 shows the tube mounted on its preparation stand.

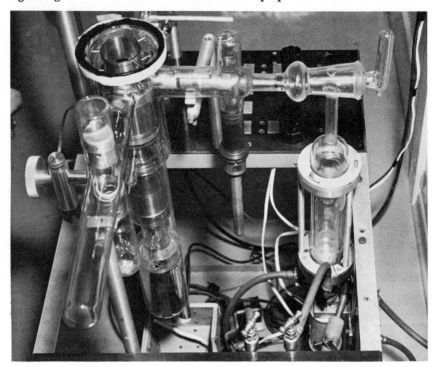

Fig. 4.—The "electronic camera" on the preparation stand

The tube is evacuated with a small oil-diffusion pump. To remove as much water as possible, the system is given a bake at 350° C during evacuation except for the emulsions and photocathode. When the tube is again cool, liquid air or nitrogen is placed in the dewar *13* for refrigeration of the emulsions and in a second dewar (not shown in Fig. 4) for cooling the photocathode. After the tube is thoroughly cooled, barium getters are evaporated. The tube can then be valved off from the pump. The photocathode is next placed in position. Its glass container *9* is first cracked by the magnetic hammer *8* and it is then drawn into position by the electromagnet *2*. The tube is then ready for positioning at the telescope. The whole operation requires about 8 hours. More recent designs use a titanium pump to maintain the vacuum (Lallemand 1961; Walker 1961). This pump increases the photocathode life to about 2 days and reduces the background caused by ionization of the residual gas. The maximum permissible exposure time has thus been increased from about 30 minutes to 4–6 hours.

The electron lens is similar to the electrostatic one discussed earlier. The magnification is 0.75. Resolution is maintained over two-thirds of the photocathode diameter, or about 14 mm. Lallemand (see Lallemand, Duchesne, and Walker 1960) is of the opinion that the paraxial resolution is not limited by the aberrations in the electron lens but by the length and size of the electron tracks in the nuclear emulsion. The electron path length for a 30-kv electron is about 10 μ.

One factor that may affect the resolution more than any other is the quality of the optical focus on the photocathode. The photocathode is about 50 mm behind the entrance window *1* in Figure 3. The difficulty in focusing can be illustrated by the procedure followed by Lallemand, Duchesne, and Walker (1960) in their application of the tube to stellar spectroscopy at the Lick Observatory:

In order to focus the tube, the regular photographic plate holder was loaded with a plate on which some focus marks had been made, and placed in the correct photographic focus of the [spectrograph] camera. The [spectrograph] grating was then replaced by a plane mirror, which reflected the beam from the camera to a collimating telescope. Since the spectrograph uses a 6.5-inch collimator and grating, a 6-inch aperture collimating telescope was used. The telescope was carefully focused on the plate in the plate holder. Next, the plate holder was removed and the Newtonian mirror [to reflect the light from the camera to the image tube, see Fig. 8] put in place. The tube was then moved along the optical axis of the camera until a focusing spot, which is provided in the center of each cathode, was sharply in focus in the collimator. With proper illumination of the cathode, the accuracy of focusing was about ±0.001 inch (0.025 mm), which is only marginally sufficient for the [monochromatic] *f*/3 beam of the camera.

Nuclear emulsions about 10 μ thick with extra plasticizer for vacuum use are employed in the camera—in particular, Ilford G5 and C2 emulsions. The latter is approximately four times slower than the G5, but the G5 has a mean grain diameter of 0.3 μ, while the C2 emulsion has a grain diameter of 0.16 μ. These emulsions have several interesting characteristics. First, the background is remarkably low. This is illustrated in Figure 5, where the G5 and C2 emulsions are compared with the familiar 103*a*-O. Second, the nuclear emulsions, when exposed to electrons, give a linear relationship between density and the number of electrons or with the intensity of the incident light (Vernier 1959). For the G5 and C2 emulsions this relationship is satisfied to density 3 (see Fig. 6).

The gain in speed over classical photography is a function of the light-intensity, the exposure time, and the amount of information required. Since a single 30-kv electron produces an identifiable track in a G5 emulsion and since the G5 emulsion has almost no background noise, the device may be used for counting electrons. This permits the detection of a luminous flux much

fainter than by the classical methods of inspection and analysis of photographic emulsions. Certain conditions must be met. First, the range in density
must be limited; otherwise the grains become too numerous to be counted in the
more dense areas. Second, the exposure time must be very short, to avoid a
general tube background. Under these conditions gains in speed up to 10,000
over an Eastman 103a-O emulsion have been reported (Lallemand, Duchesne,
Goldzahl, Duflo, and Banaigs 1959). The gain steadily decreases with increase

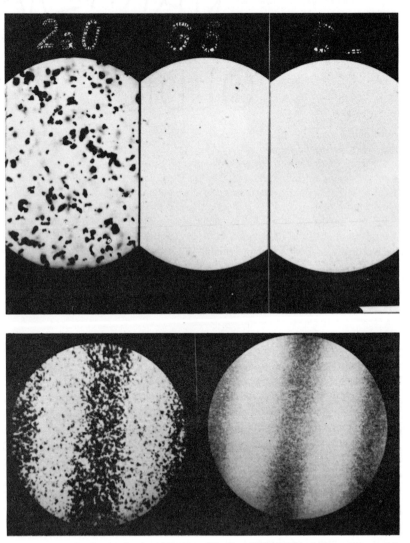

FIG. 5.—*Above:* background noise of Eastman IIa-O and Ilford G5 and C2 nuclear emulsion.
Below: enlargement of Eastman IIa-O and Ilford G5. After Lallemand (1960).

in exposure time and higher densities. At normal densities and exposures of 1 hour, the gain is from 30 to 40. Since there is no reciprocity failure when the emulsion is exposed by electrons, the above gain figures appear to be paradoxical. However, the gains of 10^4 can be realized only at very low densities, where the light-sensitive emulsions can yield essentially no information because of background.

Lallemand, Duchesne, and Walker (1960) have discussed the inconveniences of this technique. First, to retrieve the exposed emulsions from the tube, it is nec-

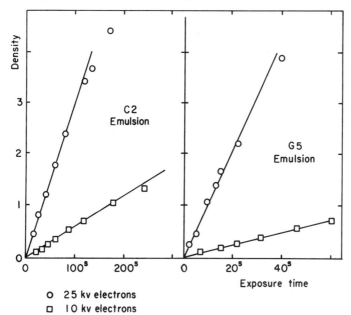

O   25 kv electrons
□   10 kv electrons

Fig. 6.—Linearity of Ilford G5 and C2 emulsions when exposed by 10- and 25-kv electrons. After Vernier (1959).

essary to disassemble the unit. This, of course, destroys the photocathode. The greatest difficulty encountered by opening the tube is in the danger of contamination of the interior. This contamination may seriously reduce the sensitivity of the photocathode when the tube is reassembled for the next operation. Also, in the present design, the photocathode is approximately 50 mm back of the front window of the tube. This causes inconvenience when fast cameras are to be used. The inability to take "focus plates" may lead to soft focus caused by improper focus of the optical lens in front of the photocathode.

This development has been applied, primarily in spectroscopy, at various observatories in France and at the Lick Observatory in the United States. Figure 7 shows the installation at the coudé spectrograph of the 120-inch Lick reflector. It was installed at the focus of a 20-inch Schmidt camera. To minimize the obstruction of light, the tube was placed to one side of the beam. A

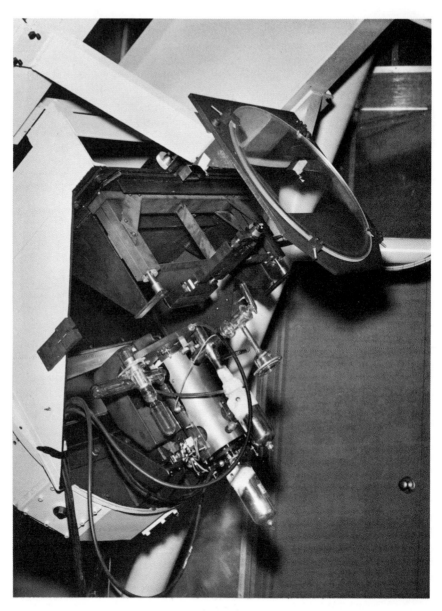

Fig. 7.—Image tube mounted at the focus of the 20-inch Schmidt camera of the 120-inch coudé spectrograph.

45° flat mirror reflected the focus to the image-tube photocathode. The dispersion at the photocathode was 45 A/mm. However, since the magnification of the electron optics is about 0.75, the final dispersion was 60 A/mm. Two spectrograms of AE Aqr—a variable star that displays explosive outbursts—are shown in Figure 8. The upper spectrogram was taken at minimum light and the lower one during an explosion when the star was 1–1.5 mag. brighter.

Walker (1961) reports that spectrograms can now be obtained of sixteenth magnitude (photographic) stars at 60 A/mm with exposures for 4–6 hours. The gain over classical photography increases from about 10 for short exposures to about 40 for 1-hour exposures when a photocathode of average sensitivity (30 μA/L) is used.

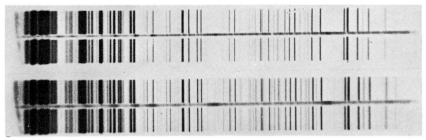

FIG. 8.—Two spectrograms of AE Aqr. The top one was taken at minimum light and the lower one during a flare. *Above:* 1960, August 14, 9:09:33 to 9:27:05 U.T.; m_v equal to about 12.6 and constant during the exposure. *Below:* 1960, August 14, 9:36:25 to 9:49:00 U.T.; M_{uv} varied from 12.1 to 11.0 to 11.5 during the exposure. The resolution in the center of the field is limited by the difficulty in bringing the tube into the correct optical focus of the spectrograph. A fairly wide slit was used.

5.2. Thin-Foil Image Converter

An alternative for preserving a photocathode for electronography is the separation of the photocathode chamber from the emulsion chamber by an electron-transparent window (Hiltner 1953; also see Hall, Ford, and Baum 1960; Hiltner and Pesch 1960). The technique is illustrated schematically in Figure 9. An emulsion is placed in the first vacuum chamber (*on the right*). When this chamber has been evacuated, the second door is opened and the emulsion placed near the foil for exposure (see Hiltner 1958). A vacuum is maintained in this inner chamber at all times, for the foils cannot withstand atmospheric pressure. The foil may be made of a variety of materials—aluminum, silicon monoxide, carbon, aluminum oxide, etc. Aluminum oxide is used at Yerkes Observatory. Foils of this material only 1000 A thick have great strength and consequently are easy to form and handle. Also, they have the same coefficient of expansion as the material (Kovar) on which they are mounted. Figure 10 is a scale drawing of a tube used at Yerkes Observatory, and Figure 11 is a photograph of a tube of this design manufactured by the Rauland Corporation.

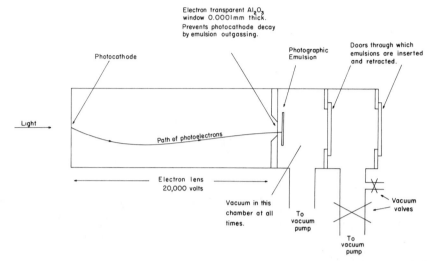

FIG. 9.—A schematic drawing of an image converter with an electron-transparent window. The emulsion is first placed in the right chamber. After evacuation, the left door is opened and the emulsion moved in position for exposure. After exposure, the procedure is reversed.

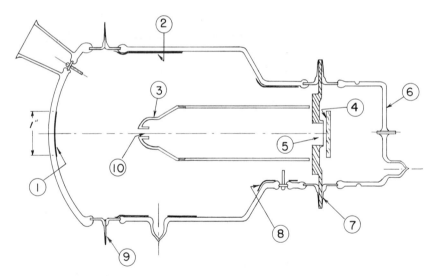

FIG. 10.—Schematic diagram of the image converter with Al₂O₃ foil. *1*, Photocathode; *2*, cylindrical focus electrode; *3*, anode; *4*, photographic emulsion (inserted after tube is placed in operation); *5*, aluminum oxide foil; *6*, removable section (to permit insertion of emulsions); *7*, Kovar flanges (helian-welded); *8*, high-voltage section of tube; *9*, Kovar flanges (heliarc-welded); *10*, anode aperature lens.

To place a tube in operation, it is first installed on a vacuum lock such as that shown schematically in Figure 9. When the desired vacuum is obtained, the back part of the tube is removed (see Hall, Ford, and Baum, 1960). This then permits access to the foil with photographic emulsions that may be inserted and retracted through the back whenever desired.

The photocathode life in this technique is of primary importance and will be a function of the gas-diffusion rate through the foil. Theoretical calculations from the approximate relationship

$$q = \frac{k_0}{d} \sqrt{(p)} \, e^{-b_0/T},$$

where k_0 and b_0 are constants characteristic of the gas-foil combination, d the thickness, p the pressure, and T the temperature, give little information. The

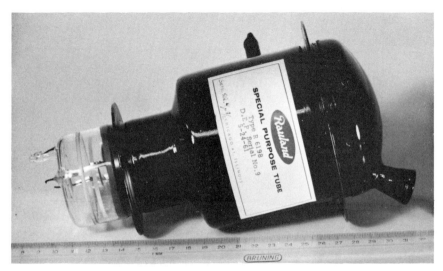

Fig. 11.—Image converter for electronography

available constants refer to bulk material, not to thin foils, in which imperfections are of prime importance. However, in the laboratory the life of a photocathode protected by a 1000 A foil appears to be unlimited.

Except for angular scattering in the foil, the resolution for this technique should be similar to that in which the cathode is protected wholly by low temperature. No data are available for aluminum oxide foils at 20 kv. However, to illustrate the order of magnitude, the scattering by a 100 A foil of polycrystalline gold is shown in Figure 12 after Marton, Simpson, and McGraw (1955a). The energy absorption is insignificant, as well as the angular scattering. From these curves and also from published data, Marton, Simpson, and McGraw (1955b) found that the intensity change in 1.2×10^{-2} radians (half-angle) for different foils are as follows: beryllium, 200; carbon, 200; gold, 500; aluminum, 10,000.

Reliable data for 1000 A Al₂O₃ foils and 20-kv electrons would be most useful, but experiments at Yerkes Observatory have shown that the resolution
will be limited by other factors than scattering in the foil if the emulsion is
placed within 0.1 mm. of the foil. A photograph of a resolution pattern and a
spectrogram taken with the tube just described is shown in Figure 13. Forty
line pairs per mm are resolved on the test pattern.

When the same accelerating voltage is used, the gain in this system should be
essentially identical with the electronographic technique described in the previous section, for the resolution is similar (it varies from tube to tube; from a
minimum of 40 lp/mm to a maximum of 56) and the electron energy loss within
the foil, as illustrated above, is insignificant.

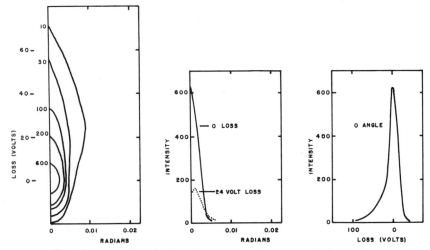

FIG. 12.—Scattering of 20-kv electrons by 100 A polycrystalline gold

The development of this system has been delayed by a high tube background.
The background in an image tube, as discussed earlier, has its origin primarily
in field emission within the tube. The field emission, given approximately by

$$J \approx 6.2 \times 10^{-6} \frac{E^2}{\phi} e^{-6.8 \times 10^7 \phi^{3/2}/E} \text{ amps/cm}^2,$$

where E is the field and ϕ the work function, varies rapidly with work function
—nearly 20 orders of magnitude per factor 2 in work function. When the photocathode is an integral part of an image tube, the work function is altered by
cesium (used in photocathodes because of its low work function) adsorbed by
the metal electrodes. Consequently, much greater precautions must be taken
than when the photocathode is processed in a separate container. In 1961
Hiltner and Niklas reported on a tube in which the background had been reduced by many orders of magnitude. This was done by applying a semiconduc-
tive internal wall coating between the focus electrode and the high-voltage sec-

tion (see Fig. 10). This coating consists essentially of chromium oxide applied by means of a binder. The binder, if properly prepared and treated, consists of an amorphous inorganic oxide with the property of gettering a predetermined amount of cesium vapors when the photocathode is processed. The cesium adheres quite strongly to the binder. This wall coating, consisting of chromium oxide, binder, and cesium, yields a controlled conductivity between the focus electrode and the anode. This equalizes local potential gradients in such a manner that the probability of field emission is appreciably reduced. The background has been further reduced by restricting the photocathode to the desired

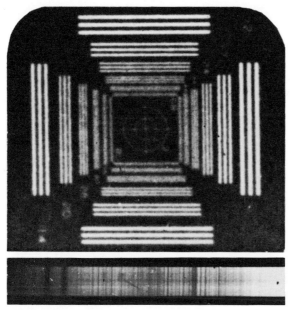

Fig. 13.—Photograph of a resolution pattern taken with the tube described in the text and illustrated in Fig. 12. Enlarged 22 times. The spectrum below was enlarged 10 times.

area. This was done by external evaporation of the antimony. Under these conditions the evaporation is more easily controlled. The final background has been reduced sufficiently that 8-hour exposures are possible with an accelerating potential of 20 kv. Ilford G-5 emulsion and the photocathode cooled with solid CO_2.

The principal advantages of this technique for electronography are as follows: First, the tube has a life of many months or years. This is especially true when the vacuum system has a liquid-nitrogen trap. Second, emulsions may be inserted, exposed, retracted, and developed at will. Third, the tube may be focused either by visual inspection of a phosphor or by a series of trial exposures. An evaporated phosphor with a resolution of 100 line pairs per mm may be inserted in place of an emulsion. This phosphor is then inspected by a low-power

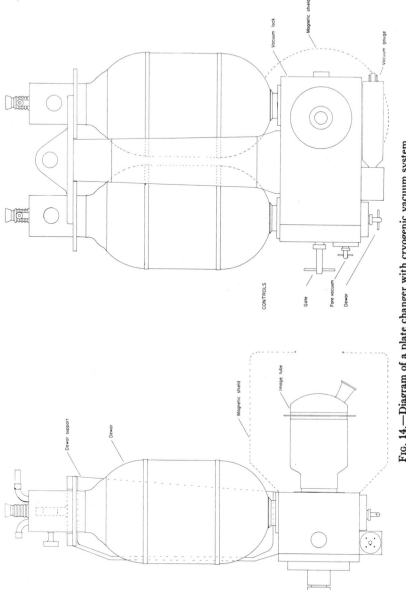

Fig. 14.—Diagram of a plate changer with cryogenic vacuum system

(about 30) microscope as the optical and electronic foci are varied. Also, in addition to the nuclear emulsions mentioned above, other electron-sensitive emulsions, such as the fast but coarse-grained Ilford XM, may be used.

The principal disadvantage is that of providing a kinetic vacuum throughout the life of the tube. Small oil-diffusion pumps trapped with liquid nitrogen (or air) are adequate. However, they are inconvenient to instal at the eye-end of a telescope (except at the coudé focus) because of their sensitivity to gravity and

FIG. 15.—Photograph of plate changer with cryogenic vacuum system attached to 40-inch Yerkes refractor for direct photography.

the need for a fore vacuum. Ion pumps are insensitive to gravity and require no continuous fore vacuum after initial evacuation. However, they radiate (internally) ultraviolet radiation and also must have a strong magnetic field for their operation. Cryogenic pumping is now used at Yerkes Observatory. Two nitrogen-shielded dewars with a capacity of 1.2 liters each of liquid hydrogen or helium evacuate either side of the vacuum lock. With hydrogen, this system, when given a partial vacuum (25–50 μ) with a fore pump (to remove atmospheric helium and neon), has an equilibrium pressure near 10^{-7}mm Hg. The dewars must be serviced with parahydrogen twice per week, for the consumption is approximately 0.3 liter per 24 hours.[1] A schematic drawing is given in Figure 14, and a photograph of the two dewars on the vacuum lock is shown in Figure 15. This particular lock has a magazine that holds three plates and a phosphor for focusing.

§ 6. CASCADED IMAGE CONVERTERS

It was shown in an earlier section that a simple image converter with a photocathode and phosphor has a light-gain of about 25–50. Therefore, a "light-amplifier" with high gain can, in principle, be made by placing two or more image converters in series. This suggestion for a light-amplifier dates back a quarter-century, when it was proposed by von Ardenne (1936). The present era for the actual development of the system, however, dates back only about one decade, when Morton and Reudy (1949) began development on a tube with three stages. In 1955 Zavoiskii et al. (1955) reported on a five-stage tube that could photograph single electrons from the first photocathode. This tube was used to photograph the track of nuclear particles in scintillation chambers. Recently, experimental photography of faint galaxies with this same tube (see Butslov et al. 1958) has been attempted at the Crimean Astrophysical Observatory and the Pulkovo Observatory (see Draft Reports for 11th Assembly, I.A.U., p. 41). Stoudenheimer et al. (1960) have continued the development of two- and three-stage tubes at the Radio Corporation of America. Magnetically focused two-stage tubes have been made by International Telephone and Telegraph Laboratories. Tests for possible astronomical applications have been made by Tuve et al. (1958) and others (see *Carnegie Institution of Washington Year Book*, No. 59, 1960).

To couple the stages together efficiently, a thin sandwich is made. This sandwich consists of the phosphor of the preceding stage separated from the photocathode of the following stage by a thin glass or mica disk. The disk is thin, in order to prevent unnecessary loss in resolution (see § 4.2). However, the proximity of the phosphor and anode requires that the potential on the tube be likewise cascaded. A photograph of three cascaded developmental tubes is shown in Figure 16, one with three stages and two with two stages.

---

[1] The service period can be extended to more than one week by more complete thermal shielding and by using parahydrogen.

The resolution of the cascaded tube seems to be limited at near 15–20 line pairs per mm. It is limited by the resolution of the phosphors and the separation of the phosphor and its following photocathode. Furthermore, the electrostatic focused tubes suffer from image distortion caused by field curvature. The image-plane curvature of the preceding tube is of the opposite sense to the object-plane curvature of the following tube. For the earlier two-stage tube, the useful field was only about 6 mm, with a resolution of 15 lp/mm (Tuve *et al.* 1958). However, recent magnetically focused two-stage tubes have given resolutions up to 16 lp/mm over a field nearly 80 mm in diameter (Draft Report for the 11th Assembly, I.A.U., p. 41). In Figure 17 two photographs, taken with a two-stage magnetically focused image tube, are shown. The typical total light-gains are 10^3 and 10^4 for two- and three-stage tubes, respectively, at 10–15 kv per stage.

FIG. 16.—Photograph of three cascaded image converters. The top one has three stages and the others two stages each. Courtesy Radio Corporation of America.

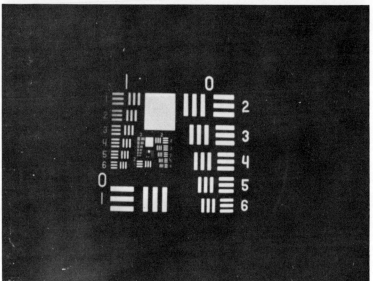

Fig. 17.—Two photographs taken with a magnetically focused two-stage cascaded image converter. The resolution is 16 line pairs per mm over an 80-mm-diameter field. Courtesy Radio Corporation of America.

The most extensive astronomical tests have been made by the Carnegie Committee on Image Tubes for Telescopes (see *Carnegie Institution of Washington Year Book*, Nos. 58 and 59, 1959 and 1960, and Draft Report for the 11th Assembly, I.A.U.). Experimental tubes (two stages, supplied by RCA) have been used for both spectroscopy and direct photography. The rate of blackening gain of the emulsion was about 30 when the same emulsion type (Eastman IIa-D) was used both in place of the image tube and to photograph the phosphor (green) at an operating potential of 18 kv. The phosphor was photographed with two $f/1.3$ lenses front to front. With 2-minute exposures, the threshold magnitude was $V = 18$, whereas the threshold of the direct unaided 2-minute exposure was 16.5. However, the threshold magnitude of an exposure with a fully exposed sky was less faint than that of the unaided emulsion. This was accounted for by the lower resolution of the tube and hence larger images. The intrinsic background of the tube was about five times less than the sky background. Spectroscopic tests at the Perkins Observatory gave a similar value for the rate of blackening. However, when corrected for the loss in resolution, the effective gain or figure of merit of the tube was only 2 or 3. This gain was more than nullified by the limited field. Recently (Tuve 1961), the Carnegie Committee has reported figures of merit from 5 to 10 for magnetically focused tubes and fields up to 80 mm in diameter.

§ 7. SECONDARY-EMISSION IMAGE INTENSIFIER

An alternative technique for internal amplification within an image tube has been described by Sternglass (1955), Wachtel, Doughty, and Anderson (1960), Wilcock, Emberson, and Weekley (1960), and Wachtel, Doughty, Goetze, Anderson, and Sternglass (1960). The technique is essentially an image-forming photomultiplier. A series of plane-parallel thin films is used as secondary emitters. Photoelectrons from a photocathode are focused by an axial magnetic field on the first dynode, which is plane-parallel to the cathode. The secondaries from this first dynode are focused by the same field on a second dynode. This process may be repeated until the desired internal amplification is achieved. The secondary electrons from the last dynode are focused on a phosphor for the light-output. If the electron gain per stage is about 7—a high, but reasonable, figure—and if the light-gain of an image tube without internal amplification is 25, it follows that the total gain of a four-dynode tube is about 50,000. This is adequate for the observation and photography of a single electron from the photocathode. Figure 18 is a schematic drawing, and Figure 19 is a photograph of a sample tube.

The secondary emitter in the dynodes is an alkali halide such as KCl or BaF_2. The halide is supported on a conductor such as aluminum. The halide and conductor may be given further support by an Al_2O_3 foil or by a fine-wire coarse-mesh screen. The total thickness of a dynode is about 1000 A. Dynodes up to several inches in diameter can be satisfactorily made. Secondary emission with

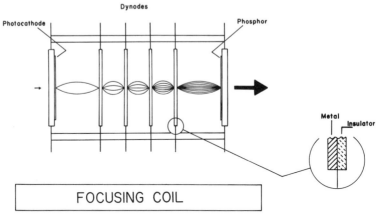

FIG. 18.—Schematic diagram of an image converter with secondary-electron multiplication

FIG. 19.—Photograph of an image converter with secondary-electron multiplication. Courtesy Westinghouse Electric Corporation.

a typical yield of 5–7 and occasionally up to 7 is achieved at voltages of from 3 to 4 kv per stage. Fortunately, and perhaps somewhat surprisingly, the secondaries have relatively small spread in normal velocities. This permits focusing of the secondary electrons on the next dynode. However, the few primaries (about 20 per cent) that do penetrate the film may have velocities sufficiently different from the secondaries that critical focusing is not possible. These "stray" electrons then cause a general lessening in picture contrast. To increase the over-all gain, the output stage—that is, from last dynode to phosphor— receives a higher potential: 10–15 kv is typical.

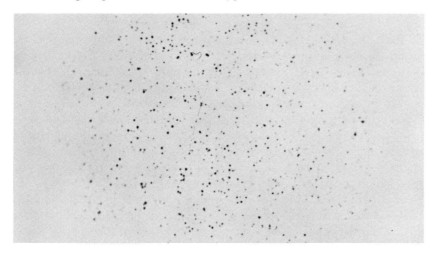

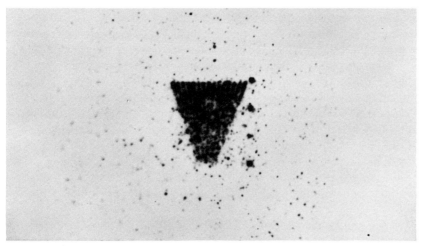

Fig. 20.—Photographs of single electrons from the photocathode of an image converter with secondary-electron multiplication. *Top:* thermal electrons. *Bottom:* resolution pattern projected on photocathode. (Wilcock *et al.* 1960.)

Two photographs taken with an image tube of the type just described are shown in Figure 20. The figure shows single electrons from the photocathode; the top corresponds to the tube background and the other to a resolution pattern projected onto the photocathode. The individual pulses have a diameter near 40 μ on the phosphor (Wilcock, Emberson, and Weekley 1960).

The resolution is no doubt determined by the focus quality from one dynode to the next. In practice, each stage must be focused independently by a series of approximations until the best image is seen on the output screen. Under these conditions the resolution is near 15 line pairs per mm over the entire field, up to 1 inch in diameter, thus far. A magnetic field, provided by either a permanent magnet or a solenoid, of 180–500 gauss is used for focusing.

If the background in image converters is due primarily to field emission, the transmission secondary-emission image-forming photomultiplier should in principle be less subject to background than all tubes previously discussed. This is so because the field emission is more probable when high voltage is used in the chamber where the photocathode is processed. In this photomultiplier, voltages of about 5 kv are used in the first stage instead of the more typical 15–30 kv in single-stage and cascaded image tubes. Background emission of 100 cathode electrons/cm²/sec have been reported. This corresponds to about 7 mag. fainter than the moonless sky background at the focus of an $f/3.5$ optical system. The background reported for a recent Westinghouse tube (Sternglass 1961) is about 10^3 counts/cm²/sec when the tube is operated at a gain of 50,000 at 28 kv.

The astronomical tests reported thus far are limited. Goetze, Sternglass, Ford, and Frederick made some preliminary tests in 1960 (see *Annual Report of the Carnegie Institution of Washington, 1960–1961*). The resolution was about 7.5 lp/mm, about half the optimum attainable, because fixed-stage voltages and a permanent magnet were used for the sake of operational simplicity. The best results were obtained on the emission lines of planetary nebulae in a slitless spectrographic arrangement. A photograph of the installation is shown in Figure 21. The image tube, together with its focusing magnet, is mounted in a 6-inch-diameter brass tube seen on the right side of the grating spectrograph. The tube installation weighed about 20 pounds. Weak emission lines of planetary nebulae were recorded in exposure times up to 15 minutes. The exposure times were approximately 150 times less than those required to reach the same density with unaided photography when 103-G and IIIG emulsions were used at the position of the photocathode. Because of a 4:1 optical magnification employed and the lowered resolution of the tube as actually used, the gain in the rate of accumulation of information over classical photography was only 3:1 in these tests.

Wilcock and Baum (see *Annual Report of the Carnegie Institution of Washington, 1960–1961*) tested a tube of the Wilcock, Emberson, and Weekley (1960) design at the $f/16$ Cassegrain focus of a 24-inch reflector. Two 50-mm $f/2$ lenses, front to front, transferred the phosphor image to the recording photographic emulsion. The telescope scale was 21 seconds of arc per mm and the resolution 12 lp/mm. To reach a given magnitude, the intensifier had a speed gain of 10 at 25 kv and 90 at 30 kv. However, the 30-kv exposure was "distinctly coarse grained or speckled." At 30 kv, the gain was sufficient to expose clumps of grains instead of individual grains. The sky-limited threshold magnitude was 1.5 mag. brighter than a direct classical exposure with an emulsion of the same grain characteristic. In other words, the gain was higher than necessary, and hence the information capacity of the emulsion was wasted.

The same tube was used experimentally by Ford, Baum, and Wilson (see *Annual Report of the Carnegie Institution of Washington, 1960–1961*) at the focus of the 114-inch camera in the 100-inch coudé spectrograph. Although the rate of blackening was greater at 27 kv by a factor of 12, the information gain over unaided photography was only a factor of 3 or 4 after a correction was made for the loss in resolution.

Several years ago Schneeberger (Sternglass 1961) at the Westinghouse Research Laboratories suggested that the secondary-emission yield of insulating layers could be further increased by the use of low-density smoke deposits. However, the presence of instabilities due to charging phenomena had prevented the realization of useful high-yield dynodes. Recent studies by Goetze (Stern-

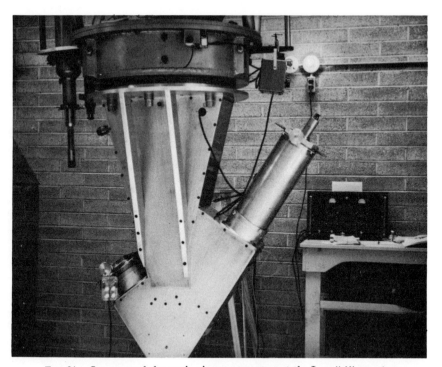

FIG. 21.—Spectrograph for testing image converters at the Lowell Observatory

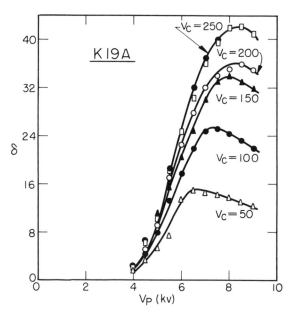

Fig. 22.—Yield-curves for a low-density deposit of KCl as a function of primary energy for various surface potentials. The surface potential is controlled by a fine grid placed at a short distance from the insulator or exit side of the dynode.

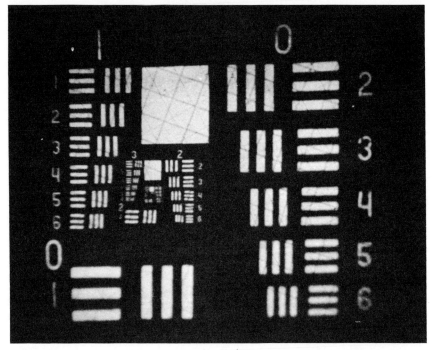

Fig. 23.—Photograph of a test pattern taken with an image converter with one stage of amplification. The total photon gain was 1000 and the resolution 22 line pairs per mm.

glass 1961) on such layers revealed the possibility of controlling the charging process by the proper choice of materials, particle sizes, and potentials. Yields up to 50 have been attained with a single film.

Figure 22 shows a typical yield-curve for a low-density deposit as a function of primary energy for various surface potentials. The surface potential is controlled by a fine grid placed immediately back of the insulator (or exit side of the dynode). In the stable range of operation, the effect of the surface charge is believed to increase the probability that secondaries will reach the surface and escape.

Single-stage devices with such a film have been built with a photon gain of 1000 and a resolution of 22 line pairs per mm. Because of the high ratio of secondary electrons (which can be focused) to primaries (not focusable), the contrast is considerably improved over the earlier four- or five-stage tubes where the dynodes were prepared by vacuum evaporation. Figure 23 is a photograph of a test pattern.

§ 8. CONCLUDING REMARKS

As this is written, it seems impossible to forecast which of the methods discussed, if any, will prove most useful for astronomical research. The data as published are, first, limited and, second, of such nature that the data of various techniques cannot be intercompared. However, a few general remarks can be made. Electronography gives the highest resolution; the full theoretical gain, since it is capable of recording an individual cathode electron (either photoelectric or thermal) on an emulsion without additional statistical processes; satisfactory low tube background; linear response to light; and probably the largest information capacity. There are emulsions, such as the Kodak HR with grain size less than $0.05\,\mu$, that have sufficient storage capacity to permit the detection of 27–28-magnitude stars with 1 second of arc resolution and a scale of 10 seconds per mm (Vernier 1956). However, the exposure time must be prolonged sufficiently to accommodate the full capacity of the emulsion. The principal unfavorable characteristic of electronography is its technical complexity. To those who are accustomed to laboratory techniques, this criticism is not crucial. Perhaps electronography may be simplified if experiments by McGee and Wheeler (1960) with a Lenard window sufficiently strong to withstand atmospheric pressure are successful, that is, capable of high resolution and low background.

The thin mica-window tube discussed in § 4.2 is remarkably simple in its application to direct photography and stellar spectroscopy. However, when the same light-sensitive emulsions are used to record the phosphor output as are now used for classical photography, the information capacity will remain unchanged or be somewhat reduced because of the lower resolution. For many spectroscopic problems this handicap may be of no particular consequence.

Because of its general simplicity, the cascaded image converter is favored by some experimenters. If the gain is sufficient, the limited resolution may be compensated for as long as there are sufficient picture elements for the problem at hand. The information capacity may be enhanced by an optical enlargement from phosphor to the recording emulsion.

The secondary-emission image intensifier discussed in § 7 may offer the lowest background noise. The chamber in which the photocathode is located has a total of not more than 5 kv, in contrast to 15–30 for all other image converters. As seen in § 5.2, low potential is conducive to low field emission. Its limited resolution can also be compensated for by sufficient gain. However, at present, it is handicapped with scattered light probably from unfocused primary electrons.

For long exposures, where image converters will have their greatest value, the tube background must be reduced to a level sufficiently low to permit the desired spectroscopic exposure and significantly below that of the sky for direct photography. The former is the more rigid requirement. Low backgrounds can be achieved, first, by proper design and processing of the tube (see Hiltner and Niklas 1961), second, by optimum installation and operation, and third, by refrigeration of the photocathode. The need for corrective measures to prevent corona discharge cannot be overemphasized if the lowest tube background is to be had.

The accelerating voltage must be regulated even for relatively short exposures. The degree of regulation, which can be easily determined experimentally, is a function of the tube and its environment. Otherwise, critical focus will not be maintained throughout the exposure. The typical electrostatically focused tube requires only a constant voltage ratio for critical focus. However, if the tube is not completely shielded from stray magnetic fields, both internally and externally, critical focus will be absent and the electron image will shift with any variation in voltage. Extra precaution against stray fields will be required where tubes are placed at movable foci, such as the prime and cassegrain foci.

As discussed in chapter 2, bundles of large diameter in stellar spectrographs lead to high light-efficiency. However, these large-diameter bundles require very fast cameras for the lower dispersions. Image converters will assist in relaxing the requirement for the fastest cameras. This can be done by electronic demagnification, that is, a reduction in image size from photocathode to target. For example, an image converter with a magnification 1/5 will produce the equivalent of an $f/0.2$ when preceded by an $f/1$ lens system. The background requirements for the image tube become more critical, of course, by $(1/m)^2$, where m is the electronic magnification. Image converters with magnifications mentioned above are used routinely in clinical fluoroscopy. Lallemand and Duchesne (1961) have made image converters for astronomical use with a magnification of 1/7. The resolution, when referred to the photocathode, is better than 10 line pairs per mm.

The preparation of this chapter was supported in part by the United States Air Force with contract No. AF 19(604)-4951.

REFERENCES

ARDENNE, M. VON   1936   *Electr. Nachr. Tech.*, **13**, 230.

BAUM, W. A., HALL,
JOHN S., MARTON,   1955–
L. L., and TUVE, M. A. 1961   Annual Reports by Carnegie Image-Tube Com-
                                 mittee in *Carnegie Institution of Washington
                                 Year Book.*

BUTSLOV, M. M.,
ZAVOISKII, E. K.,
KALINYAK, A. A.,
NIKONOV, V. B.,
PROKOFIEVA, V. V.,
and SMOLKIN, G. E.   1958   *Doklady Akad. Nauk, U.S.S.R.*, **121**, 815.

HALL, JOHN S.   1961   Private communication.

HALL, J. S., FORD, W. K.,
and BAUM, W. A.   1960   *Photo-electronic Image Devices*, ed. J. D. McGEE
                                 and W. L. WILCOCK (New York: Academic
                                 Press), p. 21.

HILTNER, W. A.   1953   Paper read at the Conference on Photoelectric
                                 Photometry at Flagstaff, Arizona, August 31,
                                 September 1, 1953. An abstract was published
                                 in *A.J.*, **60**, 26–27, 1955.

                        1958   *The Present and Future of the Telescope of Moderate
                                 Size*, ed. F. B. WOOD (Philadelphia: University
                                 of Pennsylvania Press), p. 11.

HILTNER, W. A., and
NIKLAS, W. F.   1961   Paper read at the 108th meeting of the A.A.S. at
                                 Nantucket, Mass.

HILTNER, W. A., and
PESCH, P.   1960   *Photo-electronic Image Devices*, ed. J. D. McGEE
                                 and W. L. WILCOCK (New York: Academic
                                 Press), p. 17.

KRASSOVSKY, V. I.   1958   Reported by W. A. BAUM in *Trans. I.A.U.*, **10**,
                                 146.

LALLEMAND, A.   1936   *C.R.*, **203**, 243 and 990.
                        1960   *A.R.L. Technical Report 60-324*. Publications from
                                 1936 to 1960 by Lallemand and co-workers are
                                 given.
                        1961   Draft Report for the 11th Assembly, I.A.U.,
                                 p. 35.

LALLEMAND, A., and
DUCHESNE, M.   1961   Draft Report for the 11th Assembly, I.A.U., p. 35.

LALLEMAND, A.,
DUCHESNE, M., GOLD-
ZAHL, L., DUFLO, J.,
and BANAIGS, J.   1959   *C.R.*, **248**, 2191.

LALLEMAND, A.,
  DUCHESNE, M., and
  WALKER, M.   1960   *Pub. A.S.P.*, **72**, 268.
LALLEMAND, A.,
  DUCHESNE, M., and
  WLERICK, G.   1960   *Photo-electronic Image Devices*, ed. J. D. McGEE and W. L. WILCOCK (New York: Academic Press), p. 5.

McGEE, J. D., and
  WHEELER, B.   1960   *Royal Photog. Soc. Conf., London*, December.
MARTON, L.,
  SIMPSON, J. A., and
  McCRAW, T. F.   1955*a*   *Phys. Rev.*, **99**, 495.
                     1955*b*   *Ibid.*, p. 1648.
                     1961   Draft Report for the 11th Assembly, I.A.U., p. 39.

MORTON, G. A., and
  REUDY, J. E.   1949   *Contract Rept. Nobsr-39371* (classified).
NIKLAS, W. F.   1961   *Am. J. Roentgen, Rad. Ther. Nucl. Med.*, **85**, 323.
SHCHEGLOV, P. V.   1960   *Astr. Zh.* **37**, 586.
STERNGLASS, E. J.   1955   *Rev. Sci. Instr.*, **26**, 1202.
                     1961   Private communication.

STOUDENHEIMER, R. G.,
  MOORE, J. D., and
  PALMER, H. L.   1960   *I.R.E. Trans. Nuclear Sci.*, June-September, p. 136.
TUVE, M. A.   1961   Private communication.
TUVE, M. A., FORD, W.
  K., JR., HALL, J. S., and
  BAUM, W. A.   1958   *Pub. A.S.P.*, **70**, 592.
VERNIER, P.   1956   *C.R.*, **242**, 1006.
                     1959   *Bull. Astr.*, **22**, 83.

VOLKOV, I. V.,
  YESIPOV, V. F., and
  SHCHEGLOV, P. V.   1959   *Doklady Akad. Nauk, U.S.S.R.*, **129**, 288.
WACHTEL, M. M.,
  DOUGHTY, D. D., and
  ANDERSON, A. E.   1960   *Photo-electronic Image Devices*, ed. J. D. McGEE and W. L. WILCOCK (New York: Academic Press), p. 59.

WACHTEL, M. M.,
  DOUGHTY, D. D.,
  GOETZE, G., ANDER-
  SON, A. E., and
  STERNGLASS, E. J.   1960   *Rev. Sci. Instr.*, **31**, 576.
WALKER, M.   1961   Private communication.
WEBB, J. H.   1948   *J. Opt. Soc. America*, **38**, 312.

WILCOCK, W. L.,
  EMBERSON, D. L., and
  WEEKLEY, B.   1960   *Nature,* **185,** 370.
YESIPOV, V. F.   1960   *Astr. Zh.,* **37,** 588.
ZACHAROV, B., and
  DOWDEN, S.   1960   *Photo-electronic Image Devices,* ed. J. D. McGEE
                                and W. L. WILCOCK (New York: Academic
                                Press), p. 31.

ZAVOISKII, E. K.,
  BULSLOV, M. M.,
  PLAKHOV, A. G., and
  SMOLKIN, G. E.   1955   *Doklady Akad. Nauk, U.S.S.R.,* **100,** 241.

CHAPTER 17

Photographic Photometry

J. STOCK AND A. D. WILLIAMS*†

Kitt Peak National Observatory
and
Yerkes Observatory, University of Chicago

§ 1. INTRODUCTION

Aᴌᴛʜᴏᴜɢʜ the last decade or two has seen a tremendous rise in the popularity
of photoelectric photometry because of the increasing sensitivity, accuracy, and
simplicity of its methods, a good part of astronomical photometry is still carried
out by photographic means. This is due to what has been aptly termed the
"panoramic" property of the photographic emulsion. This ability of the photographic plate to record simultaneously a large number of objects makes photography an efficient method for investigations involving a large number of stars
in a limited field, particularly if the utmost in precision is not required. The sav-
ings in telescope time brought about by the use of photographic methods in
studies such as those encountered in stellar statistics, variable-star surveys, or
investigations of rich star clusters are considerable.

To counterbalance its advantages, the photographic method is not without
its defects. The fundamental principle of photographic photometry is that equal
intensities produce equal photographic effects under identical conditions. These
conditions involve not only the emulsion, the spectral energy distribution of the
exposing light, the exposure time, and the processing of the plate, but also such
factors as the pre- and postexposure treatment of the plate, the size and structure of the optical image, the temperature and humidity during exposure, etc.
Because of the difficulties involved in controlling or accounting for the changes
in some of these conditions, the establishment of magnitude scales or the transfer of magnitude sequences from one part of the sky to another by photographic
methods must be done with great care if reliable results are to be obtained.
These difficulties are best avoided by making use of photoelectric magnitude
sequences in the areas being investigated.

* Present address: Costa Mesa, Calif.
† Section 7.2 prepared by Barbara M. Middlehurst.

The photographic emulsion is often the subject of criticism because of its low sensitivity (quantum efficiency) as compared with a photoelectric cell, its lower photometric accuracy, and its non-linear response. Its non-linear response can be calibrated more or less satisfactorily (Section 2.2) and, with exceptions, its lack of sensitivity can be compensated for by extended exposure times. The principal advantage of the photographic emulsion, as noted above, is the number of image points per unit area ($\sim 10^6/cm^2$) and its integration quality.

Earlier discussions of photographic photometry are found in the *Handbuch* articles by Eberhard (1931, 1936) and Kienle (1937). The history of astronomical photometry has been traced, with extensive reference to the literature, by Weaver (1946). Mees (1954) provides an excellent introduction to the theory of the photographic process, with an extensive survey of the literature dealing with this subject. Of value in a search of the recent literature concerning the photographic process is the *Monthly Abstract Bulletin* published at Rochester, New York, by the Eastman Kodak Research Laboratories.

§ 2. THE PHOTOGRAPHIC EMULSION AND ITS SENSITIVITY

2.1. The Photographic Emulsion and Its Reaction to Light

The most sensitive photographic materials currently available depend on the reaction to light of a suspension of silver halide in an "emulsion" of gelatin, to which is added a number of other ingredients which improve the sensitivity of the material or alter its spectral response. Silver halide is photochemically active, and, upon exposure to light of the proper wave length and sufficient intensity, an invisible *latent image* is formed which renders the associated silver halide more readily reducible than is unexposed silver halide when it is subjected to a suitable reducing agent. After a certain time this process of *development* may be stopped, and the remaining silver halide may be removed from the emulsion by *fixation*, leaving an image of metallic silver. The last steps of photographic processing are washing the emulsion, to remove various processing materials and reaction products, and drying. At every step of the way from the time the emulsion is being manufactured until it is finally measured, it is subjected to conditions that will affect its photometric performance.

The silver halide of importance in the highly sensitive emulsions is silver bromide, although such emulsions also contain a small percentage of silver iodide. Silver bromide is present in the emulsion in the form of very fine crystals, or "grains." Silver bromide is an ionic crystal composed of positively charged silver ions and negatively charged bromide ions. There is considerable evidence that the latent image material is actually metallic silver, which acts as a catalyst in the reduction of the immediately associated silver bromide. Such latent image silver is probably formed by photolysis by reactions similar to

$$Br^- + h\nu \rightarrow Br + e \tag{1}$$

and

$$e + Ag^+ \rightarrow Ag, \tag{2}$$

where $h\nu$ is a quantum of radiation and e an electron. The basis of the currently accepted theory of latent image formation was presented by Gurney and Mott (1938). Their theory considered the photoconductivity of the silver halide crystal. Both the photoelectrons and the silver ions are mobile, and at certain sites on or within the crystal they combine to form a speck of metallic silver. A review of the Gurney-Mott theory as applied to the interpretation of observed latent image phenomena has been presented by Berg (1948). More recently, the theory has been reviewed and modified by Mitchell and Mott (1957). A detailed discussion of the theory is beyond the scope of this chapter.

Neither the number of quanta necessary to produce one atom of metallic silver nor the number of atoms of metallic silver necessary for the formation of a latent image is known. In the vicinity of 4000 A, the action of two light-quanta, absorbed within a few seconds of each other, is required for the formation of a stable (but not developable) *sublatent image* (Webb 1950). According to the theory proposed by Mitchell and Mott (1957), the sublatent image is a neutral pair of silver atoms and requires two photoelectrons for its formation; the minimum stable latent image is composed of four silver atoms with a unit positive charge (Ag_4^+) and requires an additional photoelectron for its formation. On the basis of experiments made with single-grain-layer plates, Webb (1948) concluded that, in the region of 4000 A, about ten absorbed quanta per grain are required for the formation of a latent image.

From such data, a picture of the sensitivity of the photographic process may be obtained. The *responsive quantum efficiency* of a detector is defined as the ratio of the number of output events to the number of input events. If we take this ratio to be the ratio of the number of grains made developable to the number of photographically effective absorbed photons, then the Mitchell-Mott theory predicts an efficiency of 33 per cent, while Webb's observations indicate an efficiency of about 10 per cent. A ratio that is of greater interest to those using photographic materials is the ratio of the number of developable grains to the number of photons incident upon the emulsion. In the region of 4000 A, about 40 per cent of the light incident upon the emulsion is reflected or transmitted, while some 50 per cent is lost through scattering and absorption in the gelatin. Only about 10 per cent of the incident light is absorbed by the silver halide grains. On this basis, the optimum efficiency possible with present emulsions is in the neighborhood of 1–3 per cent, provided that the light is most efficiently used. This requires that all the quanta absorbed by a grain be utilized in the formation of a latent image and that no grain absorbs more than the minimum number of photons required for the formation of a latent image. This is seldom the case in practice, where "effective" quantum efficiencies on the order of 0.1 per cent are encountered.

The spectral region in which a plain silver halide emulsion is sensitive to light corresponds to the region absorbed by the silver halide and is confined largely to the ultraviolet, violet, and blue regions of the spectrum. The long-wave-length limit of sensitivity for silver bromide is, for all practical purposes, about 5000 A. The sensitivity actually extends to about 7000 A, but it is so low beyond 5400 A as to be of no practical importance.

Various organic dyes exist which, when adsorbed by the silver halide, are capable of extending the sensitivity of the emulsion to a longer wave-length limit, by transferring to the silver halide the energy absorbed by the dye. Although the adsorption of the dye by the silver halide is necessary for sensitization, not all dyes adsorbed by the silver halide act as sensitizers. With suitable

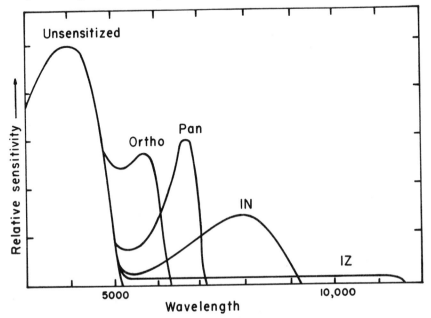

FIG. 1.—Relative spectral sensitivities of typical unsensitized, orthochromatic, panchromatic, and infrared-sensitive emulsions. The maximum infrared sensitivity of the IZ emulsion has been exaggerated to allow it to be seen on the same scale.

dye sensitizers, it is possible to extend the long-wave-length limit of sensitivity to almost 12,500 A. The strong absorption starting at about 14,000 A caused by water present in the gelatin imposes an upper limit on the range of sensitivity of the emulsion.

Figure 1 schematically illustrates the spectral sensitivities of a number of typical dye-sensitized emulsions, together with the spectral sensitivity of a non-sensitized silver iodobromide emulsion. The sensitivity at maximum has been taken as the unit of sensitivity for each emulsion in the figure. Although all the emulsions in common use are most strongly sensitive in the blue-violet region, since they all contain silver halide, their absolute sensitivities in this region vary. This is due partly to the fact that the sensitizing dyes are capable of desensitizing the photosensitive material over the entire spectral range in a manner not connected with the absorption spectrum of the particular dye. The competition between the selective sensitizing and the general desensitizing actions of a given dye result in an optimum concentration of the dye, at which the sensitivity in the spectral region absorbed by the dye reaches a maximum. A considerable loss in sensitivity in the blue-violet region may result from dye sensitization.

2.2. The Characteristic Curve

The action of light upon a photographic emulsion and the subsequent processing of the emulsion produce an image composed of minute grains of metallic silver. A measure for the photographic action which has taken place in a small area on a photographic plate would therefore be the number of grains in that area. It is more usual, however, to discuss the photometric properties of an emulsion in terms of the *transparency*, T, or the *density*, D, of the exposed and developed emulsion. The transparency is the fraction of incident light transmitted by the plate and is defined such that $T = 1$ for clear areas of the plate, while T approaches zero or a very small value with an increasing number of developed grains per unit area. The density, D, is defined by the relation $D = -\log T$. If the size of the individual grains is approximately uniform, the density is roughly proportional to the number of grains per unit area.

Of particular interest in photometric work is the relation of the transparency of the exposed and developed emulsion to the intensity of the incident light, I, forming the image during an exposure of duration t. To represent the large range of exposure conditions, it is convenient to employ logarithmic scales in graphical representations of the response of photographic emulsions to light. Thus the density is plotted versus $\log It$ to form a *characteristic curve* of the emulsion. The characteristic curve of a typical emulsion, as shown in Figure 2, consists of four regions: (1) a toe, (2) a straight portion, (3) a shoulder, and (4) a region of solarization. The toe and straight portion of the curve are due to the particular response of the emulsion to light, while the shoulder of the curve is caused primarily by the fact that the emulsion is not entirely untransparent when all the grains are developed. Solarization seems to be due to the rehalogenation of the surface latent image by the halogen liberated as in reaction (1), which in the case of strong exposures is not effectively prevented from recombining with the surface silver.

The straight portion of the characteristic curve is known as the "region of correct exposure," and for this part of the curve the relationship between the transparency of the plate and the energy producing the image is given by

$$D = -\log T = \gamma (\log It - \log i) . \tag{3}$$

The gradient of the straight portion, γ, is a measure of the contrast of the plate, while the $\log It$-axis intercept, $\log i$, is a measure of the sensitivity. The range of $\log It$ for which equation (3) is valid is called the *latitude* or, more recently, the *linear exposure scale* of the plate. The range of $\log It$ between the point on the toe and the point on the shoulder where the gradient dD/d (log It) becomes zero is called the *total scale* of the plate. The total scale is thus the intensity range within which the plate is capable, in a single exposure, of rendering intensity differences as density differences, while the linear exposure scale is the intensity range within which the maximum density change results for a given percentage change in intensity. The total scale, the linear exposure scale, the *inertia i*, and γ are all dependent not only on the emulsion but also on the exposure and processing conditions.

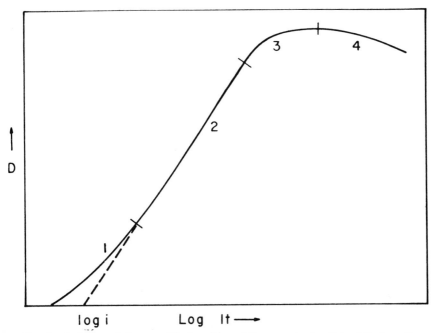

FIG. 2.—A characteristic curve. The logarithm of the exposure, log It, is plotted as a function of the density. The four regions are described in the text.

The value of γ for a given material and a given exposure is dependent on the constitution, temperature, and degree of agitation of the developer and the time of development. If γ_∞ is the maximum attainable value of γ for a given material, then, approximately,

$$\gamma = \gamma_\infty(1 - e^{-k\tau}), \tag{4}$$

where τ is the time of development and k is the velocity constant of development, which is dependent on the constitution, temperature, and degree of agitation of the developer. The value of γ is also dependent on the wave length of the exposing light. No general relationship for this dependence is known, although usually γ increases with increasing wave length.

As already mentioned, the inertia, i, is a measure of the sensitivity of the emulsion. The form of equation (3) is such that the exposure It necessary to produce a given density with materials having differing values of γ is dependent on the choice of the density at which the comparison is made. Thus the inertial speed, which is proportional to $1/i$, is only a measure of the sensitivity at the toe of the curve. A comparison of the various plate materials at a density level of 0.6 gives more significant results. Such density is necessary and adequate, for instance, for the detection and measurement of weak absorption lines in stellar spectra. Accordingly, the speeds of astronomical plates are often taken as being inversely proportional to the exposure It required to produce a density of 0.6 above fog when the plate is developed to a γ of about 80 per cent of γ_∞.

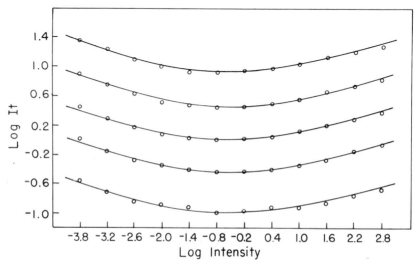

FIG. 3.—Reciprocity-curves for constant densities: O, experimental values; solid lines calculated from catenary equations. From Mees 1954.

2.3. RECIPROCITY FAILURE AND THE INTERMITTENCY EFFECT

The transparency of an exposed and developed plate is not just a function of the total exposure It but depends on the actual values of both the intensity and the exposure time. The deviation from a reciprocal relationship between these two quantities is known as *reciprocity failure* and is commonly displayed in the form of a plot of the logarithm of the exposure It necessary to produce a given density as a function of the logarithm of either the intensity or the time (Fig. 3). In the former case, lines of constant exposure time are straight lines of unit slope. Reciprocity failure varies greatly from emulsion to emulsion. Most modern materials have reciprocity-curves such that the optimal intensity, that is, the intensity at which the minimum exposure It is required to produce a given density, corresponds, for medium densities, to an exposure time on the order of 0.1–10 seconds. There are certain specially prepared emulsions, however, which have optimum exposure times on the order of 1–10 minutes. These rough figures refer to average use, since there are a number of factors which influence the reciprocity characteristics of the emulsion and are at least partially capable of being controlled by the user. These factors include the temperature of the emulsion during exposure and pre- and postexposure treatment of the plate; their control for the purpose of effectively increasing the sensitivity of the emulsion is discussed below (§ 3.5).

Various relationships between T or D and I and t have been presented, one of the most frequently quoted being Schwarzschild's law, which states that T is a function of $It^{1/q}$, where $q > 1$ (Schwarzschild 1900). The equation

$$T = \exp\left(-aI^q t\right), \tag{5}$$

where a is a constant, incorporates Schwarzschild's law and gives a fair representation of the observed characteristic curves for $0.2 < T \le 1.0$, as long as the intensities are low and, correspondingly, the exposure times long. The characteristic curve derived from equation (5) fails, however, to show a shoulder or a region of solarization. It is possible to overcome part of this difficulty by taking into account the minimum transparency of the plate. Equation (5) may then be written as

$$T = T_{(min)} + (1 - T_{min}) \exp\left(-aI^q t\right), \tag{6}$$

where T_{min} is the transparency of areas of the plate where all the grains have been developed. Even equation (6) has only a limited application, since the value of q depends on the value of I itself, decreasing with increasing I and finally becoming less than unity. An equation of the form

$$T = T_{(min)} + (1 - T_{min}) e^{kt} \left[\cosh(Lt) - \frac{k}{L} \sinh(Lt)\right], \tag{7}$$

where

$$-2k = a + (b + c)I \tag{8}$$

and

$$-2L = [a^2 + 2a(b + c)I + (b - c)^2 I^2]^{1/2}, \tag{9}$$

with a, b, and c being constants, gives a more satisfactory representation of the empirical data for the entire range of I for which $q \ge 1$ (Stock 1956).

The density produced by a number of discrete exposures will lie between the density produced by a continuous exposure to the same intensity with a duration equal to the sum of the durations of the discrete exposures and the density produced by a continuous exposure to an intensity equal to the average over both light and dark periods with a duration equal to the total elapsed time between the start of the first discrete exposure and the end of the last. As indicated above, these two continuous exposures will not generally produce the same density. This *intermittency effect*, being closely related to reciprocity failure, is clearly a function of the intensity level and the frequency of interruption of the exposure for a given emulsion. Only for fairly high frequencies is the response equivalent to that of a known continuous exposure, and then to one of an intensity equal to the average intensity of the intermittent exposure with a duration equal to the total elapsed time of the intermittent exposure. The frequency above which such a condition is obtained is a function of the particular emulsion.

A possible mechanism for reciprocity failure and the intermittency effect seems to lie in the fact that the successive absorption of several light-quanta is required in order to produce a latent image, as outlined above, and that, in the formation of the stable sublatent image, one of the intermediate "energy levels" is unstable and decays at a certain rate if no more light is absorbed. Equation (7) was, in fact, derived from such a theory. That a continuous exposure and an intermittent exposure become equivalent when the frequency of interruption of the intermittent exposure exceeds a critical value can thus be explained on the basis of the quantum structure of light.

Since light of high intensity is considerably more efficient in building up a stable sublatent image than is light of low intensity, the density produced by a multiple exposure to light of different intensities depends on the order in which the exposures are taken. The density produced is generally higher if the initial exposure is the high-intensity one (Webb and Evans 1938). In astronomical photography, this effect is often referred to as the *fog effect* (Barber 1940). In the first of a series of exposures on one plate, the light of a stellar image builds up more sublatent image for the subsequent sky-background exposure to work on than the initial sky background produces for subsequent stellar images. The stellar images of the first exposure are therefore generally more effective photographically than those of subsequent exposures. The fog effect is also present in the case of trailed images, such as widened objective-prism spectra. The magnitude of the effect depends on the characteristics of the emulsion, the intensity and wave length of the exposing light, the structure of the image, and the exposure times.

Over a wide range of exposure times, it has been shown experimentally that the reciprocity failure of an emulsion is nearly independent of wave length when points of the same density and exposure time are compared (Webb 1933; Biltz and Webb 1948). It was also found that, provided that the intensities were adjusted to produce equal densities in equal times, successive exposures to light of two different wave lengths were simply additive.

Various other exposure phenomena are known to occur. The fact that if an emulsion is exposed to increasing intensities, the densities of the developed images do not increase indefinitely but tend to diminish when a certain intensity level is surpassed has already been mentioned (§ 2.2). For this part of the characteristic curve (the region of solarization) the reciprocal Schwarzschild exponent, q, is less than unity. For very strong exposures, even a re-reversal of the characteristic curve may occur. If the emulsion is given a very short pre-exposure to intense light, followed by an exposure to light of moderate intensity, the high-intensity exposure may effectively desensitize the emulsion toward the secondary exposure and even appear reversed on development (the *Clayden effect*). Postexposure to red or infrared radiation of an emulsion that has previously been exposed to blue light may result in the destruction of some of the original latent image (the *Herschel effect*). Exposure during processing may result in a reversal of the original image (the *Sabattier effect*). These effects generally have very little, if any, bearing on photometric work, provided that proper precautions are taken in the handling of plates. It therefore seems unnecessary to discuss these effects in this chapter.

§ 3. PHOTOGRAPHIC PROCESSING

3.1. Storage and Handling of Photographic Materials

The photolysis of silver by reactions (1) and (2) is not the only way that a developable silver speck may be formed. Silver specks may be formed during storage, for instance, as a result of thermal processes. Nor is metallic silver the only material that will catalyze the reduction of silver halide in the developing process. The most sensitive emulsions owe their sensitivity to small "sensitivity specks" of silver sulfide formed by the addition of extremely small amounts of sulfur-bearing compounds related to mustard oil during the manufacture of the emulsion. In the preparation of such emulsions, as well as during the aging process, some large silver sulfide particles are bound to be formed, and these can act as catalysts in the reduction of silver halide in much the same way as metallic silver does. Photographic materials are sensitive to a number of chemicals, to pressure, and to static discharges, as well as to radiation. To insure against a decrease in quality, proper storage of unprocessed photographic materials is important.

Proper storage requires refrigeration in a dry atmosphere free from contaminating vapors and dust. To minimize pressure marks, plates should be stored on edge. Refrigeration is required to reduce thermal effects and the rates of various chemical reactions. If storage is for less than a few months, an ordinary refrigerator which produces temperatures around 40° F may be used. For longer periods of storage, a deep freeze is required. Some precautions may be necessary to protect the material from excessive moisture. If possible, the atmosphere in the storage area should be conditioned to a relative humidity of 40–60 per cent. Among the gases that photographic emulsions should be protected from are formaldehyde, ammonia, hydrogen sulfide, sulfur dioxide, gasoline engine exhaust, and the vapors of solvents, cleaners, paint and lacquer thinners, and mercury.

If photographic material is stored at a low temperature, it is subject to rapid temperature and moisture changes when removed from refrigeration for use. The sensitivity of an emulsion is dependent on its temperature and moisture content during exposure (Dimitroff 1938). To minimize the effects of varying sensitivity during exposure, it is important that the emulsion be given sufficient time to reach equilibrium with the atmosphere prior to exposure. It is desirable that the emulsion be allowed to reach equilibrium slowly in such a manner as to prevent the condensation of moisture upon it.

Unprocessed photographic materials should be handled in such a way as to prevent the contamination of the emulsion by such things as particles of hypo, grease, etc. To avoid such contamination, darkrooms should be kept clean, and plates should be handled in such a way as to avoid contact with the emulsion. This last precaution will also reduce the likelihood of fingerprints, scratches, and abrasions.

Since various reactions may occur in improper processing that will spoil the photometric usefulness of a plate, the rules of proper processing should be strictly observed. Small variations in processing technique can greatly affect the finished product. It is particularly important to use fresh solutions and to avoid contamination. Small amounts of sulfides, copper salts, or silver halide solvents such as "hypo" in the developer can result in fog. Prolonged exposure to air of a plate during the development process may cause "aerial fog." As regards the freshness of solutions, it should be noted that the figures quoted by manufacturers for the useful life of solutions, considering exhaustion from use, do not strictly apply to the conditions met in astronomical practice. For example, the average negative of commercial photography will contain, after development, considerably less silver halide than an astronomical negative, which, aside from stellar images, is essentially unexposed. Therefore, the fixer is exhausted more rapidly in astronomical than in commercial practice.

The handling and storage of processed photographic materials require a certain amount of attention, particularly if the material is to remain in usable condition for a relatively long period. For black-and-white materials, a relative humidity between 40 and 50 per cent, a temperature near $70°$ F, and protection from such chemical agents as sulfur dioxide and hydrogen sulfide, as well as adequate fixation and washing, are required conditions for archival storage.

3.2. DEVELOPMENT

If reactions (1) and (2) were allowed to occur repeatedly, a visible image of photolytic silver would be produced, although the amount of energy required to produce such an image would be excessive. Most of this energy can be supplied by chemical means, during the process of development. In this sense, development may be considered a process of amplification. The amplification factor is tremendous, in some instances 10^9 or 10^{10} silver atoms are reduced for an initial group of less than 10.

The common photographic developers are compounded from: (1) one or more agents that selectively reduce the silver halide associated with a latent image and are themselves oxidized; (2) an alkali accelerator, such as a carbonate, borate, or hydroxide, which controls the pH of the solution and thus in most cases the effective concentration of the developing agent; (3) a preservative or antioxidant, such as sodium sulfite; and (4) an antifoggant or restrainer, such as potassium bromide, which restrains not only development but also the rate of fog formation relative to the rate of development. The rate of development is controlled by the composition of the developer, including the reaction products, and in the most simplified cases varies as an exponential function of the temperature. A detailed description of every phase of the developing process is beyond the scope of this chapter. We shall confine the discussion to the more important reactions that take place during the process of development.

Many developing agents—for instance, metol and hydroquinone—contain one or more hydroxyl groups and ionize in solution. In these cases, it is the negative ion so formed that is the actual developing agent. Thus, when no sulfite is present, the reaction of hydroquinone in developing a silver halide may be written as

$$C_6H_4(OH)_2 \rightleftharpoons 2H^+ + C_6H_4O_2^=, \qquad (10)$$

$$C_6H_4O_2^= + 2\ Ag^+ \rightleftharpoons C_6H_4O_2 + 2\ Ag. \qquad (11)$$

The concentration of the negative ion, which is the actual developing agent, depends on the pH of the solution. Metallic silver, formed initially by photolysis, acts as a catalyst, accelerating reaction (11).

The oxidation product of hydroquinone—quinone, $C_6H_4O_2$—accelerates development. Further reactions taking place in the developer result, however, in products that may stain the emulsion. Because of this undesirable property, the quinone is generally removed from the developer in the form of a colorless soluble product formed by its reaction with sodium sulfite. A similar function is performed by the sulfite when used with many other developers, the oxidation products of which may actually retard development.

As the reduction to metallic silver of the silver bromide progresses, the bromide content of the developer increases. As pointed out above, the effect of bromide in the developer is to restrain development, and to do this at the low-exposure end of the exposure range more than at higher-exposure levels. However, most developers are compounded with a sufficient amount of bromide that the addition of bromide by the development process will hardly change its concentration, provided that the development bromide is dispersed throughout the developer.

The developers recommended by most manufacturers of photographic materials are frequently available in prepared form. The use of commercially prepared developers is a convenient way to insure uniformity of solutions and freedom from contamination. Comparisons of various developer-emulsion combinations of interest to astronomers have been made by Barber (1940), Hansson (1954a, b), and Gollnow and Hagemann (1956), among others.

A formula for an excellent fine-grain developer has been published by Morgan (1937). The formula is 10 grams of metol, 100 grams sodium sulphite, and 1000 cc water. Development time is from 12 to 18 minutes at 20° C.

3.3. THE ADJACENCY EFFECTS

In processing photographic plates intended for photometric studies, it is desirable that all grains associated with equivalent latent images receive equal treatment, irrespective of the influence of their neighbors. The rate of development at each grain, aside from the size of the latent image, depends on the local concentration of the developer and the local rates of accumulation and elimination of reaction products. The local accumulation of reaction products in the vicinity of a developing grain and the lack of such products in a less heavily exposed region of the plate will cause irregularities in the rate of development across the plate unless adequate agitation is used. If no agitation is applied, it may happen that the transparency of the plate at a given image is not a function of the intensity of the light producing the image alone but may be governed by the neighboring images as well. If the reaction products are allowed to move preferentially in one direction, as by gravity in the case of plates developed vertically in a tank or as often happens in the case of improper agitation, *directional development* will occur, and the plate will be marked with bromide and developer streaks.

The effects due to the diffusion of the developer and the reaction products across the border between two areas of unequal exposure are illustrated in Figure 4. Such *adjacency effects* have come to be known by several names. The depression of the transparency on the less transparent side of the border is frequently referred to as the *border effect*, while the rise in transparency on the other side of the border is known as the *fringe effect*. These two effects in combination are known as the *edge effect*, and if the border is a line, they are sometimes referred to as *Mackie lines*. Frequently these effects are called the *Eberhard effect*, although, strictly speaking, the Eberhard effect is the special case of the border effect that makes the density of a small area dependent on the size of the area (see Fig. 5). A further manifestation of the same mechanism is the *Kostinsky effect*, in which the increased concentration of the reaction products between two nearby small images causes an apparent increase in the separation of the images.

The adjacency effects are sensitive to the composition of the developer and the length of time of development. An energetic, concentrated developer with a high bromide content produces the best results from the standpoint of minimizing the adjacency effects. The effects are dependent on the degree of development, and development to the maximum contrast will minimize them. A recent study of the Eberhard effect, with special regard to the composition of the developer, has been published by Hansson (1954a). This paper also includes a useful bibliography regarding the adjacency effects.

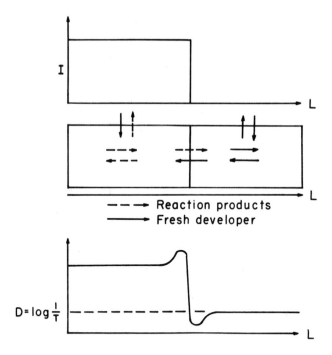

Reaction products

Fresh developer

$D = \log \frac{1}{T}$

FIG. 4.—The adjacency effects. The density (= the logarithm of the reciprocal of the transparency) of the processed emulsion in the vicinity of a sharp border of the image (*bottom*) is a function not only of the intensity of the light producing the image (*top*) but also of the diffusion of the developer and reaction products within the emulsion (shown schematically in cross-section, *center*).

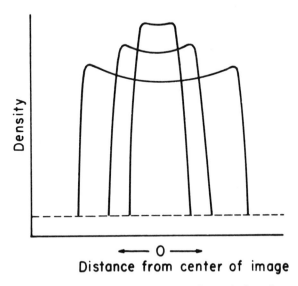

Distance from center of image

FIG. 5.—The Eberhard effect. The density of a small area is dependent not only on the intensity of the light producing the image but also on the size of the area.

Proper agitation can remove the surface film of reaction products from the plate and thus reduce the adjacency effects. Since the surface film is extremely thin and clings to the emulsion, vigorous agitation is called for. Rocking the tray or tank containing the developer will not, in general, produce sufficiently vigorous agitation for this purpose. Even when the adjacency effects are not of primary importance, simple rocking is insufficient to produce uniform development. Uniform mechanical rocking will produce a stationary condition in part of the developer, while it has been found by Ross (1936) that continuous irregular rocking may produce results inferior to those produced with no agitation of any kind, as far as the large-scale uniformity of the plate is concerned.

Constant brushing of the emulsion during development will, to a considerable extent, overcome some of these difficulties. A practical objection to brush development is that its effects on the velocity of development are not easily reproducible. To overcome this problem, various processing machines have been designed (Dobson, Griffith, and Harrison 1926; Jones, Russell, and Beacham 1937) employing paddles, plungers, rollers, or wiper blades that are moved across the plate at a small distance from the emulsion. The developer is forced at a high velocity between the blade and the emulsion, producing strong turbulence. More recently, gaseous-burst agitation has come into wide use because of its simplicity. In this method of agitation, a compressed gas (generally nitrogen) is released intermittently through holes in a distributor at the bottom of the developing tank, producing strong turbulence in the developer. The uniformity and reproducibility of results obtained by this method are comparable to those produced by other methods.

As is the case with the adjacency effects, conditions favorable to uniformity include full development and the use of developers that suffer only slight changes in activity with use.

3.4. Fixing and Washing

In addition to the metallic silver which forms the image, the developed emulsion still contains the unexposed silver halide that has not been reduced. This material is still sensitive to light and may be reduced by photolysis. In addition, it may also be reduced by chemical means, and, further, it is not completely transparent. Therefore, it must either be converted into a stable colorless material or, as is most frequently done in practice, removed from the emulsion. Since silver halide is almost insoluble in water, the removal of the silver halide remaining after development requires two steps: (1) fixation, whereby the silver halide is converted into water-soluble salts (and partially removed from the emulsion), and (2) washing, whereby the remaining salts and the fixing agents are removed from the emulsion.

Fixation may be accomplished by use of various substances, but in practice the thiosulfates, particularly sodium thiosulfate or "hypo," are most frequently used. The most probable mechanism for the chemical reactions which take place during fixation involves the reactions between thiosulfate ions and the silver ions of the silver bromide, forming argentothiosulfates of varying solubilities. The reaction

$$AgBr + 2\,Na_2S_2O_3 \rightarrow NaBr + Na_3\,Ag(S_2O_3)_2 \qquad (12)$$

produces sodium monoargentodithiosulfate, which is readily soluble, while, for instance, from the reaction

$$AgBr + Na_2S_2O_3 \rightarrow NaBr + Na\,Ag\,S_2O_3 \qquad (13)$$

sodium monoargentomonothiosulfate is obtained, which is only slightly soluble. The solubilities of the sodium argentothiosulfates follow a fairly general pattern in the sense that there is a tendency for the less soluble or insoluble complexes to be formed as the concentration of hypo is reduced. Such compounds are removed, if at all, only by prolonged washing. If they remain in the emulsion, they will decompose in time, chiefly into silver sulfide, and cause stains.

In practice, simple fixing baths composed of a thiosulfate alone in a water solution are seldom used. In the absence of a stop bath, the developer remaining in the emulsion would oxidize, causing stain. Therefore, a combination acid-fixing and hardening bath is generally used, which contains, in addition to a fixing agent, (1) an organic acid, such as acetic acid, which stops development and thus prevents staining; (2) a preservative, like sodium sulfite, which prevents the formation of sulfur by the action of the acid on the thiosulfate; and (3) a hardening agent, such as potassium or chrome alum, which forms aluminum oxide, which is adsorbed by the gelatin. The fixing and hardening properties of such baths depend on a number of factors, including the temperature, degree of agitation, and pH. During use, the bath gains "carry-over" from previous solutions, the concentration of fixing agents is reduced, and halides, such as sodium bromide, accumulate that tend to restrain the action of the fixer.

A rule of thumb in fixation is to fix "for twice the time it takes to clear." It is possible in an exhausted bath to "fix" for several times as long as it takes to clear the plates and yet not really fix them, since non-soluble argentothiosulfates are formed. A safe rule is to discard the bath when the clearing time approaches twice the time required when the bath was fresh. A further precaution is the use of two fixing baths in succession.

If alum is used as the hardening agent in the fixing bath, the presence of minute amounts of organic material in the wash water will result in an alum-organic sludge, which will adhere to the plate to form a scum on the dried plate. To prevent this scum, as well as possible contamination of the plate by other material, a well-filtered water supply might be used. Rinsing the plates before washing and swabbing them off with wet cotton at the end of washing will help guard against such damage. The latter step will also promote uniform drying.

3.5. HYPERSENSITIZATION

The inherent low sensitivity of the photographic emulsion requires long exposures to be made to record the low level of illumination common in astronomy. However, as pointed out in § 2.3, the efficiency of the emulsion is a function of the light-intensity, and for low intensities it is often greatly reduced. It is desirable in many cases effectively to increase the efficiency of the emulsion by reducing reciprocity failure. To a considerable degree, this can be accomplished in the manufacture of the emulsion. However, an increase in the efficiency of the emulsion is often accompanied by undesirable effects, such as an increase in the tendency of the emulsion to become developable spontaneously or to "fog." Thus, in the manufacture of the emulsion, the manufacturer must balance the efficiency of the emulsion against a number of other factors, such as stability and graininess. It therefore frequently occurs that certain specific treatments by the user before, during, or after the exposure may increase the effectiveness of the photographic material.

A common type of treatment employed in astronomical work is *hypersensitization*. Strictly, hypersensitization refers to treatment between the manufacture of the emulsion and its exposure, and even the methods of dye sensitization might be considered at times to be hypersensitization procedures. The hypersensitization procedures that are practiced by the user of the emulsion include, at present: (1) bathing the emulsion in water or an alkaline solution such as ammonia, (2) exposure of the emulsion to certain vapors, such as mercury vapor, (3) heating the plates in an oven for a few days prior to exposure, and (4) prefogging the plates by exposure to light (Bowen and Clark 1940; Miller, Henn, and Crabtree 1946). There is a great need for experimentation in this field, and the optimum conditions for hypersensitization are not yet known. The effectiveness of the method depends on the particular emulsion being treated.

Hypersensitization by bathing seems to depend for its effect on the increase in the concentration of silver ions at the surface of the grain, the solution removing bromide ions from the emulsion. The silver-ion concentration has an effect not only on the sensitivity of a non-sensitized emulsion but also on the transfer of energy and the desensitization by sensitizing dyes. While the response of dye-sensitized emulsions may be improved by hypersensitization by bathing, non-sensitized emulsions show little, if any, effect. The effect depends on the dye sensitizer and other properties of the emulsion and is wave-length dependent.

To illustrate some of the problems of hypersensitization, let us consider a typical process used for hypersensitizing infrared plates. Although hypersensitization may frequently be accomplished by bathing such plates in distilled water, the most commonly applied methods depend on the action of a dilute ammonia solution. The effect of ammonia hypersensitization has been found to be dependent on the rapidity of drying, and therefore the emulsion is usually treated in an alcohol bath following the ammonia bath and prior to being dried in an air blast. There is evidence, however, that, by rapidly drying ammonia-hypersensitized plates without the use of an alcohol bath, plates with a lower and more uniform fog, but otherwise almost as sensitive as alcohol-dried plates, can be obtained (Guérin and de Vaucouleurs 1950). Special precautions are necessary to insure uniform treatment and drying of the emulsion. The addition of a wetting agent to the ammonia solution appears to be beneficial in this respect. As hypersensitized plates show a tendency to fog, the addition of an antifoggant, such as benzotriazole, has been also recommended (Miller, Henn, and Crabtree 1946). To promote rapid drying, it is important that the temperature of the solution be kept below 55° F, to reduce the swelling of the gelatin. Uniformity is also promoted by adequately draining the plates before drying them in an air blast. In general, hypersensitized plates are used very shortly after preparation, although there is some evidence that the sensitivity of the emulsion may increase during the first few days following ammonia treatment, before finally deteriorating (Berthier and Morignac 1953).

The hypersensitizing effect of mercury vapor appears to be due to the reinforcement of ineffective sensitivity specks by the adsorption of mercury atoms. A critical sensitivity is soon reached, however, beyond which the further adsorption of mercury produces a rapid drop in sensitivity, together with an increase in fog (Sheppard, Vanselow, and Quirk 1945). The procedure is critically dependent on a number of outside factors, such as humidity, temperature, and pressure, and is, at best, difficult to control. The possibility of contaminating other photographic materials by mercury vapor, producing a loss of sensitivity and fog, must be carefully guarded against. While hypersensitizing by bathing affects the shape of the spectral sensitivity-curve, mercury vapor hypersensitization apparently does not. Unlike ammonia hypersensitization, where the decrease in sensitivity after treatment is accompanied by an increase in fog, the decrease in sensitivity after mercury vapor treatment—which may be attributed to the evaporation of the adsorbed mercury—is not accompanied by an increase in fog. There is thus the possibility of repeating the hypersensitization process.

Hypersensitization by heat is accomplished by baking the emulsion for a few days. A typical procedure is baking for 3 or more days at about 100° F immediately before use. Baking the emulsion produces more than an exposure effect on the plate. During manufacture, various sensitizing agents are added to the emulsion, and the chemical reactions of these adsorbed sensitizers with the silver halide are affected by the subsequent thermal history of the emulsion. To accelerate these reactions, the emulsion is subjected to an elevated temperature or after-ripening during manufacture. If this after-ripening is carried too far, it leads to fog; if not carried far enough, the emulsion continues to ripen during storage. Baking the emulsion just before use will accelerate this aging process.

Pre-exposure to light may improve the sensitivity of the emulsion by supplying stable sublatent images upon which latent images may be readily built

(§ 2.3). Ideally, this would increase the effectiveness of the subsequent exposing light by a factor of 3, according to the theory proposed by Mitchell and Mott. The intensity and duration of the pre-exposure are critical. For astronomical purposes, where the subsequent exposure is to faint light, the pre-exposure should be produced by a short flash. Argue (1954) suggests a pre-exposure flash on the order of 1/750 second or less.

Other than by hypersensitization, the efficiency of an emulsion may be improved by various procedures during exposure or between exposure and development. The loss of efficiency due to low-intensity reciprocity failure may frequently be greatly reduced by refrigerating the emulsion during exposure, provided that the temperature is not lowered too much. Roughly, the effect of reducing the temperature is to shift the reciprocity-failure curve (Fig. 3) bodily, moving the point of optimal exposure toward lower intensities and longer exposure times. The gain in efficiency to be expected from altering the temperature of the emulsion depends on the location, with respect to the optimal intensity, of the intensity range to be photographed. Although this effect has been noted in the astronomical literature for some time (see, for example, Wallace 1908), it has not, as yet, been extensively exploited by astronomers. A recent study of the astronomical application of this effect has been made by Argue (1954) and Hoag (1961). It should be noted that the spectral sensitivity of the photographic emulsion is temperature-dependent and may be considerably different at the low temperatures sometimes required for this process.

Treatment of the emulsion between exposure and development, or *latensification*, has so far found no important application in astronomical photography.

§ 4. THE MEASUREMENT OF FOCAL STELLAR IMAGES

4.1. FUNDAMENTAL CONSIDERATIONS

The fundamental principle of photographic photometry is that equal intensities produce equal photographic effects under identical conditions. Generally, the transparency of the developed photographic image is the photographic effect used as the measure of the intensity of the exposing light. However, since the response of the photographic emulsion is not linear, the integrated transparency of the photographic image depends not only on the integrated intensity of the optical image but on the intensity distribution as well. The intensity distribution in the optical image is dependent on a large number of factors, including the seeing and guiding during the exposure, the properties and the adjustment of the optical system, and photographic turbidity. The problem is further complicated by the photographic adjacency effects. The variation of these factors from one exposure to another, with position on the plate and with wave length, is largely responsible for the difficulties encountered in transferring magnitudes photographically (§ 5.13), for field errors (§ 5.2), and for the photographic Purkinje effect (§ 6.2). To a considerable extent, these difficulties may be overcome by special techniques, such as Fabry photometry (§ 7.1).

In the absence of aberrations, the seeing produces roughly a Gaussian image. That is, the intensity distribution along a radius, r, in a focal stellar image may be written as

$$I(r) = \frac{I}{\pi R^2} \exp\left(-\frac{r^2}{R^2}\right), \tag{14}$$

where $\bar{I}$ is the total light flux in the stellar image, while the "scattering radius," R, is a constant for a given exposure (Gyldenkerne 1950; Hawkins, and Whipple 1958). Equation (14) will also, to a first approximation, represent the central diffraction image of a focal stellar image.

The focal stellar image may be deformed because of field rotation, atmospheric refraction, and instrumental flexure. These effects have been discussed at length by Arend (1948). On long-exposure photographs and particularly in the presence of aberrations, these effects may produce field errors that, since they will vary from exposure to exposure, will be exceedingly difficult to control (see, for example, Ross 1936). In the absence of such disturbing effects, the effects of the optical aberrations can be handled as indicated in §§ 5.2 and 6.2.

4.2. Image Diameters

Generally the diameter of a focal stellar image provides a fairly sensitive measure of the intensity of the exposing light, although it is somewhat problematic to define a diameter of an object with a "fuzzy" edge. A number of empirical or semiempirical relations between the diameter d and the intensity I of exposing light have been proposed. Ross gives the expression

$$d = a' + \Gamma \log I, \tag{15}$$

with a' and Γ constants to be determined. The factor Γ has been named "astro-gamma," in analogy to equation (3). The expression

$$d^v = a + b \log I \tag{16}$$

is a slightly more general variation, with a and b as constants. Many other relations have been proposed in the literature (see, for example, Eberhard 1931; Lundmark 1932; Edwards 1942). The large number of complicating factors previously mentioned do not allow a general theory of the structure of the photographic stellar image. The empirically derived expressions may be regarded as merely convenient interpolation equations and apply to material gathered with a given instrument under given conditions of use. All these equations may therefore introduce systematic errors, and a better procedure would be to construct for each plate a calibration-curve, as indicated in § 5.1.

Although the measurement of image diameters under proper conditions may yield fairly accurate magnitudes, a far simpler method of similar accuracy is to compare visually the images with a scale, or *fly-spanker*, of comparable images. Such a scale is obtained by taking a series of exposures of different lengths on one plate, offsetting the telescope slightly between exposures. Usually a series of exposure times which follow a geometric progression is used. Since the structure of the images is important in estimating equality between two images, the fly-spanker should be exposed on a plate similar to the plates being measured, with the same instrument, and under similar conditions of guiding, seeing, etc. A comparison between fly-spanker images and images on the plate being measured is made, interpolating between the fly-spanker steps. The conversion of these measures into magnitudes is discussed in § 5.1. The fly-spanker method takes into account both the size and the density of the image and is therefore capable of yielding better results than measurements of diameter alone, particularly for very small, faint images. The probable error of a single measure obtained by either method may be as small as a few hundredths of a magnitude, although probable errors on the order of ± 0.05 to ± 0.1 mag. are more commonly encountered.

4.3. Photometers

The most accurate photographic photometry requires the use of an objective physical method for the measurement of the photographic image. Although a considerable variety of photometers exists for this purpose, there are essentially only two basic types of photometer: the constant diaphragm type and the variable diaphragm type. The constant diaphragm photometer was introduced by Stetson (1915, 1916) and is also associated with the names of Schilt (1922, 1924) and Ross (1936). Various types of variable, or iris, diaphragm photometers, first introduced by Siedentopf (1934), have been described by Eichner, Hett, Schilt, Schwarzschild, and Sterling (1947), Jäger (1949), Cameron (1951), Haffner (1953), Becker and Biber (1956), and Cuffey (1956). The basic optical arrangement is nearly identical in both types of instrument. Figures 6 and 7 schematically illustrate two different optical arrangements suitable for either type of instrument. The functions of the various optical components are indicated below. In both arrangements, the components are arranged so that a uniformly illuminated light-spot falls on the emulsion, while the light-distribution on the detector (generally a photocell) is independent of the light-distribution in the emulsion.

In the optical system outlined in Figure 6, the lens L_1 forms an image of the filament of the photometer lamp on L_{2A}. An iris diaphragm, placed either directly in front of or behind L_1, is projected on a reduced scale on the photographic emulsion by L_{2A} and L_{2B}. Then L_3, usually a replica of L_2, projects an image of the emulsion on L_4 and is in turn imaged at point S by L_4. Finally, L_5 projects the image at S on the cathode of a photocell. By inserting a beam-splitter at H, an image of the emulsion may be projected on a viewing screen by L_3, thus providing the operator with the means for checking the centering of the image during measurement. Since the area of the plate illuminated by the photometer lamp is very small, field illumination must be provided for purposes of orientation and identification of stars. This is done by means of a field lamp, which is imaged on L_{2B} by L_6 when the retractable mirror M is placed on the optical axis of L_{2B}; an image of L_6 is then formed on the emulsion by L_{2B}.

This optical arrangement may be used for either constant or variable diaphragm work. For constant diaphragm use, the size of the iris—usually chosen so that its projected image on the emulsion is somewhat larger than the largest stellar image to be measured—is kept constant, and the output of the photocell may be used as a measure of the transparency of the plate. It is more common, however, to produce a given output of the photocell by using a neutral-density

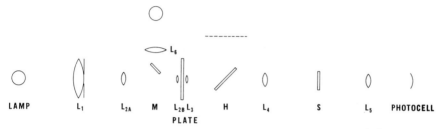

FIG. 6.—Basic optical arrangement of a photometer for the measurement of photographic plates. The components are described in the text.

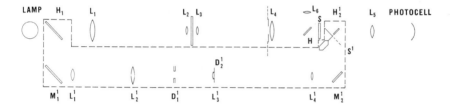

FIG. 7.—An alternate optical arrangement for a photometer for the measurement of photographic plates. The components are described in the text. The optics inclosed in the dashed lines form a comparison beam, which could also be used with the optical arrangement shown in Fig. 6.

wedge, such as is indicated near point S in the figure, as the measuring unit. For variable diaphragm use, the iris is used as the measuring unit. As the iris is opened or closed to produce a given photocurrent, the size of the light-spot on the emulsion varies. Thus the variable diaphragm photometer measures the effective diameter of the image, while the constant diaphragm photometer measures the transparency of a given constant area surrounding and including the image.

The optical system illustrated in Figure 7 may also be used as either a constant diaphragm or a variable diaphragm instrument. The principal difference between it and the system shown in Figure 6 is that, while the system of Figure 6 projects an image of the diaphragm on the emulsion, the system of Figure 7 images the emulsion on the diaphragm. The optical arrangement shown in Figure 6 thus suffers less from the effects of light-scattering in the emulsion than does the arrangement shown in Figure 7. The lens L_1 forms an image of the filament of the photometer lamp on L_2, which in turn projects an image of L_1 on the emulsion; L_3 images the emulsion on the diaphragm close in front of L_4 and is imaged at S by L_4. The image at S is projected on the photocathode by L_5. In this arrangement no extra field illumination generally is required. The converging cone of light from L_4 is intercepted by the beam-splitter H, and part of it is passed on to L_6, which images the diaphragm on the viewing screen.

For measurements in which a constant photocurrent has to be produced by varying the position of a wedge or the opening of an iris, it is convenient to compare the output directly with that from a *comparison beam*. The purpose of such an arrangement is to provide a reference for null measures in such a way as automatically to compensate for certain changes in the instrument, as, for instance, changes in the intensity of the photometer lamp. Modern photometers are generally equipped with a comparison beam and a suitable electrical circuit which indicates when equality of the intensities of the comparison and measuring beams is achieved. The optical arrangement of such a comparison beam is indicated inside the broken lines of Figure 7. The same arrangement could, of course, also be added to the system of Figure 6. A beam-splitter, H_1', is used to pass some of the light from the photometer lamp to the lens L_1', via the mirror M_1'; L_1' projects an image of the filament of the lamp on L_2', which in turn images L_1' on the diaphragm D_1'; L_3' images the diaphragm on L_4' and is imaged by S' by L_4' and M_2'. A rotating sector, or "chopper," alternately interrupts the comparison beams at S' and the measuring beam at S. A second beam-splitter, H_2', redirects the comparison beam, the image at S' being imaged on the photocathode by L_5. The intensity of the comparison beam may be varied by altering the size of the diaphragm D_1', while the size of the image at S' may be changed by varying D_2'. It is advantageous to adjust this latter diaphragm so that the comparison beam and the measuring beam produce images of the same size at the photocathode.

To compensate changes in the intensity of the lamp filament properly, it is important that the comparison beam see the same part of the filament, and from the same angle, as does the measuring beam. Similar design considerations also apply to the illumination of the detector if, for instance, variations in the dynode potential of a photomultiplier are to be compensated for. Even with a properly adjusted comparison beam, however, the compensation will not be perfect, since a variation in the filament current will alter not only the intensity of the lamp but the color of the lamp also. Since the transparency of the optical components and the emulsion is color-dependent, the variations in both measuring beam and comparison beam may, therefore, be slightly different. To reduce such effects, the lamp voltage should be stabilized, and color filters should be used to reduce the spectral range of the light.

The optical design of either type of photometer described here may be easily modified to make a microphotometer suitable for the measurement of fine details in spectra or extended objects. A slit or small diaphragm of the desired shape is placed immediately behind L_1 and is projected on the emulsion by L_2. In microphotometry, the light scattered in the emulsion and in the optics of the microphotometer becomes very important, and special steps must be taken to allow for it (Schwarzschild and Villiger 1906). To limit such effects, a second slit or diaphragm must be placed before L_4, arranged so that the image of the first slit is projected on it by L_3. A similar arrangement could be used to reduce the problem of scattered light, which may become important in the photometry of a rich star field, in the photometers described above. In the case of a variable diaphragm photometer, two iris diaphragms, at L_1 and L_4, geared together, would serve this purpose.

In those arrangements where null measurements are made, the null indication may be obtained from a meter or an oscilloscope. In the other arrangements, a meter or strip-chart recorder may be used. A strip-chart recorder is particularly valuable in microphotometry, where, for instance, a spectrographic plate is made to move at a constant rate in the direction of the dispersion. A large number of modifications have been proposed or put in practice toward the purpose of developing fully automatic recording photometers. Provision can be made for automatically converting the photometer readings into intensity readings if the calibration-curve is known beforehand or, in certain cases, if calibration plates of the proper type are available. Electronic and mechanical provisions can be made to convert any of the basic optical systems described into isophotometers, which automatically trace curves of equal density for the images of extended objects (Mohler and Pierce 1957).

The technique of measuring focal stellar images with either constant or variable diaphragm photometers has been discussed by a number of authors; we may mention Ross (1936) for the case of constant diaphragm instruments and Cameron (1951) for the case of iris diaphragm photometers. After the plate is placed in the photometer, the instrument is focused, and the plate is oriented in a manner convenient for the identification of the images to be measured. One by one, the stellar images are centered in the projected image of the diaphragm, and the measurements are made. The adjustment of the instrument must be maintained throughout a series of measures, and the emulsion must be maintained in the focus of the instrument. Although most modern photometers have provision for mechanically maintaining the position relative to the focus of the back of the plate, variations in the thickness of the glass will result in a defocusing which must be removed by moving the plate. Normally, the focusing and centering are done visually. Since the stellar image will produce maximum absorption in the measuring beam when it is centered, centering may also be done by moving the image into a position where the intensity of the measuring beam becomes a minimum. This procedure is particularly advisable when the images are somewhat distorted. Since the diameter of the image will be a minimum when the image is in focus, a similar procedure may be used for adjusting the focus of variable diaphragm instruments. After the image is centered and in focus, a reading is made in one of the ways outlined above. The conversion of these readings into magnitudes will be discussed in § 5.

In instruments using a comparison beam, the intensity of the comparison beam relative to the total intensity of the photometer lamp may be chosen arbitrarily but must be kept constant during the measurement of a plate. The optimum intensity of the comparison beam for a given plate depends on the structure of the photographic image and on the magnitude range that one is particularly concerned with. In constant diaphragm work, the size of the brightest focal stellar image to be measured determines the size of the diaphragm. The intensity of the comparison beam is then determined by the transparency of the image and the characteristics of the wedge used for the measurement. In variable diaphragm work, a different approach to the problem is employed. In many iris diaphragm photometers, the reduction factor with which the iris is projected onto the emulsion (or vice-versa) can be changed. Essentially, this is done by altering the focal length of L_{2AB} in Figure 6 or L_3 in Figure 7. The iris will be most efficiently used if the reduction factor is chosen so that the projected size of the fully opened iris compares with the size of the largest images to be measured. The intensity of the comparison beam generally is then adjusted so that the faintest images to be measured just fit in the projected image of the iris when the two beams are balanced. Then the image of the iris will cut into the outer fringes of the brighter images when the beams are in balance. For plates taken with a reflector, the loss of the fringes of the brighter images is not a disadvantage. However, the presence of chromatic aberrations in the images produced by a refractor alters the situation, and various color effects may be encountered in such cases (see § 6).

4.4. Theory of the Calibration-Curve

Given the proper theory expressing the transparency, T, as a function of the intensity, I, and the exposure time, t, and with a knowledge of the distribution of intensity in the stellar image, it is possible to derive a theoretical response-curve for a given type of photometer. Such a theoretical calibration-curve, where photometer readings, $P(m)$, are plotted versus the stellar magnitudes (m), can prove useful in indicating how the various parameters influence the particular form of the curve. It will be of special interest to determine under what conditions a linear relation between magnitudes and readings may be expected. J. Stock (1958) has made an attempt to derive such theoretical calibration-curves for iris-type photometers and for constant diaphragm photometers. In the case of iris-type photometers for all stars except those close to the plate limit, a relation of the type

$$P^2(m) = -0.921 \ R^2 m + \text{const.} \tag{17}$$

(where R, the scattering radius, is constant for a given plate) is found, if the photometer reading P is proportional to the diameter of the iris diaphragm. Thus, if the photometer reading is proportional to the area of the iris, as is the case for the photometer described by Haffner (1953), a linear calibration-curve is expected. A slight transparency of fully exposed areas of the plate calibration-curve is expected. A slight transparency of fully exposed areas of the plate (see eq. [6]) has the tendency to curve the bright-star position of the calibration-curve. For constant diaphragm photometers a relatively short, straight portion is obtained on the basis of the same theory. The slope of this straight portion again is a function of R.

The effect of a variable background, due to variable sky background or to the processing of the plate, can also be theoretically predicted to a certain extent. It appears that its effect on the photometer readings for stars can be more readily controlled in the case of constant diaphragm photometers than is the case for iris-type photometers.

§ 5. THE REDUCTION OF PHOTOMETRIC MEASURES

5.1. Calibration Methods

The process of establishing the relation between photometer readings and magnitudes is known as *calibrating* a plate. Whenever possible, this is done with the aid of photoelectric sequences, which, of course, must be on the same color system as the photographically obtained magnitudes themselves (see § 6.2). Photographic determinations of magnitude scales are, however, still in use, and it seems appropriate, therefore, to discuss some of these methods. Usually two steps are necessary, one for the determination of the magnitude scale and another for the zero point of the scale.

Several methods have been devised for establishing a magnitude scale by photographic means. The most reliable methods at present make use of the known transmittance of a neutral filter (or rotating sector) or the known intensity ratio between images of different orders produced by a diffraction grating.

5.11. *Neutral filter methods.*—On a plate with two slightly separated exposures of equal exposure time, one taken through a neutrally absorbing filter, the other through a clear-glass plate (to compensate focus differences), a set of pairs of images is obtained which permits the construction of a calibration-curve. For each pair of images, the difference in the photometer readings corresponds to the absorption in the neutral filter. This absorption is usually expressed in magnitudes and is known as the "filter constant," k. If a magnitude m_0 is assumed for one photometer reading $P(m_0)$, then the readings $P(m_0 + nk)$, where n is an integer, can easily be found from a plot of the readings for the images taken through the filter versus the corresponding images taken through the clear glass. The curve $P(m)$ usually shows a straight portion where one can easily interpolate between two of the original points and find a start for another series of points that fall in between the values of $m_0 + nk$ obtained first.

This method evidently yields the proper magnitude scale only if the same calibration-curve is valid for both exposures. This is the case only if the seeing, focus, extinction, and plate sensitivity remain constant for both exposures, which is seldom the case. It is possible to overcome these difficulties by using a neutral filter that covers only half the plate, the other half being covered by a glass plate of equal thickness. Thus both absorbed and unabsorbed images are obtained at the same time, but on different parts of the plate. To eliminate a number of effects—for instance, difference in the background on both halves of the plate—it is necessary to interchange the neutral filter and the glass plate and to take a second exposure of equal length. There are two methods which may be used to calibrate such a plate.

a) The two components of each pair may be treated as outlined above. Thus two calibration-curves will be obtained, one for each side of the plate. If the two curves are identical, it is safe to assume that they represent the correct calibration-curve. If the two curves do not coincide, the average calibration-curve is probably closer to the correct one than either of the two but may still be greatly in error. If the filter is arranged so that, at least for one area on the plate, both exposures are obtained through it, the determination of systematic differences between the two exposures may be made. The differences found there have to be applied to the readings for the images of one exposure over the entire plate to reduce it to the other. This method, however, can be used successfully only if the background reading is constant over the entire plate.

b) Each exposure may be separately compared with photometer readings obtained for the entire area from "reference plates" taken without the half-filter. If these readings are plotted against those of one exposure of the half-filter plate, two curves will be found, one for the obscured, the other for the un-obscured, part of the plate, as shown in Figure 8. The two curves are displaced by the filter constant k in units of the readings of the reference plate, and the calibration-curve can be constructed in the way indicated in the figure. Since this procedure makes a comparison between images exposed simultaneous-ly, the objections mentioned above cannot be raised here. However, field[1] errors affecting the two halves of the plate differently may cause difficulties. In such cases the two calibration-curves obtained from the two exposures will be differ-ent. Here the averaged calibration-curve may be expected to be close to the truth. For short exposures it is possible to overcome such difficulties by using a third exposure without the half-filter on the same plate as "reference."

The use of a rotating sector as an absorbing medium is sometimes preferred because of its truly neutral absorption, a property not shared by all "neutral" filters. If placed in the proper position, the rotating sector does not affect the structure of the images. It is, however, necessary to employ a sufficiently high

[1] And plate errors (see § 5.2).

frequency to avoid the intermittency effect (see § 2.3). When this precaution is taken, the procedure described above for the neutral filter methods may be used for the reduction of such exposures. The difficulties arising from changes in focus, seeing, plate sensitivity, and field and plate errors are also present in methods using rotating sectors.

5.12. *Objective-grating method.*—For plates taken with a coarse objective grating, the intensity ratio between diffraction images of different orders can be predicted from the structure of the grating. Most of the objections in connection with neutral filter methods do not apply to objective-grating plates, since all images are obtained simultaneously. Nevertheless, the application of the grating is limited, primarily because the diffraction images are all spectra, with a dis-

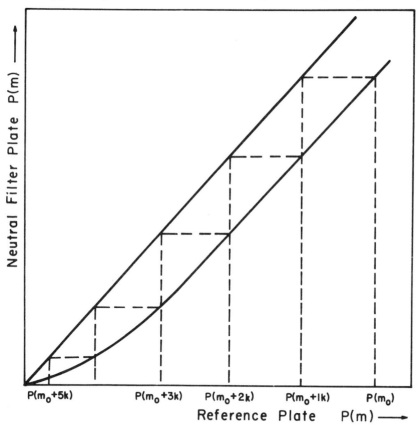

FIG. 8.—The construction of a calibration-curve from a neutral half-filter plate. The photometer readings for one of the two exposures of the half-filter plate are plotted as a function of the readings for the reference plate. Two curves, one for each side of the half-filter plate, displaced by the filter constant K in units of the readings of the reference plate, are produced. A calibration-curve may be formed by plotting the readings of the reference plate for integral multiples of the filter constant, $P(m_0 + nk)$, as a function of the magnitudes $(m_0 + nk)$.

persion depending on the order. Hence the internal structure of the various images is different unless the spectral range is very narrow. Irregularities in the spacing of the rods or their thickness also affect the structure of the images and cause additional difficulties. Frequently it is found that the "grating constant" determined empirically differs from the theoretical value and, furthermore, often depends on the color of the stars. Therefore, very thorough tests of an objective grating under various conditions are necessary before it can be successfully used for the determination of magnitude scales.

5.13. *Photographic transfers.*—Photoelectrically established magnitude sequences should be used whenever possible. If a sequence is sufficiently close to an area under study, a transfer of the magnitude scale by photographic means may be possible. If the two areas are so close that they can be covered by one exposure, only field errors and plate errors have to be eliminated. This problem is treated in § 5.2. If the two areas are more than a plate diameter apart, at least two separate exposures of the same length have to be taken on one plate, one exposure centered on the area under study, the other on the sequence. In order to eliminate the errors due to changes in the plate sensitivity, or time-dependent changes in the extinction coefficient, the seeing, or the focus, between the two exposures, it is necessary to take another plate in the reverse order. Actually, more than a pair of such plates will be required in most cases. The two fields to be compared should have approximately the same zenith distance during the transfer process, not so much because of the atmospheric extinction, which can be allowed for in most cases, but because of the seeing. The seeing is a function of the zenith distance, and it affects the calibration-curve, particularly for telescopes of long focal length. If the internal adjustment of the telescope changes with the declination and the hour angle, it is usually rather difficult to obtain satisfactory transfers of magnitude sequences.

If confined to photographic means, such transfer processes have to be used to secure the zero point for magnitude scales determined by neutral filter or grating methods. Since it is sufficient to determine the zero point for the brightest stars, only very short exposures are required. Here the objections based on possible changes in the atmospheric conditions, etc., cannot be raised, while difficulties caused by an unstable internal adjustment of the telescope still remain.

Weaver (1947) has developed a reduction method that offers a means of eliminating systematic scale errors caused by changes in seeing, guiding, and focus.

5.2. PLATE ERRORS AND FIELD ERRORS

In the previous sections the methods of obtaining photometer readings and how these readings are related to a magnitude or intensity scale has been discussed. When a large field of the sky is photographed, as, for instance, with a Schmidt telescope or a wide-angle refractor, the question arises whether one and the same relation between photometer readings and magnitudes holds over the entire plate. Whether or not this is the case depends primarily on two factors: (1) the uniformity of the sensitivity over the plate, including effects due to the processing, and (2) the uniformity of the image structure. If such uniformities do not exist, the readings will systematically or erratically deviate from the calibration-curve found to be valid for a small area of the plate. Systematic errors of this nature are called "plate errors" if they are due to non-uniform sensitivity of the plate and "field errors" if they are due to imperfections of the optics or maladjustment of the plateholder. Aside from the large-scale sensitivity variations, there are, of course, random fluctuations of the grain density which produce a small-scale scatter.

Plate errors caused by the statistical grain distribution and by a large-scale non-uniform sensitivity pattern are, in general, different from plate to plate. It should be noted that plates from the same emulsion lot might show non-uniformities of a systematic nature and that the processing procedure might also introduce systematic effects. With proper processing, however, these errors can be eliminated or greatly reduced if the average of a sufficient number of plates is taken. This is not the case with field errors. Errors due to optical imperfections are more likely to be a permanent feature of the telescope and to have similar effects on all plates. Thus they cannot be eliminated by averaging several plates; only the variations of the field errors from plate to plate can be removed in this way. It is evidently necessary to provide means to check on the field errors and to eliminate them if they exist. Stock (1951) has discussed this problem in the case where the errors are of radial symmetry. A more general discussion has been presented by Stock and Wehlau (1956). Every telescope has its own characteristic field errors. These may also be different for different plate-filter combinations, because of chromatic effects, as well as non-uniformities in the filter, and may depend on the seeing, the exposure time, the focus, etc. Since these field errors are due to structural effects in the focal (or intrafocal or extrafocal) images and to variations in the transmittance of the telescope, they are not erratically distributed over the field but depend clearly on the co-ordinates on the plate, generally in a simple manner. The types of field errors are many fold, and therefore no general recipe can be given for detecting and eventually removing them. At present a more or less general type of field error has been found only for Schmidt telescopes. Since the method used to detect such errors can be readily adapted to discuss other types of field errors, it will be presented here. The type of field error found to be present in several Schmidt telescopes seems to indicate that a tilt of the plateholder is the most common maladjustment.

On plates taken with a perfectly adjusted Schmidt telescope no field errors except vignetting should be expected. The diffraction pattern of the focal images may have a slight effect, depending on the position of the star on the plate, but this will normally occur only for stars that are heavily overexposed. If the plateholder is tilted, the plate deviates from the focal surface in a systematic way, so that, if x and y are rectangular co-ordinates with their origin at the plate center, the deviation Δf from the focal surface may be written as

$$\Delta f = a_0 + a_1 x + a_2 y . \tag{18}$$

From focus plates, the dependence of the photometer readings, $P(m)$, for a star of magnitude m is generally found to be related to Δf by

$$P(m, \Delta f) = P_0(m) - A^2(m)\Delta f^2 . \tag{19}$$

Substituting equation (18) in equation (19), the expression for the field error,

$$\begin{aligned}
\phi(x, y, m) &= (P_0 m) - P(x, y, m) \\
&= A^2(m)(a_0^2 + 2a_0 a_1 x + 2a_0 a_2 y \\
&\quad + 2a_1 a_2 xy + a_1^2 x^2 + a_2^2 y^2) ,
\end{aligned} \tag{20}$$

is obtained. The first term in this expression is independent of the co-ordinates and hence of no interest. It is therefore sufficient to write ϕ as

$$\phi(x, y, m) = A^2(m)2a_0(a_1 x + a_2 y) + A^2(m)(a_1 x + a_2 y)^2 . \tag{21}$$

If the three constants a_0, a_1, and a_2 and the function $A(m)$ were known, all readings could be reduced to the plate center and then transferred to a uniform magnitude system. A method is needed to determine these quantities. It turns out that different procedures are necessary to determine the linear and the quadratic terms.

If the telescope is reversed, the linear term changes its sign while the quadratic term remains the same. Thus, by averaging two exposures of equal exposure time taken with the telescope reversed between exposures, the linear field errors can be removed. It is assumed that the adjustment of the telescope is independent of the position of the telescope. If this is not the case, a comparison with a photoelectric sequence is the only safe way to determine the linear term. Changes in the seeing or the focus between the two exposures may also spoil the results, but, by reversing the order of exposures on another plate and taking a sufficient number of plates, these difficulties can be overcome. It should be noted that the linear field error vanishes if the plate center is in the focal surface.

The quadratic terms in equation (21) can be determined if two exposures of the same field with somewhat different centers are taken. Thus each star will have two images on the plate, one with the photometer reading P_1 at x_1, y_1; the other with the reading P_2 at x_2, y_2. If, for instance, the displacement between the two centers is made along the x-axis, then

$$x_2 = x_1 + x_0 \quad \text{and} \quad y_2 = y_1 \tag{22}$$

relate the two sets of co-ordinates, x_0 being a constant. Neglecting the linear terms, the differences in the photometer readings can be expressed as

$$P_1 - P_2 = P(x_1, y_1, m) - P(x_2, y_2, m)$$
$$= A^2(m) (a_1^2 x_0^2 + 2a_0 a_1 x_0 \qquad (23)$$
$$+ 2a_1^2 x_0 x_1 + 2a_1 a_2 x_0 y_1) + B(m),$$

where $B(m)$ is a function of m that takes into account changes in the plate sensitivity, the seeing, etc., between the two exposures.

In order to find the quantities $A(m)a_1$ and $A(m)a_2$ by means of equation (23), the stars have to be divided into groups of small magnitude range. For each group, the dependence of $P_1 - P_2$ on x_1 and y_1 yields the desired results. In most cases, however, no magnitudes will be known, and hence no groups of small magnitude range can be formed. In such cases a preliminary grouping has to be done on the basis of the mean values of P_1 and P_2. With these groups, first approximations to $A(m)a_1$ and $A(m)a_2$ can be found and, with these, approximations for the P_0 values, using equation (20). A second grouping may then be carried out on the basis of the first approximations for the values of P_0, and the entire process repeated, yielding second approximations for all quantities. It has seldom been found necessary to go beyond the first approximation.

The more general type of field errors,

$$\phi(x, y, m) = b_1 x + b_2 y + b_3 x^2 + b_4 xy + b_5 y^2, \qquad (24)$$

where the coefficients b_1–b_5 are functions of m, can be treated the same way, in principle. However, more than two displaced exposures would be necessary to determine all the quadratic terms. This will in most cases be too impractical and may be of interest only when the photometric performance of a telescope, rather than the magnitudes of stars, is the subject of the study.

For parabolic reflectors, a term caused by coma may be expected in addition to the possible effects of a plate tilt. It should be possible to express this component of the field error as a function of the distance D from the plate center. Some refractors are known to have field errors of the type

$$\phi(D, m) = A^2(m)D^2. \qquad (25)$$

Here again the function $A(m)$ can be determined on plates taken with two displaced exposures. For refractors it is possible that A is a function not only of the brightness of the stars but also of the color. Thus, for the determination of $A(m, c)$, where c is the color index, the stars have to be divided into groups of small magnitude and color range. This will obviously be too complicated in practice, and refractors with a color- and magnitude-dependent field error should not be considered suitable for photometric work.

The effects of field errors can be greatly reduced by appropriate observational procedures in certain types of investigations. For instance, in the construction of color-magnitude diagrams of clusters, the colors are needed with a higher accuracy than the magnitudes themselves. In such cases, it would be advantageous to take multicolor exposures on the same plate (Günther 1950), changing the filter between exposures and slightly offsetting the telescope. The B and U colors in the U, B, V system or the G and U colors in Becker's could be exposed on the same blue plate, the images placed as close together as possible. By this technique, the effects of the plate errors are reduced to almost the statistical grain fluctuations. If the exposure times are chosen so that, for the majority of the stars under investigation, the readings of both images are similar, the effects of the field errors on both images can be expected to be nearly the same. This is, of course, true only for achromatic optics, and even then the field errors cannot be expected to drop out entirely, since they depend on the readings themselves and also on the spectral range, because the scattering of light in the emulsion, which is partially responsible for the image growth, changes somewhat with the wave length.

In this connection it is of interest to mention a method devised by J. Hardorp (1960) which allows the transfer of a magnitude sequence from one part of the field of a telescope to another without serious effects from field errors. It involves a pair of exposures centered in the middle between the object under study and the sources of the magnitude sequence, with the telescope reversed between the exposures.

§ 6. REDUCTION TO A STANDARD SYSTEM

6.1. SPECTRAL RANGES OF MAGNITUDE SYSTEMS

A system of magnitudes is defined not only by a mathematical expression or a graph relating measured intensities to a magnitude scale but also by the spectral range in which the measures are made. This spectral range may be roughly described by two quantities—its position and its band width. The band width varies from that encountered in wide-band photometry, such as when no filters are used, to that of narrow-band or monochromatic photometry, as in spectrophotometry. The positions of the bands vary greatly with the type of plate and color filter used and are commonly expressed as wave lengths, derived in a number of ways. The two quantities, the *isophotal wave length*, λ_i, defined by

$$I(\lambda_i) = \frac{\int_0^\infty I(\lambda)\,s(\lambda)\,f(\lambda)\,q(\lambda)\,p(\lambda)^{F(z)}\,d\lambda}{\int_0^\infty s(\lambda)\,f(\lambda)\,q(\lambda)\,p(\lambda)^{F(z)}\,d\lambda}, \qquad (26)$$

and the *effective wave length*, λ_{eff}, given by

$$\lambda_{\text{eff}} = \frac{\int_0^\infty \lambda I(\lambda)\,s(\lambda)\,f(\lambda)\,q(\lambda)\,p(\lambda)^{F(z)}\,d\lambda}{\int_0^\infty I(\lambda)\,s(\lambda)\,f(\lambda)\,q(\lambda)\,p(\lambda)^{F(z)}\,d\lambda}, \qquad (27)$$

are commonly used for this purpose (King 1952, Greaves 1952; see also Becker 1950; pp. 6 and 24). Here $I(\lambda)$ represents the energy distribution in the stellar spectrum, $s(\lambda)$ the sensitivity of the photographic plate, $f(\lambda)$ the transmission of the filter, $q(\lambda)$ the transmission of the telescope, $p(\lambda)$ the zenith transmission coefficient of the atmosphere, all at the wave length λ, and $F(z)$ is the air mass corresponding to the zenith distance z. The isophotal wave length is of importance when magnitude systems with different sensitivity functions are being compared, and particularly when the relationship between wide-band and monochromatic magnitudes is being discussed, since equation (26) gives the monochromatic intensity, which is equivalent to the wide-band intensity. On the other hand, effective wave lengths can be determined empirically from the displacement of diffraction images on objective-grating plates.

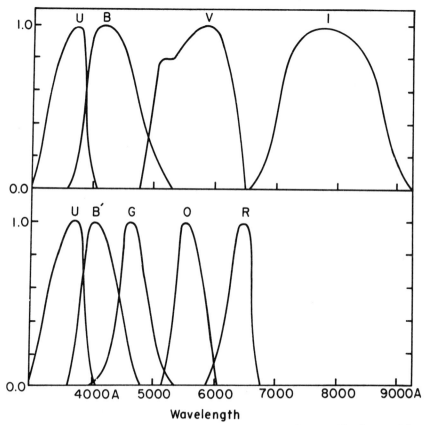

Fig. 9.—The relative spectral responses of some typical plate-filter combinations used for the determination of magnitudes and colors. The curves have been plotted for equal energy at all wave lengths, neglecting absorption by the telescope and atmosphere and taking the maximum sensitivity of each combination as unity. The various combinations are tabulated in Table 1.

As may be seen from equations (26) and (27), the wave lengths indicating the position of the spectral range within which a magnitude is measured vary with the stellar energy distribution and the atmospheric extinction, as well as with instrumental factors. It is frequently convenient for certain purposes to consider certain terms of these equations as constant. Thus, frequently, $I(\lambda)$ is set equal to unity, and the response of the system to equal energy at all wave lengths is considered. Similarly, $p(\lambda)$ is set equal to unity—or $F(z)$ to zero—on occasion, and the measuring system is discussed as being outside the atmosphere. The narrower the spectral range, the smaller is the variation of λ_i and λ_{eff} with changes in $I(\lambda)$, $p(\lambda)$, and $F(z)$, which are the variable factors beyond the control of the observer. In narrow-band photometry, λ_i and λ_{eff} are identical and independent of these factors.

To obtain accurate information concerning the energy distribution in stellar spectra, it is therefore desirable to make the band width as narrow as possible, while the study of faint stars requires the opposite. Photographic plates without any color filters have a response function with a width of several thousand angstroms. Blue-sensitive plates when used without filter, for instance, cover the range from 5000 A to somewhere between 3300 A and 3800 A, depending on the ultraviolet absorption in the telescope optics. Bands with a width of several hundred angstroms can be obtained by combining plates with one or two color filters. For wave lengths between 4700 A and 8000 A, the cutoff at the short-wave-length side is produced by a filter, while the long-wave-length cutoff is produced by the spectral sensitivity of the emulsion. For wave lengths shorter than 4700 A, the cutoff on both sides has to be achieved by filters.

The relative spectral response of a number of plate-filter combinations now in use to equal energy at all wave lengths, neglecting absorption by the telescope or atmosphere, is shown in Figure 9. The effective wave lengths, under the same conditions, and the band widths of these combinations are presented in Table 1. The U, B, V combinations are the photographic equivalents to the

$$\lambda_{eff} = \frac{\int_0^\infty \lambda \ \text{Plate-filter} \ d\lambda}{\int_0^\infty \text{Plate-filter} \ d\lambda} \ .$$

U, B, V system (Johnson and Morgan 1953), while $R, G,$ and U are the combinations proposed by W. Becker (1938, 1942, 1948; Becker and Steinlin 1956). German Agfa plate–Schott filter combinations for the U, B, V photometry are discussed by K. H. Schmidt (1956). It is important to note that blue and ultraviolet filters generally have leaks in the red and therefore should not be used with panchromatic materials.

The effects of the neglected terms of telescope transmission, atmospheric extinction, and stellar energy distribution on the total effective response are illustrated in Figures 10 and 11. In Figure 10, the effect of the optics of the telescope and the altitude of the observatory on the response of B combination is demonstrated. For an equal energy source, the effective wave lengths are 4340 A and 4460 A for a reflector with two freshly aluminized mirrors at an altitude of 4400 meters and for a strongly absorbing photographic refractor at sea level, respectively. The effect of the color of the star on the spectral range of the same combination as used with the high-altitude reflector of the previous example is shown in Figure 11. In this case, the effective wave length of the system is 4280 A for a black body of 27,500° K, which approximates a B-type

TABLE 1

PLATE-FILTER COMBINATIONS FOR VARIOUS MAGNITUDE SYSTEMS

System	Plate-Filter Combination	λ_{eff}* (A)	$\Delta\lambda$ (A)
V........	Kodak 103a-D+2-mm Schott GG11	5750	1400
B........	Kodak 103a-O+2-mm Schott GG13	4330	950
U........	Kodak 103a-O+2-mm Schott UG2	3540	600
B'........	Kodak 103a-O+2-mm Schott BG3+1-mm Schott GG13	4250	670
G........	Kodak 103a-O+2-mm Schott GG5	4690	470
O........	Kodak 103a-G+2-mm Schott OG5	5600	530
R........	Astro Pan+2-mm Schott RG1	6340	400
I........	Kodak IN+2-mm Schott RG8	8040	1660

* For equal energy at all wave lengths, neglecting telescopic and atmospheric absorption.

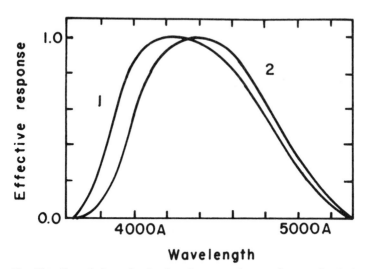

FIG. 10.—The effect of absorption by the telescope and atmosphere on the B plate-filter combination of Fig. 9. The response to equal energy at all wave lengths, using the average zenith extinction, is shown for (*1*) a reflector with two freshly aluminized mirrors at an altitude of 4400 meters, and (*2*) a strongly absorbing photographic refractor at sea level.

star and 4510 A for a black body of 3000° K, representing an M-type star. In all four examples, average zenith extinction has been used. The effects of extinction in regard to extended band widths have been discussed by Seares and Joyner (1943), Velghe (1949), and King (1952).

Equations (26) and (27) can be applied to photographically obtained magnitudes only if no chromatic aberrations are present in the equipment used. Otherwise $s(\lambda) f(\lambda) q(\lambda)$ is not representative of the weight with which the light of each wave length contributes to the photometer reading. Thus $s(\lambda)$ depends also on the distribution of light of different wave lengths within the image. In addition the magnitude obtained is dependent on the type of photometer used.

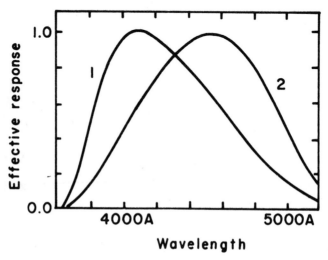

FIG. 11.—The effect of the color of the star on the spectral response of the B plate-filter combination. For the high-altitude reflector of Fig. 10 (1), the response is shown to (1), a black body of 27,500° K and (2) a black body of 3000° K.

The effects mentioned in the last two paragraphs vanish when the band width of the system is sufficiently small. A band width from a few hundred angstroms down to a few angstroms can be obtained by the use of interference filters. Sometimes additional color filters are needed to cut out secondary transmission bands. For telescopes with large fields, particularly Schmidt telescopes, the use of interference filters is problematic because the position and width of the transmission band depend on the incident angle of the light, which varies across the field. Recently, liquid-dye filters with band widths of 50–150 A have been successfully used (Wurm 1955). Kopal and Millns (1956) report on work with liquid-dye filters, which, combined with suitable plates, produce pass bands of the order of 100 A.

6.2. Color Equations

The difference between the magnitudes measured in two different color systems is, in general, a function of the magnitude and color of the star for which the measures are being compared,

$$m_1 - m_2 = V(m, C) . \qquad (28)$$

In this relationship, m_1 and m_2 are the magnitudes in the two systems, m is a magnitude of one of the systems, and C is a color index. (It is convenient in practice to represent $V(m, C)$ as a polynomial in color and magnitude.) Such a relationship is known as the *color equation* between the two systems. Provided that the plates have been properly calibrated, we should expect the magnitude scales on both systems to be identical and the terms of the expansion which involve the magnitude to have zero coefficients. Aside from a constant term representing the difference in zero points between the two systems, which may be readily determined, the color equation may therefore often be expressed as polynomial in color alone. Thus the color equation between two systems of slightly different color characteristics can often be expressed as a linear function of the color index,

$$m_1 - m_2 = vC , \qquad (29)$$

where v is a constant, if stars of peculiar intensity distribution or of relatively low temperature are excluded. Such a color equation represents observations surprisingly well over a wide spectral range, provided that no light with a wave length shorter than 3800 A contributes considerably to any of the magnitudes considered, including those from which the color index has been formed. For precise work, however, a linear equation is often insufficient, and higher-order terms involving the color may have to be included. Since equation (28) is itself only an approximation, it should be kept in mind that the various coefficients may depend on the luminosity class of the star, the amount of interstellar reddening, etc.

In photographic photometry, terms in the polynomial expansion of equation (28), which involve both the color and the magnitude, are liable to be important. Put in another way, this is to say that the coefficients v are often not constant but are functions of the magnitudes themselves, $v(m)$. This is due to two facts: (1) the color distribution of the light in the stellar images projected on the photographic emulsion is not uniform, and (2) the characteristic curve of the photographic emulsion changes with wave length. The non-uniformity of the color occurs in particular with refractors, which have chromatic aberrations. It exists, however, to a small degree in reflector images also, since the light of different colors is scattered differently within the emulsion itself. For small apertures, the dispersion of the diffraction rings also contributes to a radial variation in the color of the photographic stellar image. Bearing in mind that, for faint stars, only the central part of the image is developable, while, for bright stars, the fringes of the image with their color characteristics are the main contributors to the size of the image, it is evident that a change can be expected in the over-all color characteristics of photographically obtained magnitudes with the size of the image. Also, it is evident that effects influencing the internal structure of the image, such as changes in the seeing or focus, can affect the color characteristics. For reflectors, the change in the coefficients v with magnitude is usually rather small and may in most cases be neglected. Likewise, when the band width of the plate-filter combination is narrow, the effect vanishes. For refractors, when used with all but the narrowest band pass, a careful study of the dependence of the color system on the magnitude (actually, on the photometer reading) for the various plate-filter combinations is advisable before any photometric program is undertaken. In spectral regions where the focal length changes rapidly with the wave length, even narrow-band photometry may be impractical. In the case of refractors, the effect of chromatic aberration may lead to a strong dependence of the coefficients v on the magnitude, and an equation of the form

$$m_1 - m_2 = v_1(m)C + v_2(m)C^2 + \ldots, \qquad (30)$$

including higher-order terms, may be necessary to represent the relationship between two magnitude systems. Effects of this type, where the color terms relating two magnitude systems to each other also depend on the magnitudes themselves, are occasionally referred to as the *photographic Purkinje effect*, although they are of a different nature from those encountered in visual photometry.

When photographic magnitudes of one color system are to be compared with those of another, the color equation between the two systems can be determined without any difficulty, provided that both systems are free of scale errors. A plot of the differences in magnitude for stars common to both systems versus the color reveals the nature of the color equation, and the proper mathematical representation can be taken from the graph or determined by the method of least squares.

More frequently, one is confronted with the problem of deriving the calibration-curve and the color equation from the same comparison stars. This is the case when a photoelectric sequence is available in the field under study. When the color characteristics of the two systems are different, a plot of the photometer readings versus the photoelectric magnitudes will give only an approximation for the calibration-curve. The plot may be expected to show a scatter with red stars preferring one side of the average relationship between magnitudes and readings, while the blue stars prefer the other side. In such a case, after drawing a mean calibration-curve, a plot of the displacements of individual points from the curve in the direction of the magnitude axis versus the colors may be used to determine the color equation. It is necessary to subdivide the stars into fairly narrow magnitude ranges when determining the color equation by this method, since the average calibration-curve may have been drawn through stars of different average color in different magnitude intervals. Thus, if only linear terms are taken into account, a relation of the type

$$m_{\mathrm{pg}} - m_{\mathrm{pe}} = vC_{\mathrm{pe}} + w(m) \tag{31}$$

may be found. For reflectors or for narrow-band magnitudes, the coefficient v will be independent of the magnitude, while w may very well vary from one magnitude group to the other, as mentioned above. Once v is determined, the photoelectric magnitudes can be transferred to the photographic system by

$$m_{\mathrm{pg}} = m_{\mathrm{pe}} + vC_{\mathrm{pe}}, \tag{32}$$

and a new calibration-curve may be drawn, which is the final relation between the readings and the magnitudes if another plot of the displacements from this curve versus the colors reveals no more color-dependent terms. Otherwise, a second approximation for v has to be computed and another calibration-curve drawn, using magnitudes derived with the new value of v.

§ 7. SPECIAL TECHNIQUES

7.1. PHOTOMETRY OF EXTENDED IMAGES

The photometry of extended objects, such as galaxies or emission nebulosities, presents problems different from those encountered in the photometry of focal images of point sources. While the readings obtained for focal images are strongly affected by even slight changes in the internal structure of the images, this is not the case for surface objects. Only details in the objects of a size comparable to the scattering radius or the radius of the optical aberrations can be affected by such changes. On the other hand, the adjacency effects, which in stellar focal photometry have to be taken into account only in the case of double stars, may play an important role. This is particularly true for galaxies with a bright nucleus. Field errors, with the exception of vignetting, will not occur, while plate errors are, of course, present. Chromatic errors are also absent. The effect of a luminous sky background can be readily eliminated, since the density obtained is strictly the density corresponding to the combined light of the object and the background. Calibrating methods for surface densities are quite different from those used for focal images of stars. If certain precautions are taken, they can be carried out by laboratory means. So far, it appears that the photometry of extended objects presents fewer difficulties than the photometry of point images. For this reason, methods have been developed artificially to extend the images of point sources in order to avoid the problem inherent in focal images. Such methods will also be discussed in this section. The problems of photographic spectrophotometry are also related to those of extended objects and will be treated here.

The measuring procedure followed in the case of extended objects varies greatly with the size and internal structure of the object. For this reason, only some of the basic principles will be discussed here. Generally, an analyzing slit or diaphragm scans over the object, while a recorder traces the densities on tracing paper. The deflections on the tracing paper are then converted into magnitudes or intensities, depending on the final result desired. The size of the analyzing opening must be carefully considered. It is desirable to keep the opening as small as possible, in order to preserve the resolving power of the photograph. At the same time, it is useless to make the opening smaller than the scattering radius or the average grain separation. In order to reduce the statistical scatter or "noise," it is desirable to make the opening as large as possible. It must be remembered, however, that an integration over densities is not equivalent to an integration over intensities. Hence the analyzing opening should preferably be somewhat smaller than the structural elements of the object. This again may mean that the tracings will be noisy. In spectrophotometry it is possible to overcome this difficulty by widening the spectra extensively and by using a long and narrow slit.

Essentially three methods are used to produce surface images of point sources: (1) extrafocal images, (2) Schraffierkassette, and (3) Fabry exposures. The first method requires the extrafocal images to have a sufficiently large area of uniform density. Furthermore, in order to avoid field errors, the structure of the extrafocal images must be uniform over the entire field under investigation. In the second method, the focal images are moved in a zig-zag pattern over small squares on the plate during the exposure (Meyermann and Schwarzschild 1906, Christie 1933). To obtain squares with uniform structure, the separation of the lines must be small compared with the scattering radius. It must be remembered that the entire square is not exposed simultaneously but that each part is exposed intermittently whenever the focal image moves over it. Thus the intermittency effect may play an important role in the relation between densities and magnitudes. In the Fabry method, a small lens placed near the focus of the telescope is used to image the objective on the photographic plate (Fabry 1910, 1943). To limit the background light, a small aperture just large enough to include the telescopic image of the object being observed is placed in the focus of the telescope. The Fabry image formed by the small lens is of very nearly uniform surface brightness, and in most cases the light is more uniformly distributed than in an extrafocal image. The size and structure of the Fabry image is the same for both extended and point-source objects. Since the definition of the Fabry image depends on the Fabry lens, it is possible to obtain practically perfect surface images even from poor telescopes and off the optical axis. The distribution of light in the image may not be perfectly uniform, because of aberrations of the Fabry lens, excessive diffraction (due to focusing the star too sharply on the Fabry lens), or varying transmission of the objective. Shadow bands due to scintillation will be smoothed out in all but extremely short exposures, and, additionally, the image will be relatively unaffected by guiding errors and accidental refraction.

In spectrophotometry the spectra are trailed perpendicularly to the dispersion. Again, the resulting densities are not produced by a continuous exposure, and intermittency effects may occur. It is important to keep this in mind when calibration exposures are made for the purpose of comparison.

As in in-focus photometry, there are various ways in which the calibration of surface densities may be carried out. Only the more common methods will be mentioned.

7.11. *Exposure to a sensitometer or a calibrated wedge.*—Uniform illumination of the sensitometer tubes or the wedge is, of course, a basic requirement. Whenever possible, the calibration marks should be exposed simultaneously with the object under investigation, and the exposure times should be identical. Furthermore, in wide-band photometry it is necessary that the color characteristic of the calibration lamp and the object be similar. In spectrophotometry or for Schraffierkassette images, it must be remembered that the intermittency effects are present in the spectra or stellar images, while they are absent in the calibration marks. A proper calibration can be made only if the sensitometer marks are produced in exactly the same way as the spectra or stellar images. So far, no calibrating device has been designed which fulfils this requirement.

7.12. *Narrow-band magnitudes.*—Narrow-band magnitudes derived photoelectrically or photographically by in-focus photometry may be used to establish the relationship between densities and intensities on widened objective-prism plates for the wave length to which the narrow-band magnitudes apply.

7.13. *Extrafocal exposure of a stellar sequence.*—If a focal exposure of the extended object under study and an extrafocal exposure of a stellar sequence with known magnitudes are made on the same plate, the magnitude sequence may be used to establish the characteristic curve. Integration over the total surface of the extrafocal images will yield the zero point for surface magnitudes if they are to be expressed in magnitudes per unit area on the International system. Preferably, the two exposures should be taken simultaneously. This is possible if the object is near the sequence. In this case, the plate may be cut in half, one half being kept in focus for the object itself, the other half being placed out of focus for the sequence.

7.2. SURFACE PHOTOMETRY OF EXTENDED IMAGES

The class of objects whose focal images extend over an area of the plate appreciably greater than that of a point source includes planetary nebulae, galaxies, and bright interstellar matter. Information about the total integrated brightness and color, the shape and distribution of relative or absolute intensities over the surface, and the total extent of the object, both in integrated light and for selected spectral regions, are of importance. Present-day observations for these quantities are done photoelectrically (see, for example, Miller 1962 and Prendergast and Miller 1961) or by a combination of photoelectric and photographic observations in a manner not dissimilar to some photometric investigations of galactic and globular clusters (see Hoag, Johnson, Iriarte, Mitchell, Hallam, and Sharpless 1961); the photoelectric observations are needed for calibration of the more detailed photographic ones. One recent investigation of this nature on galaxies has been published by van Houten (1961).

The dimensions and total magnitude of an extended object, especially a galaxy, is difficult to measure by any technique. This difficulty arises because of the large angular size of the regions of low surface brightness that contribute appreciably to the total light.

The extent of a nebular image on a photographic plate can be estimated either by visual inspection of the plate or from a microphotometric tracing. The apparent diameter determined by either method will depend somewhat upon the exposure at the telescope. If the photographic plates are all exposed under essentially identical conditions, the resulting diameters will refer to nearly the same surface brightness. For example, the apparent diameters estimated from the Palomar–National Geographic Sky Survey correspond to an isophote with a surface brightness at 22.6 mag. per square second, about 0.6 mag. fainter than the night sky (Humason, Mayall, and Sandage 1956). For a typical E0 nebula careful photographic photometry can still detect radiation at a diameter four times greater than the above (Dennison 1954).

Holmberg (1950, 1958) has published photographic measurements of total magnitudes and colors for over 300 galaxies. An in-focus image of a galaxy was obtained on one-half of the plate and out-of-focus images of North Polar Sequence stars on the other. Photometric tracings were then made of successive sections of the galaxy, the Polar Sequence stars providing the standard intensities for calibration, and the integrated magnitude was obtained by summation. The method is slow and tedious but, apart from its transfer and the slight ambiguity of the N.P.S. standards, reliable. The accuracy of the final photographic and photovisual magnitudes was excellent, with a mean error of 0^m04. Lynga (1959) used a similar method to obtain the integrated magnitude of the Andromeda Nebula. Efimov (1959) obtained integrated magnitudes of NGC 7293 at λ 6550 from which an electron density was derived and a rather uncertain estimate of the mass of the nebula. In these two applications photoelectric standards in the Pleiades were used for calibration.

Bigay (1951a) used Fabry photometry (see Sec. 7.1) to obtain photographic magnitudes of 175 bright galaxies. He also published a critical survey and comparison of methods used up to 1951 for measuring integrated magnitudes of galaxies (Bigay 1951b). A previous similar survey for surface brightness distribution by photographic methods was made by de Vaucouleurs (1948).

The schraffierkassette method (see Sec. 7.1 for its application to the measurement of point-source intensities) has also been used for measuring magnitudes of extended objects (see Humason et al. 1956 and Zwicky et al. 1961). The schraffier images are calibrated by comparison with similar images of suitable standards, usually stars on the same plate for which magnitudes and colors are known or subsequently established. Magnitudes of the nebulae are obtained by measurement of the image densities. The limiting magnitude of this system depends, of course, on the size of the schraffier image. Humason *et al.* (1956) used 1 or 2 mm images with the 200-inch Hale reflector, and Zwicky *et al.* (1961) used 1 minute of arc on out-of-focus 48-inch Schmidt plates.

All observational procedures discussed above may be plagued by systematic errors because of the difficulty in integrating the faint outer regions of the nebulae. The schraffier image must be at least 2.5 times larger than the apparent diameter (see Humason *et al.* 1956 for a discussion of systematic errors in the schraffier method) to reduce the systematic error to less than 0.1 mag. Likewise, in the Fabry method, the diaphragm must be equally large. De Vaucouleurs (1956a, 1957, 1959) has reviewed the causes leading to discrepancies between the major catalogues of magnitudes of galaxies.

Contours of equal surface brightness, called *isophotes*, give useful information about the distribution of brightness within an extended object and about its structure. Evans (1949, 1950, 1951, 1952) obtained isophotes of a number of planetary and elliptical nebulae in several colors from conventional microphotometer tracings. He plotted the points of constant density for several cross-sections of the nebular image, calibration being made by comparison with a sequence of spots of known density (see also Redman 1936, Redman and Shirley 1937, and others). A similar technique has been applied with success by Sersic (1957). Use of an iris diaphragm photometer to plot contours of constant density has been described by de Vaucouleurs (1956b). Rasmadse, Iroschnikov and Kotok (1959) obtained isophotes for [O ɪɪ] at λ 3727 for the planetary nebula NGC 6853, using photographs obtained with a 70-cm meniscus telescope.

A photographic method of obtaining isophotes suitable for nebulae of intricate structure has been described by von Hoff (1937) and recently applied by H. M. Johnson (1960). Plates of the Southern Milky Way were enlarged directly onto Eastman Kodalith film of very high contrast, and the resulting boundaries between black and white areas were calibrated from tube sensitometer spots (a number of which, depending on the exposure time, disappeared on the positives). The boundaries, or isophotes, were then mapped onto a grid representing the star field. It should be noted that in this method care is needed in relating the independently obtained contours to each other and to the field.

Williams and Hiltner (1940, 1941, 1943) describe an adaptation of their direct-intensity microphotometer which enables direct continuous traces of isophotal contours for a series of intensity steps by a null method. A plate of suitable density of the object for which isophotal contours were to be obtained was placed on a carriage which could be driven in a given direction X while movement of the plate was also possible in a direction Y at right angles. One beam of light passed through the plate, while one of several calibration spots was centered in a comparison beam. Means were provided for directing the two analyzing light beams alternately onto the common photocell. The position of the nebular plate was automatically driven by a servo system in direction Y until the light beams were of equal intensity, i.e., the instrument selected a point on the nebular plate whose density was equal to that of the calibration or comparison spot. As the motion in direction X proceeded, a curve of constant density on the plate was traced photographically, the final photograph being one of a family of such traces corresponding to a number of different densities. It should be noted that for the recording of isophotes for a planetary or elliptical nebula, the carriage was run twice in the direction X for each calibration spot, in order to trace the contour for the other side of the nebula. The two traces then complete one closed contour. The principal disadvantage of this type of photometer is that for areas involving a large number of density peaks, as in some nebulae, the instrument must be carefully monitored to insure the inclusion of all proper details.

A later version of the Michigan isophotometer has been described by Dennison (1954) and Mohler and Pierce (1957), and further modifications have been made in the instrument now (January 1962) in use. Dr. Orren Mohler has kindly provided the following data. He writes:

"A series of modifications in the original instrument was begun some ten years later in order to adapt the direct-intensity microphotometer more specifically to its use as an isophotometer. No change in the fundamental principle was necessary, and it was possible to improve enormously the sensitivity and stability. A discrimination between density differences of 0.003, and a stability such that no changes were necessary over a period of years were finally achieved.

"The Williams-Hiltner machine produces a curve connecting all points of constant selected density in the photographic image being investigated. An isophotometer may also be constructed that will scan a complete area of photographic plate according to a preselected routine (Babcock 1950, Michelson 1953, Mohler and Pierce 1957). Two machines of this type have been constructed at the McMath-Hulbert Observatory of the University of Michigan. In the Michigan machines an analyzing light beam moves the full length of the plate (the X-direction), then is displaced a small step in the perpendicular direction (the Y-direction), after which it again traverses the X-direction on the plate in a sense opposite to the preceding trace. This procedure is followed until the entire area of the plate has been covered by the analyzing beam. A record is made on a paper tape by an inking pen whenever the intensity of the light beam transmitted through the photographic plate to the photoelectric cell reaches any one of a number of preselected levels. The preselected levels of intensity correspond to definite photographic densities.

"Early in 1958 a second model of an isophotometer with an X-Y scan was completed at the McMath-Hulbert Observatory. The second X-Y scanning isophotometer incorporated many improvements indicated by experience with the earlier versions. The later instrument produces isophotal contours at more than four times the speed with approximately twice the precision of the first X-Y

machine. Neither of the X-Y isophotometers is as precise as the Williams-Hiltner instrument. It should be mentioned, however, that the X-Y machine will run unattended for days at a time when this is necessary for plotting iso-photes covering large areas of a photograph.

"All isophotometers that record data only for certain preselected densities of the photographic image under study omit recording of the density at the un-selected values. It is generally necessary to make more than one isophotal tracing of a plate with such instruments so that the trace of the region scanned on a first trail will be supplemented by a record filling in the gaps.

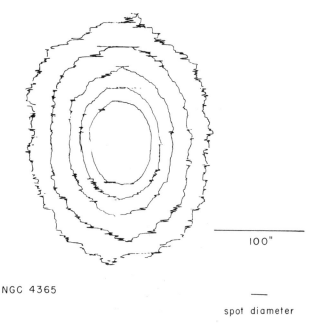

100"

NGC 4365

spot diameter

FIG. 12. —A family of isophotes for NGC 4365 drawn by the University of Michigan isophotometer (Liller 1960).

"Developments now under way at the McMath-Hulbert Observatory are di-rected toward the elimination of this defect. It is proposed that the X and Y positions of the scanning motions of a light beam and the intensity of the analyzing beam be recorded directly in a digital form. Results from a machine of this kind can be mechanically displayed in the form of tables containing the X and Y coordinates of each element of area on the plate and the photographic density within the area. The same data can be used to produce microdensito-metric tracings in either the X or the Y direction. A microdensitometric tracing may also be produced for any combination of the scanning coordinates, or for the production of isophotal contours. The preliminary developments so far carried out indicate that a digital analysis of an astronomical image of ordinary degree of complication and the tabulation of the data will require a considerable period of time. However, the presentation will be complete and in principle it is possible to record all significant photographic changes of density in any given image. The process can be speeded up by the investigator at the cost of sacrificing some degree of completeness in the results. Indications are that a machine of the type contemplated here will be significantly slower than either the original Williams-Hiltner machine or the McMath-Hulbert X-Y recorders in the production of isophotal curves to equivalent degrees of precision. It is an unfortunate fact that so far none of the recent models of isophotometers have equaled the Williams-Hiltner machine in precision."

A family of isophotes for NGC 4365 drawn by this isophotometer, with modifications introduced by Dennison (1954), is shown in Figure 12 (Liller 1960).

The preparation of this chapter was supported in part by the United States Air Force under contract No. AF 19(604)-4955 with the University of Chicago.

REFERENCES

AREND, S.	1948	*Mono. Obs. R. de Belgique*, No. 2.
ARGUE, A. N.	1954	*Observatory*, **74**, 213.
BABCOCK, H. W.	1950	*P.A.S.P.*, **62**, 18.
BARBER, D. R.	1940	*M.N.*, **100**, 180.
BECKER, W.	1938	*Zs. f. Ap.*, **15**, 225.
	1942	*A.N.*, **272**, 179.
	1948	*Ap. J.*, **107**, 278.
	1950	*Sterne und Sternsysteme* (2d ed.; Dresden and Leipzig: Steinkopff).
BECKER, W., and BIBER, C.	1956	*Zs. f. Ap.*, **41**, 52.
BECKER, W., and STEINLIN, U.	1956	*Zs. f. Ap.*, **39**, 188.
BERG, W. F.	1948	*Trans. Faraday Soc.*, **44**, 783.
BERTHIER, P., and MORIGNAC, B.	1953	*J. des Observateurs*, **36**, 119.
BIGAY, J. H.	1951a	*C.R.*, **232**, 312 (Pub. Obs. Haute-Provence, 2, No. 15).
	1951b	*J. des Observateurs*, **34**, 89.
BILTZ, M., and WEBB, J. H.	1948	*J. Opt. Soc. America*, **38**, 561.
BOWEN, I. S., and CLARK, L. T.	1940	*J. Opt. Soc. America*, **30**, 508.
CAMERON, D. M.	1951	*A.J.*, **56**, 92.
CHRISTIE, W. H.	1933	*Ap. J.*, **78**, 313.
CUFFEY, J.	1956	*Sky and Telescope*, **15**, 258.
DENNISON, E. W.	1954	Thesis, University of Michigan.
DIMITROFF, G. Z.	1938	*Harvard Circ.*, No. 430.

DOBSON, G. M. B.,
GRIFFITH, J. O., and
HARRISON, D. N.   1926   *Photographic Photometry* (Oxford: Clarendon Press).

DUNHAM, T.   1931   *Bericht VIII, Internat. Kong. Photog.*, Dresden, p. 287.

EBERHARD, G.   1931   *Hdb. d. Ap.*, **2**, 431.
                           1936   *Ibid.*, **7**, 90.

EDWARDS, D. L.   1942   *M.N.*, **102**, 242.

EFIMOV, Y. S.   1959   *A.J.* (U.S.S.R.), **36**, 457.

EICHNER, L. C., HETT,
J. H., SCHILT, J.,
SCHWARZSCHILD, M.,
and STERLING, H. T.   1947   *A.J.*, **53**, 25.

EVANS, D. S.   1949   *M.N.*, **109**, 94.
                           1950   *Ibid.*, **110**, 37.
                           1951   *Ibid.*, **111**, 526.
                           1952   *Ibid.*, **112**, 606.

FABRY, C.   1910   *Ap. J.*, **31**, 394.
                           1943   *Ann. d'ap.*, **6**, 65.

GOLLNOW, H., and
HAGEMANN, G.   1956   *A.J.*, **61**, 399.

GREAVES, W. M. H.   1952   *Trans. I.A.U.*, **8**, 355.

GUÉRIN, P., and
VAUCOULEURS, G. DE   1950   *Ann. d'ap.*, **13**, 203.

GÜNTHER, S.   1950   *Zs. f. Ap.*, **27**, 107.

GURNEY, R. W., and
MOTT, N. F.   1938   *Proc. R. Soc. London, A*, **164**, 151.

GYLDENKAERNE, K.   1950   *Ann. d'ap.*, **13**, 97.

HAFFNER, H.   1953   *Veröff. U. Sternw. Göttingen*, No. 106.

HANSSON, N.   1954a   *Lund Medd.*, Ser. I, No. 181.
                           1954b   *Ibid.*, No. 182.

HARDORP, J.   1960   *Astr. Abh. Hamburger Sternw.*, **5**, No. 7.

HAWKINS, G. S., and
WHIPPLE, F. L.   1958   *A.J.*, **63**, 283.

HOAG, A. A.   1961   *P.A.S.P.*, **73**, 301.

HOAG, A. A., JOHNSON,
H. L., IRIARTE, B.,
MITCHELL, R. I.,
HALLAM, K. L., and
SHARPLESS, S.   1961   *Pub. U.S. Naval Obs.* (2), Vol. **17**, pt. 7.

HOFF, H. VON   1937   *Zs. f. Astrophys.*, **14**, 104.

HOLMBERG, E.   1946   *Lund Medd.*, Ser. II, No. 117.
                           1950   *Ibid.*, No. 128.
                           1958   *Ibid.*, No. 136.

HOUTEN, C. J., VAN   1961   *Bull. Ast. Inst. Netherlands*, **16**, 1.

HUMASON, M. L., Mayall,
 N. U., and SANDAGE,
 A. R.   1956   *A.J.*, **61**, 145.
JÄGER, F. W.   1949   *Zs. f. Ap.*, **26**, 341.
JOHNSON, H. L., and
 MORGAN, W. W.   1953   *Ap. J.*, **117**, 313.
JOHNSON, H. M.   1960   *Mem. Mt. Stromlo Obs.*, Vol. **3**, No .15.
JONES, L. A.,
 RUSSELL, M. E., and
 BEACHAM, H. R.   1937   *J. Soc. Motion Picture Engineers*, **28**, 73.
KIENLE, H.   1937   *Hdb. d. Experimentalphys.*, **26**, 649.
KIENLE, H., WEMPE, J.,
 and BEILEKE, F.   1940   *Zs. f. Ap.*, **20**, 91.
KING, I.   1952   *Ap. J.*, **115**, 580.
KOPAL, Z., and MILLNS,
 P. Y.   1956   *Astr. Contr. U. Manchester*, No. 3, p. 40.
LILLER, M. H.   1960   *Ap. J.*, **132**, 306.
LUNDMARK, K.   1932   *Hdb. d. Ap.*, **5**, 296.
LYNGÅ, G.   1959   *Lund Medd.*, Ser. II, No. 137.
MEES, C. E. K.   1954   *The Theory of the Photographic Process* (rev. ed.; New York: Macmillan Co.).

MEYERMANN, B., and
 SCHWARZSCHILD, K.   1906   *A.N.*, **170**, 277.
MICHELSON, N. N.   1953   *Pub. Pulkovo Obs.*, **19**, 69.
MILLER, H. A., HENN,
 R. W., and CRABTREE,
 J. I.   1946   *J. Photog. Soc. America*, **12**, 586.
MILLER, R. H.   1962   *Ap. J.*, **135**, 638.
MITCHELL, J. W., and
 MOTT, N. F.   1957   *Phil. Mag.* (8th Ser.), **2**, 1149.
MOHLER, O. C., and
 PIERCE, A. K.   1957   *Ap. J.*, **125**, 285.
MORGAN, W. W.   1937   *Ap. J.*, **85**, 380.
PRENDERGAST, K. H., and
 MILLER, R. H.   1961   Paper presented at the 109th meeting of A.A.S.
RASMADSE, N. A.,
 IROSCHNIKOV, R. S., and
 KOTOH, E. V.   1959   *Bull. Obs. Abastumani*, No. 24, p. 31.
REDMAN, R. O.   1936   *M.N.*, **96**, 588.
REDMAN, R. O., and
 SHIRLEY, E. G.   1937   *M.N.*, **97**, 416.
ROSS, F. E.   1936   *Ap. J.*, **84**, 241.
SCHILT, J.   1922   *B.A.N.*, **1**, 51.
     1924   *Ibid.*, **2**, 135.
SCHMIDT, K. H.   1956   *Die Sterne*, **32**, 30.
SCHWARZSCHILD, K.   1900   *Ap. J.*, **11**, 89.

SCHWARZSCHILD, K., and
  VILLIGER, W.   1906   *Ap. J.*, **23**, 284.
SEARES, F. H., and
  JOYNER, M. C.   1943   *Ap. J.*, **98**, 261.
SERSIC, J. L.   1957   *Observatory*, **77**, 146.
                              1958   *Revista Astr.*, **29**, 65, 68, 109, 113, 117.

SHEPPARD, S. E.,
  VANSELOW, W., and
  QUIRK, R. F.   1945   *J. Franklin Inst.*, **240**, 439.
SIEDENTOPF, H.   1934   *A.N.*, **254**, 33.
STETSON, H. T.   1915   *Pop. Astr.*, **23**, 24.
                              1916   *Ap. J.*, **43**, 253.
STOCK, J.   1951   *A.N.*, **280**, 121.
                              1956   *J. Opt. Soc. America*, **46**, 17.
                              1958   *A.J.*, **63**, 496.

STOCK, J., and
  WEHLAU, W. H.   1956   *A.J.*, **61**, 80.
VAUCOULEURS, G. DE   1948   *Ann. d'ap.*, **11**, 247.
                              1956a   *Mem. Mt. Stromlo Obs.*, Vol. **3**, No. 13.
                              1956b   *Occ. Notes R.A.S.*, No. 18.
                              1957   *Ann. La Houga Obs.*, Vol. **2**, pt. 1.
                              1959   *A.J.*, **64**, 397.
VELGHE, A.   1949   *Mono. Obs. R. de Belgique*, No. 9, 33.
WALLACE, R. J.   1908   *Ap. J.*, **28**, 39.
WEAVER, H. F.   1946   *Pop. Astr.*, **54**, 211.
                              1947   *Ap. J.*, **106**, 366.
WEBB, J. H.   1933   *J. Opt. Soc. America*, **23**, 316.
                              1948   *Ibid.*, **38**, 312.
                              1950   *Ibid.*, **40**, 3.

WEBB, J. H., and
  EVANS, C. H.   1938   *J. Opt. Soc. America*, **28**, 249.
WILLIAMS, R. C., and
  HILTNER, W. A.   1940   *Pub. Univ. Michigan Obs.*, **8**, 45.
                              1941   *Ibid.*, p. 103.
                              1943   *Ap. J.*, **98**, 43.
WURM, K.   1955   *Phys. Verh.*, **5**, 133.
ZWICKY, F., HERZOG, E.,
  and WILD, P.   1961   *Catalogue of Galaxies and Cluster of Galaxies*
                                      (Zurich: California Institute of Technology), **1**.

CHAPTER 18

Measuring Engines

W. J. ECKERT AND REBECCA JONES
Watson Scientific Computing Laboratory

§ 1. INTRODUCTION

Measuring engines are used in astronomy to measure the position of images, such as star images, spectral lines, scale readings, and physical features that have been recorded on photographic plates or film. Since plate errors resulting from film distortion are of the order of half a micron on good plates (Land 1950), errors in the measuring engine of a tenth of a micron might be important in precise measurement, but, generally, somewhat less precision is considered adequate. Small distances can be measured in the field of the engine's microscope by means of a micrometer eyepiece. For large distances, a microscope with a fixed reticle is mounted with the optical axis perpendicular to the plate and is moved parallel to the plate from image to image. In some engines motion is provided in only one co-ordinate. These engines are used to measure photographs that are essentially one-dimensional, such as spectrograms and scale readings.

For measurement of a two-dimensional photograph, facilities are provided to move the microscope with respect to the plate in two perpendicular directions. Generally, the microscope moves in one direction and the plate in the other. Although a few engines have been constructed to measure both co-ordinates simultaneously, most engines measure only one co-ordinate, and the second co-ordinate is obtained by a remeasurement of the images after the plate has been rotated 90°. We shall refer to the co-ordinate being measured as the "x-co-ordinate" and to the other as the "y-co-ordinate." When only one co-ordinate is measured, a rough value of the y-co-ordinate is often recorded to facilitate identification of the image when this co-ordinate is measured after the 90° rotation. Engines have also been made for the measurement of polar co-ordinates on the plate. Some engines will measure in either rectangular or polar co-ordinates.

A photograph of a star field is the projection on a plane of a portion of the

424

celestial sphere; the center of projection is the optical center of the camera objective. Measuring engines have been built to measure the spherical co-ordinates directly. In these engines the index telescope is pivoted at a distance from the plate equal to the focal length of the camera, and angular distances corresponding to right ascension and declination are measured directly.

In much early photographic work in astrometry, the plates were measured with the aid of a "réseau," or rectangular grid of fine reference lines, superposed on the star field on the plate. The réseau was applied by a second exposure of the plate made in contact with a master glass plate on which were engraved the standard grid lines. Once the grid was calibrated, the position of a star image on a plate could be determined by measurement of its distance from the adjacent réseau lines.

The use of the réseau greatly influenced the design of many early measuring engines, but their design was such as to make them useful for general astrometric work. Typical of these engines was one produced by Repsold that provided the following: a micrometer microscope to measure distances of the star image from the réseau lines in the two co-ordinates; two precision scales to measure rectangular co-ordinates on plates without a réseau and for calibrating the réseau; and a precision-graduated circle for the measurement of polar co-ordinates. These engines were very convenient for measuring small distances between pairs of images in differential measurement of proper motions.

After the réseau was abandoned, measuring engines with scales were replaced by engines with a long micrometer screw. The screw was used to drive a microscope with a fixed reticle from one image to another. Screw engines were made at a number of observatories and by several instrument makers, including Brashear, Gaertner, and, more recently, Mann.

During recent years, many laboratories have worked on the development of devices that will perform automatically the various operations of the measuring and recording process. The measuring process involves the identification of the image to be measured, the setting of an index on the image, and the recording of the measurement of the distance that the index moves in traveling from one image to another. Finally, the precision with which the values of the measurements agree with the true values involves the calibration of the instrument and operational precautions. There is considerable variety in the details of indexing, moving the plate, and reading and recording the measurements; these details will be outlined in the following sections.

§ 2. SETTING THE INDEX ON THE IMAGE

The most common type of index for setting on an image is a microscope (Fig. 1) with a fixed reticle at the focus of the objective and an eyepiece to magnify the image and reticle. If the reticle contains two lines at right angles, one in the x-direction and one in the y, indexing in x consists of bisecting the image with the y-line at, or near, its intersection with the x-line. When the reticle contains a pair of y-lines, the operator places the image midway between the two lines.

One modification of the basic microscope separates the eyepiece from the objective and reticle. This modification contributes to the accuracy of measurement, since bumping the eyepiece will not disturb the optical axis of the objective and reticle, and it also contributes to the ease of measurement, since refocusing of the eyepiece is possible. In the simplest case the eyepiece is detached from the microscope and mounted on an auxiliary slide that moves along parallel to the slide carrying the **microscope**. In another arrangement, which is more

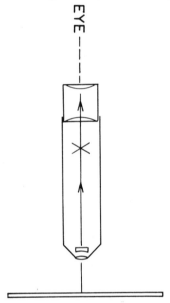

FIG. 1.—Microscope with a fixed reticle

elaborate than the one just mentioned, the eyepiece maintains a convenient, fixed position (Fig. 2) independent of the moving microscope. Since the beam of light between the collimating lenses, L_1 and L_2, is parallel, the distance between the eyepiece and reticle can be changed without disturbing the focus or the collimation (Schlesinger and Barney 1933).

In another modification of the basic microscope, the eyepiece is replaced by a lens that projects the image and cross-wires onto a screen (Schlesinger and Bennett 1933). With this device the observer does not need to look through an eyepiece; he sees the enlarged image of the field of the microscope projected on a screen (Fig. 3) at a convenient distance from his eye.

Indexing has also been performed by the optical superposition of images. The image to be measured and a comparison image are brought together into the field of the eyepiece through a reflecting system and are made to coincide by an

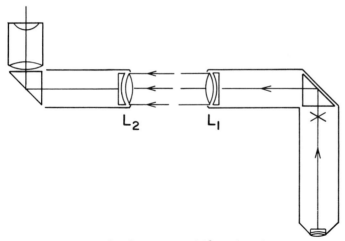

FIG. 2.—Eyepiece independent of the moving microscope

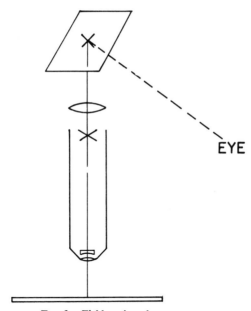

FIG. 3.—Field projected on a screen

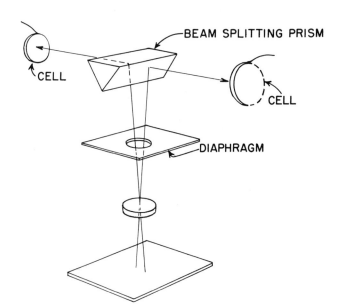

FIG. 4.—Two photocells and a beam-splitter

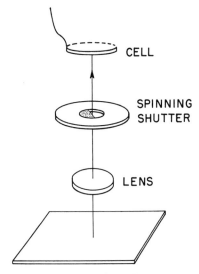

FIG. 5.—Rotating knife-edge

adjustment of the reflections. A well-known instrument that uses this type of indexing is the Hartmann spectrocomparator (Hartmann 1906).

The development of electronic techniques has permitted the substitution of photronic or photoelectric cells for the human eye. A simple form of such a device uses two cells to compare the light reflected from two faces of a beam-splitting prism (Fig. 4) onto which the objective lens has projected a small area of the plate containing the star image. A diaphragm with a circular opening defines the boundary of the bright area striking the prism. The current flowing from each cell varies with the amount of light shining on it, and a comparison of the two currents is used to determine when the image is bisected by the edge of the prism. In an early form for setting on star images, the currents are subtracted, and a meter indicates the resultant current (Mehlin 1935). The observer moves the index until the meter reads zero. The output from the two cells has been used in connection with a servomechanism to set automatically on a spectral line (Harrison 1935), on scale graduations (Watts 1950), and on the moon's limb (Watts and Adams 1950).

Another type of photoelectric sensing device uses a single cell in connection with a rotating shutter at the focus of the lens (Fig. 5). The rotating shutter has a semicircular opening, with the axis of rotation at the center of the circle. When the aperture is illuminated uniformly or when there is angular symmetry in the illumination, the current from the cell will be constant. If, however, the illumination is more intense in one sector than in another, the current will fluctuate periodically as the shutter rotates. This device provides an effective means of centering on a photographic image (Lentz and Bennett 1954). The shutter is driven by a synchronous motor, and the current from the cell is analyzed according to the phase angle of the shutter. The phase components of the current corresponding to the x- and y-directions operates through servos to produce the centering motion; centering occurs simultaneously in both co-ordinates.

§ 3. MEASURING THE CO-ORDINATES

The familiar micrometer microscope is generally used for measuring small distances between images that can be seen simultaneously in the field of the eyepiece. The precision measurement of large distances, especially in two co-ordinates, presents more serious problems, and the micrometer microscope is an important auxiliary in some of the methods for measuring these large distances.

The measurement of the co-ordinates of the images involves moving the index from one image to another and measuring the corresponding change in each co-ordinate. It is important that these motions conform to the geometry on which the instrument is based and that the instrument be extremely stable, so that given distances are always indicated by the same readings.

The various methods of setting an index on the image as described in § 2 involve pointing the optical axis of a lens at the image. Since the image is at some distance from the lens, the indicated distance from one image to another depends not only on the translation but also on any possible rotation of the optical axis.

For the measurement of rectilinear co-ordinates, the index is mounted on a carriage that slides on carefully ground ways with three points of contact. One common design utilizes a **V**-way and a flat way, with contact on the **V**-way at the two ends of the carriage and contact with the flat way in the middle of the carriage (Fig. 6). These ways are ground on a single casting with great care, to insure that the carriage will move parallel to itself in a straight line. Another design uses cylindrical ways and bearings (Fig. 7). The cylindrical ways are carefully mounted parallel to each other.

Three devices have been used to drive the carriage along the ways: a screw and nut, a rack and pinion, and a cord or belt and pulley. It is important that

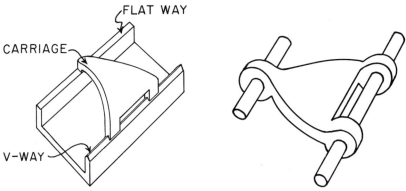

FLAT WAY

CARRIAGE

V-WAY

FIG. 6.—Carriage on ways   FIG. 7.—Cylindrical ways

the driving mechanism be mounted so as to impart only translational motion to the carriage and not to lift or tilt it from the ways; in precision measurement, a slight pressure can produce effects much greater than the required precision of measurement. Precise measurement of the motion of the carriage has been made mostly by means of a scale or a screw.

The position of a carriage can be read from a scale, which is mounted parallel to the way, by means of a microscope attached to the carriage. The operator determines the position by setting the reticle of the micrometer on one or both of the scale divisions nearest to the center of the field. In the Repsold engine, the microscope that is used for setting on the star image is also used for setting on the scale; it is tilted slightly about an axis parallel to the scale to bring the scale or the image into the field (Scheiner 1897).

The scale provides a simple, accurate method of measuring distances, but it requires the operator to note a scale division and two or three micrometer readings and to perform some arithmetic for the interpolation process. By reason of this lengthy measuring process, scales have been abandoned for most measuring engines, and the screw with its problems has been substituted for the scale.

However, since the advent of automatic methods of setting, reading, and computing, the merits of the scale should be re-examined. The automatic reading of the scale could be accomplished photoelectrically at the engine, or the scale could be photographed and the photograph measured elsewhere, as Watts (1950) has done for the meridian circle.

In recent years most engines have had a single, long screw and nut to move the carriage and to measure the distance traveled. The screw is mounted in bearings, so that it is free to rotate. The nut on the screw is attached to the carriage in such a manner that the carriage prevents the nut from rotating and the nut drives the carriage along the ways. The prevention of any motion other than that of translation from being imparted to the carriage requires careful construction. To insure uniform pressure on the screw and carriage assembly (Fig. 8), a single thrust bearing positions the screw longitudinally, and a cord and counter-

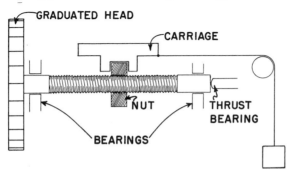

FIG. 8.—Screw-thrust bearing and weight

weight pull the carriage, nut, and screw toward the thrust bearing. The position of the carriage is indicated by the number of whole turns of the screw, as shown on a scale or counter, and by the fraction of a turn, as shown on the graduated head.

The Michelson interferometer, an exceedingly accurate device for measuring distances, has been used effectively in the ruling of diffraction gratings (Harrison and Archer 1951). It has been suggested for use on measuring engines, especially since it has become feasible to count fringes automatically. However, the accuracy required for astronomical photographs has not seemed high enough to warrant the added complication of interference methods.

To measure two-dimensional photographs, a second set of ways and carriage is provided to move the plate at right angles to the motion of the index; the second carriage is mounted so that the plate is inclined from 30° to 60° to the horizontal for the observer's convenience in looking through the microscope and to reduce flexure. A pulley and counterweight are used to balance the weight of the carriage and plate. Needless to say, the ways carrying the plate must be parallel to the surface of the plate, and the ways carrying the index must be parallel to the plate and at right angles to the other ways. The optical axis of the index should be perpendicular to the plate.

Some engines have been built to measure precise co-ordinates simultaneously in x and y. Scale engines require a precision scale and micrometer for the y-direction and a filar micrometer that will set on the star in two co-ordinates. Many of the scale engines, such as the Repsold, were of this type.

In using an engine that measures one co-ordinate at a time, the operator must turn the plate 90° to measure the second co-ordinate. He can turn the plate by removing it from the engine and reinserting it, or he can rotate the plateholder. In some engines the device for rotation has a precision-graduated circle with two micrometers for reading position angle.

For the measurement of spherical co-ordinates, the index is mounted on a device that has two perpendicular axes of rotation, each having accurately graduated circles and reading micrometers; the device is similar to an accurate theodolite (Scheiner 1897).

Although most precision photographs are on glass plates, roll film is con-

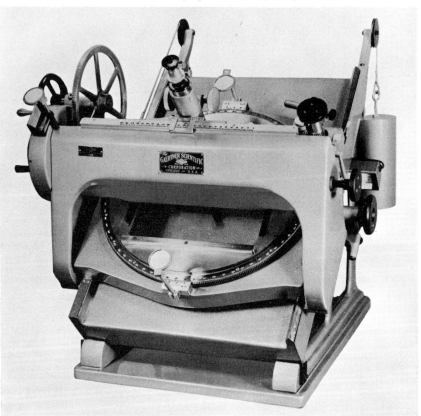

FIG. 9.—Gaertner measuring engine

venient for many purposes, such as photographing scale settings. The camera can have automatic means of advancing the film between exposures, and the measuring engine can be equipped with a similar device for advancing the film for measurement (Watts 1950).

§ 4. OBSERVING TECHNIQUES AND CALIBRATION OF THE ENGINE

In any measuring program the observer must assure himself that the instrument and the method of use will give measurements of the required accuracy. For precision measurement, it may be necessary to study the instrument carefully and conduct an extensive calibration program. The first requirement is, of course, that the instrument repeat itself with the necessary accuracy under circumstances that can be controlled by the operator. The next step is to determine quantitatively how the readings from the engine are related to the desired co-

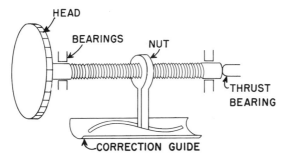

FIG. 10.—Self-correcting attachment

ordinates, by isolating the various parameters that affect the measurements and constructing a calibration-curve or table for each effect.

Calibration-curves can be used in three ways: (1) as a guide to adjust or rework the engine, (2) to instal self-correcting attachments to the engine that produce corrected readings directly, and (3) to apply arithmetic corrections to the readings. Circumstances usually dictate how the calibration-curves are to be used.

The correction of major mechanical troubles, such as those arising from the faulty cutting of the screw and ways, is a problem for the maker and not for the user. There are, however, several adjustments that can be made with the aid of adjusting screws or shims. An example of a self-correcting attachment to an engine is a device for correcting the readings of a screw. The nut is permitted to rotate slightly with respect to the carriage, and the rotation is controlled by an extension of the nut that is constrained to move in a calibration slot in a sheet of metal (Fig. 10).

Keeping the engine simple and relegating as much of the calibration problem as possible to the arithmetic of the reduction procedure constitute the more attractive approach, especially when the reductions are made on automatic computing machines. When the calibration corrections are applied arithmetically, the readings from the engine may differ widely from the nominal value, and the only requirement is that the instrument repeat with the required accuracy and that the calibration-curves be reasonably smooth.

The measuring engines that are used for large programs, such as the Yale Zone Catalogs (Schlesinger and Barney 1933) and the AGK_2, are carefully calibrated; the published results offer good working examples of the calibration investigations. Other examples may be found in the reports of Lee and Steele (1917) and Newkirk (1913). Here we shall discuss briefly the principal types of errors.

An important group of errors varies with the value of the co-ordinate being measured; these errors depend on the irregularities in the ways for transporting the index and on the screw or scale assembly. They are usually combined and discussed only as periodic and cumulative or progressive errors. Periodic errors in the screw arise from the shape of the thread and nut, the thrust bearing on the end of the screw, and an eccentric mounting of the graduated head of the screw; they have the period of rotation of the screw, and they are treated as the same for each revolution. The progressive errors depend on the ways and the screw, and, generally, they vary smoothly along the screw. In the case of a scale, the periodic errors are in the reading microscope, and, corresponding to the progressive error in the screw, each scale division has its own error.

To evaluate the progressive errors, one can employ the following procedure with the aid of a glass scale or a glass plate spattered with small dots of India ink. The images (dots or divisions) that are chosen for measurement should be parallel to the x-co-ordinate and at suitable distances apart. The glass plate, which may be oriented conveniently by means of two dots widely separated in y, is moved successively by its own length, and the locations of the dots are measured in each position. These measures of several distances, or intervals, in several parts of the screw can be combined to yield the distances between the images (in terms of the average screw revolution or scale division) and the errors along the screw at the points where the readings were taken. The measurement of one interval on a standard bar or scale determines the average value of a screw revolution or scale division, which is not required with high accuracy in many cases.

The periodic errors of the screw or micrometer can be treated in a similar manner, with smaller intervals than those used to determine progressive errors. The scale value of the micrometer is very sensitive to focal setting, and it is determined frequently by settings on a pair of graduations of the scale.

The measuring screw is subject to two troublesome errors that affect the method of observing. There is always considerable end-play or backlash to prevent binding of the assembly. This slack is taken up by the cord and counterweight that hold the carriage against the nut and the screw against the thrust bearing. To reduce the effect still further, it is customary to approach all images in the same direction, namely, the one that lifts the counterweight. Second, as the nut moves along the screw, the oil piles up ahead of it by an amount that varies with the distance of travel. To reduce this effect, the operator moves the index past the image, back over it, and then makes the standard approach.

Irregularities in the ways for movement in y will cause errors in x, depending on y; these errors can be determined with the aid of a fine, tight wire in a frame or with a straight line ruled on a glass plate. With the wire or plate mounted parallel to the y-co-ordinate, settings in x are made for a suitable number of positions in y. The plate or frame is then rotated 180° about the line as axis, and the measurements are repeated. If the plate or frame has two lines at right angles, the measurements will indicate whether or not the x- and y-directions of motion are mutually perpendicular.

There may be some tendency of the plate carriage to twist in one direction or the other, depending on the direction of its motion in y. To reduce this effect, the operator should always approach all images for the final setting in the same direction.

In setting an index, most observers have personal equations that vary with the size of the image; they can eliminate the error by measuring the plate in two positions 180° apart or by using a reversing prism in the eyepiece. In photo-electric indices there are similar effects, such as the lack of balance in the two photocells. An improper adjustment of the index introduces two effects. If the optical axis is not perpendicular to the plate, the setting will vary with the distance of the objective from the plate, caused by irregularities in the plate. The second effect arises when the index line in the reticle is not perpendicular to the co-ordinate being measured; the resulting error varies with the part of the line that is used in the setting. This effect can be eliminated by careful adjustment of the reticle or by measurement of all images at the same position on the index line. The same condition holds true for a photoelectric setting if a reflecting prism is used.

In the photoelectric setting device that uses a spinner, the sensitivity of a setting in the x-direction is reduced if there is a large error signal in y. The engine moves simultaneously in both co-ordinates to reduce the error signal to zero, but it is unable to reduce the error if the motion in y is not sufficiently smooth. To overcome this difficulty, an auxiliary device is provided to make the final adjustment of the position of the image in y without a corresponding motion of the carriage (Lentz and Bennett 1954).

The photocell requires more intense illumination than the diffuse light that is used to illuminate the plate for visual measurements. A collimated beam of light meets this requirement, and the motion of the collimated source must be equal to that of the index system. It is also necessary to make sure that variations in the uniformity of the illumination coupled with changes in collimation will not introduce systematic errors.

Temperature changes generally affect the scale of an instrument, and they also introduce warping of the geometry during the changes. This temperature effect is especially troublesome for large engines and long measuring sessions. It is customary to inclose engines for these programs in an insulated room. For high-precision measurements, temperature control should be installed, with baffles to prevent intermittent local heating from the heat source.

The calibration of the engine should be considered in connection with the observing program; measures made in the program itself may be useful in the calibration, and the calibration necessarily depends on the program. In zone work, for example, high precision is required, but the large number of standard comparison stars and the nature of the plate solutions greatly simplify the calibration process. On each plate there are about fifty standard stars, and for each star there is an equation of condition in each co-ordinate to determine zero point, scale, orientation, and the coefficients of the quadratic terms. As Schlesinger and Barney (1933) have pointed out, any progressive errors that can be represented by linear and quadratic terms need not be determined or applied.

§ 5. AUTOMATION

An important attribute of a measuring engine is its convenience for the user; it affects not only his feelings but also the quantity and quality of his output. The measurement of large numbers of images involves an important man-machine relation that should not be underestimated in the over-all program.

In the present state of technology, it is feasible to automatize essentially all the operations of locating images on the plates from approximate co-ordinates, setting the index on the image, recording the measurements, performing the calculations, and preparing the finished copy for reproduction by lithography or zinc etchings. For large, systematic programs, such as the construction of star catalogues and the measurement of a number of well-populated plates, the automatic process is not only feasible but economically sound. In cases where this degree of automation is not warranted, there are many lesser degrees of kindness to the observer. We have already mentioned the indexing aids, including the detached eyepiece, the projected image, and the photoelectric devices. Another important area of convenience is associated with the reading of scales and micrometers both for setting and for measurement. For visual reading, figures on a dial are more convenient than marks on a scale, and many engines now use such devices (Fig. 11).

Dials may be attached to the engine near the moving part whose motion is being measured or in more convenient locations by means of flexible connections. A convenient form of remote connection is the electrical system involving a pair of Autosyn motors (Lentz and Bennett 1954). The Autosyns may be connected so that one drives the other, or, for greater precision of following, they can be arranged so that the difference in phase between them produces an error signal to control an auxiliary drive. Photography offers another convenient

method of remote reading. A small, automatic camera can be used to photograph
a scale or dial, and the films are read or measured elsewhere (Watts 1950).

The readings from dials, scales, screws, or photographs may be observed
visually or converted into electrical impulses for controlling automatic equipment. The equipment may be attached to the engine, or the readings may be
recorded in digital form in punched cards or other media for remote processing.
Counters and registers that are equipped for read-out by means of electrical
contacts are now generally available. The electronic counter keeps track of the
position of a part of the engine by simply counting impulses from marks on a
scale or from interference fringes. Electrical signals from the engine can be used

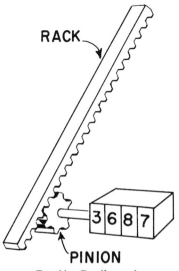

FIG. 11.—Reading scales

in a servoloop to control the motions of the engine for automatic setting at a
given location on the plate.

Associated with every measuring program is the problem of processing the
results. In-line continuous computers can be attached to the engine to perform
these simple calculations. If the engine is equipped with card readers and
punches, an automatic digital computer can be used as a link in the chain.

The following working examples illustrate many of the principles described in
this section. The automatic engine for measuring spectra at the Massachusetts
Institute of Technology sets photoelectrically on the spectral lines, applies a
reduction formula to the measures by means of an in-line continuous computer,
and exhibits the results as photographs of dial readings.

In the meridian-circle program of the U.S. Naval Observatory, automatic
cameras photograph the circle graduations on 35-mm films. The measuring en-

gine measures these films and records the results in punched cards. Another device at the Naval Observatory measures the irregularities in the edge of the moon. A plate rotates about a point near the center of the moon's image, and photocells track the edge of the moon. The displacements from the moon's edge are amplified and traced on a large-scale sheet of paper.

The engine at the Watson Laboratory (Eckert and Jones 1954; Lentz and Bennett 1954) was designed for use in connection with an electronic calculator and a table-printing device to provide an automatic system for programs such as the construction of precise star catalogues. For each star to be measured, the identification and approximate co-ordinates are punched into a card. The cards are sorted into groups according to the plate on which the represented stars will appear and in the order in which they will be measured. The plate and the associated cards are presented to the engine. After reading each card, the engine proceeds to the indicated location. The operator inspects the image projected on the screen and signals the machine to measure the image when it is within the range of the sensing device. The photoelectric device then centers on the image, and the precise measurement is recorded in the card. The processing of the cards includes the application of all the calibration effects and the necessary reductions. The final results are then prepared as copy for reproduction by lithography.

Automatic measurement has many advantages over manual methods: the precision of setting is much higher (photoelectric setting on a star image, for example, has a probable error of one- or two-tenths of a micron, whereas the error of a visual setting is about 1 micron); there are fewer errors of setting and reading; and more images can be measured in a single session, with a corresponding decrease in the effects of instrumental changes and of change in personal equation.

REFERENCES

ECKERT, W. J., and		
JONES, R. B.	1954	*A.J.*, **59**, 83.
HARRISON, G. R.	1935	*J. Opt. Soc. America*, **25**, 169.
HARRISON, G. R., and		
ARCHER, J. E.	1951	*J. Opt. Soc. America*, **41**, 495.
HARTMANN, J.	1906	*Ap. J.*, **24**, 285. Translated by PHILIP FOX from *Zs. f. Instrumentenk.*, **21**, 205.
LAND, G.	1950	*A.J.*, **55**, 145.
LEE, O. J., and STEELE, H. B.	1917	*A.J.*, **30**, 128.
LENTZ, J., and BENNETT, R.	1954	*Electronics*, **27**, 158.
MEHLIN, T. G.	1935	*A.J.*, **44**, 169.
NEWKIRK, B. L.	1913	*Pub. Lick Obs.*, **7**, 135.
SCHEINER, J.	1897	*Die Photographie der Gestirne* (Leipzig).

SCHLESINGER, F., and
    BARNEY, I.   1933   *Trans. Yale Obs.*, Vol. **9.**
SCHLESINGER, F., and
    BENNETT, A. L.   1933   *M.N.*, **93,** 382.
SCHORR, R., and KOHL-
    SCHÜTTER, A.   1951   *AGK*$_2$, **1,** E12.
WATTS, C. B.   1950   *Pub. Naval Obs.*, **16,** 347–359.
WATTS, C. B., and
    ADAMS, A. N.   1950   Reported in *Sky and Telescope*, **9,** 134.

CHAPTER 19

Techniques for Visual Measurements

P. MULLER

Observatoire de Paris

§ 1. MICROMETERS

THE invention of the telescope not only has enabled astronomers to observe stars too faint to be seen with the naked eye or to distinguish details of the nearer members of the solar system but also has contributed to positional astronomy. The telescope has made it possible to measure the direction of a star with incomparably greater precision than that obtained by the alignment of reference points in front of the eye. The telescope has also permitted differential observations of two objects simultaneously visible in the field of the eyepiece. Although most differential measurements are now done photographically, visual observations still remain the superior technique under some circumstances and the only one in the case of double stars with small separations. Micrometers are therefore still of interest to the astronomer and may still occasionally undergo improvements.

A complete review of the subject, with a description of all the micrometers invented in the last two or three centuries, is beyond the scope of this chapter. Such a review has been published by Becker (1889). This chapter will be limited to a description of the devices now in use or those that have unique and interesting features.

1.1. FILAR MICROMETER

The filar micrometer was described for the first time by Auzout (1667) in a form not essentially different from modern instruments. Since this instrument is familiar to physicists, who use it in many laboratory instruments, as well as astronomers, only a brief description will be given here.

A screw of very small pitch (generally only a few tenths of a millimeter) moves a small frame mounted in a rectangular box. A spider thread is stretched across the box at right angles to the axis of the screw. To make it possible to read the displacement of the thread, a graduated drum with a revolution

440

counter is attached to the screw. A second frame in the box supports a fixed thread parallel to the first. Since the two threads are in slightly different planes, the movable wire can be projected on the stationary one when the drum reads L_0. Since the translation of the movable threads per revolution of the screw is known, the separation of the two threads can be computed for any other setting of the drum. The pitch of the screw is usually expressed in seconds of arc for the telescope to which it is attached. The screw pitch is rarely less than 10 seconds of arc.

A micrometer, as described above, would permit measurements in only one co-ordinate. To provide the second co-ordinate, either of two arrangements is possible: (1) a second system of two threads, one fixed and one movable, at right angle to the first; (2) the micrometer can be mounted so that it can rotate on the optical axis of the telescope. The orientation is then read on a divided position circle. The first system, which gives the relative position in rectangular co-ordinates, is used on meridian or auxiliary instruments. The second system, which gives the relative position in polar co-ordinates in the tangent plane of the celestial sphere, is used on equatorially mounted telescopes. The fiducial mark for the position-angle circle is oriented so that the circle reads either 0° or 180° when the screw lies approximately along an hour circle. The position-angle circle will increase in the direction northeast-southwest. To facilitate the measurement of the position angle, a fixed thread is installed normal to the two threads described above. Position angles are referred to this second fixed or transverse thread. Although the micrometer is attached to the telescope to satisfy the above conditions, a small zero correction to the position angle always remains. This correction is evaluated by trailing a star along the thread by diurnal motion.

As a rule, filar micrometers are provided with a second screw, the box screw, parallel to the micrometer screw but without a divided head. It is used to shift both the fixed and the movable threads together without altering their separation. Details for facilitating the reading of the drum and circle by magnifiers, the use of verniers, illuminations of the threads, automatic recording, etc., will not be discussed in this chapter. The filar micrometer of the Yerkes Observatory is shown in Figure 1.

1.11. *Measuring technique.*—The problem is to find the difference in co-ordinates of two stars, A and B, visible simultaneously in the field of view. First, the fixed wire Ff is oriented to bisect both A and B (Fig. 2, a). The circle reading, corrected for the zero error, then gives the position angle θ of B relative to A. The micrometer is then rotated 90°, so that the two parallel wires will be normal to the line connecting A and B. The fixed wire Ff is set on A with either the telescope's slow motions or, preferably, by the box screw referred to above. The movable wire Fm is then set on B by means of the micrometer screw (Fig. 2, b). The distance AB can be read on the drum. In practice, the settings are repeated several times. Instead of applying the coincidence reading L_0 of the

FIG. 1.—Filar micrometer at the Yerkes Observatory. Photograph by J. Tapscott

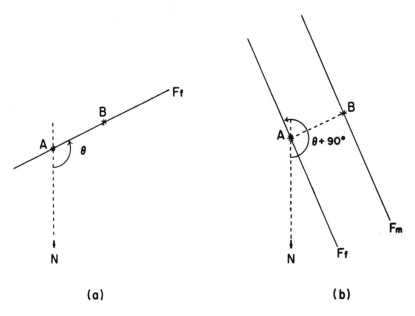

(a)   (b)

FIG. 2.—Measurement of a double star with a filar micrometer: (a) for position angle, (b) for separation.

fixed and movable threads to obtain the distance AB, it is preferable to repeat the measurement by placing the fixed wire on B and the movable one on A. The difference between the two drum readings immediately gives twice the separation. As briefly mentioned above, a micrometer generally has a transverse thread. This removes the necessity of rotating the micrometer by 90° between the position angle and the separation measures.

The same procedure is followed in diameter measures. Settings are made with the two threads tangential to the disk. Here also, when symmetrical observations are made to give twice the diameter, the zero reading L_0 need not be determined.

1.12. *Errors in the measurements.*—The filar micrometer measures only small separations at the focus of a telescope. It was originally designed to refer a planet or comet to nearby fixed stars in the same field of view or to refer one star to another. Separations may be several minutes of arc, in which case low magnification is used. This reduces the accuracy of the measurement. Also the accuracy may be limited by the shape of the object—for example, comets. Photography has largely replaced this type of visual observations because of its higher precision and greater convenience. Today, only close double stars and small diameters are measured visually where distances of only a few tens of microns are encountered. Errors have entered that were previously neglected when only larger distances were measured. The screw may display either a periodic or a progressive error or both. Furthermore, when high magnification is used, the threads appear relatively thick and partly translucid. The least irregularity of the telescope drive, wind pressure on the telescope, and small motions of the stellar image caused by anomalous atmospheric refraction will vitiate the bisection of the images with the threads. When measuring diameters, there is the additional uncertainty of judging when a thread of sensible thickness is tangent to a curved limb.

These limitations of the filar micrometer have not escaped the attention of astronomers. Numerous devices have been proposed and constructed to lessen or suppress them. It is not possible to give a complete review here. Moreover, the majority of them, sometimes unjustifiably, have not remained in use, and some have not been given serious tests.

1.13. *Modified filar micrometers.*—Jonckheere (1950) introduced a modification in the filar micrometer by a rearrangement of the threads. The movable thread was replaced by an intersecting pair that made an acute angle with the axis of the screw (Fig. 3). The fixed thread is oriented so as to bisect the obtuse angle formed at the intersection of the two movable threads. This thread is used for measuring the position angle, say of a double star, after which, without reorientation of the micrometer, the movable cross-thread is shifted until the two stars are bisected. The shift of the cross-thread is not the separation of the stars but the height of a triangle of which the stars form the base. This height is proportional to, but always several times greater than, the separation of the stars. Again, as for the classical filar micrometer, the position of coincidence is eliminated by the method of measuring double distances. This modification has two interesting features: (1) the screw value is greatly reduced (Jonckheere's instrument had a screw value equal to 1.078 seconds of arc per revolution); (2) the two movable threads, since they are fixed relative to each other, can be stretched in essentially the same plane. Consequently, both threads remain in critical focus under high power. This is never the case with the fixed and movable threads in the usual arrangement. The fixed thread, since it is used only for angle measures, need not be so critically focused. If desired, another thread parallel to the fixed one may be installed on the movable frame to permit measures of separations too great for the two intersecting threads. In this case, the screw would assume a different value.

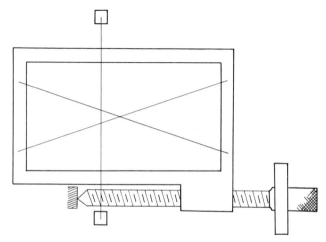

FIG. 3.—Jonckheere's micrometer with skew threads

Other materials, such as quartz and tungsten, have been substituted for spider thread. However, the thread remains the finest. It can be elastically stretched and will resist changes in humidity and temperature so that even the focal image of the sun does not cause damage. A well-set spider thread will give many years of service.

An interesting experiment was made by Bigourdan (1895), who replaced the spider threads by sharp, tapered points of glass. Such points are easily made by drawing a thin glass rod heated at one place. These points were then attached to the fixed and movable frames of the micrometer. A measure is made not by superposition but by "presentation" (Fig. 4). The stars are "pointed at" by the glass points. Diameters are measured in the same way. This method gives measures with greater certainty than with threads, the settings are easy, and, since the stars are not hidden, the limiting magnitude should be fainter. A thread is still needed for measuring position angles.

One group of micrometers has no moving parts. The môvable and fixed threads are replaced with a graticule at the focal plane. The graticule may have a variety of forms—lozenge, circle, two concentric circles (ring micrometer), etc. The relative co-ordinates of two stars are obtained by noting the instants of contacts as the stars drift over the graticule. The accuracy of such observations is, however, much inferior to those obtained with a filar micrometer.

1.2. Non-filar Micrometers

Attempts have been made to substitute for the classical bisection with threads a direct comparison with an image produced in the focal plane. Micrometers of this general type form two groups: (1) comparison-image micrometers, where an artificial double star is projected onto the focal plane, and (2) double-image micrometers, where a second image of the double star itself is used.

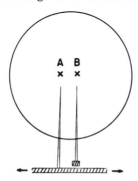

FIG. 4.—Measurement by "pointing" with Bigourdan's glass points.

1.21. *Comparison-image micrometers.*—It is not difficult to project into the field of view an image of an artificial double star and to adjust the pair in both relative magnitude and color. Two devices of this nature have been in regular use after some earlier trials, and a third system has been proposed recently.

The micrometer constructed at Greenwich Observatory was originally designed by Hargreaves (1932) and modified into its present form by Davidson and Symms (1938). The artificial double star is obtained from a single light-source by means of a birefringent prism. Two rotatable Nicol prisms enable one to vary at will the total brightness and magnitude difference. A set of reflecting prisms brings the image into the field of view. Rotation on the optical axis of the telescope takes care of measurements of position angle. A thread must be used momentarily to determine the parallel correction. This instrument is now in constant use and has all but replaced the filar micrometer in double-star measurements at Greenwich. A substantial improvement in accuracy, especially for separations, has been reported. Since no field illumination is necessary, the faintest stars accessible to the telescope can be measured.

The screen micrometer invented by Duruy (1938) has been used on a 27-cm refractor. With this micrometer, the real pair of double stars is observed with one eye and the artificial pair with the other eye. The artificial pair is formed by two small bright disks on a dark background. Their orientation and separation can be regulated. This micrometer, although more primitive than the preceding one and placing rather severe demands on the eyesight, has given good results (Duruy 1938).

Camichel (1956) has recently constructed a comparison-image micrometer for the Pic-du-Midi. It is similar in principle to the Greenwich instrument but differs significantly in detail. The artificial double star is produced with a birefringent designed prism by Muller. The first series of measures with it have been published (Camichel 1956). The measured separations are good, but the position angles can doubtless be improved. Unfortunately, these preliminary trials were made under unfavorable atmospheric conditions.

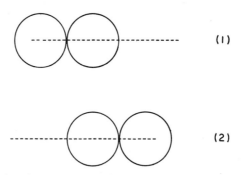

FIG. 5.—Diameter measurement by the double-image method

1.22. *Double-image micrometers.*—Suppose an instrument is designed and constructed so that an image A' of a star A can be placed in the same field. Furthermore, the instrument can place the image A' in any measurable position relative to the star A. Such a device will enable one to measure diameters and double stars. For diameters, the two images are separated until the two disks are tangent, first on one side and then on the other. The total displacement of the movable disk gives twice the diameter (Fig. 5). For double stars, the four images are arranged (Fig. 6) in characteristic patterns (alignment for position angle, squares, or equidistance for separation). These patterns will not be discussed further except for a word of caution. Contrary to what is sometimes proposed, the superposition of images (so as to obtain, for instance, a configuration of three equidistant stars with a coincidence in the center) must be avoided.

The double-image micrometer has several significant advantages. The small motions of the stellar image, whatever their cause, have no influence on the stability of the pattern. Field illumination is not required, nor is the box screw. Laboratory tests have shown that the alignment of the image for the position angle and the pattern of equidistance for the separation give a representation of these quantities equal to those obtained with a filar micrometer. In measuring diameters, the setting for tangency of two disks is more precise than the setting of a thread tangent to a disk.

The earliest representative of the double-image micrometer was an objective one, the heliometer by Bouguer. It was modified by Dollond and given its definitive form by Fraunhofer (1831). The telescope objective is cut along a diameter, and the two halves slide along this diameter in opposite directions. This gives rise to two images at the focal plane, the separation of which is equal to the displacement of the two objective halves. Originally, as its name implies, the instrument was designed for the measurement of the sun's diameter. As a rule, it is not possible to view the whole solar disk in the field of an eyepiece and simultaneously to place threads tangent to opposite limbs. The heliometer

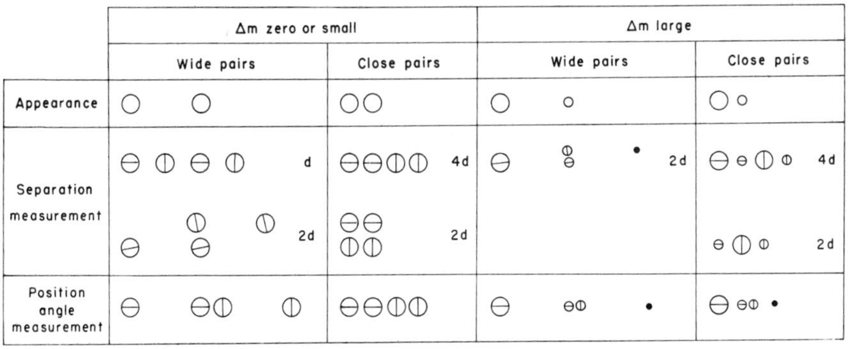

	Δm zero or small			Δm large		
	Wide pairs	Close pairs		Wide pairs	Close pairs	
Appearance	◯　◯	◯◯		◯　○	◯ ○	
Separation measurement	⊖ ① ⊖ ① d	⊖⊖①① 4d	⊖	⊖ • 2d	⊖ ⊖ ① ⓪ 4d	
	① ① 2d ⊖ ⊖	⊖⊖ ①① 2d			⊖ ① ⓪ 2d	
Position angle measurement	⊖ ⊖① ①	⊖⊖①①	⊖	⊖① •	⊖ ⊖① •	

FIG. 6.—Different ways of measuring a double star by the double-image method. The third row (and also the fourth for angle measurement) illustrate the proper procedure for the polarizing micrometer where the images of the components can be made equally bright.

has given many measurements of planetary diameters, some of which are still used in the classical ephemerides. However, relatively few measures of double stars have been made. The high magnification required for double stars emphasizes the aberrations caused by half an objective.

Instead of sacrificing an objective (heliometers have not exceeded 30 cm in aperture), one lens of the eyepiece can be cut in half. The micrometers of Amici (1815) and Airy (1846) were of this type. These instruments had all the advantages of the heliometer, with the addition that the movable parts (the half-lenses) could be moved with greater precision. Furthermore, this micrometer could be adapted to any telescope. The Airy micrometer has been used for numerous double-star measures (Kaiser 1872a, b).

Double-image micrometers also have been designed in which the second image is produced by a system of mirrors or prisms. One such instrument has been described by Steinheil (1848).

A whole family of double-image micrometers has been built around birefringent prisms. Certain types of double refraction prisms can give, with the proper displacement, the desired variations in the relative positions of the two images. Although it is one of the most recent origin, Lyot's micrometer will be described first. It consists of a simple plate of calcite with the crystal axis inclined 45° to the parallel faces. The plate can rotate about an axis perpendicular to the crystal axis and parallel to the faces. When placed immediately in front of the eyepiece, this plate produces two images of excellent quality. The separation can be varied from zero to a computable upper limit, and orientation of the two images is accomplished by rotation of the whole assembly about the axis of the telescope. This micrometer has been successfully used at the Pic-du-Midi principally by its inventor until his premature death in 1952 and by Camichel (1949, 1956).

A much older and almost equally simple instrument has been described by Dollond. Instead of a calcite plate, this crystal micrometer used a rotatable calcite sphere equivalent to a plate in which the crystal axis could be rotated by 360°. This rotation gave an image separation proportional to the sine of twice the angle of rotation. The maximum separation was proportional to the diameter of the calcite sphere. The author has tested such an instrument at the Strasbourg Observatory. The images are excellent and the system easy to use.

The first micrometer with a birefringent prism was invented by Rochon (1783) nearly two centuries ago. The prism used by Rochon now carries his name. It consists of two prisms, made of either quartz or calcite, cemented along their hypotenuses. The two prisms are cut so that light travels along the axis of the first prism and perpendicular to the axis of the second (Fig. 7). A Wollaston prism, a modification of the Rochon, is also given in the figure. When mounted on the axis of a telescope, either prism produces two images, the separation of which is proportional to the distance of the prism from the focal plane. This permits measurements of double stars or small diameters by the double-image method. This instrument had a novel and important characteristic: the image separation varied slowly with the translation of the prism. The reduction factor was from 100 to 200 times. Therefore, a fine precision screw was no longer necessary. The Rochon micrometer had, however, a serious defect in regard to image quality. As the prism was moved away from the focal plane for greater separation, the various aberrations became more objectionable.

In 1937, Muller (1937, 1939, 1949) showed that, since the prism (Wollaston, for example) was in a convergent bundle, the variation in separation of the two stellar images could be achieved by a prism displacement perpendicular to the optical axis (Fig. 8). The prism can therefore be mounted on the movable frame of an ordinary filar micrometer. It is near the focal plane, where aberrations except chromatic will be at a minimum. The screw value is reduced by a large factor (85 for the prism adopted by Muller). To reduce the ill effects of dispersion in the birefringent prism, Muller designed a prism as shown in Figure 7. This prism also gives an image separation proportional to the displacement, with zero near the center of the prism. Micrometers of this design

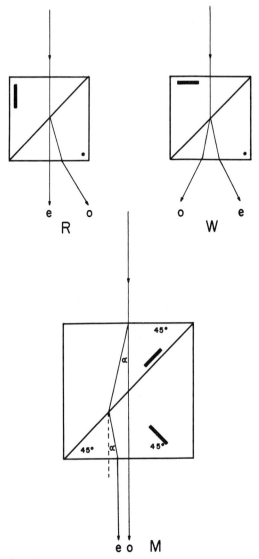

FIG. 7.—Orientation of crystal axes and the optical paths in the Rochon (R), Wollaston (W), and Muller (M) prisms.

give excellent measures of double stars and small diameters. About ten such instruments are in use throughout the world. Modifications are under consideration for extending the instrument to measure larger diameters and for special applications, several of which will now be discussed.

Instantaneous phenomena, such as occultations by the moon and the occultations and transits of Jupiter's satellites, cannot be observed by repeated settings. However, the double-image micrometer provides a means of observing a series of pseudo-phenomena, either before or after the true phenomenon takes place. If the two images are separated in the direction of the moon's motion toward or from a star or of a satellite toward or from a planet, the apparent contact of one image (the ordinary image, for example) of the star and the other image (the extraordinary in the example) of the moon's limb will appear to take place sometime before or after the true contact. If the time of this pseudo-contact is noted, a measure of the distance between the star (or satellite) and the true contact point is obtained at that instant. After the first observation, the image separation may be altered and a second observation made. A simple linear extrapolation then gives the instant of the true phenomenon, even if the true contact is frustrated by poor seeing or haze at the critical moment or if the nature of the phenomenon (emersion, for example) gives the observer no warning.

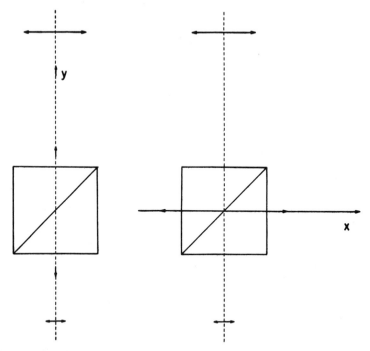

FIG. 8.—Displacement of a birefringent prism in Rochon's telescope (*left*) and in the Muller instrument (*right*).

In the case of Jupiter's satellites, the relative motion is sufficiently slow that the range of the normal double-image micrometer is sufficient to permit observations for several minutes with most telescopes. Even in the smallest telescopes, however, the moon's motion across the background of stars is too rapid for this method to be applicable. Preliminary tests (Muller 1951, 1952*a*) have shown promise, provided that the range of the double-image micrometer is extended and automatic registration is introduced.

The double-image birefringent prism has also been used in stellar photometry. Pickering (1879) designed a polarization photometer in which an analyzer was followed by a Wollaston prism. Since the two emergent beams from the Wollaston are polarized at right angles, a rotation of the analyzer permitted the relative brightness of the two images to be varied. Therefore, for a double star, the ordinary image of one star was made equal to the extraordinary image of the other, and vice versa. The double-image micrometer with the Muller prism can be transformed into a photometer of this type by introducing a rotatable analyzer on a divided circle. The analyzer may be a Polaroid plate sufficiently thin that it can be placed immediately in front of the eyepiece.

For the highest accuracy, it is important that the images to be compared be carefully adjusted for position in the field of view. First, the stars should be placed close together and always at the same separation. Second, the stars should be in a line either parallel or, if necessary, perpendicular to the line joining the eyes. Any skew adjustment should be avoided. Under these conditions, the eye is capable of judging equality to about one-tenth of a magnitude. One systematic error remains that must be eliminated: It is a position error in which either the left or the right image is favored in brightness. This is a variable quantity that may amount to at least one- or two-tenths of a magnitude. But it is easily eliminated by reversing the images.

The double-image micrometer by Muller (1937) converted to a polarizing photometer has two advantages over the original Pickering instrument for observing magnitudes of double stars: first, because of its micrometer characteristics, the stellar images may be accurately placed; and, second, the prism design produces images of higher quality. Muller has measured the difference in magnitude of double stars with separations of only 2 seconds of arc with a 16-cm telescope, $0\rlap{.}''7$ with a 49-cm, and $0\rlap{.}''45$ with the Pic-du-Midi 60-cm telescope. The average mean error is only 0.04 mag. for observations made in one night.

The relative magnitude can also be measured at different effective wave lengths, although the limiting magnitude will be brighter. If the combined color index or that of one component is known, the color indices of the two individual stars can be computed. Such data serve as a substitute for spectral classification. Generally, such information is not available for close pairs.

§ 2. INTERFEROMETERS

The telescopic image of a star is not a point but a small round disk surrounded by alternately dark and bright diffraction rings. The brightness of the latter diminishes rapidly from the center outward. Even for the brighter stars, only two or three bright rings are seen. It is well known, of course, that this phenomenon is a consequence of the wave nature of light. The rays that arrive in the focal plane from opposite ends of a diameter of the objective have a path difference that increases with distance from the central image. This path difference gives rise to a phase difference that produces constructive and destructive interference. It can be shown that, for a complete conical beam, the angular radius of the first dark ring, as seen from the center of the objective, is given by

$$a = 1.22 \, \frac{\lambda}{D} \, (\text{in radians}),$$

where λ is the wave length of the light and D is the free aperture of the objective. By convention, a is defined as the resolving power.

Particular diffraction patterns can be obtained by obscuring different parts of the objective by an opaque screen. The simplest of such screens is obviously one with two openings at the opposite ends of a diameter. Nearly the same effect is obtained, but with a more luminous image, with two parallel slots. The diffraction pattern, obviously much larger because of the greatly reduced free aperture, is then crossed by several interference fringes. On the assumption that the slots are narrow, the fringe space is given by

$$\epsilon = \frac{\lambda}{d},$$

when d is the separation of the two slots. If the source of light is now a close double star and the slots are oriented perpendicular to the line joining the components, the two fringe systems will partially overlap. This superposition will result in a strengthening of the partially overlapping diffraction patterns if the separation of the double star is an integer number of times the fringe spacing. Likewise, the contrast diminishes (or disappears for double stars of equal magnitude) if the separation is equal to an integer plus one-half. Therefore, the separation of the double star can be measured by adjusting the separation of the two slots until a characteristic pattern is recognized.

This, in its simplest form, is the principle of the interferometer. For a given telescope, the theoretical limit of separation $(d = D)$ is given by

$$a' = \frac{\lambda}{2\,D}.$$

When this is compared with the theoretical resolving power of a telescope, it is seen that the theoretical gain in resolution is 2.44.

The interferometer can also be applied to the measurement of small diameters. The theory then leads to somewhat different constants, so that, based on the disappearance of contrast in the fringe pattern, the limit is equal to the visual resolving power. Even so, an advantage is present; for a small disk of diameter a is impossible to measure by ordinary methods. Diameters no smaller than $3a$ or $4a$ are measured with micrometers (Muller 1952b, c, 1953).

2.1. HISTORICAL

Fizeau (1862) was the first to point out the possibilities of using interferometer methods in astronomy. He was followed by Stephan (1874), who observed the fringes of several bright stars in the telescope at Marseilles. An upper limit (0″.15) was assigned to stellar diameters. The first practical application, preceded by an intensive study of the subject, nevertheless falls to Michelson. His name is justly coupled with Fizeau as the originator of the method. In 1890, Michelson (1890a, b, 1891, 1892) obtained reliable determinations for the diameters of Jupiter's Galilean satellites. Somewhat later, Schwarzschild (1896) published a paper that has received only limited attention. In this paper he described an instrument that was essentially an objective grating in two halves. The two halves, placed on the objective like a roof, were adjustable so that the angle at the apex could be changed. The separations of the higher-order images (spectra) formed at the focal plane on either side of the central image of the star were therefore likewise adjustable. In this way, the separation of a double star could be measured. In addition, the grating was rotatable about the telescope axis, so that position angles could be measured. The multiple slots transmitted appreciably more light than the two slots in Michelson's interferometer. However, close double stars could not be measured. Michelson's work was followed by Hamy (1899), who also obtained good measures for the diameters of the Galilean satellites.

In about 1920, Michelson returned to the problem. He succeeded in measuring a few stellar diameters, first at Yerkes Observatory with the 40-inch refractor and later with the Mount Wilson 100-inch reflector. To increase the resolution, Michelson attached movable 45° mirrors on a 6-meter bar mounted on the end of the 100-inch telescope. These mirrors could travel by equal amounts in opposite directions. Starlight reflected from two mirrors was directed toward two other 45° mirrors, which in turn reflected the light toward the primary mirror. A 15-meter bar was later planned, but the instrument was never brought to fruition. Although compensators were provided, it seems that, with an instrument of such dimensions, the required constancy in path difference can no longer be assumed.

Immediately after Michelson's success with stellar diameters, Anderson (1920) used the interferometer method for the measurement of close double stars. The apertures were placed near the focus instead of at the objective. They were set at a fixed distance apart, somewhat greater than the distance for minimum visibility (for Capella), then rotated to determine the four position angles that gave minimum visibility.

The first systematic program for the measurement of double stars was started soon thereafter by Maggini (1925). Since then the method has become general practice by H. M. Jeffers, W. S. Finsen, and R. H. Wilson, Jr. More recently Danjon (1936) has described a half-wave interferometer.

2.2. Types of Instruments

In this section, the properties of two instruments now in regular use will be described. In addition, a discussion of Danjon's (1936) half-wave interferometer will be given. Some modifications that have been proposed will not be discussed here. It will suffice to state that the opaque screen with slots has rarely been abandoned.

2.21. General conditions of measurement.—The opaque screen with two slots has a fundamental defect, since it critically limits the amount of light received by the objective. In general, this loss of light restricts observations to magnitude 7 or brighter. Therefore, a compromise must be made between slot dimensions and loss of sensitivity. The complete theory on slot dimensions has been given by Jones (1922).

The fringe spacing depends, of course, directly on wave length. Therefore, the fringes become increasingly more colored with increasing distance from the achromatic central image. However, this coloration does not prevent critical observations for the maximum and minimum contrast. Atmospheric dispersion produces a short spectrum of the stellar image. The effect of this dispersion depends on the zenith distance and the position angle of the slots. When the slots are horizontal, the central fringe becomes a spectrum, but, unless the star is quite low, the two dispersions counterbalance at another fringe, so that it becomes achromatic. In most cases this compensation is sufficient to permit unhindered measurement. In extreme cases a horizontal prism of variable dispersion can be introduced to provide complete compensation. When the slots are inclined, the fringe space varies along the fringes themselves, so that they diverge toward the red. This effect increases as the vertical position is approached. However, in general, this does not appreciably hinder the measurements.

An important source of error, not yet mentioned, arises from the difference in brightness for the two components of a double star. It is obvious that the variation in the fringe pattern as the interferometer is adjusted must decrease as the magnitude difference increases. The practical limit is much narrower than originally thought. A conservative value is 1 mag. or possibly less.

The color of the observed stars requires precaution in the reductions. In principle, an effective wave length dependent on spectral type should be adopted. For a refractor, the wave length corresponding to the wave length of the minimum focus may be safely assumed.

All observers agree that the interferometer measures are less affected by poor seeing than are all micrometer measures. Although the interferometer has not lowered the practical resolution to the theoretical one, it has given considerably more accurate results than the micrometer in the domain near this limit. Also the technique offers an opportunity for the discovery of new double stars such as has been done by Finsen in his survey at Johannesburg. Of course, this requires even more skill than needed for known pairs.

2.22. *Anderson interferometer of Lick Observatory.*—This instrument was built by Aitken (see Jeffers 1945) following Anderson's design briefly discussed in § 2.1. Except for an interruption for World War II, it has been used regularly by Jeffers since 1939 on the Lick 36-inch refractor. It has a rotatable mounting on which two disks, A and B, are attached. Each disk has four apertures; one is available for direct inspection of the star, and the other three are closed by an opaque screen with double slots of three different separations. The following slots, as projected on the objective, are available: disk A, slot width 125 mm, slot length 245 mm, slot separations 366, 542, and 721 mm; disk B, slot width 180 mm, slot length 245 mm, slot separations 363, 549, and 683 mm. The minimum stellar separations measurable, for an F0 star, are therefore $0''16$, $0''11$, and $0''08$ for either disk. These limits are not much below the separations that can be measured by a micrometer on the 36-inch refractor. However, the interferometer gives greater accuracy for separations less than $0''35$. The limiting magnitude is 7.0, and the difference in magnitude for the pair must be less than 1.5 mag. The effective wave lengths have been determined with the aid of an objective grating and are given in the accompanying table for A0 and M0 stars.

	A0	M0
No filter..............	5730 A	5845 A
Wratten 16.............	5855	5968
Wratten 16+40.........	5638	5738

Since the slots and therefore their separations are fixed, double stars are measured by rotation of a preselected slot pair. When the slots are parallel to the line joining the two components of the double, a pattern for a single star is obtained, that is, maximum contrast, regardless of the difference in magnitude. When the interferometer is rotated, the contrast decreases until that position is reached where the projection of the pair separation on the perpendicular to the slot equals half the fringe space. At this position, there is extinction of contrast if the components are equal or at a minimum if there is a difference in brightness. Upon further rotation, the contrast increases to a secondary maximum, 90° from the first. This repeats itself in the four quadrants, that is, there are two primary maxima, two secondary maxima, and four minima in two pairs. The individual minima in a pair are 180° apart. The position angles of the minima give the position angle of the double star and its separation. However, there would be a 90° ambiguity in the position angle and consequently a choice of two values for the separation if it were not for the observation of the two primary maxima. The use of a free aperture for a direct observation is also valuable for eliminating any doubt about the correct position angle for the pair. When the fringe space is twice the separation of the pair, there are only two maxima, 180° apart, and two minima midway between. For wider pairs, the minima show a characteristic zigzag effect, as the two fringe patterns do not exactly overlap, because the double star is inclined to the fringes. This aspect

Fig. 9.—The eyepiece interferometer of the Union Observatory

is, of course, altered and difficult to observe when the pair has unequal components.

2.23. *Finsen's eyepiece interferometer of the Union Observatory.*—After experiments with an Anderson interferometer, Finsen (1951) designed and constructed an instrument with movable slots. Modifications (Fig. 9) were added later (Finsen 1954). The slots are not in the convergent beam as·in the Lick instrument. The slots are preceded by a collimator and followed by a miniature telescope for the observation of the interference pattern. Either of two screens may be used: one has rectangular slots, and the other has slots with curved edges. The limiting values for the slot constants are 0″087 and 0″143 for the screen with rectangular slots and 0″087 and 0″32 for the other. The interferometer is used on the 26½-inch refractor of the Union Observatory. All the optical parts were fixed in the 1954 modification, leaving only the slots and position angle circle to rotate. This makes centering easier and more stable. At large zenith distances, atmospheric dispersion can be compensated for by a variable-dispersion prism.

There is no need for a lengthy discussion of the measuring technique. It differs from that for the Lick interferometer, since the slots are movable. The separations are measured by varying the fringe space, not by a rotation of the interferometer. Finsen (1954) estimates that the limiting magnitude is about 7.5 for the $26\frac{1}{2}$-inch refractor.

2.24. *Danjon's half-wave interferential micrometer.*—Danjon has described (1936) an interferometer of new design in which the whole objective glass is used. The limiting magnitude for double stars is a function of the separation but is fainter than for the conventional slot interferometer.

Suppose that a path difference of one-half wave length could be introduced in the light coming from opposite halves of a telescope objective. The diffraction image of a point source would then consist of two patterns separated by a dark fringe. The separation depends on the free aperture of the objective. Therefore, a variable diaphragm provides a scale for the measurement of double stars, either by disappearance of the dark fringes or by double images. Small diameters could likewise be measured, for this dark fringe would again disappear for the proper aperture-diameter ratio. Since a compensator equal in size to half the objective is difficult to achieve, a much smaller unit is placed immediately after a collimator near the focal plane. A variable diaphragm is also located in the same bundle (Fig. 10). The diaphragm is a "cat's eye," that is, two square apertures that can slide in opposite directions along one of the diagonals (Fig. 11). The half-beams are separated parallel to one of the sides.

As mentioned above, the limiting magnitude of a double star that can be measured by the disappearance of the dark fringe depends on the separation, for the measurement is done with a variation in the aperture. Danjon (1936) gives the accompanying table for the limiting magnitude (equal components),

Magnitude	Maximum Separation	Aperture (cm)	Magnitude	Maximum Separation	Aperture (cm)
3.0........	4.0	3	8.0.......	0.40	32
4.0........	2.5	5	9.0.......	.25	51
5.0........	1.6	8	10.0.......	.16	81
6.0........	1.0	13	11.0.......	0.10	129
7.0........	0.63	20			

maximum separation, and minimum aperture. Danjon (1936) has given a full analysis of the successive appearance of the diffraction pattern when the aperture is varied near the limit of fringe disappearance. At the critical aperture there is, in reality, a pattern of minimum contrast. This pattern consists of three

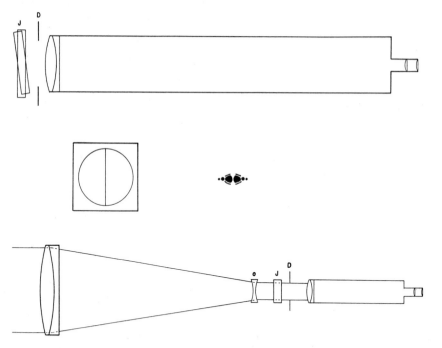

FIG. 10.—Danjon's half-wave interference micrometer. The principle is shown above. *J* is a Jamin compensator and *D* the objective diaphragm. An end-on view is shown in the center, along with the image appearance. The actual mounting is shown at the bottom, where *o* is a negative lens.

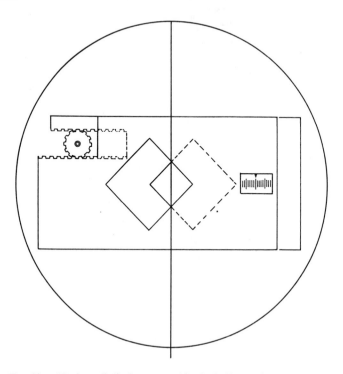

FIG. 11.—"Cat's-eye" diaphragm used in the half-wave interferometer

equal maxima, in which the middle one either rapidly increases or decreases as the aperture is modified. The separation, ρ, of the double star is then given by

$$\rho = 0.770 \frac{\lambda}{D},$$

where D is the aperture of the entrance pupil and λ the effective wave length. If the aperture of the diaphragm is increased from this critical position, two well-separated stellar images are seen. Their separation equals that of the double star when the aperture is about doubled. A square is produced when the compensator is turned with the separation of the aperture perpendicular to the line that joins the two components in the double star. Or the method of equidistant alignment can be used if the separation is doubled once more. The coefficient in the numerator then becomes 1.321 for the square and 2.65 for the alignment. For a given double star, the double-image method has an advantage, in that a larger aperture and hence more light are used.

When small diameters are measured, the dark fringe disappears for

$$d = 1.84 \frac{\lambda}{D}$$

or

$$d = \frac{1.65 \text{ cm}}{\delta}$$

for the Strasbourg installation. Actually, the diameter measurements were made with an experimental instrument that had a circular aperture (Danjon 1933). The constant 1.84 then becomes 1.86, but D is now the diameter instead of the side of the square diaphragm, so that the constant in the second formula becomes 1.17 cm. The double-star measurements, however, were made with a definitive instrument. A first series accompanied the description of the interferometer. A second series was published later (Danjon 1952). The precision is comparable to that of the best double-image measurements.

REFERENCES

AIRY, G. B.	1846	*Mem. R.A.S.*, **15**, 199.
ANDERSON, J. A.	1920	*Ap. J.*, **51**, 263.
AMICI, G. B.	1815	*Mem. mat. e fis. Soc. ital. sci.*, **17**, 344.
AUZOUT, A.	1667	*Traité du micromètre* (Paris).
BECKER, E.	1889	*Handwörterbuch der Astronomie* (Breslau: Maruschke & Berendt), **3**, 64.
BIGOURDAN, G.	1895	*Paris Ann.*, **21**, E1.
CAMICHEL, H.	1949	*J. Obs.*, **32**, 94.
	1956	*Ibid.*, **39**, 198.
DANJON, A.	1933	*C.R.*, **196**, 1720.
	1936	*Ann. Obs. Strasbourg*, **3**, 135.
	1952	*J. Obs.*, **35**, 85.

DAVIDSON, C. R., and
  SYMMS, L. S. T.   1938   *M.N.*, **98**, 176.
DURUY, M.   1938   *J. Obs.*, **21**, 97.
FINSEN, W. S.   1951   *M.N.*, **111**, 387.
     1954   *Union Obs. Circ.*, **114**, 240.
FIZEAU, M.   1862   *C.R.*, **54**, 1237.
FRAUNHOFER, J.   1831   *A.N.*, **8**, 397.
HAMY, M.   1899   *Bull. Astr.*, **16**, 257.
HARGREAVES, F. J.   1932   *M.N.*, **92**, 453.
JEFFERS, H. M.   1945   *Lick Obs. Bull.*, **19**, 175.
JONCKHEERE, R.   1950   *J. Obs.*, **33**, 57.
JONES, H. S.   1922   *M.N.*, **82**, 513.
KAISER, F.   1872*a*   *Ann. Leiden*, **3**, 179.
     1872*b*   *Ibid.*, p. 209.
MAGGINI, M.   1925   *Mem. Soc. astr. ital.*, N.S., **3**, 231.
MICHELSON, A.   1890*a*   *Phil. Mag.*, **30**, 1.
     1890*b*   *Amer. J. Sci.*, **39**, 115.
     1891   *Phil. Mag.*, **31**, 338.
     1892   *Ibid.*, **34**, 280.
MULLER, P.   1937   *C.R.*, **205**, 961.
     1939   *Rev. opt. théor. et instr.*, **18**, 172.
     1949   *Bull Astr.*, 2d ser., **14**, 177, 257.
     1951   *J. Obs.*, **34**, 105.
     1952*a*   *Ibid.*, **35**, 83.
     1952*b*   *C.R.*, **234**, 812.
     1952*c*   *Ann. d'ap.*, **15**, 79.
     1953   *Ann. Obs. Strasbourg*, Vol. **5**, No. 4.
PICKERING, E. C.   1879   *Harvard Ann.*, Vol. **11**.
ROCHON, A. M.   1783   *Recueil de mémoires sur la mécanique et la physique* (Paris).
SCHWARZSCHILD, K.   1896   *A.N.*, **139**, 353.
STEINHEIL, C. A.   1848   *A.N.*, **26**, 133.
STEPHAN, M.   1874   *C.R.*, **78**, 1008.

CHAPTER 20

Astrometry with Astrographs

A. KÖNIG

Sternwarte Königstuhl, Heidelberg

§ 1. INTRODUCTION

THE methods of photographic astrometry have been known in their fundamental aspects for over half a century. In this time further developments have taken place in only a few minor respects. On the one hand, it became necessary to modify procedures to some extent—not so much in the development of the formulae as in the taking and measurement of the plates—when it became possible to construct optical systems that could cover appreciably larger fields than the objectives with only two components used at first. On the other hand, special methods were devised for the case when the position of a single object, such as a minor planet or comet, had to be obtained from a plate.

In the present exposition, both the normal case, when the positions of many objects on the plate have to be obtained, and the special case just mentioned will be treated. Unfortunately, available space does not permit giving the complete derivation of the formulae, for which reference must be made to already existing literature. Unless a special reference is given in the text, these derivations will be found in *Handbuch der Astrophysik 1933*, Volume **1**, chapter 6.

§ 2. TAKING THE PLATES

2.1. OBJECTIVES

The principal condition, which must be satisfied by an objective to be used for the determination of photographic position, is that the image definition be as good as possible and especially that it be uniform within the part of the plate that is used. Otherwise, systematic errors in the resulting positions will be unavoidable. Curvature of the field, astigmatism, and coma should therefore be eliminated as much as possible. Field distortion, on the other hand, is relatively unimportant: if it is small, it is automatically taken care of by the scale factor; if greater, it is not difficult to correct for (Schlesinger *et al.* 1926; König and Heckmann 1928).

For the present purpose, the following types of objectives are to be con-- sidered:

A. *Triple objectives of the Cook-Taylor type.*—The anastigmatic flat field extends $6° \times 6°$; aperture ratio can go to about $1:4$. Distortion, however, cannot be corrected and amounts to about $5''$ at $3°$ from the axis.

B. *Quadruple objectives of the Ross type.*—The field has about the same or greater extent as under A, but the aperture ratio is smaller. Distortion is small, less than $1''$ at $3°$ from the axis.

C. *Quadruple objectives of Zeiss.*—Field extent as under A, and distortion as under B, but the aperture ratio is greater—$1:5$ or even more. So far, no astrometric experience is available for this type, but it should be well adapted for the purpose.

D. *Schmidt reflectors.*—As is well known, astigmatism and coma have been largely eliminated in these optical systems. A difficulty—at least in the case of the "classical" Schmidt—is the curvature of the field, which requires that the plate or film be suitably bent. Good astrometric results are, however, possible, as the curvature is easily allowed for (Dieckvoss 1955).

Types A, B, and C are usually color-corrected for the range of wave length that affects the ordinary blue-sensitive plates. In principle, other spectral regions can also be used by means of suitably sensitized plates in combination with filters, but this may introduce defects in optical homogeneity through the glass of the filter, and the image quality may be destroyed to some extent by going to a different spectral range. It has to be remembered, while reducing such cases, that the refraction depends on wave length. For the Schmidt reflectors, chromatic aberration is negligibly small and has hardly any effect on image quality.

2.2. DETERMINATION OF FOCUS

It is important to determine the best focus setting by putting on the plate a series of exposures of equal duration of the same object, close together, altering the focus setting by equal steps from exposure to exposure. It then becomes easy to select the best setting. This is not constant, but depends on (A) temperature, (B) distance of the stars from the plate center or axis, and (C) the brightness of the stars.

Though the effect of temperature is usually small for the types of objectives here mentioned, it should nevertheless be allowed for. Determination of focus should therefore be made over a range of temperatures. The other two effects are caused by field curvature and spherical aberration. They are always small for well-made objectives. Effect (C) becomes, in practice, important only for the very bright stars, which cannot be accurately measured in any event. One should therefore concentrate on the faint stars and strike a mean between plate center and edge for the best focal setting.

To judge the best setting, double stars of suitable separation may be recommended as test objects. In view of the preceding remarks, it is, however, advisable to select a rich star field. Then one obtains, at the same time, a numerical determination of the curvature of the field and of a possible skewness of the plate with respect to the optical axis.

2.3. EXPOSURE

For astrometric purposes, accurate guiding is of crucial importance. Neglecting this may introduce systematic error, especially magnitude error. Apart from atmospheric unsteadiness and unevenness of the clock drive, accurate guiding is influenced by differential flexure between camera and guiding telescope and by the telescope's lack of precise equatorial adjustment. If, as will usually be the case, differential flexure obeys a sine law in the first approximation, it will make itself felt principally in right ascension. Küstner (1920) has given a simple correcting procedure.

Error of polar adjustment produces an apparent rotation of the field around the guiding star. The effect, therefore, becomes more serious as the field becomes larger and the exposure time longer. In moderate declinations and small hour angles, azimuth error of the instrumental pole dominates. For fields in high declinations, close attention to polar adjustment is necessary (Küstner 1920). Furthermore, it should be remembered that near the pole the slow motion in right ascension no longer suffices; guiding can then be done only by moving the plateholder in a double slide, with an eyepiece affixed at the side.

Furthermore, it is necessary to check that the plates are plane, as it is assumed in the reductions that the representation of the region is projected on a true plane. The larger the field, the greater the error introduced by unevenness of the plate. For a star 3° from the optical axis, a deviation of only 0.1 mm. results in an apparent shift of the image greater than 5μ. The plate material in normal use does not satisfy these requirements; deviations of 0.2 mm. or more occur (see Schlesinger and Barney, 1939).

§ 3. MEASUREMENT OF THE PLATES

3.1. MEASUREMENT IN RECTANGULAR CO-ORDINATES

In the early days of photographic astrometry, a réseau (usually consisting of 5-mm squares) was frequently imprinted on the plate, defining a system of rectangular co-ordinates. Measurement then consisted simply in referring the star images micrometrically to the surrounding réseau lines. The measuring machine was therefore quite simple and measurement more rapid, as only small distances had to be measured. Nowadays this procedure is rarely applied, because réseau errors enter fully into the results, while to correct accurately for them needs lengthy determinations, especially for large fields.

For this reason, measuring machines now in use generally have a measuring device (scale or screw) which covers the entire plate field. Many such machines, especially the older ones, allow accurate measurement of only one co-ordinate at a time, with rough measurement of the other for identification purposes, so that the plate must be turned 90° for the measurement of the other co-ordinate. Newer machines, such as that of Zeiss, permit simultaneous measurement of both co-ordinates (König 1932).

To obtain great accuracy, it is necessary to measure each co-ordinate in two positions of the plate, differing by 180°, so as to eliminate systematic errors of a physiological nature, especially the magnitude equation. In addition, this gives information on the accuracy of the measurement through the differences between the two orientations. This, with careful measurement in a good machine, depends in practice on the quality of the object to be measured. Experience shows that, in favorable circumstances, a mean error a little below 1μ may be obtained for the mean of the two orientations (König 1932) (see § 4.5).

3.2. Measurement in Other Co-ordinate Systems

If the measuring machine is provided with a position circle, it is possible in principle to measure position angles and distances, but this procedure is of little importance for the purposes here discussed, except under special circumstances.

Of practical application has been a measuring machine introduced by Kapteyn (1892). It is essentially a small equatorial, so constructed that the hour, declination, and telescope axes meet in one point. This point is put in the perpendicular to the plate at the tangent point (see § 4.2), at a distance equal to the focal length of the telescope with which the plate was taken. If the plate has been correctly oriented, differences of right ascension and declination are read directly on the circles of the equatorial measuring machine. As correct adjustment causes some trouble in practice, this procedure has been of limited application, in spite of its theoretical elegance, but it is, nevertheless, sometimes used for the determination of positions of minor planets and comets (see van Biesbroeck 1955).

§ 4. REDUCTION

4.1. Introductory Remarks

It is assumed that rectangular co-ordinates of a number of objects on the plate, corrected for errors of the measuring machine if necessary, have been obtained. It is obvious that such results give information only on the relative positions of these objects: a relation to the usual spherical co-ordinates a and δ can be derived from the known data on plate exposure only as a very rough approximation. To obtain this relation in accurate form, it is necessary to know a and δ for a certain number of the stars measured on the plate, the so-called reference stars. The positions to be determined for the other objects are therefore based on the known spherical co-ordinates of the reference stars. In the following the methods of doing this will be given.

4.2. Tangential Co-ordinates

4.21. DEFINITION

The picture of a portion of the celestial sphere, made on a photographic plate by an objective free from errors, may be mathematically described as the central projection from the center of the sphere on a tangent plane. This at once suggests the introduction of rectangular co-ordinates in this plane which will be called "tangential co-ordinates."

In the absence of a statement to the contrary, a tangential co-ordinate system[1] will henceforth be defined thus:

A. The co-ordinate system lies in a plane tangent to the celestial sphere, the tangent point T being the origin of the co-ordinates.

B. The axis of Y is tangent to the declination circle through T, positive in the direction in which the distance of T from the north celestial pole is $<180°$.

C. The axis of X is perpendicular to the axis of Y and positive in the direction of increasing right ascension.

D. The unit of length is the radius of the sphere (in practice, the focal length of the objective with which the plate has been taken).

[1] In the literature other designations ("standard co-ordinates," "ideal co-ordinates") are frequently used, but here we restrict ourselves to the designation "tangential co-ordinates," as a reminder of their definition and to stress the difference from measured co-ordinates.

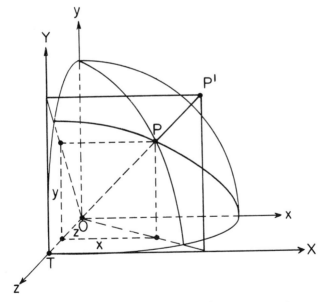

Fig. 1.—Definition of the tangential co-ordinates. P' is the image point of P arising by central projection from O. Relationship of the spatial co-ordinate system $Oxyz$ and the tangential co-ordinate system TXY.

E. The tangential co-ordinates X and Y of a point P on the celestial sphere are the rectangular co-ordinates, in the system here defined, of the point P', the central projection of P on the tangent plane from the center of the sphere (Fig. 1).

The radius of the sphere has been chosen as the unit of length, because the formulae then assume their simplest form. In practice, another unit, e.g., the second of arc, is, of course, preferable. One should therefore remember to add the conversion factor to the formulae in numerical applications.

4.22. RELATIONS BETWEEN TWO TANGENTIAL CO-ORDINATE SYSTEMS

Let a three-dimensional rectangular co-ordinate system x, y, z be adjoined to the tangential system X, Y, as shown in Figure 1. Then the relations

$$X = \frac{x}{z}, \qquad Y = \frac{y}{z}, \tag{1}$$

are immediately obvious from Figure 1.

Now, if X', Y', and x', y', z' are the co-ordinates of P in a second tangential system and its adjoined spatial system, then we have

$$X' = \frac{x'}{z'}, \qquad Y' = \frac{y'}{z'}. \tag{1'}$$

The systems x, y, z and x', y', z' have the same origin—the center of the sphere—so that their relative orientation is uniquely defined by the direction cosines. Let $\langle xx' \rangle$ represent the cosine of the angle between the axes of x and x', etc.; then we have the equations

$$x' = \langle xx' \rangle x + \langle yx' \rangle y + \langle zx' \rangle z \, ,$$
$$y' = \langle xy' \rangle x + \langle yy' \rangle y + \langle zy' \rangle z \, , \tag{2}$$
$$z' = \langle xz' \rangle x + \langle yz' \rangle y + \langle zz' \rangle z \, ;$$

$$x = \langle xx' \rangle x' + \langle xy' \rangle y' + \langle xz' \rangle z' \, ,$$
$$y = \langle yx' \rangle x' + \langle yy' \rangle y' + \langle yz' \rangle z' \, , \tag{2'}$$
$$z = \langle zx' \rangle x' + \langle zy' \rangle y' + \langle zz' \rangle z' \, .$$

Dividing in equations (2) and (2') the first two equations by the third, we find, from equations (1) and (1'),

$$X' = \frac{\langle xx' \rangle X + \langle yx' \rangle Y + \langle zx' \rangle}{\langle xz' \rangle X + \langle yz' \rangle Y + \langle zz' \rangle},$$
$$Y' = \frac{\langle xy' \rangle X + \langle yy' \rangle Y + \langle zy' \rangle}{\langle xz' \rangle X + \langle yz' \rangle Y + \langle zz' \rangle}; \tag{3}$$

$$X = \frac{\langle xx' \rangle X' + \langle xy' \rangle Y' + \langle xz' \rangle}{\langle zx' \rangle X' + \langle zy' \rangle Y' + \langle zz' \rangle},$$

$$(3')$$

$$Y = \frac{\langle yx' \rangle X' + \langle yy' \rangle Y' + \langle yz' \rangle}{\langle zx' \rangle X' + \langle zy' \rangle Y' + \langle zz' \rangle}.$$

Equations (3) and (3') are valid in the general case, independently of conditions B and C above. If we now assume these conditions to be satisfied and the relative situation of the two systems to be given by the declinations δ_0 and δ'_0 and the difference in right ascension Δa of the two tangential points, the direction cosines in equations (3) and (3') are found—after some simple, though somewhat lengthy, arithmetic—to be given by the formulae in schedule (4).

	x	y	z
$x'\ldots$	$\cos \Delta a$	$\sin \delta_0 \sin \Delta a$	$-\cos \delta_0 \sin \Delta a$
$y'\ldots$	$-\sin \delta'_0 \sin \Delta a$	$\cos \delta_0 \cos \delta'_0 +$ $\sin \delta_0 \sin \delta'_0 \cos \Delta a$	$\sin \delta_0 \cos \delta'_0 -$ $\cos \delta_0 \sin \delta'_0 \cos \Delta a$ (4)
$z'\ldots$	$\cos \delta'_0 \sin \Delta a$	$\cos \delta_0 \sin \delta'_0 -$ $\sin \delta_0 \cos \delta'_0 \cos \Delta a$	$\sin \delta_0 \sin \delta'_0 +$ $\cos \delta_0 \cos \delta'_0 \cos \Delta a$

If the relative situation is defined by the spherical distance s of T and T' and the position angles P and P' which the great circle through T and T' forms at these points, then the equations in schedule (5) follow.

	x	y	z
$x'\ldots$	$\cos P \cos P' +$ $\sin P \sin P' \cos s$	$-\sin P \cos P' +$ $\cos P \sin P' \cos s$	$-\sin P' \sin s$
$y'\ldots$	$-\cos P \sin P' +$ $\sin P \cos P' \cos s$	$\sin P \sin P' +$ $\cos P \cos P' \cos s$	$-\cos P' \sin s$ (5)
$z'\ldots$	$\sin P \sin s$	$\cos P \sin s$	$\cos s$

Formulae (3) and (3'), together with schedules (4) and (5), transform a tangential co-ordinate system to a different tangent point. In practice, equations (3) and (3') are required when several plates must be taken to cover a portion of the sky larger than the field of a single plate (Dieckvoss 1954). Furthermore, they can be used to advantage for several developments of formulae.

Schedule (5) leads to an important transformation of equations (3) if the tangent points are so close together that s^2 can be neglected. Putting $P' - P = \Delta P$, we have

$$\langle xx' \rangle = \cos \Delta P, \quad \langle xy' \rangle = -\sin \Delta P, \quad \langle zz' \rangle = 1,$$

$$\langle yx' \rangle = \sin \Delta P, \quad \langle yy' \rangle = \cos \Delta P.$$

If we also put

$$\langle xz'\rangle = \sin s \sin P = m, \quad \langle yz'\rangle = \sin s \cos P = n,$$

we find, from the familiar relations between direction cosines,

$$\langle zx'\rangle = -m \cos \Delta P - n \sin \Delta P,$$
$$\langle zy'\rangle = m \sin \Delta P - n \cos \Delta P,$$

and equations (3) become

$$X' = \frac{(X-m)\cos \Delta P + (Y-n)\sin \Delta P}{1+mX+nY},$$

$$Y' = \frac{-(X-m)\sin \Delta P + (Y-n)\cos \Delta P}{1+mX+nY}.$$

Under the above assumption about s, m and n are also so small that their squares and products may be neglected. This applies also to ΔP, if high declinations are excluded. So we may put

$$\cos \Delta P = 1, \quad m \cos \Delta P = m, \quad n \cos \Delta P = n,$$
$$\sin \Delta P = \Delta P, \quad m \sin \Delta P = 0, \quad n \sin \Delta P = 0,$$

and

$$\frac{1}{1+mX+nY} = 1 - (mX+nY).$$

The above equations simplify to

$$X' = X - m + Y\Delta P - (mX+nY)X,$$
$$Y' = Y - n - X\Delta P - (mX+nY)Y. \tag{6}$$

The transfer from a tangential co-ordinate system to another with nearby tangent point therefore results in a shift of the origin by the amounts m and n, a rotation over ΔP, and a small change in the unit of length, which, however, depends on the co-ordinates. As is easily seen, the origin of the X' Y' system has the co-ordinates m and n in the XY system (neglecting higher terms).

4.23. TRANSFORMATION OF TANGENTIAL CO-ORDINATES TO α, δ AND VICE VERSA

4.231. *The rigorous formulae.*—Let α and δ be the right ascension and declination of a star, X and Y its tangential co-ordinates, and α_0 and δ_0 the right ascension and declination of the tangent point T. The required transformation formulae are easily obtained by introducing a second tangential co-ordinate system X', Y', with the north celestial pole as tangent point.

The orientation defined under § 4.21 here loses its meaning; we therefore specify that the X'-axis shall be parallel and in the same direction as the X-axis and that the Y'-axis shall be taken so that T has a negative value of Y'. Figure 2 shows the situation in the X' Y'-plane: P is the pole, T' and S' the central projections of the tangent point T and the star S. Let the star's co-ordinates be X', Y' and put $a - a_0 = \Delta a$; then the figure shows that

$$X' = \cot \delta \sin \Delta a , \quad Y' = -\cot \delta \cos \Delta a . \tag{7}$$

The relation between X', Y' and X, Y is given by equations (3) and (3'). The direction cosines are easily read from Figure 3, which shows the adjoined three-dimensional co-ordinates, except that the x- and x'-axes are not shown,

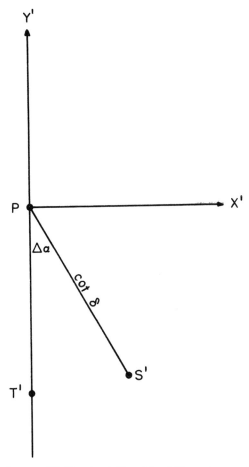

Fig. 2.—Relation between X', Y' and a, δ. Here T' and S' are the central projections of the tangent point and the star, respectively, from the center of the sphere on $X'Y'$, the tangent plane at the celestial pole.

as they coincide and are perpendicular to the plane of the figure at the central point. We get the accompanying schedule:

	x	y	z
x'..........	1	0	0
y'..........	0	$\sin \delta_0$	$-\cos \delta_0$
z'..........	0	$\cos \delta_0$	$\sin \delta_0$

so that equations (3) and (3') take the form

$$X' = \frac{X}{Y \, \cos \delta_0 + \sin \delta_0},$$

$$Y' = \frac{Y \, \sin \delta_0 - \cos \delta_0}{Y \, \cos \delta_0 + \sin \delta_0};$$

(8)

$$X = \frac{X'}{\sin \delta_0 - Y' \, \cos \delta_0},$$

$$Y = \frac{\cos \delta_0 + Y' \, \sin \delta_0}{\sin \delta_0 - Y' \, \cos \delta_0}.$$

(8')

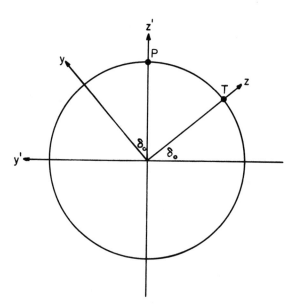

Fig. 3.—For the derivation of the directive cosines for the transformation from X, Y to X', Y' and conversely. P = celestial pole, T = tangent point. The coincident x- and x'-axes are perpendicular to the plane of the figure.

Substituting equations (7) in equations (8'), we obtain the required formulae for transforming a, δ into X, Y:

$$X = \frac{\cos \delta \sin \Delta a}{\sin \delta \sin \delta_0 + \cos \delta \cos \delta_0 \cos \Delta a} ,$$

$$Y = \frac{\sin \delta \cos \delta_0 - \cos \delta \sin \delta_0 \cos \Delta a}{\sin \delta \sin \delta_0 + \cos \delta \cos \delta_0 \cos \Delta a} .$$

$$(9)$$

Substituting equations (7) in equations (8), we obtain

$$\cot \delta \sin \Delta a = \frac{X}{\sin \delta_0 + Y \cos \delta_0} ,$$

$$\cot \delta \cos \Delta a = \frac{\cos \delta_0 - Y \sin \delta_0}{\sin \delta_0 + Y \cos \delta_0} ,$$

$$(10)$$

from which

$$\tan \Delta a = \frac{X}{\cos \delta_0 - Y \sin \delta_0} ,$$

$$\tan \delta = \frac{\sin \delta_0 + Y \cos \delta_0}{\cos \delta_0 - Y \sin \delta_0} \cos \Delta a .$$

$$(9')$$

For many purposes we require a formula for δ which does not contain Δa. Squaring and adding equations (10) and remembering that

$$\sin \delta = 1/\sqrt{(1 + \cot^2 \delta)},$$

we get

$$\sin \delta = \frac{\sin \delta_0 + Y \cos \delta_0}{\sqrt{(1 + X^2 + Y^2)}} .$$

$$(11)$$

4.232. *Numerical treatment.*—For numerical treatment the often used formulae (9) and (9') need a transformation, not only to simplify the computation, but also because X and Y are expressed in units of the radius, whereas in practice another unit, such as the second of arc, is preferred. Only a small selection of the numerous methods and auxiliary tables given by different authors for different purposes can be given here (see references at end of chapter). The transformation of the formulae can proceed in two ways: by the introduction of auxiliary quantities and by development in series.

Putting $Y = \tan q$ and $\delta_0 + q = d$, equations (9') give

$$\tan \Delta a = X \sec d \cos q, \qquad \tan \delta = \tan d \cos \Delta a . \qquad (12')$$

The same formulae can be used for the converse transformation by putting them in the form

$$\tan d = \tan \delta \sec \Delta a , \qquad q = d - \delta_0 ,$$

$$X = \tan \Delta a \cos d \sec q , \qquad Y = \tan q .$$

$$(12)$$

This transformation goes back to the days when computations of this nature were nearly always performed by logarithms. The equations are, however, also adapted to the computing machine, if one uses suitable auxiliary tables (König 1933, Appendix 1).

The quantity $d - \delta$ is always small, even in high declinations. Formulae to compute $d - \delta$ directly would therefore be still more convenient. Such formulae, as well as elaborate auxiliary tables for the transformation, have been given by Peters (1929). These tables were mainly intended, and are entirely satisfactory for use if a large number of such transformations is to be made. For a small number, it may be more convenient to proceed as follows: From the first and last equation of equations (12) and (12') we may derive δ from d or vice versa by a development into series familiar in spherical astronomy (Brünnow 1880). We find

$$d = \delta + \tan^2 \frac{\Delta a}{2} \sin 2d + \tfrac{1}{2} \tan^4 \frac{\Delta a}{2} \sin 4d + \dots,$$

$$q = d - \delta_0 ,$$

$$X = \tan \Delta a \cos d \sec q ,$$

$$Y = \tan q ,$$

and

$$\tan q = Y ,$$

$$d = \delta_0 + q ,$$

$$\tan \Delta a = X \sec d \cos q ,$$

(13)

(13')

$$\delta = d - \tan^2 \frac{\Delta a}{2} \sin 2d + \tfrac{1}{2} \tan^4 \frac{\Delta a}{2} \sin 4d - \dots .$$

The terms of higher order in the series remain under $0''.01$ if $\Delta a < 30^m$ The series may therefore be used, for a $6° \times 6°$ field, up to declinations of $65°$ (König 1933, Appendix 1). We should also mention here the formulae and tables given by Vick, Dieckvoss, and Cox (see Schorr 1924, 1934, 1935), which are very convenient and of general application.

If we put $\Delta \delta = \delta - \delta_0$, we may express X and Y directly by a series in Δa and $\Delta \delta$ and vice versa by equations (9), (9'), and (11):

$$X = \Delta a \cos \delta_0 - \Delta a \Delta \delta \sin \delta_0 + \tfrac{1}{6} (\Delta a)^3 \cos \delta_0 (3 \cos^2 \delta_0 - 1) + \dots,$$

$$Y = \Delta \delta + \tfrac{1}{2} (\Delta a)^2 \sin \delta_0 \cos \delta_0 + \tfrac{1}{2} (\Delta a)^2 \Delta \delta \cos 2\delta_0 + \tfrac{1}{3} (\Delta \delta)^3 + \dots;$$

(14)

$$\Delta a = X \sec \delta_0 + X Y \sec \delta_0 \tan \delta_0 - \tfrac{1}{3} X^3 \sec^3 \delta_0$$

$$+ X Y^2 \sec \delta_0 \tan^2 \delta_0 + \dots, \quad (14')$$

$$\Delta \delta = Y - \tfrac{1}{2} X^2 \tan \delta_0 - \tfrac{1}{2} X^2 Y \sec^2 \delta_0 - \tfrac{1}{3} Y^3 + \dots .$$

It is to be noted that the coefficients in these series depend only on δ_0. They are therefore constant for the same tangent point, or even for different tangent points having the same declination, which is, of course, very advantageous in practical applications. Nevertheless, formulae (14) and (14') are of limited value for our purposes, mainly because, for accurate results in a large field, the higher orders cannot be neglected, even in moderate declinations. They are, however, useful for approximate computations, such as identification (König 1933, Appendix 1). Another form of the series will be given in § 5.

4.3. Corrections To Be Applied

4.31. General Remarks

The aim of the reduction is the derivation of the spherical co-ordinates α, δ of the objects measured on the plate. As a rule (for exceptions, see § 5.2), this aim is achieved in two steps. To begin with, the measured co-ordinates x, y are transformed into tangential X, Y; then these again into α, δ. This second step has already been dealt with under § 4.2, so only the first remains. In practice, it is always possible to make the system x, y a close approximation to X, Y and to express it approximately in the desired unit, such as the second of arc. Then only small corrections will be needed. These corrections may be divided into two groups: "instrumental" corrections,[2] depending on the state of the telescope while taking the plate, namely, scale, orientation, zero point, plate skewness, and "spherical" corrections, due to astronomical causes, namely, refraction, aberration, precession, and nutation.

For the second group, formulae can be given, from which they can be computed with all required accuracy, simply on the basis of the known exposure data (time, hour angle, etc.). For the first group, on the contrary, at least some of the coefficients have to be determined empirically, and this is done by means of the known positions of the reference stars.

4.32. Instrumental Corrections

4.321. *Scale, orientation, zero point.*—The scale and orientation of the tangential co-ordinates are fixed by their definition. The system of the measured co-ordinates, on the contrary, is dependent on the measuring machine and the accidental orientation of the photographic plate in it. Consequently, the two systems will differ, as to both scale and orientation. Furthermore, the measured co-ordinates will always require a zero-point correction because the position of the tangent point on the plate is never known to the accuracy required of the star positions that must be found. One therefore adopts as the "computational" tangent point that point on the plate which has exactly the right ascension α_0 and declination δ_0 already assumed (§ 4.4). The relations between the

---

[2] It should be emphasized that these do not include corrections for eventual errors of the measuring machine; it is assumed (see § 4.1) that these have already been applied.

tangential co-ordinates X, Y and the measured co-ordinates x, y then are of the form

$$X = (1 + A)x + By + C,$$
$$Y = -Bx + (1 + A)y + D,$$

or, putting $X - x = \Delta x$, $Y - y = \Delta y$,

$$\Delta x = Ax + By + C,$$
$$\Delta y = -Bx + Ay + D. \tag{15}$$

As x, y approximate to X, Y, the coefficients A, B, C, and D, which are called the "plate constants," are always small. This not only is of importance from a computational point of view but is fundamental to the application of all correction formulae. For the determination of the plate constants see § 4.4.

The meaning of equations (15) is that the measured co-ordinates require a linear orthogonal transformation, whose coefficients are to be determined empirically. If, therefore, the measured co-ordinates were falsified by any cause whatsoever, whose effects could be represented by formulae of form (15), the errors would be eliminated automatically by the adjustment to the reference stars and could not influence the final result. From this we draw the important conclusion that, in the reductions of a plate, any correction that can be represented by a linear orthogonal transformation may be omitted.

4.322. *Plate skewness.*—As has already been said, a "computational" tangent point has been substituted for the true one; it follows from the definition of the tangential co-ordinates that this is theoretically not admissible. Nevertheless, this does not give rise to appreciable errors if both points are sufficiently close together. We therefore need a formula which enables us to compute the effect of the error we have committed on the co-ordinates. In principle, this is already given by equations (6).[3] It is easily seen that the measured co-ordinates require the corrections

$$\Delta x = (px + qy)x, \quad \Delta y = (px + qy)y, \tag{16}$$

where p and q are the co-ordinates of the true referred to the computational tangent point. As equations (6) are valid for tangential co-ordinates, we have once more made the assumption that the measured co-ordinates x, y differ only little from the tangential X, Y and may be substituted for them for the purpose of computing the small corrections Δx and Δy. It is emphasized again that this assumption is made in all correction formulae.

The error represented by equations (16) will be called "plate skewness,"

---

[3] The terms $X \Delta P$ and $Y \Delta P$ may be omitted, as they represent only a change in orientation.

because an imaginary plate whose true tangent point coincides with our assumed computational point is inclined to the actual plate. This shows, at the same time, that we have here something different from the zero-point error, mentioned earlier, though in the literature the two are sometimes combined under this name.

The error resulting from plate skewness is quadratic in the co-ordinates; hence it increases greatly for large fields. In the accompanying table, the maxi-

FIELD	p			
	10″	20″	40″	60″
1°× 1°....	0″.001	0″.002	0″.003	0″.005
2°× 2°....	.003	.006	.012	.018
5°× 5°....	.02	.04	.08	.11
10°×10°....	0.08	0.15	0.30	0.46

mum error for different sizes of field and different values of p is shown, with the simplifying assumption $q = 0$. One sees that for large fields the position of the tangent point on the plate must be known to an accuracy that is not easy to achieve in practice.

The oldest method of determining the tangent point is due to Olsson (1898). This procedure is based on the consideration that the tangent point is practically given by a perpendicular to the plate through the center of the objective. The very simple means used by Olsson give sufficient accuracy only for fields up to about 2° × 2°. Schlesinger and Barney (1925) and Küstner (see König and Heckmann 1928) have refined the method, using mechanical and optical devices and providing adequate accuracy for fields of 5° × 5° and more.

Another method consists in determining p and q from plates specially arranged for the purpose (König and Heckmann 1928; König 1933). The procedure is, of course, unsuitable for the determination of the position of the tangent point on a single plate but is of value as a check on other determinations. Finally, p and q may be derived from the positions of the reference stars (see under § 4.4).

4.33. SPHERICAL CORRECTIONS

4.331. *Refraction.*—As is well known, the refraction may be given as a function either of the apparent zenith distance z or of the true ζ. For astrophotographic purposes, one prefers the latter and puts

$$\Delta z = \beta \tan \zeta , \qquad (17)$$

where Δz is the total refraction in zenith distance and β is the coefficient of photographic refraction. This coefficient is weakly dependent on the zenith distance and also on the state of the atmosphere (temperature, pressure).

Furthermore, investigations by Henry (1892) and Wilsing (1898) have shown that the photographic refraction is obtained from the visual by multiplication by a constant factor κ, which is found to be 1.0155 as the mean of the two investigations. A photographic refraction table is therefore easily derived from the known tables of visual refraction; it gives β with argument ζ and corrections for temperature and pressure (De Ball 1906; König 1929, 1933; Schorr 1934).

For large zenith distances, allowance has to be made for the variation of β within the field of the plate; in practice, it always suffices to put

$$\beta = \beta_0 + \beta' \tan^2\zeta , \tag{18}$$

where β_0 and β' are constants. The neglected terms of higher order remain below $0\rlap{.}''1$ for a field of $6° \times 6°$ and $\zeta = 70°$ (König 1933).

The derivation of the formulae to correct for refraction has already been the subject of numerous publications, and various ways have been explored. The reader is referred to Vick (1934) for references to papers published before 1934. The simplest method seems to be one applied first by Turner (1893, 1897) and later by Heckmann (1932), which may be described thus:

A. One starts from the apparent tangential co-ordinates and the apparent tangent point but, deviating from the usual definition, orients them so that the axis of ordinates points to the zenith. These co-ordinates are then transformed to the zenith as the tangent point.

B. In this system, correction for refraction becomes simple, because the refraction now has symmetry with respect to the tangent point.

C. The corrected co-ordinates are transformed back to the true tangent point, and the normal orientation toward the celestial pole is restored by rotation round the tangent point.

The data are the apparent, normally oriented tangential co-ordinates and the true position of the tangent point, i.e., declination and hour angle as given by the record of exposure. To be found are the corrections for refraction Δx, Δy which are to be applied to the apparent co-ordinates. The mathematical relations between the data and the required corrections are extremely complicated. For practical application, only development into series can be considered; it is therefore necessary to state which terms must be retained and which can be neglected.

In the following formulae only terms of order βK, βK^2, βK^3, and $\beta' K$ are retained, where K quite generally signifies a co-ordinate. It is advisable, in order to obtain the simplest possible expressions for the coefficients of the series, to introduce the following auxiliary quantities:

$$\begin{aligned} k_1 &= \tan \zeta \sin \chi , \quad k_3 = 1 + k_1^2 , \\ k_2 &= \tan \zeta \cos \chi , \quad k_4 = 1 + k_2^2 , \end{aligned} \tag{19}$$

where χ is the true parallactic angle at the tangent point and ζ its true zenith distance; k_1 and k_2 have a simple geometrical meaning: they are the tangential co-ordinates of the zenith in the plane of the plate.[4]

The correction formulae for refraction, then, are

$$\Delta x = 2[\beta + 2\beta'(1 + k_1^2 + k_2^2)]k_1 k_2 y - \beta k_1 k_3 x^2$$
$$-2\beta k_1^2 k_2 xy - \beta k_1 k_4 y^2 + \beta k_3^2 x^3$$
$$+3\beta k_1 k_2 k_3 x^2 y + \beta(k_3 k_4 + 2k_1^2 k_2^2)xy^2$$
$$+\beta k_1 k_2 k_4 y^3 ,$$

$$(20)$$

$$\Delta y = [\beta + 2\beta'(1 + k_1^2 + k_2^2)](k_2^2 - k_1^2)\, y - \beta k_2 k_3 x^2$$
$$-2\beta k_1 k_2^2 xy - \beta k_2 k_4 y^2 + \beta k_1 k_2 k_3 x^3$$
$$+\beta(k_3 k_4 + 2k_1^2 k_2^2)x^2 y + 3\beta k_1 k_2 k_4 xy^2$$
$$+\beta k_4^2 y^3 .$$

It must be stated that, proceeding in the way indicated, one first obtains formulae which contain in each co-ordinate two terms linear in x, y with β and β'. These terms do not have the form of formulae (15), i.e., they are not orthogonal and may not therefore be simply omitted. An orthogonal part can, however, be split off and neglected. In equations (20) this has already been done, and there remains in each co-ordinate only one linear term, the residual refraction (Pingsdorf 1909; König 1933), which can also sometimes be neglected (see § 4.42). The terms retained in equations (20) are in general sufficient, even for a large field.[5] Cases may, however, occur where terms of higher order cannot be neglected. It should be noted that the derivation of the formulae is based on a certain assumption about the tangent point, to which the co-ordinates are finally referred, and their orientation. This assumption is not the only possible one; it also matters which equinox is used in the reduction (see § 4.41). For the terms contained in equations (20) it makes no difference what assumption one makes, but this is not so for terms of higher order. This fact has caused differences in the results of various authors. Vick (1934) has clarified the rather involved situation in this respect. Terms of higher order can be taken from this publication, if they should be needed.

For the numerical computation one needs to find the auxiliaries k_1 and k_2, which give at once k_3 and k_4, also ζ, to enter the refraction table. A

[4] For this reason several authors use the letters X and Y. The designations here used, as well as the introduction of k_3 and k_4, which causes an additional simplification, are due to Zurhellen (1904).

[5] A table showing the amounts which the principal terms may reach in various cases is given in König (1933, p. 531).

very useful procedure has already been given by Bessel (1841). If t_0 and δ_0 represent hour angle and declination of the true tangent point (as supplied by the exposure data) and ϕ the altitude of the pole, then we define two auxiliaries n and N by

$$\sin n \cos N = \sin \phi ,$$

$$\sin n \sin N = \cos \phi \cos t_0 , \qquad (21)$$

$$\cos n = \cos \phi \sin t_0 ;$$

and the spherical triangle pole-zenith-tangent point gives

$$k_1 = \frac{\cot n}{\sin (N + \delta_0)} ,$$

$$k_2 = \cot (N + \delta_0), \qquad (22)$$

$$\cos \zeta = \sin n \sin (N + \delta_0).$$

As β changes only very slowly with ζ, this is always determined with sufficient precision by its cosine. Formulae (22) are the most convenient if one has available a so-called parallactic table for the latitude in question, from which one can take directly, with argument t_0, the quantities N, $\cot n$, and $\sin n$.[6] Then one obtains β, if necessary allowing for temperature and pressure, from a refraction table (De Ball 1906; König 1929, 1933; Schorr 1934) and puts $\beta' = -0.082$. This completes our knowledge of the quantities required in formulae (20). More than four decimals are practically never required; usually three suffice (slide rule or graph).

If many plates have to be reduced for a certain latitude, it pays to compute special tables, giving, with arguments t_0 and δ_0, the coefficients of the separate terms in formulae (20) (Küstner 1920). Plates taken in very high declinations, of course, require special treatment (König 1934; Vick 1934).

It remains to be decided for which moment of the exposure time the refraction should be computed, for it is doubtful whether the obvious procedure of taking simply the middle of the exposure suffices in case of long exposures.

[6] If the table should give N and $\cot n$, but not $\sin n$, one finds ζ from

$$\cos \zeta = \frac{\sin \phi}{\cos N} \sin (N + \delta_0)$$

or

$$\tan \chi = \frac{k_1}{k_2}, \qquad \tan \zeta = \frac{k_1}{\sin \chi} = \frac{k_2}{\cos \chi} .$$

If no table at all is available, the following formulae are recommended:

$$\tan N = \cot \phi \cos t_0 ,$$

$$k_1 = \frac{\tan t_0 \sin N}{\sin (N + d_0)}, \qquad k_2 = \cot (N + \delta_0),$$

ζ as before.

Zurhellen (1909) has gone into this question and comes to the conclusion that it is best to take a mean of the constants computed for the beginning, middle, and end of the exposure, giving double weight to the middle.

4.332. *Aberration.*—If s be the distance of a star from the apex of the earth's motion and k the aberration constant, then the total amount Δs of the aberration is given by

$$\Delta s = k \sin s . \qquad (23)$$

The law of aberration closely resembles that of refraction. To derive the aberration formulae, one may therefore to a large extent use the developments which led to the refraction formulae; naturally, the apex takes the place of the zenith. As the law of aberration contains the sine instead of the tangent and as, moreover, k is only about one-third of β, the terms of the aberration formulae are considerably smaller than those of the refraction formulae. Therefore, it seems justified to neglect terms of the third order.[7]

The derivation shows that the linear terms in x and y are orthogonal and consequently not required; furthermore, terms corresponding to those in β' in the refraction cannot appear, as k is constant. Only the quadratic terms in x and y remain.

Here, also, it is advisable to introduce auxiliaries for simplification, defined by

$$R = h \sin (H + a_0) , \quad S = h \cos (H + a_0) \sin \delta_0 + i \cos \delta_0 , \qquad (24)$$

where a_0 and δ_0 are the right ascension and declination of the true tangent point and h, H, and i are the well-known independent day numbers of the almanacs.

If the corrections to the co-ordinates to be found are called Δx and Δy, the formulae are

$$\Delta x = S x y + \tfrac{1}{2} R (x^2 - y^2), \quad \Delta y = R x y - \tfrac{1}{2} S (x^2 - y^2). \qquad (25)$$

As in the case of refraction, it should be remembered that equations (25) are valid only under a special assumption about the co-ordinate system. If this assumption is not satisfied, the formulae are modified, but the deviation is very small (Vick 1934), so that even for a field of $10° \times 10°$ it becomes noticeable only in declinations above $70°$.

4.333. *Precession and nutation.*—It is well known that precession and nutation do not affect the relative situation of the celestial bodies. Obviously, then, their effect on tangential co-ordinates must be rigorously orthogonal and can only be a rotation of the system around the tangent point. If, therefore, ξ and η represent the corrected co-ordinates and ΔP the amount of the precession and nutation in position angle at the tangent point, we have

$$\xi = x \cos \Delta P + y \sin \Delta P , \quad \eta = -x \sin \Delta P + y \cos \Delta P . \qquad (26)$$

[7] If higher-order terms are required in exceptional cases, they may be taken from Vick (1934).

For the numerical application of these rarely used formulae, we refer to the literature (König 1933).[8]

4.4. Adjustment to the Reference Stars

4.41. PREPARATIONS

The assumption is now made that the spherical corrections have been applied at least to the measured co-ordinates of the reference stars and, furthermore, that the zero point, used as "computational" tangent point, is sufficiently close to the true tangent point (see § 4.322). The first step is then to determine the spherical co-ordinates a_0 and δ_0 of the computational tangent point. This can be done by one of the methods given in § 5. As, however, even in unfavorable cases an accuracy of a few seconds of arc suffices, this is hardly necessary. It is good enough if one interpolates a_0, δ_0 by means of the measured co-ordinates x, y between a, δ of such pairs of reference stars as are near the tangent point and lie approximately on a straight line with it; there will then be no error resulting from the effect of the still unknown orientation. Should there be a reference star in the immediate neighborhood of the tangent point, then one needs only to convert its x, y approximately into Δa, $\Delta \delta$ and to subtract these small amounts from the reference star's a and δ.

In theory, the epoch of the reference star positions should be for the date of the exposure, but in practice a difference of a few years will hardly matter. For longer intervals the proper motions should be applied. If these are not, or only imperfectly, known, there may result an uncertainty in the final outcome that is difficult to estimate.

On the other hand, the choice of the equinox is arbitrary within wide limits. One may, for instance, take the nearest standard equinox; then the positions of the other objects are automatically found for that equinox. It should only be noted that, in principle, the values a_0, δ_0 should be referred to the equinox of date for computing the constants in the refraction and aberration formulae; in practice, this will be needed only if the interval is long. Finally, the a, δ of the reference stars must be transformed into tangential co-ordinates X, Y referred to the tangent point a_0, δ_0 (equinox of the reference star positions).

4.42. ADJUSTMENT

In formulae (15)

$$\Delta x = Ax + By + C , \quad \Delta y = -Bx + Ay + D ,$$

applied to the reference stars, all quantities are now known, except the plate constants A, B, C, and D. As every reference star supplies two equations of condition, two reference stars are, in theory, sufficient to determine these constants and hence for the complete reduction of the plate. It need hardly be

---

[8] The formulae (62) given there on p. 533 contain a printing error and should read exactly like (26) given here.

stated that this minimum number will not allow the full accuracy which the plate is capable of attaining. How many reference stars should be used depends on various circumstances and cannot be given as a general rule. To give some indication, it may be mentioned that for the reductions of the AGK2 plates performed at Hamburg-Bergedorf and Bonn, about twelve to fifteen reference stars were available in a field of $5° \times 5°$.

In practice, the number of equations of condition is therefore always considerably greater than the number of unknowns, whose most probable values are consequently obtained by least-squares adjustment. The special form of the equations of condition simplifies the computation (König 1933).

Conditions (15), called "orthogonal" for short, lead to the greatest weight for the unknowns; their application presupposes, however, that both the system of the X, Y computed from the reference star positions and that of the measured x, y are orthogonal and that abscissae and ordinates are expressed rigorously in the same units. This assumption is, in practice, not automatically justified; at any rate, to realize it for the system x, y requires great care in the measurement, as many influences, such as changes of temperature during a long series of measurements, may cause deviations (König and Heckmann 1928). Obviously, the larger the plate, the easier it is for errors to be introduced. For this reason, one often prefers for astrographs a general linear condition over the orthogonal one:

$$\Delta x = Ax + By + C, \quad \Delta y = A'x + B'y + C', \qquad (27)$$

increasing the number of plate constants to six. An additional advantage of this procedure is that in the correction formulae all linear terms, not only the orthogonal ones, may be omitted. Against this, equations (27) result in weights for A, B, A', and B' only about half as much as those for A and B given by equations (15). It is obviously possible to go a step further and to introduce quadratic terms in the adjustment. The most general equations of condition then take the form

$$\Delta x = Ax + By + C + Dx^2 + Exy + Fy^2,$$
$$\Delta y = A'x + B'y + C' + D'x^2 + E'xy + F'y^2. \qquad (28)$$

In this case one may, of course, omit the quadratic terms in the correction formulae. The saving in the labor of computing is insignificant, as only the reference stars are concerned and the least-squares adjustment becomes much more laborious. Furthermore, the introduction of additional constants is not without danger; at any rate, a correspondingly larger number of reference stars will be required to determine them with adequate precision. One would have to investigate whether three additional terms are really needed in both co-ordinates. For instance, in the case of large fields, the position of the tangent point will frequently not be sufficiently accurately determinable. To allow for the plate skewness caused thereby, terms of the form (16) suffice, so that only two additional unknowns appear. Schlesinger, for his reobservation of the AG catalogues, has largely proceeded in this manner, using forty to fifty reference stars for a field of over $10° \times 10°$ (Schlesinger and Barney 1933).

4.43. COMPUTATION OF THE POSITIONS RESULTING FROM THE PLATE

For the reference stars, the residuals v_x and v_y left by the adjustment represent directly the corrections (if the signs are suitably defined) of their X, Y according to the plate. For the corrections of their a, $δ$, one may usually put, even for large fields,

$$\Delta a = v_x \sec δ , \quad \Delta δ = v_y . \qquad (29)$$

For the other objects measured on the plate, the same corrections must first be applied to the measured co-ordinates as in the case of the reference stars. The corrected co-ordinates are then transformed into tangential co-ordinates X, Y by equations (15) or (27) or (28), using, of course, for the plate constants the values resulting from the adjustment. In practice, it is simpler to combine these equations with the correction formulae into a single set of the two equations, giving the tangential co-ordinates X, Y directly from the measured co-ordinates x, y. Finally, the tangential co-ordinates are transformed into a, $δ$ (see § 4.23); obviously, the same values a_0, $δ_0$ should be used as in the inverse transformation of the reference stars.

4.44. SPECIAL CASES

Here we must refer, first of all, to plates taken in high declinations, the polar area itself included. These invariably require special treatment, which may differ from one case to the next (König 1934; Vick 1934; Schorr 1951).

Special treatment may also be advisable when a large area of the sky is covered by overlapping plates so that every star is contained on two or more plates. The obvious method—so far invariably applied—of reducing every plate separately and taking the mean of the resulting positions is not the best or most exact, for not only the reference stars but all other stars may be used for interconnecting the overlapping plates. The device to be used for this purpose, which also allows one, in principle, to take account of the color and magnitude equation, is exceedingly complicated (Eichhorn 1960). Where there is a large number of plates, as, for instance, in the case of the AGK2, only electronic computers will manage the computations required. However, one obtains in this way the maximum possible uniformity of the system of star positions and at the same time one has the advantage that one requires fewer reference stars, for equal accuracy, than in the conventional treatment.

4.5. ACCURACY OF THE RESULTING POSITIONS

The accuracy of the positions obtained depends, of course, on many circumstances: focal length, size of field, image quality, seeing during exposure, etc.

A rough idea is given by the experience that the mean error of a position derived from an astrographic plate (size 5° × 5° or more), in linear measurement
on the plate, is of the order ±2 μ. It may be stated that the greater part of this
error is inherent in the plate itself, i.e., due to the entire photographic process,
while the part resulting from the measurement is considerably less (König
1932). Without doubt, a major part of the uncertainty is the result of distortions
of the sensitive layer. The question of the character and amount of such
distortions has been the subject of repeated investigation, but the conclusions
are not free from contradictions. According to the results of Meurers (1954),
which largely confirm earlier ones of Land (1942, 1948, 1950), it appears to be
certain that they show a systematic run and, as had been suspected for a long
time, are especially to be feared near the edges of the plate; these should be
avoided in the measurement, as far as possible. It is remarkable that the maximum amounts are decidedly smaller for large plates (18 × 24 cm) than for
small plates, where they may surpass 10 μ.

§ 5. DETERMINATION OF SINGLE POSITIONS

5.1. METHOD OF CO-ORDINATES

The case where only one, or a few, positions are to be derived from the plate
occurs frequently with minor planets or comets. If one were to use the method
outlined above for this purpose, the final result would in no way justify the
labor. Various devices have been given that require less trouble and use approximate formulae, because the nature of the objects measured precludes great
accuracy in the positions.

The method of co-ordinates is the simplest as to theory. It can be briefly
described as follows: We limit ourselves to the minimum number of two reference stars, so situated that the object lies as close as possible to the middle of
the line joining them and as near together as possible. Only the differences of
the co-ordinates are measured on the plate and need not be corrected for refraction, etc., because it may be assumed that, for the short interval in question,
all corrections are nearly enough linear. Only three transformations are needed:
two from spherical to tangential co-ordinates for the stars and one the other
way for the object. Instead of the rigorous formulae, the developments in
series (14) and (14′) may be used for this, but it is still simpler to put these
in such a form that, instead of δ_0, the declination δ of the stars appears in the
coefficients; we thus have

$$X = \Delta a \cos \delta + \tfrac{1}{6} (\Delta a)^3 \cos \delta (3 \cos^2 \delta - 1) + \tfrac{1}{2} \Delta a (\Delta \delta)^2 \cos \delta + \ldots ,$$
$$Y = \Delta \delta + \tfrac{1}{4} (\Delta a)^2 \sin 2 \delta + \tfrac{1}{3} (\Delta \delta)^3 + \ldots ; \tag{14*}$$

$$\Delta a = X \sec \delta + \tfrac{1}{6} X^3 \sec \delta (\sec^2 \delta - 3) - \tfrac{1}{2} X Y^2 \sec \delta - \ldots ,$$
$$\Delta \delta = Y - \tfrac{1}{2} X^2 \tan \delta - \tfrac{1}{3} Y^3 - \ldots . \tag{14'*}$$

Auxiliary tables appreciably simplify the numerical computation, and the third-order terms may be either retained or neglected, depending on the circumstances. Furthermore, as formulae (15) are applied to differences of co-ordinates, the zero-point constants fall away, and only A and B are to be found; another simplification results from the fact that a rough approximation suffices for the determination of the tangent point (König 1949, 1951). The method therefore strongly resembles an interpolation.

5.2. INTERPOLATION METHOD

As the name suggests, this method has the character of a pure interpolation (Reger 1906; Kaiser 1914; König 1951). Here the transformation from sphere to tangent plane is abandoned completely, and one deals only with the spherical differences $\Delta\alpha$, $\Delta\delta$, on the one hand, and the differences of the measured co-ordinates Δx, Δy, on the other hand. To establish a relation between the two systems, one applies to the $\Delta\alpha$ a "reduction for declination" by means of simple formulae, so that $\Delta\alpha$ and $\Delta\delta$ are expressed in the same unit. The tangent point is not required, and all terms of the third- and higher-order are neglected; in spite of this, the approximation is entirely adequate in practice if the reference stars are suitably chosen (see the remarks under § 5.1). The method is extremely simple in computation and has the great advantage that the arithmetic is automatically checked.

5.3. METHOD OF DEPENDENCES

The method of dependences, given by Schlesinger (1926), is without doubt the most elegant and the one most often applied nowadays. Apart from considerable simplification of the reduction, it has the special advantage that, though it can be applied to two reference stars, one can at will use three or more. Schlesinger reflects that the co-ordinates x, y of the object must be linear functions of the co-ordinates of the reference stars. So he puts (for the case of three stars)

$$x = D_1 x_1 + D_2 x_2 + D_3 x_3, \quad y = D_1 y_1 + D_2 y_2 + D_3 y_3, \qquad (30)$$

where x_1, y_1, etc., represent the co-ordinates of the reference stars; x, y those of the object; and D_1, D_2, D_3 are the dependences, which obey the condition $\Sigma D = 1$. Their geometrical significance is as follows: If one joins the corners of the triangle formed by the reference stars with the object (situated inside the triangle), the dependences are the ratios of the areas of the three partial triangles to the area of the large triangle. It follows that they are entirely independent of the co-ordinate system; equations (30) are valid for both the measured and the tangential co-ordinates but not for spherical co-ordinates or their differences. In the transformation to the sphere, which is done by the development into series in this case also, terms of higher order—under certain circumstances, to the fourth inclusive—must be taken into account. As only a few decimal places suffice, the labor of computing is small and may be greatly simplified by suitable auxiliary tables (Arend 1933; Land 1945). The only drawback of the method is that automatic checks are not so easily devised as for the interpolation method and to some extent for the method of co-ordinates.

REFERENCES

A. COMPLETE TREATISES

BERGSTRAND, Ö.   1899   *Stellarphotografiens användning vid Bestämmingen af fixstjärnornas parallaxer* (Uppsala).

KÖNIG, A.   1933   "Reduktion photographischer Himmelsaufnahmen," *Hdb. d. Ap.* (Berlin: Springer Verlag), Vol. **1**, chap. 6.

RAYET, M.   1900   "Instructions pour la reduction des clichés photographiques de l'observatoire de Bordeaux," *Ann. Obs. Bordeaux*, Vol. **9**.

SCHEINER, J.   1897   *Die Photographie der Gestirne* (Leipzig).

TREPIED, C.   1903   *Carte photographique du ciel* (Paris: Observatoire d'Alger), Introduction.

ZURHELLEN, W.   1904   *Darlegung und Kritik der zur Reduktion photographischer Himmelsaufnahmen aufgestellten Formeln und Methoden*. Inaugural-Dissertation, Bonn.

B. AUXILIARY TABLES FOR THE TRANSFORMATION OF CO-ORDINATES

KÖNIG, A.   1933   *Hdb. d. Ap.* (Berlin: Springer Verlag), Vol. **1**, chap. 6, Appendix 1.

PETERS, J.   1929   *Veröff. d. astr. Recheninst.* (Berlin-Dahlem), No. 47.

PETERS, J., and
    NOWACKI, H.   1936   *Veröff. d. astr. Recheninst.* (Berlin-Dahlem), No. 52.

SCHORR, R.   1924   *Hilfstafeln der Hamburger Sternwarte*, Sec. G.
                        1934   *Hilfstafeln der Hamburger Sternwarte*, Sec. H.
                        1935   *Hilfstafeln der Hamburger Sternwarte*, Secs. J, K.

C. TABLES FOR PHOTOGRAPHIC REFRACTION

DE BALL, L.   1906   *Refraktionstafeln* (Leipzig), Table 11.

KÖNIG, A.   1929   *A.N:*, **236**, 81.
                        1933   *Hdb. d. Ap.* (Berlin: Springer Verlag), Vol. **1**, chap. 6, Appendix 2.

SCHORR, R.   1934   *Hilfstafeln der Hamburger Sternwarte*, Sec. H.

D. GENERAL

AREND, S.   1933   *Bull. astr. Obs. Uccle*, **1**, 199.
BESSEL, F. W.   1841   *Astr. Untersuch.*, **1**, 167.
BRÜNNOW, F.   1880   *Lehrbuch der sphärischen Astronomie*, p. 16.

DIECKVOSS, W.	1954	*Mitt. d. AG*, p. 40.
	1955	*A.N.*, **282**, 25.
EICHHORN, H.	1960	*A.N.*, **285**, 233.
HECKMANN, O.	1932	*Veröff. d. U.-Sternw. Göttingen*, No. 30.
HENRY, P.	1892	*Bull. de la carte du ciel*, **1**, 464.
KAISER, F.	1914	*Veröff. d. Sternw. Heidelberg*, **7**, 115.
KAPTEYN, J.	1892	*Bull. de la carte du ciel*, **1**, 94, 377, 401.
KÖNIG, A.	1932	*A.N.*, **246**, 237.
	1934	*Ibid.*, **252**, 189.
	1949	*Ibid.*, **277**, 264; *Mitt. d. Sternw. Heidelberg*, No. 72.
	1951	*Ibid.*, **280**, 49; *Mitt. d. Sternw. Heidelberg*, No. 84.
KÖNIG, A., and HECKMANN, O.	1928	*Vierteljahrschr. d. AG*, **63**, 282, 284, 291.
KÜSTNER, F.	1920	*Veröff. d. U.-Sternw. Bonn*, No. 14.
LAND, G.	1942	*A.J.*, **50**, 51.
	1945	*Ibid.*, **51**, 104.
	1948	*Yale Trans.*, **15**, Part. 3, 164.
	1950	*A.J.*, **55**, 141.
MEURERS, J.	1954	*A.N.*, **281**, 233.
OLSSON, K.	1898	*A.N.*, **146**, 137.
PINGSDORF, F.	1909	*Der Sternhaufen in der Cassiopeia M52.* Inaugural-Dissertation, Bonn.
REGER, F.	1906	*Pub. d. Ap. Inst. Heidelberg*, **2**, 167.
SCHLESINGER, F.	1926	*A.J.*, **37**, 77.
SCHLESINGER, F., and BARNEY, I.	1925	*Yale Trans.*, **4** (5).
	1933	*Ibid.*, **9** (13).
	1939	*Ibid.*, **11** (5).
SCHLESINGER, F., HUDSON, C. F., JENKINS, L., and BARNEY, I.	1926	*Ibid.*, **5** (13), (14).
SCHORR, R.	1951	*AGK2*, **1**, E25.
TURNER, H.	1893	*M.N.*, **54**, 11.
	1897	*Ibid.*, **57**, 133.
VAN BIESBROECK, G.	1955	*Vistas in Astronomy*, ed. A. BEER (London and New York: Pergamon Press), **1**, 447.
VICK, C.	1934	*A.N.*, **253**, 277.
WILSING, J.	1898	*A.N.*, **145**, 273.
ZURHELLEN, W.	1909	*Veröff. d. U.-Sternw. Bonn*, No. 11.

CHAPTER 21

Astrometry with Long-Focus Telescopes

PETER VAN DE KAMP

Sproul Observatory, Swarthmore College

§ 1. INTRODUCTION

IN SEVERAL long-focus problems the material consists of photographic plates on which the position of the star in which we are interested—the "central" star—is referred to a "background" of three or more reference stars. The classic example is the parallax work done with the largest existing refractor (focal length 19.37 meters, aperture 102 cm) at the Yerkes Observatory near the beginning of the century. The necessary techniques of observing, measuring, and calculating were developed by Frank Schlesinger, who succeeded in obtaining parallaxes with an accuracy not achieved before (Schlesinger 1924). His methods of long-focus photographic astrometry are basic and complete; only minor improvements remained possible.

There is also the study of the relative positions of the components of double stars, first developed by Hertzsprung (1920). Both Schlesinger and Hertzsprung had visual refractors; they used panchromatic emulsions and a yellow filter (thus eliminating the blue light) to obtain sharp images in the color for which the objective was corrected.

This chapter deals, first, with a description of the long-focus photographic technique, and the methods of measurement and reduction (§§ 2, 3, 4). Next are presented the applications of the long-focus photographic technique and methods to relative star positions for individual stars (§ 5) and for groups of stars, referred to a background of field stars (§ 6). The relative positions of binary components are treated in § 7 (van de Kamp 1951, 1958).

§ 2. THE LONG-FOCUS REFRACTOR

2.1. At the Telescope; Scale Value, Atmospheric Refraction

The long-focus refractor normally has a focal ratio between $f/15$ and $f/20$. The achromatic objective usually consists of a convex crown-glass lens and a

487

concave flint-glass lens, which may be very close together or separated up to several centimeters. See, for example, the specifications for the objective of the Sproul refractor, as given in Table 1 (van de Kamp 1956a). The aperture of the Sproul refractor is 24 inches (61 cm), the focal length 36 feet (1093 cm), and the focal ratio $f/18$ (Fig. 1).

The principal off-axis aberration of a long-focus objective is "coma." Using rectangular co-ordinates in the image plane, the intersection of any ray differs from the ideal point (0, y_0) by quantities Δx and Δy, which are functions of ρ and θ, the polar co-ordinates of the point in the objective through which the ray passes. The coma equals

$$\Delta x = \gamma y_0 \rho^2 \sin 2\theta ,$$

$$\Delta y = \gamma y_0 \rho^2 (2 + \cos 2\theta) ,$$

i.e., the rays passing through a zone of the objective of radius ρ intersect the image plane in a circle of radius $\gamma y_0 \rho^2$, whose center is a distance $2\gamma y_0 \rho^2$ from the ideal image point (0, y_0).

Hence, the "flare" due to coma varies linearly with the distance from the optical center and with the square of the diameter of the largest zone of the objective through which light is allowed to pass. To obtain the highest optical quality, it is therefore desirable to limit the size of the field, while a reduction in the aperture may often prove effective.

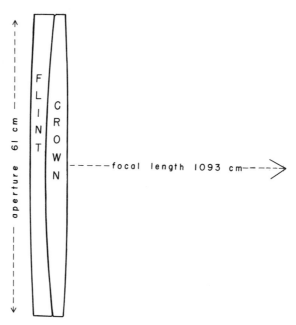

FIG. 1.—Diagram of Sproul 24-inch objective

A recent comparison of plates taken on one night of the star cluster NGC 1039 with the Sproul refractor at full (24-inch) and at reduced (12-inch) aperture shows improved images off center for the smaller aperture, accompanied by a scale reduction of 0.0005.

Photographs taken of the cluster IC 4756 at full aperture with a grating giving a two-magnitude reduction show a magnitude coma-effect amounting to a scale increase of 0.00008 per increase of one magnitude.

Hartmann tests indicate systematic changes in the performance of the Sproul objective due to changes of temperature during the course of the night; the zonal focus difference at times amounts to as much as 6 mm.

The scale value in the focal plane is defined as the number of seconds of arc per millimeter; for a focal length of F mm, the scale value is $206,265/F$ seconds of arc/mm. For the Sproul refractor the scale value is 1 mm = 18″.87, or 0.053 mm for 1 second of arc. To illustrate this the focal image of the moon is nearly 4 inches across and fills the greater part of the useful field portrayed on the photographic plates of 5 × 7 inches (13 × 18 cm).

A more precise definition of scale value involves atmospheric refraction. At moderate zenith distances the atmospheric refraction at zenith distance ζ may be represented to a high degree of approximation by the formula

$$(\mu \doteq 1) \tan \zeta ,$$

TABLE 1

Specifications of 24-Inch Objective of Sproul Visual Refractor

	Radii of Curvature		
Front lens (flint)......	$\left\{\begin{array}{l}+284.20 \text{ inches}\\ +101.82 \text{ inches}\end{array}\right\}$	Central thickness	1.33 inches
		Spacing between lenses*	0.005 inch
Rear lens (crown).....	$\left\{\begin{array}{l}+101.82 \text{ inches}\\ -457.15 \text{ inches}\end{array}\right\}$	Central thickness	1.85 inches
	+ ....convex toward source		
	− ....concave toward source		

* The current spacing between the two components is 0.002 inch.

WAVE LENGTH	REFRACTIVE INDICES	
	Crown	Flint
C............	1.510484	1.605533
λ 5614........	1.514290	1.612663
F............	1.518980	1.621876
G............	1.524140	G′ 1.631756
h............	1.526685	1.637993

where μ is the index of atmospheric refraction at the observer's location. We write the above relation as

$$R \tan \zeta ,$$

where R, the atmospheric refraction at $\zeta = 45°$, is the refraction constant.

Because of atmospheric refraction, any vertical angular distance suffers a minute contraction, whose first-order term is represented by the factor $R (1 + \tan^2 \zeta)$; any horizontal distance, measured along the great circle, suffers a contraction R. For a wide range in wave length in the visual spectrum, R is close to 60''; hence the scale reduction in the zenith amounts to 0.00029. The scale value in use for various telescopes refers to the zenith and includes the factor 0.00029, to allow for the contraction caused by refraction. Relative to the zenith, there is no additional first-order horizontal scale reduction, while the additional vertical reduction due to refraction is given by the term $R \tan^2 \zeta$, which is tabulated in Table 2, together with its effect on the Sproul scale value.

TABLE 2

SCALE REDUCTION

ζ	Additional Vertical Scale Reduction	Addition to Sproul Vertical Scale Value	ζ	Additional Vertical Scale Reduction	Addition to Sproul Vertical Scale Value
0°.......	0.00000	0''.0000	40°.......	0.00020	0''.0038
10.......	.00001	.0002	50........	.00041	.0077
20.......	.00004	.0008	60........	0.00087	0.0164
30.......	0.00010	0.0019			

In practice, the scale value may refer to the pitch (revolution) of the screw of a measuring engine; this pitch is generally very close to 1 mm or a simple fraction thereof. For example, the scale values at the zenith for the Sproul refractor (Strand 1946) are 18''.8733 for the Gaertner long-screw measuring machine and 18''.8723 for the St. Clair–Kasten long-screw measuring machine in use at the Sproul Observatory. These values vary slightly with the focal setting of the telescope and the observing temperature. Except in special problems, where extreme accuracy may be reached, the rounded-off scale value 18''.87 is used.

2.2. PHOTOGRAPHIC TECHNIQUE; ATMOSPHERIC DISPERSION

Guiding is accomplished by using a double-slide plate carrier, permitting an accurate slow motion of the plateholder. Residual guiding error is minimized by aiming at magnitude compensation. This may be accomplished by reducing the brightness of a "central" star by means of a small rotating sector in front of the plate. The Sproul Observatory has a set of 43 sectors, with extinctions ranging in steps from very close to 0.2 mag. up to 8.3 mag. Sector openings of less than about 2.5 per cent (extinction 4 stellar mag.) lead to a slight increase in positional error and should generally be avoided (Alden 1949; Land 1949a).

"Coarse" diffraction gratings, in front of the objective, may be used to provide faint companion images, symmetrically placed on each side of the star images (see, e.g., § 7.1, Fig. 15). Both sectors and gratings play an important role in reducing differences in the apparent sizes of star images, with a resulting increase in the ultimate accuracy of measurement.

Color effects are due primarily to dispersion in our atmosphere, but imperfect collimation of the objective may contribute its share also. The refraction constant R and its dispersion per 100 A are tabulated in Table 3 (Hertzsprung 1912).

Except at the zenith, each star appears as a spectrum, whose blue end is closer to the zenith than is the red end. For stars of different spectral types the energy distribution is different; moreover, the spectra differ in brightness. For positional work, the spectral range should be reduced, in order to have as nearly "monochromatic" images as possible. The approach to monochromatism is obtained by the triple combination of objective, emulsion, and filter. Sharp, round

TABLE 3

ATMOSPHERIC DISPERSION

λ (A)	R	Dispersion per 100 A	λ (A)	R	Dispersion per 100 A
4000......	61″34	−0″108	6500.......	60″06	−0″021
4500......	60.89	− .072	7000.......	59.96	− .017
5000......	60.58	− .050	7500.......	59.89	− .014
5500......	60.33	− .037	8000.......	59.83	−0.011
6000......	60.19	−0.028			

star images are obtained as long as the effective radiation is within Rayleigh's (visual) criterion for focal accuracy. According to the latter, all images obtained within $4f^2\lambda$ of the focus of a theoretically perfect objective are equally good. In this expression λ is the wave length that corresponds to a minimum focal length and f is the focal ratio. The same criterion holds closely for photographs as well. Generally, for long-focus refractors, Rayleigh's limit is between 0.5 and 0.7 mm (Schlesinger 1936); for the Sproul refractor it is 0.7 mm.

2.3. Photovisual Technique; Focal Curve, Emulsion, and Filter

Proper choice of emulsion and filter keeps the range of light close to the wave length corresponding to the minimum focal length of the focal curve (also called "color-curve," "achromatization-curve," or "secondary spectrum") of the objective (Bell 1922). The photographic position still depends on the residual energy distribution of the star's spectrum, as "filtered" by the objective (transparency and focal curve), filter, and emulsion. The effective wave lengths of the star images depend on the spectrum and, to some extent, on the magnitude; however, with proper choice of filter and emulsion, this dependence may be reduced to a minimum.

The rapid decrease in atmospheric dispersion toward longer wave lengths gives an advantage to the photographic technique as applied with visual refractors—referred to as "photovisual technique." As an illustration, the Sproul visual refractor with its aperture of 61 cm has its minimum focal length of 1093 cm for λ 5607. A minus-blue (No. 12) Wratten filter is used in contact with the 5 × 7-inch plate, eliminating practically all radiation on the blue side of approximately λ 5100. A suitable range of radiation is admitted to the photographic plate by using the Eastman G-type emulsion, for which the sensitivity is greatest at λ 5650 but extends hardly beyond λ 6000. Sharp images are obtained with effective wave lengths ranging only from about λ 5480 for a blue star of spectral type A to about λ 5525 for a red star of spectral type M. This corresponds to a small difference in refraction constant of $\Delta R = 0\rlap{.}''017$ at an

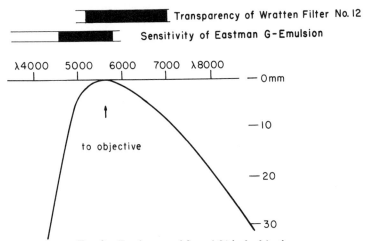

FIG. 2.—Focal curve of Sproul 24-inch objective

altitude of 45°. The A star is comparatively that much closer to the zenith than the M star. Figure 2 gives the focal curve for the Sproul 24-inch objective.

In addition, there is a delicate effect which was first noted by Bergstrand (1905) for positions obtained on ordinary photographic emulsions: the photographic position for one and the same spectrum depends on the brightness. This is explained by the contribution of radiations of different colors to the formation of the photographic star image. Generally, the distribution of these relative intensities is asymmetrical with respect to the wave length. Initially, only a limited range of radiation is effective, while, with increased exposure or brightness, other radiations begin to contribute to the formation of the photographic image. For one and the same stellar spectrum the relative contribution of the different colors changes gradually with increasing exposure or brightness. The resulting change in effective wave length or color depends on the character of the focal curve and selective absorption of the objective and on the type of emulsion and filter.

2.4. Residual Dispersion in Right Ascension and Declination

Even with the best possible spectral compensation, small differences in effective wave length are likely to remain. It is advisable to avoid any variation in this residual systematic error, such as would be caused by a large variation in hour angle. Let ΔR be the difference in refraction constant for a certain pair of wave lengths. Assuming the refraction and hence the dispersion to vary with $\tan \zeta$, the dispersion component in right ascension is given by

$$R \sin t \cos \phi \sec \zeta ,$$

where t is the hour angle and ϕ is the latitude. For observations near the meridian, the formula may be written as

$$\Delta R t \cos \phi \sec (\phi - \delta) .$$

While for observations near the meridian the refraction and hence the dispersion in declination are practically constant, the component in right ascension depends strongly on the hour angle. For observations not exceeding an hour angle of 1 hour, the change in the dispersion effect in declination is negligible. In right ascension the dispersion effect is very nearly proportional to the hour angle and changes signs at the meridian; an increase in altitude corresponds to a shift toward the meridian. For latitude 45° and $\Delta R = +0\rlap{.}''01$, the values are given in Tables 4 and 5 (Schlesinger 1924).

TABLE 4

Dispersion Effect in Right Ascension for $\Delta R = +0\rlap{.}''01$

DECLINATION	HOUR ANGLE				
	60^m E.	30^m E.	Meridian	30^m W.	60^m W.
$-20°$......	$-0\rlap{.}''0046$	$-0\rlap{.}''0022$	$0\rlap{.}''0000$	$+0\rlap{.}''0022$	$+0\rlap{.}''0046$
$0°$......	$-\ .0027$	$-\ .0013$	$.0000$	$+\ .0013$	$+\ .0027$
$+20°$......	$-\ .0021$	$-\ .0010$	$.0000$	$+\ .0010$	$+\ .0021$
$+40°$......	$-\ .0019$	$-\ .0009$	$.0000$	$+\ .0009$	$+\ .0019$
$+60°$......	-0.0019	-0.0009	0.0000	$+0.0009$	$+0.0019$

TABLE 5

Dispersion Effect in Declination for $\Delta R = +0\rlap{.}''01$

DECLINA-TION	HOUR ANGLE				
	60^m E.	30^m E.	Meridian	30^m W.	60^m W.
$-20°$....	$+0\rlap{.}''0224$	$+0\rlap{.}''0216$	$+0\rlap{.}''0214$	$+0\rlap{.}''0216$	$+0\rlap{.}''0224$
$0°$....	$+\ .0104$	$+\ .0101$	$+\ .0100$	$+\ .0101$	$+\ .0104$
$+20°$....	$+\ .0049$	$+\ .0047$	$+\ .0047$	$+\ .0047$	$+\ .0049$
$+40°$....	$+\ .0010$	$+\ .0010$	$+\ .0009$	$+\ .0010$	$+\ .0010$
$+60°$....	$+0.0026$	$+0.0027$	$+0.0027$	$+0.0027$	$+0.0026$

Variations in the flexure of the objective and possible relative displacement of the two lens components may further cause prismatic effects having the same effect as refraction.

It is customary to limit the photographic observations as much as possible to the meridian. These hour-angle restrictions are particularly stringent for the ordinary photographic technique but much less so in photovisual work (Slocum 1924).

§ 3. MEASUREMENT

Long-focus astrometric problems are customarily studied in rectangular co-ordinates x and y which coincide closely with the directions of right ascension and declination of the equatorial co-ordinate system. The rectangular co-ordinates are in the tangential co-ordinate system (also called "standard" or "ideal") as described in chapter 20 by König. For an extended stellar path, an increasing disparity between rectangular and spherical co-ordinates develops, which may be represented, to a high approximation, as a slowly changing orientation of the equatorial with respect to the rectangular co-ordinate system, amounting to

$$\Delta\theta = +\Delta x \sin \delta ,$$

where Δx is the projection of the path on the x-co-ordinate and δ is the declination (Fletcher 1931). In comparing results expressed in rectangular and in equatorial co-ordinates, the above change in position angle must be kept in mind. Secular effects should be considered, especially for stars of large proper motion situated at high declination. The effect on the components of the annual parallactic motion is generally negligible.

Referred to the optical axis, an angular extent a on the celestial sphere corresponds to a plane extent on the plate of $\sin a$. Hence a third-order "distortion," $a^3/3$, between plane and angular portrayal exists, amounting to $206{,}265\ a^3/3$ in seconds of arc, or $F(a^3/3)$ in linear value. For the case of long-focus refractors, the field is generally well below $1°$ in diameter. For an extreme value of $a = 20'$, the distortion amounts to $0\rlap{.}''02$. In most long-focus problems, a is rather less, and the third-order distortion may be neglected.

3.1. AT THE MEASURING MACHINE

The positions of star images in any one co-ordinate may be obtained with a long-screw measuring machine. The plate is mounted on a carriage which can be moved along sliding ways and is oriented by two or more star images. The plate is viewed with a low-power (say 20×) microscope mounted on a second carriage by means of a nut which fits a horizontal long-precision screw, perpendicular to the sliding ways. The screw has a pitch of, say, 1 mm; by turning the screw and moving the plate carriage, all portions of the plate may be viewed. Instead of direct viewing, the projection method may be used. The microscope contains a vertical wire (and a horizontal one to indicate the center of the field), for bisecting the star images. At one end the screw is provided with a graduated dial, so that the amount of turning and hence the distance moved can be read and recorded to 0.001 mm (1 μ).

Two successive settings are made on each image; the central star is usually measured twice. The plates are measured in four positions, differing by 90° each, representing the "direct" and "reversed" directions of the rectangular celestial co-ordinates; the averages of the direct and reversed values in each co-ordinate are thus reasonably free from systematic errors of bisection, varying with the measurer and the intensity of the photographic image. It is customary to record the measurements to 0.001 mm, but to carry out averages and further calculations to 0.0001 mm.

The accuracy of the positions is much higher than the photographic resolving power; the smallest star images are rarely below 1″ in diameter. Although the diameters of star images ordinarily range from 0.04 to 0.20 mm, or even more, the relative location of two stars may be deduced with an uncertainty only a small fraction of the size of the image. With the Sproul refractor, the relative location of two star images is obtained with a probable error of ± 0.002 mm, or about $\pm 0.''04$. Experience has shown that the positional accuracy is almost independent of atmospheric turbulence or "seeing," provided that inferior definition is avoided. Apart from such obvious image quality as symmetry, the most important requirement for high positional accuracy is that the images shall be well blackened, i.e., give a good representation of the position of the star; the sharpness of the image is of secondary importance.

3.2. Plate and Night Errors

Astrometric series of plates often extend over several decades. It is not always feasible or advisable to measure all the plates of a series during a limited span of time. Where measurements are made at different times, the stability of the measuring technique is of prime importance. Experience with the long-screw measuring machines of the Sproul Observatory has shown that the measuring technique is generally quite stable. Repeated measurements have seldom revealed systematic differences of more than 1 μ in the measured positions of the central star on the reference background; most of these systematic differences are below $\frac{1}{2}$ μ. The average of two measurements of a plate increases the effective plate weight by a factor 1.15, three measurements by 1.25. The resulting gain is limited, and, generally, the additional effort is not warranted, apart from its value as a test of the stability of the measuring machine (van de Kamp 1945a).

Increase in positional accuracy on any one night may be obtained by increasing the number of exposures per plate and the number of plates. Plate errors, common to all exposures on one and the same plate, are to a great extent due to emulsion shifts, which rarely amount to as much as 10 μ. Generally, no more than three or four exposures per plate are taken. Appreciable reduction of film errors is obtained by the use of "double plates," obtained by turning the same

photographic plate 180° in its own plane between the two successive sets of exposures, representing the two "single plates." The two sets of exposures for the
central star are close together on the emulsion; here the effects of a general film
shift are virtually equal and are opposite for the two successive single plates.
The double-plate procedure is especially desirable for large configurations,
where this source of error is to a great extent responsible for the decreased positional accuracy of single sets of exposures. The number of plates on any one
night is limited by the night errors, which are probably due to refraction anomalies. These positional night errors are assumed constant during all the exposures
of one and the same field, within the same night (Land 1944).

Generally, it is not warranted to take more than four exposures on any one
plate and more than four plates on any one night. The resulting positional accuracy (probable error) is about 0.001 mm (1 μ), or about 0".02, for plates taken
with the Sproul refractor. The accuracy for any one night may be regarded as
the limit beyond which it is not easy to go. Measurements of relative positions
of stars close together, such as visual double stars, are less affected by plate and
night errors, and an appreciably higher accuracy may be obtained (§ 7).

3.3. Other Errors; Attainable Accuracy

It is important to keep the optical performance of the telescope as constant
as possible. The remounting of an objective may lead to a systematic error of the
nature of a color equation. Any slight lateral maladjustment of the lens has its
effect on the position of the stars as a function of the color. At Sproul Observatory the lens was taken out of its cell in 1941, because of maladjustment, and
again in 1949, when the old aluminum cell was replaced with a fine-grain cast-
iron cell. While in declination there has been hardly any effect, in right ascension
the position of a red M star, as compared with a blue A star, suffered a color
equation of 0".046 ± 0".005 in 1941 and a very much smaller equation in 1949
(Lippincott 1957).

Apart from night errors, there is good evidence that there are long periods of
time, extending perhaps from one night to several months, over which the
measured position for any one star has a slight systematic shift, the origin of
which has not yet been traced. Are these shifts of atmospheric origin, or are they
due to maladjustment of the telescope?

Possible sources of systematic error are improper or changing collimation and
focus. Maladjustment of focus results in displacements relative to the optical
axis, depending on the distance of the plate to the focal plane, the distance of
the star from the optical axis, and the brightness of the star. For plates taken with
the Yerkes refractor, Schlesinger (1911) found a shift of 0".01 for each millimeter
that the plate was outside the focal plane, for a difference of one magnitude
at a distance of 11' from the optical axis. The displacement was in the sense
that the brighter star was shifted toward the optical axis, relative to a fainter
star, on either side of the focal plane. Since plates with extreme positive
and negative parallax factors in right ascension are taken at dusk and dawn,

respectively, systematic differences in focus may easily occur if the same focal setting is used for any one night, or even if only partial adjustment is made, say at midnight. The possible effect on such sensitive data as stellar parallax could be serious.

The dome can heat up quite appreciably on a hot day, and, if no proper ventilation is provided ahead of time, one must expect, on opening the dome, a very important temperature gradient for an hour or so after sunset. In his Darwin lecture entitled "Some Aspects of Astronomical Photography of Precision," Schlesinger (1927) urged the importance of good ventilation as a prerequisite for good seeing. One should have good ventilation not only between the inside of the dome and the outside, but also between the inside of the telescope tube and its surroundings. Accordingly, following Schlesinger, at Sproul Observatory the two armholes just below the objective cell—armholes for cleaning the inside surface of the lens—are opened in the daytime, while three ventilating fans installed in the windows of the dome are operated when needed. In the daytime the telescope is kept in a horizontal position.

A recent investigation on astrometric accuracy by Miss Lippincott (1957) includes 53 star series, extending anywhere from one to four decades, taken with the Sproul refractor over the interval 1912–1954. The least-squares solutions yield 3123 residuals in both right ascension and declination. Over the years 1938–1951, fourteen successive years in which most of the measured Sproul material is concentrated, normal places for the residuals for each year have been formed. The average weight of these yearly mean residuals is 402, using the usual Sproul weighting system, in which night errors have been allowed for (van de Kamp 1945a). The weights used correspond to an average probable error of unit weight of ± 0.00175 mm. This would correspond to a probable error of

$$\frac{\pm 0.00175 \text{ mm}}{\sqrt{402}} = \pm 0.00009 \text{ mm},$$

probably a spuriously low value, for the yearly normal places. The observed average residuals, for what we may call the "composite Sproul star," range from -0.00032 to $+0.00021$ mm in right ascension and from -0.00038 to $+0.00027$ mm in declination. The average absolute values are ± 0.00015 mm in right ascension, ± 0.00017 mm in declination, or ± 0.00016 mm in both co-ordinates. The corresponding probable value is ± 0.00014 mm, thus leaving a probable "year" error of

$$\pm \sqrt{[(0.00014)^2 - (0.00009)^2]} = \pm 0.00011 \text{ mm or } \pm 0\overset{''}{.}002 .$$

There is reason to believe that any systematic errors of a yearly or seasonal nature and any residual orbital effects, undiscovered or not allowed for in the least-squares solution for individual stars, have canceled out to a great extent in the yearly mean residuals of the "composite" star. This probable year error of ± 0.00011 mm or $\pm 0\overset{''}{.}002$ would then appear to set a limit to the attainable photographic accuracy in any one year. As for the case of normal points based on six or more multiple-exposure photographs of relative positions of double-star components, the quantity $\pm 0''.002$ (probable error) appears to represent the ultimate in positional accuracy obtainable for yearly normal positions with the long-focus photographic technique (van de Kamp 1957).

§ 4. REDUCTION OF STELLAR PATH

The long-focus photographic method is now applied to the study of the path of a star. The star may be under observation for parallax, in which case useful information may be obtained in a few years. Or the star may be under observation for orbital motion, and hence a prolonged interval of time—several decades or even centuries—may be necessary to obtain the required observational material. In all cases the path of the star is referred to and measured on a background of virtually "fixed" reference stars. While the largest known parallactic displacement for a star is less than $1''$, there are numerous stars whose annual proper motion exceeds $1''$. The largest known annual motion is $10''.3$ for Barnard's large-proper-motion star. Appreciable displacements are the rule, at least for the more interesting nearby stars. The measured positions must be properly adjusted or "reduced" so as to permit a precise analysis of the star's path.

4.1. Scale and Orientation Effects; Standard Frame

The principal effects on the measured positions may be summarized as changes in scale and orientation, resulting from the following causes:

1. Observational (König, this volume, chap. 20)
   a) Instrumental (measuring engine, telescope)
   b) Spherical (refraction, aberration)
2. Cosmic: proper motions of reference (and orientation) stars (van de Kamp 1935a, 1939b, 1947a)

Accidental errors in the angle of orientation may be kept well below 0.0002 radians when orienting by star images. Proper motions of the orientation stars may introduce a systematic effect; a yearly change in orientation of the order of 0.0001 is not excluded, and its accumulation over many years may become serious. To avoid a progressive change in orientation and its effect on the measurements, the proper motions of the orientation stars should be sufficiently known so that they may be allowed for. Variations in scale due to changes in temperature and barometric pressure are negligible for the present purpose. The maximum scale effect due to aberration is a factor 0.0002. Its possible effect on parallax is negligible. Because of the small angular extent of the long-focus plates, the small changes in refraction and aberration may be considered as linear functions of the position of the star on the plate.

The effect of plate tilt is generally negligible for long-focus instruments. Let p and q be the rectangular co-ordinates of the base or "optical center" of the plate, i.e., the point obtained by letting fall a perpendicular from the center of the objective onto the plate, or also the location of the point of tangency with the celestial sphere relative to the intersection of the optical axis. The resulting corrections are

$$px^2 + qxy \quad \text{in } x, \qquad qy^2 + pxy \quad \text{in } y.$$

For an extreme x or y of $20'$ and a value of $1'$ for p and q, the quadratic terms in the above expressions would be only $0\rlap{.}''002$ (König 1961).

For the Sproul 24-inch telescope in the normal position of the plateholder, i.e., the long dimension parallel to the equator, Olsson's method as refined by Schlesinger and Barney (1925) yields values of $p = 7$ mm west, and $q = 11$ mm north of the geometrical plate center. For an extreme x or y of $20'$, the corresponding tilt effect would be less than $0\rlap{.}''01$.

When comparing the different plates of a series of observations of one and the same field, all that is necessary, therefore, is to reduce the measurements by a linear transformation to a common origin, scale, and orientation. In order to permit a comparison of measured positions on different plates, a reduction is made to a "standard frame" as defined by the reference stars (van de Kamp 1942). Use is made of rectilinear co-ordinates closely oriented to the directions of right ascension and declination. Let X', Y' and x', y' be the measured positions of central and reference stars as recorded at the measuring machine. The zero point is arbitrary, the scale and orientation are close to that of the adopted standard frame given by the configuration of n reference stars—at least three and seldom more than four in number. The co-ordinates of the standard frame will be denoted by the subscript s; the positions x_s and y_s, defining the standard frame of reference, are relative to their mean position, i.e.,

$$[x_s] = [y_s] = 0 . \tag{1}$$

4.2. Plate Constants; Dependences

All measured positions can now be reduced to the scale, orientation, and origin of the reference frame (x_s, y_s) through plate constants a, b, and c, which are given by the linear equations of condition,

$$
\begin{aligned}
a_x x_s + b_x y_s + c_x &= x_s - x' , \\
a_y x_s + b_y y_s + c_y &= y_s - y' .
\end{aligned}
\tag{2}
$$

A least-squares solution gives

$$a_x = \frac{[y_s^2][x_s(x_s - x')] - [x_s y_s][y_s(x_s - x')]}{[x_s^2][y_s^2] - [x_s y_s]^2} ,$$

$$b_x = \frac{[x_s^2][y_s(x_s - x')] - [x_s y_s][x_s(x_s - x')]}{[x_s^2][y_s^2] - [x_s y_s]^2} , \tag{3}$$

$$c_x = \frac{[x']}{n} ,$$

and similar expressions for a_y, b_y, and c_y.

For the central star the position X and Y reduced to the standard frame is given by

$$X = X' + a_x X_0 + b_x Y_0 + c_x,$$
$$Y = Y' + a_y X_0 + b_y Y_0 + c_y,$$

(4)

where X_0 and Y_0 are values of X and Y rounded off to a sufficient number of significant figures. Thus the position X_0, Y_0 is rigorously corrected for plate constants, while the rounding-off leads to the neglect of the following quantities:

$$a_x(X - X_0) + b_x(Y - Y_0) \ldots \text{ in } x,$$
$$a_y(X - X_0) + b_y(Y - Y_0) \ldots \text{ in } y.$$

(5)

Schlesinger has shown that, for the case of linear plate constants, considerable time may be saved and insight gained by expressing the reduced position as an explicit linear function of the measured co-ordinates (Schlesinger 1911, 1924; van de Kamp 1942). The necessary transformation is obtained by substituting equations (3) in equations (4), which leads to

$$X = X' + \left\{ \frac{X_0\{x_s[y_s^2] - y_s[x_sy_s]\} + Y_0\{y_s[x_s^2] - x_s[x_sy_s]\}}{[x_s^2][y_s^2] - [x_sy_s]^2} \right.$$
$$\left. \times (x_s - x') \right\} - \frac{[x']}{n},$$

$$Y = Y' + \left\{ \frac{X_0\{x_s[y_s^2] - y_s[x_sy_s]\} + Y_0\{y_s[x_s^2] - x_s[x_sy_s]\}}{[x_s^2][y_s^2] - [x_sy_s]^2} \right.$$
$$\left. \times (y_s - y') \right\} - \frac{[y']}{n}.$$

(6)

The resulting reduction statement, regardless of the zero point of the measured co-ordinates, therefore is

$$X = X' + [D_i(x_s - x')_i], \qquad Y = Y' + [D_i(y_s - y')_i], \qquad (7)$$

where $i = 1, \ldots, n$. The quantities

$$D_i = \frac{X_0\{x_{si}[y_s^2] - y_{si}[x_sy_s]\} + Y_0\{y_{si}[x_s^2] - x_{si}[x_sy_s]\}}{[x_s^2][y_s^2] - [x_sy_s]^2} + \frac{1}{n}, \qquad (8)$$

are Schlesinger's "dependences." It is obvious that $[D] = 1$, and, because of the least-squares procedure, that $[D^2]$ is a minimum. In the plate-constant method, X and Y are implicit functions of (x') and (y'); the dependence method provides an explicit expression which greatly simplifies the reduction calculations.

4.3. PLATE SOLUTIONS; DEPENDENCE CENTER AND DEPENDENCE BACKGROUND

The "dependence reductions" (7) may be written as follows:

$$X = [Dx_s] + X' - [Dx'], \qquad Y = [Dy_s] + Y' - [Dy']. \qquad (9)$$

The position $[Dx_s]$ and $[Dy_s]$ defines a point close to the central star, which is rigorously corrected for plate constants and is called the "dependence center"; $[Dx']$ and $[Dy']$ are the measured "dependence background."

The dependence method leaves only a small segment uncorrected, the so-called "plate solution," sometimes called "offset":

$$\zeta = X' - [Dx'], \qquad \eta = Y' - [Dy'], \qquad (10)$$

which remains uncorrected to the small amount given in equation (5). Theoretically, the plate solutions should vanish for the position X_0, Y_0, but, because of the limited number of decimals in D, small plate solutions exist for this position. Because of their explicit use in the dependence reduction method, it is convenient to substitute the plate solution ζ and η in the reduced positions, so that

$$X = [Dx_s] + \zeta, \qquad Y = [Dy_s] + \eta. \qquad (11)$$

The zero point of the measurements is eliminated for the plate solutions; the co-ordinates of the standard frame, the quantities x_s and y_s used in the computation of the dependence center, refer to their mean.

In general, if the plates are carefully oriented, the plate constants are factors less than 0.0002, and their effect on the plate solutions is well below the observational errors. If the uncorrected segments or plate solutions are kept sufficiently small—say, less than 0.5 mm—plate-constant reduction is obtained within the errors of observation, and a number of plates can be reduced with one set of dependences calculated for one position X_0, Y_0 of the central star.

The dependence method has another advantage: it reveals the relative significance, or the weight, of the individual reference stars. The dependence method gives no information about the plate constants, which are eliminated; in general, however, the plate constants are of no particular interest.

4.4. CHANGE OF DEPENDENCES

There are problems such as conventional parallax determinations, in which the path covered by the central star is small enough to be served by one set of dependences. In this case the plate solutions as such, i.e., the positions with respect to the dependence background of the reference stars, may be used, and no further reduction is necessary. But in several problems it is necessary to use more than one dependence center, either because of appreciable change in the position of a central star due to proper motion, or because it is desired to study the relative position of two or more stars on the same plate which are widely separated. In all such cases a reduction to the origin of the standard frame commends itself.

For the case of appreciable proper motion of the central star, successive dependence sets are so chosen that the dependence center is kept close to the central star. As before, the uncorrected segments, or plate solutions, ζ, η, are kept sufficiently small so that, mainly through careful orientation, rigorous linear plate-constant reduction is obtained within the errors of observation for the duration of each dependence set. Since many measured positions are reduced by the same set of dependences, the economy of the dependence method is maintained, and it remains a desirable substitute for the plate-constant method.

In many long-focus problems (parallax, mass ratio, perturbation, perspective acceleration) there is no obvious need for knowledge of the accurate positions of the reference stars. If, however, the position and proper motion of the central star or stars as such are of importance, accurate knowledge of the positions and proper motions of the reference stars is ultimately necessary. The required data can be obtained by referring the reference stars to a more comprehensive group of stars. In this case an eventual reduction $(\Delta x_s, \Delta y_s)$ to a more precise reference system requires the addition of $[D\Delta x_s]$ and $[D\Delta y_s]$ to the dependence centers $[Dx_s]$ and $[Dy_s]$.

4.5. CALCULATION OF DEPENDENCES

A set of dependences for an initial position X_0, Y_0, and the standard frame (x_s, y_s), may be computed by the linear formula:

$$D_i = f_i X_0 + g_i Y_0 + \frac{1}{n}. \tag{12}$$

Here

$$f_i = \frac{x_{si}\,[y_s^2] - y_{si}\,[x_s y_s]}{[x_s^2]\,[y_s^2] - [x_s y_s]^2}, \tag{13}$$

and

$$g_i = \frac{y_{si}\,[x_s^2] - x_{si}\,[x_s y_s]}{[x_s^2]\,[y_s^2] - [x_s y_s]^2}$$

with the control equations,

$$[fx_s] = 1 \quad \text{and} \quad [gy_s] = 1. \tag{14}$$

The quantities D_i must satisfy the equations

$$[D] = 1, \qquad [Dx_s] = X_0, \qquad [Dy_s] = Y_0. \tag{15}$$

The first equation must be rigorous, in order to provide accurate elimination of the zero point of the measured co-ordinates. The calculated dependence center, $[Dx_s]$, $[Dy_s]$, must equal the position X_0, Y_0 within the errors due to rounding off the dependences.

In practice it will be found convenient to adopt for X_0 and Y_0 the position in a certain year. For any other year the dependences can then be easily computed through the use of their annual variations, D, which are given by

$$\Delta D_i = f_i \mu_X + g_i \mu_Y. \tag{16}$$

Here μ_X and μ_Y are the rectangular components of the yearly proper motion of the central star; the control equations are

$$[\Delta D] = 0, \qquad [\Delta D x_s] = \mu_X, \qquad [\Delta D y_s] = \mu_Y. \qquad (17)$$

By means of these formulae an ephemeris for both dependences and dependence centers is easily computed (Land 1942). For plates taken with the 24-inch Sproul refractor (scale 1 mm = 18″87), x_s and y_s are used to 0.01 mm; the scale and orientation errors of the adopted standard frame are usually below a factor 0.0001. Using two decimals in X_0 and Y_0, the dependences are computed to four decimals, but rounded off to three, always taking care that their sum shall rigorously equal unity. The dependence centers are computed to 0.0001 mm.

The rounding-off to three places in the dependences leads to values of the plate solutions that are rarely over 0.1 mm near the dependence epoch. By spacing the dependence centers not more than about 1 mm apart in each co-ordinate, the solutions seldom exceed 0.5 mm, and errors due to extreme orientation (and scale) constants are rarely above 0.0001 mm.

4.6. CHOICE OF REFERENCE STARS; POSITIONAL ACCURACY

The choice of reference stars is guided by various considerations. Generally one need have little concern about the proper motions and parallaxes of the reference stars; almost any set of faint stars represents an acceptably close approximation to a fixed background. The choice depends on the exposure time and limitations due to required magnitude compensation. In any long-term astrometric problem it is important to study carefully any possible choice of reference stars, so that one will not be faced with early obsolescence but, instead, will have a well-planned foundation for the present, and possibly future, configurations of reference stars. Other things being equal, the greatest astrometric accuracy is reached for small configurations of stars. However, a larger configuration may often be preferred because of its longer life, while the practical choice of a set of reference stars is very much determined by the actual availability of stars.

The chief consequence of the central star's motion is the varying accuracy of its geometrical fixation due to its changed location within the configuration (van de Kamp 1943, 1947c). We shall neglect the possible variation in intrinsic positional accuracy of each reference star with its location on the photographic plate. The geometrical accuracy of the reduced position of the central star depends on the distribution of the dependences for the reference stars. The error squared of the position measured on the dependence background is proportional to

$$1 + [D^2], \qquad (18)$$

a quantity which we call the "inverse weight." In the case of a central star of appreciable proper motion, the dependences change and result in a corresponding change in accuracy for the changing dependence background. Writing

$$D_t = D_0 + t\Delta D,$$

the inverse weight becomes

$$1 + [D_0^2] + 2t[D_0\Delta D] + t^2[\Delta D^2], \tag{19}$$

reaching a minimum value for

$$t_m = -\frac{[D_0\Delta D]}{[\Delta D^2]}. \tag{20}$$

Calling the dependences at this epoch D_m, the inverse weight at any other time is given by

$$1 + [D_m^2] + (t - t_m)^2[\Delta D^2]. \tag{21}$$

For any investigation spread over a limited time interval, the greatest accuracy is maintained if the position of greatest dependence accuracy is reached about

TABLE 6

ACCURACY ON BACKGROUNDS OF THREE AND MORE STARS
(EQUAL DEPENDENCES)

n	Inverse Weight $1+[D^2]$	Relative Error	n	Inverse Weight $1+[D^2]$	Relative Error
3........	1.333	1.031	7........	1.143	0.956
4........	1.250	1.000	8........	1.125	0.949
5........	1.200	0.981	....	....	....
6........	1.167	0.967	∞........	1.000	0.895

the middle of that interval. If the interval is not more than a few decades, it is generally not difficult to find an appropriate configuration for which the dependences vary not too much over the interval and would in any case remain positive.

The absolute minimum value of $[D^2]$ in the configuration occurs at the origin, defined by

$$[x_s] = [y_s] = 0,$$

where each of the dependences equals $1/n$. For any central star, therefore, to insure a satisfactorily small $[D_m^2]$, it is important to choose a configuration whose origin will not lie too far off the path of the star.

As to the number of reference stars, even for a central star at the origin, the accuracy does not increase much with the number of reference stars. This is illustrated in Table 6. Considering the extra work involved, not much is generally gained by using more than four reference stars.

In the case of a limited problem such as a conventional parallax determination, nothing is therefore more desirable than a configuration limited in number of stars and in areal extent, and with approximately equal dependences.

Graphical methods are useful for initial exploration and evaluation of the dependences of different configurations of reference stars (Schlesinger 1926; Plummer 1932; Land 1949b); they are particularly effective for three-star combinations.

For a central star with considerable proper motion, the effect of each reference star on its reduced position changes with time; thus secular effects due to magnitude, color, and proper motion are introduced. The first two are kept at a minimum by limiting the range in magnitude and spectrum for the reference stars; the dispersion effects can be minimized by photography in the longer wave lengths. In long-range astrometric problems the effect of the proper motion of the reference stars becomes important (van de Kamp 1935a, 1939b, 1947c). This particular effect is studied in § 5.10.

4.7. LONG-RANGE PROBLEMS; TRANSITION FROM ONE CONFIGURATION TO ANOTHER

For a star of appreciable proper motion which is to be observed over a long interval, a sufficiently large configuration should be chosen (avoiding stars near the edge of the plate) so that the same reference system may serve well for as long a time as possible. Limited by the size of the telescopic field and the photographic plate, any configuration has a limited lifetime within which maximum usefulness is reached. It is advisable to choose a configuration which the central star has recently entered, so that long use can be made of the reference system. The importance of a reference star in a long-range problem should be judged not only by its present dependence value but by the annual dependence variations as well. The advantage of having one long-range reference system more than offsets the possible temporary occurrence of negative dependences at the beginning and end of its period of usefulness.

When planning measurements for a region that is to be observed for a long time, one should make a survey of potential configurations. The proper motion of the central star should be known, so that its future path can be traced with sufficient accuracy. After considerations of magnitude compensation and exposure time, a few possible configurations are likely to be found, all of them satisfying the condition that at some time in the future the path of the central star will pass close to the center of the configuration.

For a short-term problem, it may be desirable to use a relatively small configuration, with the corresponding advantage of increased astrometric accuracy. Even in this case, however, it is wise to provide for a possible extension toward a long-range problem. This could, of course, be done by starting with a larger "long-range" configuration, even though its positional accuracy may be less. An alternative approach is to make a transition from a smaller to a larger configuration whenever future developments warrant such a procedure (van de Kamp 1943, 1947c, d).

The addition of a reference star always leads to an increase in geometric accuracy, since it leads to a new distribution of the dependences, for which $[D^2]$ represents the least-squares minimum. This minimum value equals the old value if the dependence of the additional star is zero; if not, it must be smaller, even though a negative dependence for another star or stars may have appeared. The addition of another reference star might be of little or no value at present, as would be demonstrated by a small, or even negative, dependence value. The eventual transition to a reference system involving the inclusion of one additional star is most conveniently carried out about the time of vanishing dependence value for that star. The useful procedure is to realize the potential future importance of such a star but, for reasons of economy, to refrain from measuring this star until its dependence attains an appreciably positive value. By measuring and reducing a sufficient number of common backgrounds at that time, any reductions of earlier plates to the new frame may be evaluated with adequate accuracy.

§ 5. INDIVIDUAL STARS

We now discuss the various astrometric problems for which an extended stellar path provides the observational data. Average values are formed of the plate solution ξ and η for the different exposures on each plate (§ 4). Means for each night are formed and added to the corresponding dependence center, $[Dx_s]$, $[Dy_s]$, thus yielding positions X and Y, which hold for the standard frame, (x_s, y_s).

5.1. PROPER MOTION AND PARALLAX

We first analyze a series of measured and reduced positions for proper motion and parallax. The central star has been measured on a background of faint reference stars; the reduced positions refer to the dependence background of these faint stars of, say, magnitude 10; the resulting values for proper motion and parallax are relative.

The equations of condition for a uniform, rectilinear heliocentric path are

$$X = c_X + \mu_X t, \qquad Y = c_Y + \mu_Y t. \qquad (22)$$

Here c_X, c_Y is the heliocentric position at a certain zero epoch, say 1950.000; μ_X, μ_Y is the yearly proper motion; the time t in years is counted from the adopted zero epoch. The unit of time is the solar or Besselian year, which begins when the right ascension of the mean sun is 280°. The Besselian fraction of the year, τ, is given in the *American Ephemeris and Nautical Almanac*.

The equations of condition for the corresponding geocentric path are

$$X = c_X + \mu_X t + \pi P_a, \qquad Y = c_Y + \mu_Y t + \pi P_\delta. \qquad (23)$$

Here, π is the relative parallax; P_a and P_δ are the parallax factors in right ascension (reduced to great-circle measure) and declination, respectively:

$$P_a = R(\cos \epsilon \cos a \sin \odot - \sin a \cos \odot),$$
$$P_\delta = R[(\sin \epsilon \cos \delta - \cos \epsilon \sin a \sin \delta) \sin \odot - \cos a \sin \delta \cos \odot]. \qquad (24)$$

Here R is the radius vector of the earth's orbit expressed in astronomical units, $\odot$ the sun's true longitude, and ϵ the inclination of the ecliptic on the equator. The right ascension, α, and declination, δ, of the star are reduced to the equator and equinox of, say, the year 2000; any appreciable effect of proper motion is applied up to the epoch of the observation. A precession correction of $+0\rlap{.}{''}838$ (2000 $-$ Epoch) is applied to the values of $\odot$ to refer them also to the equinox of the year 2000.

The formulae for the parallax factors are simplified by the following substitutions:

$$p = +0.9174 \cos \alpha , \qquad a = +0.3979 \cos \delta - 0.9174 \sin \alpha \sin \delta ,$$

$$q = - \qquad \sin \alpha , \qquad b = -\cos \alpha \sin \delta ,$$

whence

$$P_\alpha = R(p \sin \odot + q \cos \odot), \qquad P_\delta = R(a \sin \odot + b \cos \odot). \quad (25)$$

Here p, q, a, b, R, $\sin \odot$, and $\cos \odot$ are calculated to four decimal places. The final values for P_α and P_δ are used to three or two places.

The positions X and Y for each night are often corrected for provisional values of the unknowns c, μ, and π. This is done to facilitate the calculations and also to inspect the material for possible orbital motion. The equations of condition are assigned a night weight p, in accordance with the total plate weight and an assumed night error (van de Kamp 1945a). The least-squares solutions are carried out for the differential corrections, which afterward are added to the provisional values, to yield the final values of c, μ, and π. All calculations are carried out in units of 0.0001 mm; the final results for the unknowns are reduced to seconds of arc by multiplying with the scale value (1 mm = $18\rlap{.}{''}87$ for the Sproul refractor).

The "classical" parallax determinations with long-focus refractors are based on some twenty to thirty plates, spread over five to seven successive observing seasons, and yield probable errors of about $\pm 0\rlap{.}{''}01$ for the relative parallax. There has been a trend to increase the number of plates, up to several hundred in certain cases, with resulting decrease in the interval probable error values as low as $\pm 0\rlap{.}{''}002$. In § 3 we concluded that a probable "year error" of $\pm 0\rlap{.}{''}002$ appeared to set a limit to the attainable accuracy in any one year. An error of this size represents an acceptable limitation in many problems, such as long-period orbital motion of sufficient amplitude. However, the same error looms large as a possible seasonal error that would put severe limitations on the attainable accuracy in parallax determinations. Systematic errors having a period of one year would be serious because of their obvious effect on parallax determinations and on perturbations with periods close to a year. Some comfort is derived from the fact that an average difference of $+0\rlap{.}{''}005 \pm 0\rlap{.}{''}002$ (p.e.) is found for the independent parallax determinations at Sproul Observatory, of 53 stars from the two co-ordinates in the sense right ascension *minus* declination (Lippincott 1957). This difference is sufficiently small to give us some reassurance on the subject of systematic errors in parallaxes.

5.2. RESOLVED ASTROMETRIC BINARIES

For the case of orbital motion, another term has to be added to the equations of condition. For a resolved binary the above geocentric equations hold for the barycenter, while the positions of the brighter component A and the fainter component B referred to the barycenter are as follows:

Orbital effect of A in x-co-ordinate: $-\text{B}\Delta x$,

Orbital effect of A in y-co-ordinate: $-\text{B}\Delta y$,

Orbital effect of B in x-co-ordinate: $(1 - \text{B})\Delta x$,

Orbital effect of B in y-co-ordinate: $(1 - \text{B})\Delta y$.

Here B is the fractional mass $M_B/(M_A + M_B)$ of the companion in terms of the combined mass of primary and companion, and Δx, Δy, is the relative position of the secondary B referred to the primary A. Hence, limiting ourselves to the primary component, the equations of condition for the geocentric position of the primary are

$$X = c_x + \mu_x t + \pi P_a - \text{B}\Delta x, \qquad Y = c_y + \mu_y t + \pi P_\delta - \text{B}\Delta y. \quad (26)$$

The relative positions in the apparent orbit may be written as

$$\Delta x = Bx + Gy, \qquad \Delta y = Ax + Fy. \quad (27)$$

Here x and y are the elliptical rectangular co-ordinates in the unit orbit (i.e., unit semi-axis major), while B, A, G, and F are the "natural" geometric, or Thiele-Innes, constants (van den Bos 1926a, b; 1961). The elliptical rectangular co-ordinates are related to the "dynamical" elements P (period), e (eccentricity), and T (periastron passage) via the eccentric anomaly E:

$$x = \cos E - e, \qquad y = \sin E \sqrt{(1 - e^2)}, \quad (28)$$

while

$$E - e \sin E = M. \quad (29)$$

Tables published by the Union Observatory (*Circular No. 71*, 1927) give x and y as functions of e and the mean anomaly M, so that E need not be computed.

The "natural" geometric elements are related to the "conventional" geometric elements as follows:

$$B = a(\cos \omega \sin \Omega + \sin \omega \cos \Omega \cos i),$$

$$A = a(\cos \omega \sin \Omega - \sin \omega \sin \Omega \cos i),$$

$$G = a(-\sin \omega \sin \Omega + \cos \omega \cos \Omega \cos i), \quad (30)$$

$$F = a(-\sin \omega \cos \Omega - \cos \omega \sin \Omega \cos i).$$

Thus Δx and Δy may be calculated if the orbital elements of the relative orbit of the two components are known. The conventional geometric elements are the "scale" of the orbit a (semi-axis major in seconds of arc), while the three "orientation" elements are the angles i (inclination), ω (counted from the line of nodes to periastron in the direction of orbital motion), and Ω (position angle from the north point to the line of nodes) (van de Kamp 1958, 1960).

The conventional elements can be found from the natural elements as follows:

$$\tan(\omega + \Omega) = \frac{B - F}{A + G},$$

$$\tan(\omega - \Omega) = -\frac{B + F}{A - G},$$

$$\cos i = \frac{m}{a^2}, \qquad a^2 = j + k,$$

$$2k = A^2 + B^2 + F^2 + G^2, \qquad m = AG - BF, \qquad j^2 = k^2 - m^2.$$

(31)

Another, more elegant and often more revealing, form of equations (26) is obtained as follows (van de Kamp 1945b): the orbits of primary and secondary are similar; the semi-axis major a of the orbit of the primary is related to the semi-axis major a of the relative orbit of primary and companion by $a = Ba$; the phases in the respective orbits differ by $180°$.

We may write the orbital displacements for the primary as follows:

Orbital displacement in x: $-B\Delta x = -\frac{a}{a}(Bx + Gy),$

Orbital displacement in y: $-B\Delta y = -\frac{a}{a}(Ax + Fy),$

(32)

or

Orbital displacement in x: $\left(-\frac{B}{a}x - \frac{G}{a}y\right)a = Q_a a,$

Orbital displacement in y: $\left(-\frac{A}{a}x - \frac{F}{a}y\right)a = Q_\delta a.$

(33)

The quantities Q_a and Q_δ are named "orbital factors"; they are the projected values in right ascension (reduced to great circle) and declination of the radius vector barycenter-primary for unit orbit. The orbital factors are analogous to the parallax factors; the latter refer to the star's parallactic orbit, the former to the star's own apparent orbit. Q_a and Q_δ may be expressed as follows:

$$Q_a = (b)x + (g)y, \qquad Q_\delta = (a)x + (f)y,$$ (34)

where

$$(b) = -\cos \omega \sin \Omega - \sin \omega \cos \Omega \cos i,$$

$$(a) = -\cos \omega \cos \Omega + \sin \omega \sin \Omega \cos i,$$

$$(g) = +\sin \omega \sin \Omega - \cos \omega \cos \Omega \cos i,$$

$$(f) = +\sin \omega \cos \Omega + \cos \omega \sin \Omega \cos i.$$

(35)

These "orientation factors" are related to the Thiele-Innes constants as follows:

$$B = -(b)a \,, \qquad G = -(g)a \,,$$
$$A = -(a)a \,, \qquad F = -(f)a \,. \tag{36}$$

We thus obtain the following equations of condition for the observed geocentric positions of the primary:

$$X = c_X + \mu_X t + \pi P_a + a Q_a \,, \qquad Y = c_Y + \mu_Y t + \pi P_\delta + a Q_\delta \,. \tag{37}$$

5.3. UNRESOLVED ASTROMETRIC BINARIES; PHOTOCENTRIC ORBIT

In many cases the distance between the components is below the resolving power of the photographic plate, in which case no separation is possible, and a composite image results. These photographically unresolved astrometric binaries are important, since so many interesting objects fall in this group. We can measure the position of the composite image, but these questions arise: What do we measure? What do the measures signify?

The smallest star images on long-focus photographs are rarely below $1''$ in diameter. Blended exposures of components separated by $1''$ or sometimes even more generally present circular images. This is certainly the case for magnitude differences of 2 or more. A self-luminous, though photographically not resolved, companion would generally draw the center of light toward the center of mass for visual separations up to $1''$ and even more. For periods of half a century and more there might be no danger of photographic blending—except for stars of small parallax. However, blending is generally to be expected for periods up to several decades, except possibly for a few of the very nearest stars. The blended image of the unresolved binary may still appear circular, but the orbit of the center of the image will generally be appreciably smaller than the actual perturbation orbit described by the primary. Since the dimensions of this orbit are a measure of the mass of the companion, the observations in the case of a blended image thus generally yield a lower limit for the mass of the companion.

We assume that the measured position of the blended image represents the weighted center of light-intensity or "photocenter" of the components. In this case the fractional distance β of the primary to the photocenter, in terms of the distance between the two components, is given by

$$\beta = \frac{l_B}{l_A + l_B} \,. \tag{38}$$

Here l_A and l_B are the luminosities of the components. Or, if we introduce the difference in magnitude Δm, companion minus primary, we have (Table 7)

$$\beta = \frac{1}{1 + 10^{(0.4)\,\Delta m}} \,. \tag{39}$$

Experiments made by R. G. Hall, Jr. (1951) at the Yerkes Observatory with artificial binaries show systematic deviations from the theoretical relation. For separations of less than 0.12 mm there is a discrepancy beginning at about $\Delta m = 2^{m}0$; for larger values of Δm the observed value of β is less than the theoretical value, reaching the value zero at $\Delta m = 4^{m}0$ (Fig. 3).

The fractional difference of photocenter to barycenter is therefore $B - \beta$, and the semi-major axis of the photocentric orbit relative to the barycenter is

$$a = (B - \beta)a .\qquad (40)$$

Referred to the barycenter, the orbits of primary, companion, and photocenter are all similar to the orbit of companion relative to primary in the ratios B, $1 - B$, and $B - \beta$ (Fig. 4). Note that a has the sign of $B - \beta$. A positive value for a indicates that photocenter and companion are on opposite sides of the barycenter; a negative value, that they are on the same side. Except for the abnormal possibility that $\beta - B > B$, i.e., a comparatively luminous companion of low mass, the photocentric orbit is always smaller than the orbit of the primary (Section 5.8).

TABLE 7

THEORETICAL RELATION BETWEEN Δm AND β

m	β	m	β
0.0........	0.500	2.0........	0.137
0.5........	.387	3.0........	.060
1.0........	.285	4.0........	.025
1.5........	.201	5.0........	.010
2.0........	0.137	6.0........	0.006

The orbital displacement of the photocenter is represented by

$$-(B - \beta)\Delta x , \qquad -(B - \beta)\Delta y ;$$

but the form aQ_a, aQ_δ remains of particular value because of the explicit way in which a appears.

The formulae for analyzing the geocentric positions of the photocenter for proper motion, parallax, and orbital motion are therefore

$$X = c_X + \mu_X t + \pi P_a - (B - \beta)\Delta x ,$$
$$Y = c_Y + \mu_Y t + \pi P_\delta - (B - \beta)\Delta y ,\qquad (41)$$

or, again,

$$X = c_X + \mu_X t + \pi P_a + aQ_a , \qquad Y = c_Y + \mu_Y t + \pi P_\delta + aQ_\delta . \quad (37)$$

5.4. PARALLAX AND MASS RATIO

As a rule, parallax and mass ratio are determined simultaneously, using formulae (26), (37), or (41). If both components are visible and well separated on the photographic plate, the orbit need not be known; Δx and Δy are directly furnished by the measurements, and B is obtained through formulae (26). Or, if the orbital elements of the relative orbit are known, Δx and Δy may be calculated, and B or B $- \beta$ may be obtained with the aid of formula (26) or (41).

In general, only the primary or the photocenter of the blended primary and secondary is measured; in this case formulae (37) are most conveniently used, assuming the relative orbit to be known. The dynamical and orientation elements are used to compute the orbital factors Q_a and Q_δ. From material covering a sufficiently extended part of the orbit, a least-squares solution yields values of π and a.

If the measured positions refer to a primary component whose image is unaffected by a well-separated or an invisible companion, then the value a yields directly a determination of the quantity B $= a/a$, i.e., the fractional mass $M_B/(M_A + M_B)$ of the companion in terms of the combined mass of primary and companion. If the measured positions refer to the blended image of primary

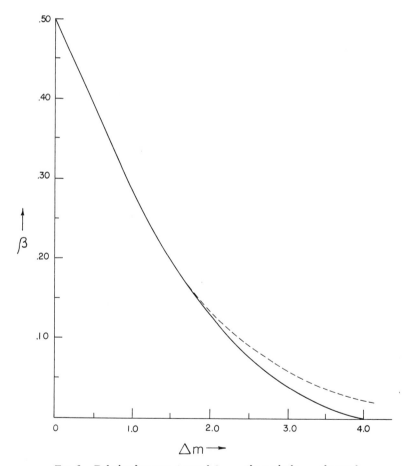

FIG. 3.—Relation between Δm and β. - - - theoretical; —— observed

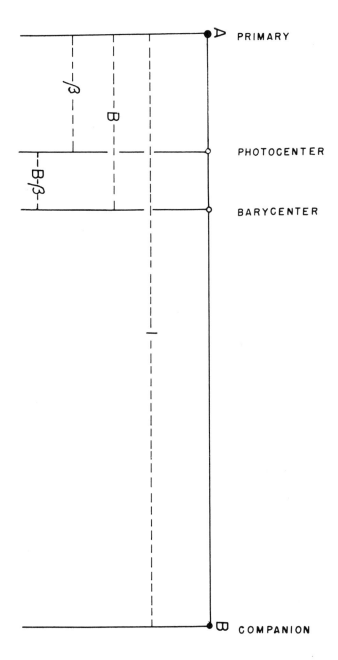

Fig. 4.—Relative spacings between components, barycenter, and photocenter for photographically unresolved binaries.

and companion, the resulting photocentric orbital displacements yield a determination of

$$B - \beta = \frac{a}{a}.$$ (42)

The general relation

$$B = \frac{a}{a} + \beta$$ (43)

shows explicitly how the total error of B depends on errors in a, a, and β. For large, well-established orbits the fractional accuracy of a is simply transferred to B. For small or provisional orbits the accuracy of B is also limited by the accuracy of a, while for blended images it is directly affected by any uncertainty in β, which in turn depends on the accuracy of Δm and on the reliability of the assumed theoretical relation between β and Δm.

In the 1930's the first serious attempts were made at accurate photographic determinations of parallax and mass ratio. Twenty to thirty plates seemed hardly adequate; gradually fifty to sixty plates were used for combined parallax and mass-ratio determinations, yielding probable errors of $\pm 0''005$ for the relative parallax and something like 2 per cent for the mass ratio. For accurate mass-ratio determinations as many as two hundred or more plates have been used, with resulting decrease in the probable errors of the parallax to $\pm 0''004$ or even $\pm 0''003$, while the mass ratio has often been found with an error of 1 per cent or even less (van de Kamp 1954).

5.5. Perturbations

The field of unresolved astrometric binaries includes the discovery and subsequent study of photocentric orbits revealed through variable proper motion. In this case, where no a priori orbital elements are known, it is convenient to use the following formulae for the orbital displacements:

$$aQ_a = a(b)x + a(g)y = (B)x + (G)y ,$$
$$aQ_\delta = a(a)x + a(f)y = (A)x + (F)y .$$ (44)

The dynamical elements P, e, and T are represented by the elliptical rectangular co-ordinates x and y in the unit orbit. The geometric constants (B), (A), (G), and (F) refer to the observed photocentric orbit of the unresolved system. They are related to the orientation factors and to the Thiele-Innes constants as follows:

$$(B) = -\left(\frac{a}{a}\right) B = a\,(\,b\,) = a\,(\,-\cos\omega\,\sin\Omega - \sin\omega\,\cos\Omega\,\cos i\,),$$

$$(A) = -\left(\frac{a}{a}\right) A = a\,(\,a\,) = a\,(\,-\cos\omega\,\cos\Omega + \sin\omega\,\sin\Omega\,\cos i\,),$$

$$(G) = -\left(\frac{a}{a}\right) G = a\,(\,g\,) = a\,(\,+\sin\omega\,\sin\Omega - \cos\omega\,\cos\Omega\,\cos i\,),$$

$$(F) = -\left(\frac{a}{a}\right) F = a\,(\,f\,) = a\,(\,+\sin\omega\,\cos\Omega + \cos\omega\,\sin\Omega\,\cos i\,).$$

(45)

The general formulae for analyzing the positions of the photocenter for proper, parallactic, and orbital motion are, therefore,

$$X = c_X + \mu_X t + \pi P_a + (B)x + (G)y,$$
$$Y = c_Y + \mu_Y t + \pi P_\delta + (A)x + (F)y.$$

(46)

These formulae are useful if the dynamical elements are known, for example, from spectroscopic information. They are very suitable if nothing whatsoever is known about the orbital elements. This is the case, par excellence, resulting from the discovery and subsequent study of an astrometric binary revealed by variable proper motion. First, the observed positions are corrected for provisional values of proper motion and parallax, aiming for the adopted proper motion to be as close as possible to that of the barycenter. The remainders are then analyzed for orbital motion; successive approximations are generally necessary.

Recall that $a = (B - \beta)a$. Experience with blended images of known binaries has commonly failed to reveal any elongation of images for separations up to $1''$ or even more and for magnitude differences as small as 2.0, for which β is as high as 0.14; for smaller separations, binaries with even smaller magnitude differences may go undetected on photographic plates.

A close companion may be too faint to be detected visually or spectroscopically, but affects the center of light by pulling it toward the barycenter. The photocentric orbit of the unresolved binary is generally smaller than the orbit of the primary. If the companion is very much fainter, or when its image is not blended with that of the primary, the measured positions refer to the primary, and β is zero.

5.6. Orbital Analysis

The dynamical elements may be determined by Zwiers' method, which in this case involves locating the invisible focus or barycenter. This procedure may be awkward, and a different method therefore commends itself. Instead of the apparent orbit, we study its projection on any co-ordinate, right ascension or declination or any other direction. This procedure has been used for "linear" orbits as they are represented by all spectroscopic binaries and by certain visual orbits seen edgewise. However, the principle of the method is also applicable to any "open" visual or photocentric orbit (van de Kamp 1947a, b).

The advantage of using displacements (R) plotted against the time is that the best-known observed datum—the time—enters explicitly. Periastron and apastron are located by the fact that their mean anomalies differ by 180° and their ordinates are equal and opposite when referred to the center of the orbit. Periastron and apastron are conveniently located by making a copy of the displacement-curve, reversing it along the central line representing the center of the orbit, and shifting the reversed curve half a period along the time axis. Generally two pairs of intersections result (Fig. 5). Of these, the single intersection on the shorter, steeper branch and the central intersection on the longer branch represent periastron and apastron, respectively.

The slopes of any displacement-curve represent projected velocities (dR/dt). The ratio of the true velocity vectors at periastron and apastron is $-(1+e)/(1-e)$, their directions being opposite. Since this ratio remains the same in projection, the ratio of the slopes $(dR/dt)_P$ and $(dR/dt)_A$ at periastron and apastron, respectively, amounts to $-(1+e)/(1-e)$ for any displacement-curve, including those of astrometric orbits seen on edge. We can thus not only distinguish periastron from apastron but also derive the eccentricity of the orbit, independently of the focus, through the relation

$$e = \frac{(dR/dt)_P + (dR/dt)_A}{(dR/dt)_P - (dR/dt)_A}. \tag{47}$$

The method becomes unreliable when periastron and apastron are close to the extreme amplitudes; this occurs if the major axis is at a small angle with the

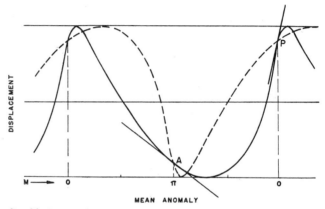

Fig. 5.—Graphical evaluation of periastron (P), apastron (A), and eccentricity, from slopes of time-displacement-curves at periastron and apastron.

line of nodes for any spectroscopic orbit and for any astrometric orbit with a high inclination. In this case a combination of graphical and analytical methods may be used to derive the eccentricity from the observed cosine of the eccentric anomaly for selected values of the mean anomaly (van de Kamp 1947a).

The method of time-displacement-curves is equally applicable to resolved and to unresolved astrometric binaries, provided that in the latter case the orbital motion of the center of light is appreciable and well separated from the proper motion and parallax of the system. The time-displacement-curve method is of particular significance for unresolved binaries. In this case the conventional geometric derivation of the eccentricity is awkward or fails, while the time-displacement-curve methods are effective, accurate, and generally applicable.

With the set of dynamical elements P, e, and T thus obtained, x and y are computed and the observations represented by the general formulae for orbital displacement. An analysis of the equations yields the four geometric constants

(B), (A), (G), and (F), from which the scale a and the three orientation elements Ω, ω, and i may be computed. Successive approximations are used and, as in the case of resolved binaries, the dynamical elements are varied, in order to test the stability of the results. While it is possible to solve simultaneously for differential corrections to all orbital elements and to parallax and proper motion, such a procedure is hardly warranted at the current stage of this problem. The process of variations is certainly to be preferred and has the great advantage of remaining in close touch with the real worth of the available material.

5.7. GENERAL CONSIDERATIONS

The discovery and study of photographically unresolved binaries consist of two parts: (1) establishing the existence of deviations which cannot be accounted for by proper motion and parallax and (2) determining the photocentric orbit from these deviations. While it may be relatively simple to detect initial deviations, the second step is much more difficult.

Thousands of parallax determinations of "single" stars have been made, and, with few exceptions, it has always been possible to represent the observed positions satisfactorily by uniform proper motion and a parallactic orbit of appropriate size. Moreover, no increase in the probable error of unit weight has been found for stars of large parallax (Schlesinger 1937). This general absence of observable orbital motion may often be due to a negligible value of the semimajor axis of the photocentric orbit. For example, a is zero if both components have the same mass and the same luminosity. However, even with an appreciable value of a, orbital motion may not be found because of the small number of plates, twenty or thirty, and the short time interval, often only 2 years, employed in conventional parallax determinations. If the period is short, the amplitude of the photocentric orbit may be too small to be detected. If the period is long, more time is required to detect orbital motion. Moreover, the orbital motion may be partly absorbed in the parallactic and the proper motions, or it may be temporarily or accidentally disguised through gaps in the series of observations. The conventional parallax determinations are generally neither suitable for the discovery of orbital motion nor affected by any existing orbital motion.

For any thorough investigation it is desirable to go beyond the extent and also beyond the occasional repetition of conventional parallax series. Observations over an interval of several decades are desirable; the chances of discovery depend on the particular portion of the orbit in which the star happens to be. Even for shorter periods an extended observational series is in order, to insure complete coverage of the orbit; plates should be taken without particular regard to the parallax factor, so as to insure as complete and uniform a distribution in time as possible. The narrow hour-angle requirements of the observations cause annual gaps of at least 6 or 7 months, which in turn may result in spurious periods; with limited accuracy, scattered position in successive cycles of a short-period orbit may be interpreted as an orbit with a period a multiple of the actual

one unless plates are also taken in close temporal succession. The danger of interpreting a long-period orbit by a spurious short period exists also. So long as
the binary is not resolved, the analysis lacks the control of the harmonic relation
$a^3/P^2 = M_A + M_B$, which for resolved binaries may serve as a guide for the
period. The danger of interpreting a limited initial set of residuals by a for-
tuitous orbit should always be avoided through additional observations.

A satisfactory orbit is generally not obtained until all phases of the orbit have
been covered. Correct dynamical interpretation is aided by the fact that the
Keplerian motion is, as a rule, observed in two co-ordinates. The blending of the
two components and variability of either component remain potential sources of
error in any analysis of a photocentric orbit.

5.8. Dynamical Interpretation; Mass Function

The analysis of the astrometric orbit of an unresolved binary gives two data
of principal interest—the period P (years) and the semi-axis major a (reduced to
astronomical units). In case of a completely dark companion or in the case of
sufficient separation of the components, $a = Ba$, and we derive the mass function

$$\frac{a^3}{P^2} = B^3 (M_A + M_B). \tag{48}$$

Compare this with the mass function for a spectroscopic binary with one component visible:

$$B^3 \sin^3 i \, (M_A + M_B). \tag{49}$$

We may write (48) as follows:

$$M_B = a P^{-2/3} (M_A + M_B)^{2/3}. \tag{50}$$

By making an assumption about the sum of the masses or about the mass of the
primary, complete knowledge of the separate masses is obtained. Generally,
however, we do not know whether the observed orbit refers to the pure image of
the primary or to the photocenter of primary and companion. In the latter case
$a = (B - \beta)a$, and our knowledge about the masses is limited to the mass
function

$$\frac{a^3}{P^2} = (B - \beta)^3 (M_A + M_B). \tag{51}$$

Thus a combined astrometric and spectroscopic study becomes significant in the
case of appreciable inclination, e.g., eclipsing binaries, since the astrometric
study furnishes the inclination i, while the spectroscopic study may not be influenced by the blend effect β. In such a combined study the mass function
$B^3 (M_A + M_B)$ and the ratio β/B may be determined. So long as the companion
remains unseen, visually or spectroscopically, the masses of the components
cannot be rigorously derived. With a reasonable assumption about $(M_A + M_B)$, however, a value for B, and hence β, can be found, and corresponding
values of M_A and M_B derived.

So long as the astrometric information is not supplemented by spectroscopic data, we remain in the dark as to the evaluation of the luminosity correction β. Generally, therefore, we are confronted with the interpretation of the mass function which contains the three unknowns M_A, M_B, and β. We may write the mass function as follows:

$$M_B - \beta (M_A + M_B) = a P^{-2/3} (M_A + M_B)^{2/3} . \tag{52}$$

This expression gives a lower limit for the mass of the companion, for an adopted value of the combined mass. Note that the astrometric observations alone do not yield the sign of a; hence the above expressions for the mass function have the double sign. In order to interpret the observations, we generally make different assumptions for the sum of the masses $(M_A + M_B)$, which will then yield different limiting values for the mass of the companion.

If we take $B - \beta$ positive, we find the following limiting values for the masses of the components: upper limit primary: $M_A + \beta (M_A + M_B)$; lower limit companion: $M_B - \beta (M_A + M_B)$.

If $B - \beta$ is negative, we find the following limiting values for the masses of the components: lower limit primary: $M_A - (1 - \beta) (M_A + M_B)$; upper limit companion: $M_B + (1 - \beta) (M_A + M_B)$. Hence, without additional information, the absolute size of the photocentric orbit fails to distinguish between the two components. A minimum value of the mass is always found for that component that is revealed as the perturbing influence on the photocenter, i.e., the component that is on the side of the barycenter opposite the photocenter.

Often a choice between the alternate interpretations can be made by considering the implications of the results for mass and luminosity. The definition of primary and companion implies in all cases $0 < B < 1$ and $0 < \beta < 0.5$. Any admissible value of β may satisfy the condition $0 < B - \beta < 1$, in which case the photocentric orbit is always smaller than the orbit of the primary. The alternate interpretation is subject to the restriction that $0 < \beta - B < 0.5$. In this case the photocentric orbit may be larger than the orbit of the primary, i.e., $\beta - B > B$ or $\beta > 2B$, which implies a value of $B < 0.25$. Generally, however, the photocentric orbit is smaller than the orbit of the primary. Since the dimensions of the latter are a measure of the mass of the companion, the observations give a lower limit for the mass of the companion. One has to be very careful, therefore, about ascribing a very small photocentric orbit to the influence of a planetary companion (van de Kamp 1956b).

5.9. Spectroscopic and Eclipsing Binaries

Although little has yet been done, astrometric research on spectroscopic and eclipsing binaries has begun, and we shall briefly report on the methods employed and the results obtained thus far.

The general formulae for the observed orbital displacements are

$$\text{In } x:\ (B)x + (G)y , \qquad \text{In } y:\ (A)x + (F)y , \tag{44}$$

where

$$(B) = a(-\cos \omega \sin \Omega - \sin \omega \cos \Omega \cos i),$$
$$(A) = a(-\cos \omega \cos \Omega + \sin \omega \sin \Omega \cos i),$$
$$(G) = a(+\sin \omega \sin \Omega - \cos \omega \cos \Omega \cos i),$$
$$(F) = a(+\sin \omega \cos \Omega + \cos \omega \sin \Omega \cos i).$$

$$(53)$$

For both known spectroscopic and eclipsing binaries the quantities P, e, and T are more accurately determined than they could possibly be obtained from astrometric data. For both spectroscopic and eclipsing binaries properly distributed astrometric material permits a determination of the geometric elements (B), (A), (G), and (F), or the related elements a, i, Ω, ω. Neither spectroscopic nor photometric observations yield Ω; this quantity can be determined from astrometric data only; furthermore, the spectroscopic observations do not yield i.

If, in addition to the dynamical elements, we adopt the value ω furnished by the spectroscopic or eclipsing data, the following formulae for the orbital displacements may be used:

$$\text{In } x: \quad (B)x + (G)y = (a \sin \Omega)U - (a \cos \Omega \cos i)V,$$
$$\text{In } y: \quad (A)x + (F)y = (a \cos \Omega)U + (a \sin \Omega \cos i)V,$$

$$(54)$$

where

$$U = -x \cos \omega + y \sin \omega, \qquad V = +x \sin \omega + y \cos \omega. \quad (55)$$

Suitable astrometric material then yields values for a, Ω, and i. For eclipsing binaries the value of i is known, and values of a and Ω are obtained in a very simple fashion. An astrometric orbit of the eclipsing binary VV Cephei has been derived from plates obtained with the Sproul 24-inch refractor (Fredrick 1960).

5.10. Secular Perspective Acceleration

On the assumption of constant space velocity and absolute magnitude, the following expressions exist for the first-order term of the secular changes in the annual proper motion (μ) and parallax (π), the radial velocity (V), and the magnitude (m):

Yearly change in μ: $\qquad -2\rlap{.}''05 \times 10^{-6} \mu \pi V,$ $\qquad\qquad$ (56)

Yearly change in π: $\qquad -1\rlap{.}''02 \times 10^{-6} \pi^2 V,$ $\qquad\qquad$ (57)

Yearly change in V: $\qquad +2.30 \times 10^{-5} \dfrac{\mu^2}{\pi} \,\text{km/sec},$ $\qquad$ (58)

Yearly change in m: $\qquad +2.22 \times 10^{-6} V\pi \,\text{mag}.$ $\qquad\qquad$ (59)

Here μ and π are expressed in seconds of arc, V in km/sec, and m in magnitudes (Schlesinger 1917).

Our first interest lies in the secular change of the proper motion—the secular perspective acceleration. This quantity is small, but the accumulated effect increases with the square of the time and therefore becomes significant as time goes on.

Attention has been drawn to the importance of using the observed secular acceleration (56) for deriving the radial velocity V independent of the Doppler shift. This procedure permits, in principle at least, a determination of the gravitational redshift, by correcting the observed redshift for the value of the radial velocity as determined geometrically from the observed perspective acceleration and the well-known values of the proper motion and parallax (Oort 1932).

In practice the situation is not favorable, since the secular changes in the proper motion and also in the parallax are unavoidably tied up with apparent secular changes caused by the reference stars (van de Kamp 1935a, 1939b, 1947c). Both the reductions from relative to absolute proper motion and parallax are subject to secular changes caused by the proper motions and parallaxes of the reference stars. The plate reduction of a measured position may be written as follows:

$$X = [Dx_s] + X' - [Dx'] , \qquad (60)$$

limiting ourselves to one co-ordinate. Here X' and x' represent the measured positions of central and reference stars. Full plate-constant reduction is insured by changing the dependence sufficiently often; hence the measured positions x' may be assumed to have been made in the co-ordinate system defined by the positions x_0 of the reference stars at an arbitrary zero epoch. Hence, in the usual notation,

$$x' = x_0 + \mu_x t + \pi P_a . \qquad (61)$$

The ideal reference system (x_0) would have neither proper motion nor parallax, in which case the reduced position would be

$$[Dx_s] + X' - [Dx_0] . \qquad (62)$$

Compared with the ideal, fixed reference stars, an effect

$$-[D(x' - x_0)] \qquad (63)$$

is therefore introduced into the reduced positions X of the central star. This effect may be written as

$$-t[D\mu_x] - P_a[D\pi] . \qquad (64)$$

The first term represents a uniformly accelerated motion,

$$-t[D_0\mu_x] - t^2[\Delta D\mu_x] . \qquad (65)$$

This is, with the opposite sign, the motion of the reference background, consisting of the reflected dependence mean proper motion at the zero epoch, $-[D_0\,\mu_x]$, and the reflected secular acceleration of this background, amounting to $-2[\Delta D\mu_x]$ yearly.

The second term of expression (64) represents a uniformly changing annual parallax of

$$- P_a[D_0\pi] - P_a{}'[\Delta D\pi] .\qquad(66)$$

This is, with the opposite sign, the effect of a uniformly changing annual parallax, consisting of the negative dependence mean parallax at the zero epoch, $-[D_0\pi]$, and the negative yearly secular change of this mean parallax, $-[\Delta D\pi]$.

The apparent secular changes in proper motion and parallax caused by the reference stars may be quite appreciable and may well be of the same order of size as the true secular changes in these quantities. Examples are Barnard's star (van de Kamp 1951) and Lalande 21185 (Lippincott 1960). A current study of Barnard's star at the Sproul Observatory shows a close agreement between the predicted secular acceleration ($+0\rlap{.}''00124\pm0\rlap{.}''00003$) and the observed acceleration ($+0\rlap{.}''00119\pm0\rlap{.}''00004$) corrected for the inherent acceleration of the reference system.

TABLE 8

REFERENCE STARS AND ROSS 614

No.	Diameter (mm)	Photo-visual Mag.	Spectrum	x_s (mm)	y_s (mm)	Dep. (1940)	ΔD/Year
1........	0.127	11.4	F0	−27.52	+08.25	0.340	−0.00052
2........	.126	11.4	F5	−25.97	−17.70	.288	+ .00001
3........	.112	11.6	F8	+19.78	+30.84	.253	− .00034
4........	.098	11.8	G:	+33.71	−21.39	0.119	+0.00085
Ross 614.	0.130	11.3	M2e	−07.79	+02.97	....	....

5.11. THE ASTROMETRIC BINARY ROSS 614

The technique and measurement of long-focus photographic astrometry will be illustrated for the interesting astrometric binary Ross 614; 06^h24^m3, $-02°44'$ (1900), photovisual magnitude 11.3, spectrum M2e. An early parallax determination at the McCormick Observatory for this red dwarf star revealed variable proper motion, from which a provisional orbital motion was determined (Reuyl 1936, Mitchell and Reuyl 1940). Subsequently, a comprehensive analysis was made. The combined photographic material of the Sproul (1938-1950) and McCormick (1927-1937) observatories (Lippincott 1951, 1955) was used. The Sproul plates were measured, using four reference stars, for which the relevant information is given in Table 8 (see also Fig. 6).

Because of the appreciable proper motion, two sets of dependences were used over the interval 1938-1950. The change of dependences and of the geometric accuracy (inverse weight) of the measured positions are illustrated in Table 9 and Figures 7 and 8. Maximum geometric accuracy is reached in the year 2083, when the minimum value of 1.253 is reached for the inverse weight. The same reference system can therefore be effectively used for several centuries to come.

The Sproul material consists of 309 plates, with 933 exposures, distributed over 92 nights and representing a total weight of 191. Since the Sproul material did not cover a sufficiently large interval for a good determination of the orbital motion, it was combined with published material from the McCormick Observatory. This material was based on measurements made on a system of five reference stars, all different from the Sproul reference stars. After correcting for a provisional value of the parallax, the McCormick measurements were reduced to the Sproul reference system by means of a linear transition, derived from a graphical adjustment, checked by appropriate measurements of the transition function (§ 4.7).

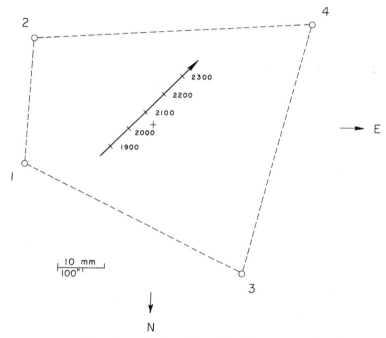

FIG. 6.—The astrometric binary Ross 614; reference stars and path

TABLE 9

ROSS 614: DEPENDENCES AND INVERSE WEIGHT

| EPOCH | DEPENDENCES | | | | INVERSE WEIGHT $1+D^2$ |
	1	2	3	4	
1900........	0.361	0.288	0.266	0.085	1.291
2000........	.309	.289	.232	.170	1.261
2100........	.257	.290	.198	.255	1.254
2200........	.205	.291	.164	.340	1.269
2300........	0.153	0.292	0.130	0.425	1.306

Analysis of combined Sproul and McCormick material yielded the following results for the photocentric orbit of the, then, unresolved astrometric binary:

Dynamical elements: $P = 16.5$ years, $e = 0.36$, $T = 1933.2$.

Geometric constants:

$$(B) = +0\rlap{.}''2166, \qquad \omega = 48°4,$$
$$(A) = +0\rlap{.}''1162, \qquad \Omega = 27°1,$$
$$(G) = +0\rlap{.}''0055, \qquad i = 52°4,$$
$$(F) = -0\rlap{.}''2606, \qquad a = +0\rlap{.}''306 \pm 0\rlap{.}''006 \text{ (p.e.)}$$
$$= 1.22 \text{ a.u.}$$

See also Figures 9 and 10.

After correction for orbital motion, the Sproul material yielded a value of $0\rlap{.}''991$ for the proper motion in position angle 134° of the barycenter, and a value of $+0\rlap{.}''2468 \pm 0\rlap{.}''0024$ (p.e.) for the relative parallax. Combining the latter value with determinations made elsewhere, an absolute parallax of $+0\rlap{.}''251 \pm 0\rlap{.}''0024$ was derived, which was used to compute the linear value of the semi-axis major of the photocentric orbit. The resulting lower limit for the mass of the companion therefore is

$$M_B - \beta(M_A + M_B) = aP^{-2/3}(M_A + M_B)^{2/3} = 0.189\,(M_A + M_B)^{2/3}\,\odot\,.$$

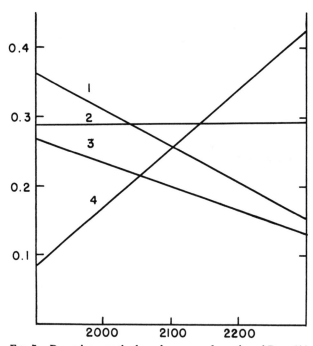

FIG. 7.—Dependence paths for reference configuration of Ross 614

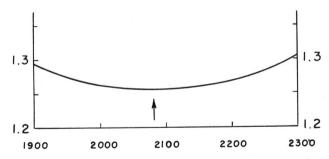

FIG. 8.—Inverse weight for position of Ross 614 at different epochs

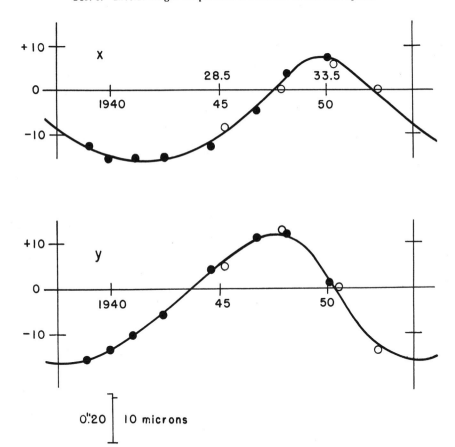

FIG. 9.—Ross 614. Time-displacement-curves in right ascension, *x*, and declination, *y*.
●—Sproul normal points; ○—McCormick normal points.

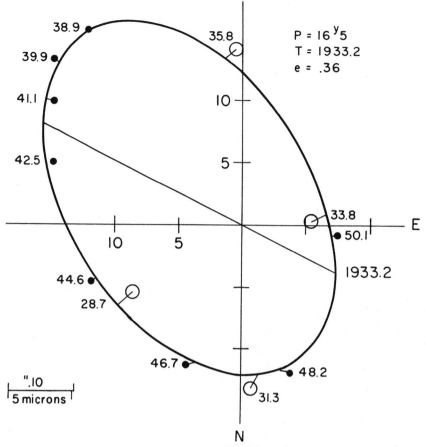

P = 16^{y}5
T = 1933.2
e = .36

".10
5 microns

FIG. 10.—Photocentric orbit of Ross 614. ●—Sproul normal points; ○—McCormick normal points. The radius in each case indicates the probable error.

FIG. 11.—Three successive 5-second exposures of Ross 614, taken by W. Baade with the 200-inch Hale telescope, March 23, 1955. Scale of original photo 1 mm = 11″.12. Enlarged 20 times.

526

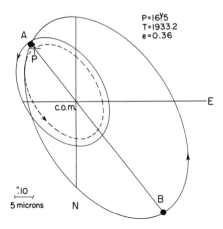

FIG. 12.—Ross 614. Orbits of components and of photocenter. The positions of A, B, and P are shown for March 23, 1955, the date of the visual discovery of Ross 614B.

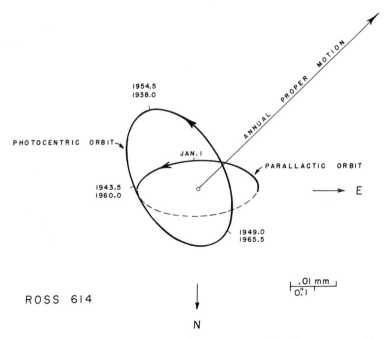

FIG. 13.—Annual proper motion, parallactic, and photocentric orbits of Ross 614. Since the observations are always made close to the meridian, only the full-drawn half of the parallactic orbit is accessible to observation.

In 1955, Ross 614 was visually and photographically resolved with the Hale reflector of Palomar Observatory by Walter Baade: distance $\rho = 1''19$, position angle $\theta = 36°$, estimated magnitude difference 3.5. The predicted value for the displacement Δ of the photocenter from the barycenter was $0''372$, the position angle $217°5$ (Fig. 11). Hence

$$B - \beta = \frac{\Delta}{\rho} = \frac{a}{a} = 0.31 ,$$

from which $a = 3.90$ a.u. and $M_A + M_B = a^3/P^2 = 0.22 \odot$. The photovisual magnitudes of Ross 614A and B are 11.3 and 14.8, respectively; the value $\Delta m = 3.5$ yields $\dot{\beta} = 0.04$. Hence B $= 0.35$ and, finally, $M_A = 0.14 \odot$ and $M_B = 0.08 \odot$. In this particular case, the principal uncertainty in the mass determination lies in the measured value of ρ. The apparent orbits of the components and of the photocenter are shown in Figure 12. Proper motion and parallactic and photocentric orbits are shown in Figure 13. The resulting path over the two decades 1938.0–1958.0 is illustrated in Figure 14.

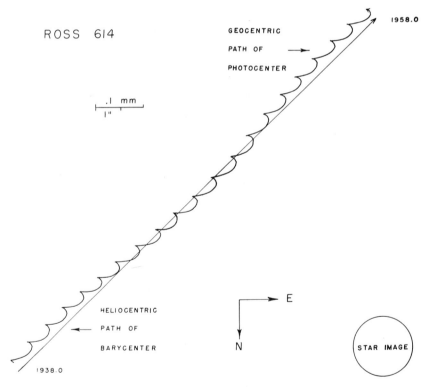

FIG. 14.—Path of Ross 614. The straight line refers to the heliocentric path of the barycenter. The helical line represents the geocentric path of the photocenter.

§ 6. GROUPS OF STARS

The technique and methods of long-focus photographic astrometry are applicable to problems involving fields of limited angular extent, where high accuracy is required. Examples of these problems are field proper motions, proper motions and internal motions of open clusters, and, finally, the measurement of the proper motions of distant companions.

6.1. REDUCTION OF RELATIVE PROPER MOTIONS

Proper motions are measured in any rectangular co-ordinate system, the one that is oriented closely to the equatorial system being most convenient. The results thus obtained are directly comparable with absolute proper-motion components measured in the equatorial co-ordinate system and referred to the sun. The orientation is found from stars of known absolute position if they occur in the field, or by a trail. For the simple case of linear plate constants, the measured differences m_x and m_y between the positions on two plates taken at different epochs are

$$m_x = t\mu_x + c_x + a_x x + b_x y + \delta_x,$$
$$m_y = t\mu_y + c_y + a_y x + b_y y + \delta_y. \tag{67}$$

Here t is the interval; μ_x and μ_y are the yearly proper motion and are practically equal to $\mu_\alpha \cos \delta$, μ_δ. The plate constants c_x, a_x, b_x, c_y, a_y, and b_y express differences in origin, orientation, scale, the first-order effects of precession, nutation, aberration, and refraction; δ_x and δ_y are accidental errors of observation. By using gratings, magnitude compensation may be provided. In case of large areas or large zenith distances, higher-order terms may have to be included.

The ideal way of determining the plate constants is from galaxies, which form an ideal frame of reference for proper motions of (inter)galactic objects. Until the practical advent of the extragalactic reference system, we shall have to use an intergalactic reference system based on stars. We may make use of stars with known proper motion. If this is not feasible, the plate constants may be derived from the stars themselves. For this purpose we consider the proper motion (μ_x, μ_y) as accidental deviations from the average reference system provided by the stars; the plate constants are obtained from the conditional equations

$$m_x = c_x + a_x x + b_x y, \qquad m_y = c_y + a_y x + b_y y. \tag{68}$$

The probable error of one equation in each co-ordinate is given by

$$R = 0.6745 \sqrt{\left\{ \frac{t^2 [\mu^2] + \delta^2}{n - 3} \right\}}. \tag{69}$$

The probable errors of the plate constants a and b are given by

$$r_a = \frac{R}{\sqrt{p_a}}, \qquad r_b = \frac{R}{\sqrt{p_b}}, \qquad (70)$$

where p_a and p_b are the weights of a and b.

In this way proper motions are obtained relative to the origin of an internal reference system represented by a plate-constant structure (c, a, b) in each coordinate. This reference system suffers a linear distortion term $(x\epsilon_a + y\epsilon_b)$ which is of the nature of proper motion. Here ϵ_a and ϵ_b are the true errors of the plate constants a and b, and are partly of cosmic origin. The motions referred to this reference system are thus affected by a systematic error $-(x\epsilon_a + y\epsilon_b)$, but we can only say that the plate-constant structure introduces a probable error, $\pm\sqrt{(x^2 r_a^2 + y^2 r_b^2)}$. No matter how small the errors of observation (δ_x, δ_y), the accuracy of the proper motions is definitely limited by the proper motions of the stars, by the "cosmic" errors.

Apart from this, the origin of the proper motion of the reference system remains undefined, and thus proper motions derived in this manner are called "relative." The part of the plate constants which is of cosmic origin for the relative motion, finds a counterpart in the cosmic part of the precession constants, which results from the same source, for the case of absolute motion (van de Kamp 1939a).

6.2. Absolute Field Proper Motions

An effective transfer from relative to absolute motions can be made for faint stars in small areas photographed with a long-focus instrument and centered on a standard star whose magnitude equation can be eliminated through a rotating sector or similar device. The importance of this method for obtaining absolute motions was pointed out by Schlesinger (1919) and again emphasized by Kapteyn (1922). The method has been further worked out, and results were obtained first by Alden and van de Kamp (1927), and later by van de Kamp and Vyssotsky (1937), and by Vyssotsky and Williams (1948).

6.3. Proper Motion of Clusters

The long-focus photographic technique can yield accurate proper motions for open clusters. Recent examples are studies of the open cluster IC 348 at the center of the ζ Persei association (Fredrick 1956) and of the open cluster NGC 6940 (Vasilevskis and Rach 1957).

6.4. Internal Proper Motions of Open Clusters

Extreme accuracy, based on large time intervals and rich plate material, may reveal the existence of internal proper motions, due to both dispersion in the space motions and perspective effects. An example is the afore-mentioned study by Fredrick (1956) of the nucleus IC 348 of the ζ Persei association from material obtained with both the Sproul and the McCormick long-focus refractors. The probable error of the annual proper motions was $\pm 0''0003$, the probable internal motion $\pm 0''0006$. Another example is the study of Praesepe by van de Kamp (1935b) from plates taken with the McCormick refractor. Measurements of the central part of the Praesepe cluster yielded a probable error of $\pm 0''00079$ and a probable internal motion of $\pm 0''00073$, in satisfactory agreement with the still more accurate values $\pm 0''00043$ and $\pm 0''00040$ from measurements made on plates taken with the Rutherfurd refractor with a time interval up to 65 years (Schilt and Titus 1938).

6.5. Distant Proper-Motion Companions

For the study of the path of a star and its distant proper-motion companion, the dependence method commends itself. Because of the spacing between the widely separated components, two different sets of dependences are generally needed. The slightly different "dependence backgrounds" must be kept in mind in interpreting any observed relative orbital motion. An example is the study of the classical visual binary σ Coronae Borealis A, B, and its companion σ Coronae Borealis c, at a distance of $633''$ from A and B (van de Kamp and Damkoehler 1953). The relative motion of c with respect to A and B, as found from the measured paths of A, B, and c, respectively, amounts to $+0''0004$ in right ascension and $+0''0071$ in declination. However, because of the proper motions (μ_x, μ_y) of the reference stars and the different dependences used for A, B, and c, the above values have to be corrected for the quantities $(D_c - D_{A, B}) \mu_x = +0''0011$ and $(D_c - D_{A, B}) \mu_y = -0''0024$, yielding a corrected value for the relative motion of c with respect to A and B amounting to $\mu_x = +0''0015$, $\mu_y = +0''0047$.

§ 7. RELATIVE POSITIONS OF VISUAL BINARIES

The photographic technique has proved to be extremely accurate for the measurement of wider pairs—about $3''$ and wider. The precise technique of long-focus photographic measurements of double stars was first developed by E. Hertzsprung (1920) with the visual refractor of 12.5-meter focal length of the Potsdam Observatory during the years 1914–1919. This type of observation has been continued by others, notably by K. Aa. Strand (1937). Again the photovisual technique has yielded positional results of extreme accuracy.

The photographic method is limited to doubles with separations exceeding about 0.15 mm on the plate. Below this limit it is, in general, difficult to obtain satisfactory exposures. The neighboring images affect each other, causing either a diminution or an increase in the separation between the images. Hence there is every reason to observe the "close" double stars visually, either by micrometer or by interferometer, and to limit the photographic observations to wider pairs for which the images are clearly resolved, i.e., separated on the photographic plate.

7.1. Magnitude Compensation

In observing the relative positions of the components of a resolved astrometric binary by the photographic method, the magnitude error is compensated by the use of a coarse grating in front of the objective. Such a grating produces diffraction images symmetrically located with respect to the central image; these images can be given any desired intensity with respect to the central image by proper choice of the thickness of the bars and of their spacing.

The linear separation, Δ, between the central and nth-order images in the focal plane is given by the formula

$$\Delta = \frac{nF\lambda}{l+d},\tag{71}$$

where F is the focal length, λ the (effective) wave length, l the width of the space between the bars, and d the width of a bar. The extinction in magnitudes for the central image is

$$5 \log \frac{l+d}{l}.\tag{72}$$

The difference in magnitude between the nth-order and central image is given by

$$\Delta m = 5 \left(\log \frac{nl\pi}{l+d} - \log \sin \frac{nl\pi}{l+d} \right).\tag{73}$$

The diffraction images are really spectra; in the photovisual technique, however, the first- and even higher-order spectra look like star images because of the narrow range in wave length (§ 2.3).

By employing a grating for which the first- (or higher-)order spectra of the brighter component are of approximately the same intensity as the central image of the fainter component, a compensation for possible magnitude error is provided by using the mean of the measured positions of the two spectral images instead of the central image. So long as the difference in intensity between the images does not exceed half a magnitude, the magnitude error is usually negligible; it is therefore sufficient to have a limited number of gratings, producing first-order spectra that are a whole number of magnitudes fainter than the central image. For example, in his work with the Sproul refractor, Strand used four gratings, made of duraluminum, giving differences of 1, 2, 3, and 4 mag., respectively, between the central image and the first-order spectra (Fig. 15, a and b).

7.2. At the Telescope and Measuring Machine

Multiple exposures are taken; each plate has two rows of exposures, in a west-to-east sequence parallel to the daily motion. After a series of about thirty to forty exposures has thus been obtained, either manually or by some automatic device, the telescope is given a small shift in declination, and the double

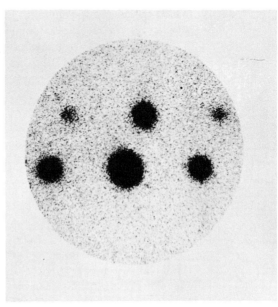

a　　　　　　　　　　　　　　　　　　*b*

Fig. 15.—*a* (*left*): A view through the slit of the dome of the Sproul refractor with one of the duraluminum gratings in front of the 24-inch objective. *b* (*right*): A 5-second exposure of Castor, enlarged 75 times. The separation of the components is 3″.74 or 0.198 mm on the plate. The first-order spectra are 1 mag. fainter than the central image. Photographed December 1, 1939, by K. Aa. Strand, with the Sproul 24-inch refractor, aperture reduced to 13 inches, Eastman IV-G emulsion, Wratten No. 12 (minus blue) filter. Scale of original photo 1 mm = 18″.87.

star itself or a neighboring bright star is used to impress a trail giving the equator of the date. As a rule, a second row of exposures is then taken, followed by a second trail. Since the exposures are taken without any guiding, the exposure times never exceed 30 seconds; on the other hand, no exposures below 3 seconds are used.

The relative position of the two components is obtained from the difference in $\Delta \alpha \cos \delta$ (Δx) and $\Delta \delta$ (Δy), measured, for example, on a precision long-screw machine. In each co-ordinate the plates are measured with the film turned toward the microscope and also through the glass, the plate being turned 180° between the two measures around an axis parallel to the vertical bisecting wire in the microscope. This eliminates errors arising from inaccuracy in the orientation between the axis of the screw, the bisecting wire, and the motion of the plate at right angles to the screw.

7.3. Accuracy

For an average plate with forty to fifty measured exposures, the relative position Δx, Δy of the two components is obtained with a probable error of $\pm 0''.006$. Part of this error, about $\pm 0''.004$, is due to the personal error of the measurer; it affects the distances rather than the position angles. As a rule, the error in orientation arising from inaccuracies in the trail is below $0°.01$ for any one plate and would therefore be less than $0''.002$ for a pair with a separation of $10''$.

One good photographic exposure with a long-focus refractor yields about the same accuracy as one visual measure with the micrometer. More than a hundred visual observations are required to obtain an accuracy comparable with that of one photographic plate, taken and measured as described above. These visual observations are all independent measures, each representing a single night's observations by one observer, and the mean result is considered to be made up of observations by many observers with different telescopes. In the case of visual observations of double stars, systematic and personal errors are appreciable; generally not more than a few settings make a single night's observation, and not more than three or four observations each year are warranted.

The superiority of the photographic observations is even more pronounced if the distances are considered. The visually observed distances between the components may be off as much as $0''.06$, even though they represent the mean of many observers with different telescopes. The systematic errors in visual measures do not cancel out, even over several decades, and may be found to depend on the separation of the components. For example, in the case of 70 Ophiuchi, the visual distances have been found to be systematically too small when the separation is over $2''.5$ and systematically too large when the separation is less than $2''.5$. Such a result may be due to one observer, who may have observed the star over several decades. In general, in very bright pairs such as γ Virginis, for example, the visual distances are measured too large. Systematic errors are not entirely absent in the photographic measures, but they are only about one-tenth as large, and their effect can be partly eliminated by repeated measurements of the same plate by different persons. In other words, photographic measurements take us one decimal further. Hence it pays to have forty to fifty measurable images on each plate and to take four to six plates each year.

REFERENCES

ALDEN, H. L.   1949   *Trans. Astr. Obs. Yale*, Vol. **15**, Part 2.

ALDEN, H. L., and
   KAMP, P. VAN DE   1927   *Mem. Nat. Acad. Sci.*, Vol. **22**, First Memoir, Part 3 ("Publications of the Leander McCormick Observatory," Vol. **4**), p. 301.

BELL, L.   1922   *The Telescope* (New York: McGraw-Hill Book Co.), p. 91.

BERGSTRAND, O.   1905   *A.N.*, **167**, 241.

BOS, W. H. VAN DEN   1926a   *Union Obs. Circ.*, **68**, 354.

                      1926b   *Bull. Astr. Inst. Netherlands*, **3**, 149.

                      1961   This volume, chap. 22.

FLETCHER, A.   1931   *M.N.*, **92**, 119.

FREDRICK, L. W.   1956   *A.J.*, **61**, 437.

                      1960   *Ibid.*, **65**, 628.

HALL, R. G., JR.   1951   *A.J.*, **55**, 215.

HERTZSPRUNG, E.   1912   *A.N.*, **192**, 315.

                      1920   *Pub. Ap. Obs. Potsdam*, Vol. **24**, No. 75.

KAMP, P. VAN DE   1935a   *A.J.*, **44**, 73.

                      1935b   *Ap. J.*, **81**, 297.

                      1939a   *A.J.*, **48**, 21.

                      1939b   *Ibid.*, p. 95.

                      1942   *Ibid.*, **49**, 149.

                      1943   *Ibid.*, **50**, 134.

                      1945a   *Ibid.*, **51**, 159.

                      1945b   *Ibid.*, p. 161.

                      1947a   *Ibid.*, **52**, 185.

                      1947b   *Ibid.*, p. 189.

                      1947c   *Ibid.*, p. 226.

                      1947d   *Ibid.*, p. 229.

                      1951   "Long-Focus Photographic Astrometry," *Pop. Astr.*, **59**, 65, 129, 176, 243; *Contr. Inst. Ap.*, Ser. A, No. 81; *Sproul Obs. Reprint*, No. 73.

                      1954   *A.J.*, **59**, 447.

                      1956a   *Photogrammetric Engineering*, **22**, 314 (No. 2).

                      1956b   *Vistas in Astronomy*, ed. A. BEER (New York and London: Pergamon Press), **2**, 1040.

                      1957   *The Present and Future of the Telescope of Moderate Size*, ed. F. B. WOOD (Philadelphia: University of Pennsylvania Press), Art. 11, p. 173.

KAMP, P. VAN DE	1958	"Visual Binaries," *Hdb. d. Phys.*, **50**, 187.
	1960	"Elements of Astromechanics," *J. Royal Astr. Soc. Canada*, **54**, 275.
KAMP, P. VAN DE, and DAMKOEHLER, J. E.	1953	*A.J.*, **58**, 25.
KAMP, P. VAN DE, and VYSSOTSKY, A. N.	1937	*Pub. Leander McCormick Obs.*, Vol. **7**.
KAPTEYN, J. C.	1922	*Bull. Astr. Inst. Netherlands*, **1**, 75.
KÖNIG, A.	1961	This volume, chap. 20.
LAND, G.	1942	*A.J.*, **49**, 153.
	1944	*Ibid.*, **51**, 25.
	1949a	*Trans. Astr. Obs. Yale*, Vol. **15**, Part 3.
	1949b	*A.J.*, **54**, 96.
LIPPINCOTT, S. L.	1951	*A.J.*, **55**, 236.
	1955	*Ibid.*, **60**, 379.
	1957	*Ibid.*, **62**, 55.
	1960	*Ibid.*, **65**, 445.
MITCHELL, S. A., and REUYL, D.	1940	*Pub. Leander McCormick Obs.*, **8**, 210.
OORT, J. H.	1932	*Bull. Astr. Inst. Netherlands*, **6**, 289.
PLUMMER, H. C.	1932	*M.N.*, **92**, 892.
REUYL, D.	1936	*A.J.*, **45**, 133.
SCHILT, J., and TITUS, J.	1938	*A.J.*, **46**, 197.
SCHLESINGER, F.	1911	*Ap. J.*, **33**, 8, 161.
	1917	*A.J.*, **30**, 137.
	1919	*Pub. Allegheny Obs.*, **4**, 19.
	1924	*Probleme der Astronomie: Seeliger Festschrift*, (Berlin: Springer), p. 422.
	1926	*A.J.*, **37**, 77.
	1927	*M.N.*, **87**, 506.
	1936	*Trans. Astr. Obs. Yale*, **8**, 8.
	1937	*A.J.*, **46**, 85, Table 3.
SCHLESINGER, F., and BARNEY, I.	1925	*Trans. Astr. Obs. Yale*, **4**, 5.
SLOCUM, F.	1924	*Ap. J.*, **59**, 108.
STRAND , K. AA.	1937	*Ann. Sterrewacht Leiden*, **18**, No. 2, 1.
	1946	*A.J.*, **52**, 3.
VASILEVSKIS, S., and RACH, R. A.	1957	*A.J.*, **62**, 175.
VYSSOTSKY, A. N., and WILLIAMS, E. T. R.	1948	*Pub. Leander McCormick Obs.*, Vol. **10**.

CHAPTER 22

Orbit Determinations of Visual Binaries

W. H. VAN DEN BOS

Union Observatory, Johannesburg, South Africa

§ 1. INTRODUCTION

THE observational data from which the orbit of a visual binary is derived
are mainly measurements of position angle and separation, made visually with
some form of micrometer and, more recently, interferometer. Photographic
observations, provided that suitable precautions as outlined by Hertzsprung
(1920) have been taken, are of greater accuracy and freedom from systematic
errors but cannot be obtained for the very close pairs which at present constitute
the majority of the double stars suitable for orbit determination.

It is found, in general, that micrometer measures of position angle are more
consistent and accurate than those of separation and that the errors of observation in both, *when expressed in seconds of arc*, diminish with decreasing separation. However, *when expressed as a percentage of the separation*, the reverse is the
case, so that for the purpose of orbit computation these errors are the more
serious, the closer the pair. The computer of a double-star orbit will therefore
never be tempted to follow the habitual practice of the computer of a first orbit
for a minor planet or comet and to derive the elements from the minimum
number of measurements, disregarding errors of observation.

A further consequence of the relatively large errors inherent in double-star
measurements is that, if the result of the computation is to be a fair approximation to the real orbit, the observations must cover a considerable fraction of the
entire ellipse. Much time has been wasted in computing meaningless orbits
based on entirely inadequate data. A diagram showing the observed arc will in
most cases enable the computer to decide whether or not orbit computation is
worthwhile.

§ 2. THE APPARENT ORBIT

The first step in the computation is to compile a list of the available observations. This would be an extremely laborious and time-consuming task, if it were

537

not for the existence of general catalogues and of up-to-date card catalogues at Lick Observatory, Mount Hamilton, California (entire sky), and Union Observatory, Johannesburg, South Africa (pairs south of $-19°$ declination).

In theory, the observations should first be reduced to a standard equator, though in practice this may often be neglected relative to the accuracy of the measurements. The correction for precession, to be added to the observed angle, is given by the approximate formula

$$\Delta\theta = -0°\!.00557 \sin a \sec \delta \ (t - t_0) \ ,$$

where t_0 is the epoch of the standard equator chosen, and the correction to be added for proper motion by

$$\Delta\theta = -0°\!.00417 \ \mu_a \sin \delta \ (t - t_0) \ ,$$

where μ_a is the proper motion in right ascension, in seconds of time per year. The separations should be reduced to the standard epoch by adding a correction for variation of the system's distance from us, given by

$$\Delta\rho = +0.00000102 p \ V\rho(t - t_0) \ ,$$

where p is the parallax in seconds of arc and V is the radial velocity in kilometers per second. If (photographic observations) the measurements have been made in rectangular co-ordinates x (declination increasing) and y (right ascension increasing), the total corrections to be added are

$$\Delta x = [+0.00000102 p V x + (0.0000972 \sin a \sec \delta$$
$$+0.0000727 \ \mu_a \sin \delta)y](t - t_0) \ ,$$

$$\Delta y = [+0.00000102 p V y - (0.0000972 \sin a \sec \delta$$
$$+0.0000727 \ \mu_a \sin \delta)x](t - t_0) \ .$$

Fletcher (1931) has shown that the observed co-ordinates ρ and θ or x and y, after reduction by the above formulae, still require the addition of the further corrections,

$$\Delta x = +\mu_x z(t - t_0) \quad \text{and} \quad \Delta y = +\mu_y z(t - t_0) \ ,$$

where μ_x and μ_y are the components of the proper motion in the direction of increasing declination and increasing right ascension, respectively, expressed in *radians* per year, and z is the third co-ordinate, along the line of sight, in seconds of arc, positive in the direction away from the observer. The appearance of this co-ordinate shows that these corrections cannot be applied until z has become approximately known by a preliminary orbit determination, combined with observations in the line of sight.

To minimize the effect of observational errors, it is advisable to plot the angles and distances or the rectangular co-ordinates separately against the time of observation and to draw smooth interpolation-curves representing the general run of the observations. If this device were completely successful in eliminating errors, then values read from these curves would satisfy two conditions (always presupposing unperturbed Keplerian orbital motion): (1) they would fall on an ellipse (the "apparent orbit") having the primary star, taken as origin of co-ordinates, somewhere inside it; (2) the law of areas,

$$\rho^2 \frac{d\theta}{dt} = x \frac{dy}{dt} - y \frac{dx}{dt} = \text{the double areal constant } c,$$

where $d\theta/dt$ is in *radians* per year.

In general, these conditions will not be satisfied, and the interpolation-curves have to be modified until they are. For difficult (close or unequal) pairs, this is often easier said than done. The corrected curves may now be used to derive the orbital elements.

§ 3. THE TRUE ORBIT

The apparent orbit is the projection of the true orbit on the plane through the primary star perpendicular to the line of sight. Two orbits, symmetrical to this plane, give the same apparent orbit, and it is only by observations along the line of sight (radial velocity, light-time) that they can be distinguished.

With the primary as origin, we have in the plane of projection the axis of x, positive toward the north, and the axis of y, positive toward east or following. The axis of z is the line of sight, positive in the direction away from the observer. It is worth noting that in positional astronomy the x-axis is usually taken positive toward the east and the y-axis positive toward the north, but in dealing with double stars this would be illogical and confusing, as the position angle is counted from north to east.

In the plane of the true orbit the axis of X is the major axis of the ellipse, positive toward periastron, and the axis of Y, the latus rectum, positive 90° from the positive X-axis in the direction in which the motion takes place. The polar co-ordinates are the radius vector, r, and the true anomaly, v.

The true and apparent orbits can be defined by a set of seven orbital elements: (1) period of revolution P in years or mean motion, $n = 360°/P$; (2) epoch of periastron passage, T; (3) eccentricity e (of the true orbit); (4) semi-major axis a (of the true orbit) in seconds of arc; (5) inclination i, the angle between the planes of true and apparent orbit (it is taken in the first quadrant when the position angles increase with the time, in the second when they decrease; when i is zero—direct motion—or 180°—retrograde motion—the true and apparent orbits coincide; when i is 90°, the apparent orbit is a straight line through the primary); (6) node Ω, the position angle of the line of intersection of the planes of true and apparent orbit (in the absence of observations in the line of sight, it is not possible to distinguish between ascending and descending nodes and the value less than 180° is taken; should the ambiguity in the plane of the true orbit have been removed, the ascending node is given); (7) longitude of periastron ω, the angle in the plane of the true orbit from node to periastron, in the direction of motion in the true orbit (it can have any value from $0°$ to $360°$ and is affected by the $180°$ uncertainty in the node).

If the inclination is zero or $180°$, the node should be taken as zero, so that, for direct motion, ω, and, for retrograde motion, $360° - \omega$, become the position angles of periastron. If the true orbit is a circle, ω should be taken as zero, so that T becomes the epoch of *nodal* passage. It will therefore require to be changed by half the period if the ascending node should be found greater than $180°$.

Unfortunately, not all orbit computers have kept to the definitions of the elements as given here and adopted by the International Astronomical Union (1935). This has caused confusion and errors in ephemeris computations, as the computers sometimes failed to indicate how their elements were to be interpreted where they did not conform to the definitions adopted by the I.A.U.

How to select the correct set of values of ω and Ω from radial-velocity observations will be shown later, under § 10.

The elements as here defined refer to the *relative* orbit of the secondary around the primary. If the mass of the primary is denoted by m_1, of the secondary by m_2, we have, for the *absolute* orbits of primary and secondary around their center of gravity,

$$a_1 = \frac{m_2}{m_1 + m_2} a \quad \text{and} \quad a_2 = \frac{m_1}{m_1 + m_2} a,$$

the other elements being the same as for the relative orbit, except that $\omega_1 = \omega \pm 180°$.

The elements can be divided into two groups: the *dynamical* elements, P (or n), T, and e, which (disregarding the effect of light-time on T and of its variation on P and n) specify characteristics of the true orbit, independent of the observer, and the *geometrical* elements, a, i, ω, and Ω, which are affected by the system's distance (a) and direction (i, ω, Ω) from the observer. In orbit and ephemeris computation, as well as differential correction of the orbit, the work may be greatly simplified by the introduction of the so-called Thiele-Innes constants, a set of parameters which will be defined in what follows.

The position at time t of the companion in the true orbit is given by the formulae

$$M = n(t - T) = E - e° \sin E \qquad (e° = 57°\!.2958e),$$

$$X = \frac{r}{a} \cos v = \cos E - \sin \phi \qquad (\sin \phi = e), \qquad (1)$$

$$Y = \frac{r}{a} \sin v = \cos \phi \sin E.$$

Tables of X and Y as functions of M and e are given in the Appendix to *Circular No. 71* of the Union Observatory.

By projection, the companion's position in the apparent orbit becomes

$$\rho \cos (\theta - \Omega) = r \cos (v + \omega) ,$$
$$\rho \sin (\theta - \Omega) = r \sin (v + \omega) \cos i ,$$
$$z = r \sin (v + \omega) \sin i ,$$

which readily reduce to

$$x = \rho \cos \theta = r \cos v \ (\cos \omega \cos \Omega - \sin \omega \sin \Omega \cos i)$$
$$+ r \sin v \ (-\sin \omega \cos \Omega - \cos \omega \sin \Omega \cos i) ,$$

$$y = \rho \sin \theta = r \cos v \ (\cos \omega \sin \Omega + \sin \omega \cos \Omega \cos i) \qquad (2)$$
$$+ r \sin v \ (-\sin \omega \sin \Omega + \cos \omega \cos \Omega \cos i),$$

$$z = r \cos v \sin \omega \sin i + r \sin v \cos \omega \sin i .$$

The Thiele-Innes constants are defined by

$$A = a \ (\cos \omega \cos \Omega - \sin \omega \sin \Omega \cos i) ,$$
$$B = a \ (\cos \omega \sin \Omega + \sin \omega \cos \Omega \cos i) ,$$
$$C = a \sin \omega \sin i ,$$
$$F = a \ (-\sin \omega \cos \Omega - \cos \omega \sin \Omega \cos i) , \qquad (3)$$
$$G = a \ (-\sin \omega \sin \Omega + \cos \omega \cos \Omega \cos i) ,$$
$$H = a \cos \omega \sin i .$$

Using equations (1) and (3), we derive from equation (2)

$$x = AX + FY, \qquad y = BX + GY, \qquad z = CX + HY . \qquad (4)$$

In formulae (4), the dynamical and geometrical elements have been separated, as the Thiele-Innes constants are functions of the four geometrical elements a, i, ω, and Ω, while X and Y are functions of the three dynamical elements P (or n), T, e, and the time t.

The relative radial velocity of the secondary with respect to the primary is found by

$$\frac{dz}{dt} = C \frac{dX}{dt} + H \frac{dY}{dt} = nC \frac{dX}{dM} + nH \frac{dY}{dM} \qquad (dM \text{ in degrees});$$

but to reduce from seconds of arc per year to kilometers per second requires the introduction of the absolute parallax p to reduce seconds of arc to astronomical units and the factor 4.737 to reduce astronomical units per year to kilometers per second. The relative radial velocity in kilometers per second is, therefore,

$$V = L \frac{dX}{dM} + N \frac{dY}{dM}, \qquad (5)$$

where

$$pL = 4.737nC \quad \text{and} \quad pN = 4.737nH. \tag{6}$$

Because of the 180° uncertainty in ω, the constants C, H, pL, and pN must be given the double sign $\pm$ or $\mp$. The *upper* signs correspond to the set ω, Ω, where Ω is less than 180°.

The Thiele-Innes constants are computed from the geometrical elements by equation (3) or by

$$A + G = a(1 + \cos i) \cos (\omega + \Omega),$$
$$A - G = a(1 - \cos i) \cos (\omega - \Omega),$$
$$B - F = a(1 + \cos i) \sin (\omega + \Omega), \tag{3a}$$
$$-B - F = a(1 - \cos i) \sin (\omega - \Omega),$$

the latter giving at once, for the reverse computation,

$$\tan (\omega + \Omega) = \frac{B - F}{A + G},$$

$$\tan (\omega - \Omega) = \frac{-B - F}{A - G}, \tag{7}$$

$$a(1 + \cos i) = (A + G) \sec (\omega + \Omega) = (B - F) \operatorname{cosec} (\omega + \Omega),$$
$$a(1 - \cos i) = (A - G) \sec (\omega - \Omega) = (-B - F) \operatorname{cosec} (\omega - \Omega).$$

The quadrants of $\omega + \Omega$ and $\omega - \Omega$ are unambiguously determined by the Thiele-Innes constants, as in equations (3a), $1 + \cos i$, $1 - \cos i$, and a cannot be negative; but, since we may add 360° to $\omega + \Omega$ without changing its quadrant, we obtain two solutions ω, Ω and $\omega \pm 180°$, $\Omega \pm 180°$. The solution with Ω less than 180° is to be taken. Checks are

$$AF + BG + CH = 0, \qquad A^2 + B^2 + C^2 = F^2 + G^2 + H^2 = a^2,$$
$$AG - BF = a^2 \cos i.$$

At periastron we have, by equations (1) and (4),

$$X = 1 - e, \qquad Y = 0, \qquad x_0 = A(1 - e), \qquad y_0 = B(1 - e),$$

and, at apastron,

$$X = -1 - e, \qquad Y = 0, \qquad x_{180} = A(-1 - e), \qquad y_{180} = B(-1 - e),$$

so that the co-ordinates of the center of the apparent orbit are

$$x_c = -Ae, \qquad y_c = -Be.$$

For the positive extremity of the minor axis we have, by equations (1) and (4),

$$E = +90°, \qquad X = -e, \qquad Y = \cos \phi, \qquad x_{+90} = -Ae + F \cos \phi;$$
$$y_{+90} = -Be + G \cos \phi \qquad \text{or} \qquad F = \sec \phi(x_{+90} + Ae);$$
$$G = \sec \phi(y_{+90} + Be).$$

The geometrical interpretation of the Thiele-Innes constants is therefore that A and B are the co-ordinates of the projected periastron, referred to the *center* of the apparent orbit as origin, and F and G are the co-ordinates of the projected point where the positive minor axis meets Kepler's auxiliary circle, referred to the *center* of the apparent orbit. The direction cosines of the positive directions of the major and minor axes of the true orbit are

$$\frac{A}{a}, \frac{B}{a}, \frac{C}{a}, \quad \text{and} \quad \frac{F}{a}, \frac{G}{a}, \frac{H}{a}.$$

§ 4. COMPUTATION OF THE ORBITAL ELEMENTS

The corrected interpolation-curves (θ, t) and (ρ, t) or (x, t) and (y, t) having been obtained, the next step is to derive the orbital elements. If the observations cover a full revolution or more, the period P is found from the recurrence of angles and separations or of the rectangular co-ordinates. This value is then used to reduce all the observations to a single revolution.

Let C be the center of the apparent orbit and x_{max}, x_{min}, y_{max}, y_{min} the extreme values of x and y read from the curves; then we have

$$x_c = \tfrac{1}{2}(x_{max} + x_{min}), \qquad y_c = \tfrac{1}{2}(y_{max} + y_{min}),$$

as a diameter is midway between the tangents parallel to it.

Periastron (x_0, y_0) and apastron (x_{180}, y_{180}) are the two points separated in time by $P/2$ for which $x_0 - x_c = x_c - x_{180}$ and $y_0 - y_c = y_c - y_{180}$. We read from the curves the co-ordinates for a few arbitrary sets of times t and $t + P/2$ and plot the differences $x_t + x_{t+P/2} - 2x_c$ and $y_t + y_{t+P/2} - 2y_c$ against t, thereby locating the times T and $T + P/2$ for which these differences are zero. Periastron is on the same side of C as the primary. Apart from errors in the curves, the same result for T should be found from x as from y; if not, the mean or, depending on the character of the curves, a weighted mean must be taken and the curves corrected so that the conditions used in locating periastron remain satisfied.

Having located T and $T + P/2$ we read from the curves the co-ordinates x_0, y_0, and x_{180}, y_{180} at these times. The eccentricity is then given by

$$e = \sin \phi = \frac{x_c}{x_c - x_0} = \frac{x_c}{x_{180} - x_c} = \frac{y_c}{y_c - y_0} = \frac{y_c}{y_{180} - y_c}.$$

The dynamical elements are now known, so that X and Y can be found for any time t by equation (1). The Thiele-Innes constants may be obtained from two positions (or more, by least squares) by equations (4), or they may be found directly from the extremities of the projected axes: the times when the companion reaches the extremities of the minor axis are given by

$$t_{\pm 90} = T \pm n^{-1}(90° - e°),$$

and the co-ordinates,

$$x_{+90}, \qquad y_{+90}, \qquad x_{-90}, \qquad y_{-90},$$

are read from the curves. Then we have

$$A = x_0 - x_c = x_c - x_{180} ,$$

$$B = y_0 - y_c = y_c - y_{180} ,$$

$$F = \sec \phi (x_{+90} - x_c) = \sec \phi (x_c - x_{-90}) ,$$

$$G = \sec \phi (y_{+90} - y_c) = \sec \phi (y_c - y_{-90}) .$$

Finally, $a, i, \omega, \Omega, C, H, pL$, and pN are computed by equations (7), (3), and (6).

Provided that the period can be determined by recurrence, the method here outlined is general; it includes the case of a straight-line or nearly straight-line apparent orbit, for which special solutions have been sought in the past.[1] For apparent orbits of this type, orbit computation will rarely be attempted before the observations cover a full revolution or more; but when the apparent orbit is more open, a preliminary orbit is usually already derived from observations covering only a part of the complete ellipse. The number of methods which have been devised to solve this problem is so large that it is quite impracticable to discuss, or even to mention, them all here. Broadly speaking, they may be divided into two categories—the graphical and the analytical methods. It must suffice to give an example of each, and the graphical method of Zwiers (1896) and the analytical method of Thiele (1883, and van den Bos 1932a) have been chosen.

4.1. Zwiers' Method

The co-ordinates of a number of points on the apparent orbit are read from the corrected interpolation-curves, plotted, and the ellipse which best satisfies them is constructed. Let its center be C and the origin of co-ordinates, which represents the primary star, O. Then CO is drawn; it meets the ellipse in the points P_0, the projected periastron, on the side of O and P_{180}, the projected apastron, on the side of C. (Should C coincide with O, then the true orbit is a circle, the major axis of the apparent orbit is the line of nodes, its length $2a$, the ratio of minor to major axis is $\cos i$, and $e = 0$, $\omega = 0°$, $T =$ nodal passage.) Construct the conjugate diameter to P_0P_{180}; this is the projected minor axis and meets the ellipse in P_{+90} and P_{-90}, P_{+90} being reached first when proceeding

---

[1] If the apparent orbit is a straight line or a very narrow ellipse, the work may be simplified by rotating the axes of co-ordinates over an angle θ', so that the new x'-axis approximately coincides with the major axis of the apparent orbit. We have

$$x' = \rho \cos (\theta - \theta') = A'X + F'Y , \qquad y' = \rho \sin (\theta - \theta') = B'X + G'Y ,$$

and derive the dynamical elements, as well as A' and F', from x', using y' only to find B' and G'. Then return to the original axes by

$$A = A' \cos \theta' - B' \sin \theta' , \qquad B = A' \sin \theta' + B' \cos \theta' ,$$

$$F = F' \cos \theta' - G' \sin \theta' , \qquad G = F' \sin \theta' + G' \cos \theta' .$$

from P_0 in the direction of motion. Let the co-ordinates of C be x_c, y_c; of P_0, x_0, y_0; etc.; then we have

$$e = \sin \phi = \frac{CO}{CP_0} = \frac{CO}{CP_{180}} = \frac{x_c}{x_c - x_0} = \frac{x_c}{x_{180} - x_c} = \frac{y_c}{y_c - y_0} = \frac{y_c}{y_{180} - y_c},$$

$$A = x_0 - x_c = x_c - x_{180},$$

$$B = y_0 - y_c = y_c - y_{180},$$

$$F = \sec \phi (x_{+90} - x_c) = \sec \phi (x_c - x_{-90}),$$

$$G = \sec \phi (y_{+90} - y_c) = \sec \phi (y_c - y_{-90}).$$

When this stage is reached, an ephemeris for x and y with argument M should be computed. From the interpolation-curves read the times at which the computed x and y for a few selected values of the mean anomaly have been observed, plot the mean anomalies against these times, and pass a straight line through the plot. Then T is the time for which this line gives $M = 0°$, and the slope of the line gives the mean motion n. If P_0 and P_{180} both lie within the observed arc, it is simpler, though less accurate, to read on the curves the times t_0 and t_{180} at which $x = x_0$, $y = y_0$, and $x = x_{180}$, $y = y_{180}$. Then $T = t_0$ and $P = 2|t_0 - t_{180}|$.

In the construction of the apparent ellipse (ellipsograph, two pins and thread, projection of a circle) its major and minor axes will already have been located. If the computer prefers to do so, the eccentricity and Thiele-Innes constants may be found without further construction. Read the co-ordinates x_c and y_c of the center, x_1 and y_1 of an extremity of the major axis, x_2 and y_2 of an extremity of the minor axis, and compute

$$a^2 = (x_1 - x_c)^2 + (y_1 - y_c)^2, \qquad b^2 = (x_2 - x_c)^2 + (y_2 - y_c)^2,$$

$$m_1 = \frac{y_c}{x_c}, \qquad \tan \psi = \frac{y_1 - y_c}{x_1 - x_c},$$

$$a = a^2 \sin^2 \psi + b^2 \cos^2 \psi, \qquad \beta = -\sin \psi \cos \psi (a^2 - b^2),$$

$$\gamma = a^2 \cos^2 \psi + b^2 \sin^2 \psi, \qquad m = -\frac{a + \beta m_1}{\beta + \gamma m_1},$$

$$e^2 = \sin^2 \phi = \frac{a x_c^2 + 2 \beta x_c y_c + \gamma y_c^2}{a^2 b^2},$$

$$A = -\frac{x_c}{e}, \qquad B = -\frac{y_c}{e},$$

$$F = \pm a b \sec \phi (a + 2 m \beta + m^2 \gamma)^{-1/2}, \qquad G = mF,$$

the sign of F being determined from the direction of motion so that the point $(F \cos \phi, G \cos \phi)$ is reached after periastron and before apastron passage (van den Bos 1927).

4.2. THIELE'S METHOD

Thiele's analytical method uses three normal places derived from the corrected interpolation-curves,

$$
\begin{array}{ccccc}
t_1 & \rho_1 & \theta_1 & x_1 & y_1 , \\
t_2 & \rho_2 & \theta_2 & x_2 & y_2 , \\
t_3 & \rho_3 & \theta_3 & x_3 & y_3 ,
\end{array}
$$

and the double areal constant,

$$
c = \rho^2 \frac{d\theta}{dt} = x\,\frac{dy}{dt} - y\,\frac{dx}{dt} ,
$$

which has been found in testing the curves for the law of areas; $d\theta/dt$ is expressed in radians per year and is, of course, negative for retrograde motion. The mean motion, μ, is also expressed in radians per year:

$$
\mu = \frac{2\pi}{P} = \frac{n}{57°2958} .
$$

The double areal constant is twice the area of the apparent orbit divided by the period; the area of an ellipse is π times the product of its semiaxes; the area of the rectangle having the axes as sides equals the area of a parallelogram having any two conjugate diameters (for which we take here the projected axes of the true orbit) as sides; hence $c = \mu \cos \phi \, (AG - BF)$. Put

$$
\Delta_{p,\,q} = \rho_p \rho_q \sin (\theta_q - \theta_p) = x_p y_q - x_q y_p = (AG - BF)(X_p Y_q - X_q Y_p) ;
$$

then

$$
\frac{\Delta_{p,\,q}}{c} = \frac{1}{\mu}\,[\sin (E_q - E_p) - \sin \phi\,(\sin E_q - \sin E_p)] ,
$$

and

$$
t_q - t_p - \frac{\Delta_{p,\,q}}{c} = \frac{1}{\mu}\,[(E_q - E_p) - \sin (E_q - E_p)] .
$$

This is Thiele's fundamental formula; after multiplication by $\tfrac{1}{2}c$, it is an expression for sector minus triangle. Put $E_2 - E_1 = u$ and $E_3 - E_2 = v$, so that $E_3 - E_1 = u + v$, then

$$
t_2 - t_1 - \frac{\Delta_{1,\,2}}{c} = \frac{1}{\mu}\,(u - \sin u) ,
$$

$$
t_3 - t_2 - \frac{\Delta_{2,\,3}}{c} = \frac{1}{\mu}\,(v - \sin v) ,
$$

$$
t_3 - t_1 - \frac{\Delta_{1,\,3}}{c} = \frac{1}{\mu}\,[(u + v) - \sin (u + v)] .
$$

The left-hand members are derived from the observational data. By trial and error, μ is to be found so that the sum of u and v from the first two equals $u + v$ from the third. If this sum is greater than $u + v$, the trial value of μ is too small. Using a table of arc minus sine (van den Bos 1932b) and plotting the differences (sum u and v minus $u + v$) against μ, or using the device given by Dommanget (1955), the correct value of μ is quickly obtained. Then $P = 6.28319/\mu$, and $n = 57°2958\mu$. As

$$\Delta_{p,\,q} = \frac{c}{\mu} \left[\sin(E_q - E_p) - \sin \phi (\sin E_q - \sin E_p) \right],$$

we have

$$\Delta_{2,\,3} \sin u - \Delta_{1,\,2} \sin v = \frac{c}{\mu} \sin \phi \sin E_2 \left[\sin u + \sin v - \sin(u + v) \right],$$

$$\Delta_{2,\,3} \cos u + \Delta_{1,\,2} \cos v - \Delta_{1,\,3} = \frac{c}{\mu} \sin \phi \cos E_2 \left[\sin u + \sin v - \sin(u + v) \right],$$

$$\Delta_{2,\,3} + \Delta_{1,\,2} - \Delta_{1,\,3} = \frac{c}{\mu} \left[\sin u + \sin v - \sin(u + v) \right]$$

so that

$$\sin \phi \sin E_2 = \frac{\Delta_{2,\,3} \sin u - \Delta_{1,\,2} \sin v}{\Delta_{2,\,3} + \Delta_{1,\,2} - \Delta_{1,\,3}},$$

$$\sin \phi \cos E_2 = \frac{\Delta_{2,\,3} \cos u + \Delta_{1,\,2} \cos v - \Delta_{1,\,3}}{\Delta_{2,\,3} + \Delta_{1,\,2} - \Delta_{1,\,3}},$$

giving $\sin \phi = e$ and E_2; $E_1 = E_2 - u$, $E_3 = E_2 + v$. Compute M_1, M_2, M_3 by $M = E - e \sin E$ and T by $T = t - M/n$; the three values for T should agree. By $X = \cos E - \sin \phi$, $Y = \cos \phi \sin E$, compute $X_1, Y_1, X_2, Y_2, X_3, Y_3$. By equations (4) we finally obtain A, B, F, G from two of the normal places, using the third as a check. An ephemeris should now be computed.

If we should find $\sin \phi \sin E_2 = 0$ and $\sin \phi \cos E_2 = 0$, then $\sin \phi = e = 0$, the true orbit is a circle, and E_2 becomes indeterminate. By convention, "periastron" will now be taken at the node, but it is, in fact, arbitrary. We take it provisionally at t_2; then we have

$$E_2 = M_2 = 0, \qquad E_1 = M_1 = -u, \qquad E_3 = M_3 = +v, \qquad \text{and}$$

$$X = \cos M, \qquad Y = \sin M.$$

We compute provisional values of the Thiele-Innes constants, as in the general case, and from them, a, i, Ω, ω by equations (7). The epoch of nodal passage T is now found from $T = t_2 - \omega/n$, and the final elements are a, i, Ω, as already found, $\omega = 0$, $A = a \cos \Omega$, $B = a \sin \Omega$, $F = -B \cos i$, $G = +A \cos i$, $C = 0$, $H = \pm a \sin i$, $pL = 0$, $pN = \pm 4.737\, n\, a \sin i$.

§ 5. COMPUTATION OF AN EPHEMERIS

In any orbit computation it is advisable to compute an ephemeris at the earliest possible stage for comparison with the observations, as this may save unnecessary labor if the orbit obtained should prove to be unsatisfactory. An ephemeris, with the mean anomaly as argument, can be computed as soon as the eccentricity and the constants A, B, F, and G are known.

To avoid unnecessary interpolation in the XY tables, it is advisable to use whole degrees of M as argument. If e is small, equal steps of $12°$ in M will in most cases be found sufficient; for larger values of e, shorter steps near periastron and longer near apastron are recommended. X and Y need be taken out for M only from $0°$ to $180°$, as x and y for negative M are found by changing the signs of FY and GY, while AX and BX remain the same:

$$\tan \theta = \frac{y}{x}, \qquad \rho = x \sec \theta = y \operatorname{cosec} \theta, \qquad t = T + \frac{M}{n}.$$

Circular orbit:

$$\rho \cos (\theta - \Omega) = a \cos M,$$

$$\rho \sin (\theta - \Omega) = a \cos i \sin M.$$

§ 6. DIFFERENTIAL CORRECTIONS

If the representation of the observations by the orbit is not deemed entirely satisfactory or if later observations show small deviations from an earlier orbit without justifying a fresh determination, the computer may wish to correct the orbit differentially.

The equations of condition, in rectangular co-ordinates, are

$$\Delta x \text{ (observed minus computed)} = X\Delta A + Y\Delta F + P_x\Delta e + Q_x n\Delta T + R_x\Delta n,$$

$$\Delta y \text{ (observed minus computed)} = X\Delta B + Y\Delta G + P_y\Delta e + Q_y n\Delta T + R_y\Delta n,$$

(8)

where

$$P_x = A \frac{\partial X}{\partial e} + F \frac{\partial Y}{\partial e}, \qquad Q_x = - A \frac{\partial X}{\partial M} - F \frac{\partial Y}{\partial M}, \qquad R_x = - (t - T)Q_x,$$

$$P_y = B \frac{\partial X}{\partial e} + G \frac{\partial Y}{\partial e}, \qquad Q_y = - B \frac{\partial X}{\partial M} - G \frac{\partial Y}{\partial M}, \qquad R_y = - (t - T)Q_y,$$

and the partial derivatives are

$$\frac{\partial X}{\partial e} = - 0.01 \left[1 + \frac{Y^2}{\cos^2 \phi (\cos^2 \phi - X \sin \varphi)} \right],$$

$$\frac{\partial Y}{\partial e} = + 0.01 \frac{XY}{\cos^2 \phi (\cos^2 \phi - X \sin \phi)},$$

$$\frac{\partial X}{\partial M} = - 0.017453 \frac{Y}{\cos^2 \phi (\cos^2 \varphi - X \sin \phi)},$$

$$\frac{\partial X}{\partial M} = +0.017453 \frac{\cos \phi (X + \sin \phi)}{\cos^2 \phi - X \sin \phi},$$

if the steps are 0.01 for Δe and the degree for ΔM as in the XY tables. The units for Δx, Δy, ΔA, ΔB, ΔF, and ΔG are seconds of arc; for ΔT, years; for Δn, degrees per year. There is no need to compute the partial derivatives by these formulae, as the mean of the preceding and following differences in the XY tables, taken horizontally for e and vertically for M, is a sufficient approximation. Their signs are fixed by the rules: $\partial X/\partial e$ always negative; $\partial Y/\partial e$ negative when X and Y have opposite signs; $\partial X/\partial M$ negative when Y is positive; $\partial Y/\partial M$ negative when $X + e$ is negative. The relative radial velocity may be computed in the same way; but near periastron, if the eccentricity is large, the formulae should be used.

If the apparent orbit is fairly open, the computer may prefer to correct the elements, semi-major axis excepted, by using the angles only, these being generally more reliable and accurate than separations. The equation of condition, then, is

$$\Delta \theta \text{(observed minus computed)} = \Delta \Omega + b\Delta i + c\Delta \omega + d\Delta e + \epsilon \Delta \tau + f\Delta n , \quad (9)$$

where the coefficients are found by

$$\tan v = \frac{Y}{X}, \qquad\qquad \tan(\theta - \Omega) = \cos i \tan(v + \omega),$$

$$g = \sin i \cos(\theta - \Omega), \qquad\qquad b = - g \sec i \sin(\theta - \Omega),$$

$$c = (1 - g^2) \sec i, \qquad\qquad l = \frac{\cos v}{X} = \frac{\sin v}{Y},$$

$$h = - l \sin v , \qquad\qquad k = + l \cos v ,$$

$$d = 57.3 c \left(h \frac{\partial X}{\partial e} + k \frac{\varrho Y}{\partial e} \right),$$

$$\epsilon = 57.3 c \left(h \frac{\partial X}{\partial M} + k \frac{\partial Y}{\partial M} \right), \qquad f = \epsilon (l - T), \qquad \Delta T = - \frac{\Delta \tau}{n}.$$

The units are degrees for $\Delta \theta$, $\Delta \Omega$, Δi, $\Delta \omega$, $\Delta \tau$; degrees per year for Δn; years for ΔT; and 0.01 for Δe. It will save labor to select the equations of condition at the mean anomalies already used for the ephemeris.

The equations may be treated by the method of least squares, but, before plunging blindly into the laborious computations required by this procedure, the computer may be well advised to consider whether simpler means will not give an orbit that will represent the observations satisfactorily, even if it does not reduce the sum of the squares to a minimum—a desideratum of doubtful value in the case of visual double-star measurements.

A correction of T shifts the computed curves in time without altering them in any other way; a correction of P or n stretches or contracts them proportionally to the time interval reckoned from T; a correction of Ω changes all com-

puted angles by that amount; a correction of a changes all computed separations in the same ratio; etc.

Where such readily made corrections fail to improve the residuals, the coefficients of a set of equations of condition should be computed, but it is then
advisable to plot these in a diagram, using time or mean anomaly as abscissa.
If two or more of the plots show a close resemblance (positive or negative proportionality) to each other in the observed part of the orbit, a least-squares
solution would meet the difficulty that the unknowns to which those plots refer
cannot be separated. For instance, if i is near $0°$ or $180°$, $\Delta\Omega$ and $\Delta\omega$ cannot be
separated; the term in $\Delta\omega$ should be omitted from the equations of condition
by taking $\Delta\omega = 0$ and throwing the correction entirely on the node. If the
eccentricity is small, it may be difficult to separate $\Delta\omega$ from ΔT and so on.

An improvement in the orbit, element by element, may often be obtained
by plotting on transparent paper the residuals on the same scale and using the
same abscissa as the plot of coefficients and superposing the transparent plot
(face up for a positive, face down for a negative correction to one of the elements) on the coefficients diagram, noting resemblance or proportionality with
the run of one of the coefficients. The proportionality factor determines the correction to be made to the element in question; the residuals are corrected by
means of the relevant coefficients in the equations of condition; the corrected
residuals plotted again; and the process is repeated until no further resemblance
can be detected. Even a simple ocular comparison often suffices to reveal the
correction to be made (van den Bos 1937).

§ 7. ORIENTATION IN SPACE

Let l, m, and n be the direction cosines of an arbitrary line in the system of
co-ordinates defined earlier—x north, y following, z line of sight—and l_1, m_1, and
n_1 those of the same line in the system x_1 vernal equinox, y_1 right ascension 6
hours, z_1 north pole, while a and δ are the right ascension and declination of the
primary and a_1 and δ_1 those of the arbitrary line; then we have

$$l_1 = \cos \delta_1 \cos a_1 = -l \sin \delta \cos a - m \sin a + n \cos \delta \cos a \,,$$

$$m_1 = \cos \delta_1 \sin a_1 = -l \sin \delta \sin a + m \cos a + n \cos \delta \sin a \,,$$

$$n_1 = \sin \delta_1 = +l \cos \delta + n \sin \delta \,.$$

The direction cosines of a line from the primary to an arbitrary point x, y, z
are: $l = x/r$, $m = y/r$, $n = z/r$ ($r^2 = x^2 + y^2 + z^2$); of the positive major axis:
$l = A/a$, $m = B/a$, $n = C/a$; of the positive minor axis: $l = F/a$, $m = G/a$,
$n = H/a$; of the positive normal to the orbit plane (motion in plane seen direct):
$l = + \sin i \sin \Omega$, $m = -\sin i \cos \Omega$, $n = + \cos i$.

The above formulae determine the orientation in space by right ascension
and declination. In the absence of observations in the line of sight, the double
signs of z, C, and H give two solutions.

§ 8. SECULAR CHANGES OF THE ORBITAL ELEMENTS

The effect of a binary's motion in space relative to the sun on its orbital elements has been studied by van den Bos (1926). For the rigorous formulae, valid as long as the relative motion of binary and sun may be taken as uniform rectilinear, the reader is referred to the above publication. Approximate formulae, sufficient in practice, are the following:

$$D = D_0 + \frac{\gamma_0}{4.737}(t - t_0), \qquad p = \frac{D_0}{D} p_0, \qquad a = \frac{D_0}{D} a_0 ;$$

$$i = i_0 + \mu_0 \sin (\psi_0 - \Omega_0) (t - t_0) ;$$

$$\omega = \omega_0 + \mu_0 \operatorname{cosec} i_0 \cos (\psi_0 - \Omega_0) (t - t_0) ;$$

$$\Omega = \Omega_0 + \mu_0 [\tan \delta_0 \sin \psi_0 - \cot i_0 \cos (\psi_0 - \Omega_0)] (t - t_0) ;$$

$$A = A_0 + \frac{A_0}{a_0}(a - a_0) + F_0(\omega - \omega_0) - B_0(\Omega - \Omega_0) + C_0 \sin \Omega_0 (i - i_0) ;$$

$$B = B_0 + \frac{B_0}{a_0}(a - a_0) + G_0(\omega - \omega_0) + A_0(\Omega - \Omega_0) - C_0 \cos \Omega_0 (i - i_0) ;$$

$$F = F_0 + \frac{F_0}{a_0}(a - a_0) - A_0(\omega - \omega_0) - G_0(\Omega - \Omega_0) + H_0 \sin \Omega_0 (i - i_0) ;$$

$$G = G_0 + \frac{G_0}{a_0}(a - a_0) - B_0(\omega - \omega_0) + F_0(\Omega - \Omega_0) - H_0 \cos \Omega_0 (i - i_0) ;$$

$$C = C_0 + \frac{C_0}{a_0}(a - a_0) + H_0(\omega - \omega_0) + C_0 \cot i_0 (i - i_0) ;$$

$$H = H_0 + \frac{H_0}{a_0}(a - a_0) - C_0(\omega - \omega_0) + H_0 \cot i_0 (i - i_0) ;$$

$$L = L_0 + \frac{4.737n}{p_0}(C - C_0); \qquad N = N_0 + \frac{4.737n}{p_0}(H - H_0),$$

where D is the distance of the binary from the sun in astronomical units, γ is the radial velocity of its center of gravity, p its parallax, and μ its total proper motion in *degrees* per year in position angle ψ. In the formulae for the Thiele-Innes constants the differences $\omega - \omega_0$, $\Omega - \Omega_0$, and $i - i_0$ are in *radians*. In the absence of observations in the line of sight, ω and Ω are subject to an uncertainty of 180°, and a double solution is obtained; in theory, it is possible to discriminate between the two possible orbit planes without having observations in the line of sight, by observing the changes in the orbit. The true period and hence the true mean motion are found as the time interval between two successive periastron passages, after each has been corrected for light-time by using the appropriate distance D.

§ 9. PARABOLIC ORBITS

Without questioning the fact that double-star orbits are ellipses, a parabolic orbit may satisfy the observations within admissible errors in the case of a partially observed orbit of long period and high eccentricity and will then give all the information that is not meaningless.

Finsen (1936a) defines the orbital elements and Thiele-Innes constants for the parabolic orbit and gives a table of X and Y as functions of the "mean anomaly," M. The Thiele-Innes constants and X and Y are obtained from the definitions valid for the ellipse by the substitution of the periastron distance in the true orbit q for the semi-major axis a. The eccentricity is unity, and the (infinite) period is replaced by the areal constant in the true orbit, $\sigma = \frac{1}{2}r^2 \, dv/dt$, the "mean motion" becoming $n = \sigma/q^2$. It is in radians per year. The elements in full are σ (or n), T, q, i, ω, and Ω, the last three being defined as for elliptic orbits. We have

$$M = n(t-T) = \tan \tfrac{1}{2} v + \tfrac{1}{3} \tan^3 \tfrac{1}{2} v \, ,$$

$$X = \frac{r}{q} \cos v = 1 - \tan^2 \tfrac{1}{2} v \, ,$$

$$Y = \frac{r}{q} \sin v = 2 \tan \tfrac{1}{2} v \, ,$$

$$x = \rho \cos \theta = A X + F Y \, , \qquad y = \rho \sin \theta = B X + G Y \, .$$

At periastron, $v = 0°$, $X = +1$, $Y = 0$, $x = A$, $y = B$. At the latus rectum, $v = \pm 90°$, $X = 0$, $Y = \pm 2$, $x = \pm 2F$, $y = \pm 2G$. The double areal constant in the apparent orbit is

$$c = \rho^2 \frac{d\theta}{dt} = x \frac{dy}{dt} - y \frac{dx}{dt} = 2\sigma \cos i \, .$$

To derive the elements from (corrected) interpolation-curves of the observed angles and distances or rectangular co-ordinates plotted against the time, the parabola best fitting the measures is drawn, as in the method of Zwiers for an elliptic orbit; or the coefficients of its equation,

$$ax^2 + 2bxy + dy^2 + 2fx + 2gy - 1 = 0 \, ,$$

may be computed from five positions, or more by least squares, as in the method of Kowalsky for an elliptic orbit. If this equation is to represent a parabola, we must have $a > 0$, $d > 0$, $b^2 - ad = 0$, and $df - bg \neq 0$. Wieth-Knudsen (1953) has adapted Thiele's method to parabolic orbits.

If the apparent parabola has been drawn, we construct an arbitrary diameter by bisecting parallel chords; the line through the primary parallel to this diameter then is the projected axis of the true orbit and meets the apparent orbit in the projected periastron, of which A and B are the co-ordinates. From the interpolation-curves we find T as the time at which $x = A$ and $y = B$. The extremities of the latus rectum are located as the two points for which $t_1 - T = T - t_2$, $x_1 + x_2 = 0$, $y_1 + y_2 = 0$, or $\rho_1 = \rho_2$ and $\theta_1 = \theta_2 \pm 180°$. If t_1 falls after T, then $v_1 = +90°$, and we have

$$F = \tfrac{1}{2}x_1 = -\tfrac{1}{2}x_2, \qquad G = \tfrac{1}{2}y_1 = -\tfrac{1}{2}y_2, \qquad \text{and} \qquad M_1 = -M_2 = +\tfrac{4}{3},$$

giving

$$n = \frac{4}{3(t_1 - T)}.$$

An ephemeris may now be computed for comparison with the observations.

Finally, q, i, ω, and Ω are computed from A, B, F, G; C, H, pL, and pN from q, i, ω; $\sigma = nq^2$; and, if the double areal constant in the apparent orbit has been found in testing the curves for the law of areas, $\sigma = \tfrac{1}{2} c \sec i$ is a check.

§ 10. COMBINATION OF DOUBLE-STAR DATA WITH OTHER DATA

If the parallax p of the system is known, the total mass is found by $m_1 + m_2 = a^3 p^{-3} P^{-2}$ for elliptic orbits or $m_1 + m_2 = q^3 p^{-3} n^2 (2\pi^2)^{-1}$ for parabolic orbits.

As, for the majority of the double stars, either the parallax is unknown or its accuracy is relatively low, it is customary to derive the "dynamical parallax," which is the parallax that makes the system conform to the mass-luminosity relation. It is derived from the quantity

$$h_1 = aP^{-2/3} \text{ (elliptic orbits)}$$

or

$$h_1 = qn^{2/3} (\pi\sqrt{2})^{-2/3} \text{ (parabolic orbits)}$$

or

$$h_1 = 0.418\rho^{1/3}w^{2/3} \text{ (slow moving pairs)}$$

(w is the relative motion in seconds of arc per year) by the procedure given by Russell and Moore (1940).

Observations connecting one or both components of the binary system with other stars give information on the absolute orbits and hence on the individual masses. Such observations are nowadays mostly obtained in the course of photographic determinations of parallax.

Radial-velocity observations of one or both components of a binary system, *provided that there is no doubt as to which spectroscopically observed component corresponds to the visual primary*, supply the following information:

Let V_A be the radial velocity of the visual primary, m_A its mass, V_B and m_B those of the secondary, $V = V_B - V_A$ the relative radial velocity, γ the radial velocity of the center of mass, p the absolute parallax, $\beta = m_B/m_A$ the mass ratio, $kp = \beta/(1 + \beta)$, and $lp = 1/(1 + \beta)$, then we have

$$V_A = \gamma - kp V, \qquad V_B = \gamma + lp V, \qquad |V_B - V_A| = \frac{1}{p}|pV|.$$

We plot the observations of V_A—and, if available, of V_B—against pV, computed by formulae (5) and (6) on the assumption that the upper signs of pL and pN are correct, and pass a straight line through the plot.

Now β, p, $\beta/(1+\beta)$, and $1/(1+\beta)$ and therefore k and l are, of necessity, positive quantities, so that, if these straight lines indicate positive values for k and l, i.e., if the variation in V_A (allowing for admissible errors in the observed velocities) definitely proves to be in the opposite, in V_B in the same, direction as that in pV, then our assumption is justified, the upper signs of C, H, pL, and pN are correct, and ω and Ω must be left unaltered. If not, then the lower signs are correct, and ω and Ω must both be changed by $\pm 180°$. The ambiguity in the plane of the orbit is removed.

The line determines γ by its zero point and k and/or l by its slope. If both V_A and V_B have been observed at at least two epochs, we have the mass ratio $\beta = k/l$ and the parallax $p = 1/(k+l)$ (see Wilson 1941). If radial velocities of only one of the components are available, the mass ratio may be found if the parallax is known (the assumption that the dynamical parallax is the best value obtainable may often be justified) by

$$\beta = \frac{pk}{1-pk} = \frac{1-pl}{pl},$$

or the parallax may be found if the mass ratio is known by

$$p = \frac{\beta}{k(1+\beta)} = \frac{1}{l(1+\beta)}.$$

The equation for $|V_B - V_A|$ shows that an independent parallax can be found from one or more simultaneous observations of the radial velocity of both components, even if it should not be possible to identify them with the visual components. Radial velocities are of maximum value if made at, or near, the times of nodal passage, where they are extreme.

It may happen that for the same binary a visual, as well as a spectroscopic, orbit (from radial velocities) can be computed. If these two computations are made independently, it cannot be expected that the elements which the two orbits have in common will agree precisely, so that it will be better to proceed with the computations together and make the common elements equal one by one as they are derived.

The visual orbit supplies the elements P, T, e, a, i, ω $(\pm 180°)$, Ω $(\pm 180°)$, and the spectroscopic P, T, e, $a_1 \sin i$, ω_1 and γ, or, if both components have been observed, in addition $a_2 \sin i$ and $\omega_2 = \omega_1 \pm 180°$.

It will be extremely rare for a parallax determination to be so relatively accurate that the additional relation $a_1 + a_2 = 149.5 \times 10^6 \, a/p$ should be considered as a further condition rather than as an independent—and much more accurate—determination of the parallax. Or, similarly in the case of a mass-ratio determination, that $a_1 = 149.5 \times 10^6 \, \{a/p\} \, \{m_2/(m_1+m_2)\}$ should be re-

garded as an additional condition between $a_1 \sin i$, a, and i. We assume, therefore, that $a_1 \sin i$ in the spectroscopic orbit is independent of the visual orbit
and that the only common elements are P, T, e, and $\omega = \omega_1 \pm 180°$.

Cases of this nature will, in general, be restricted to binaries of short period,
so that we may assume that the observations cover more than one revolution
and the period is determined by recurrence. While deriving the period from the
two sets of observations—visual and spectroscopic—the computer will be able
to judge the relative accuracy of the two determinations and weight them accordingly. The weighted mean is adopted as the final value of P and is used to
reduce all observations to a single revolution. Interpolation-curves having the
time as abscissa are now drawn for the visual x and y and the spectroscopic V
observations. We have

$$V = \gamma + K[e \cos \omega_1 + \cos (v + \omega_1)],$$

or, putting

$$\bar{V} = \gamma + Ke \cos \omega_1,$$
$$V = \bar{V} + K \cos (v + \omega_1).$$

This gives, for periastron ($v = 0°$),

$$V_0 = \bar{V} + K \cos \omega_1$$

and, for apastron ($v = 180°$),

$$V_{180} = \bar{V} - K \cos \omega_1.$$

For the nodal passages, $v + \omega_1 = 0°$ or $180°$, so

$$V_\Omega = \bar{V} + K, \text{ and } V_\mho = \bar{V} - K.$$

Therefore, $\bar{V}$ is the velocity midway between the extremes, and K is the
semi-amplitude of the velocity-curve.

Periastron and apastron are now located as the two points on the curve distant in time by $P/2$ for which $V_0 - \bar{V} = \bar{V} - V_{180}$. In the visual orbit they are
located as described earlier in § 4, and once more the computer must decide the
final value of T by weighting. The curves may have to be corrected slightly, so
that the conditions used in locating T remain fulfilled for the adopted final value
of T. The eccentricity for the visual orbit is now derived, as shown earlier. For
the spectroscopic orbit, e is determined in two ways (Zurhellen's method), their
relative accuracy depending on the value of ω_1. For the extremities of the latus
rectum we have $v = \pm 90°$ or

$$V_{+90} = \bar{V} - K \sin \omega_1 \quad \text{and} \quad V_{-90} = \bar{V} + K \sin \omega_1,$$

so that these are located as the points equidistant in time from T and in velocity
from $\bar{V}$. Also for these points $M = \pm (t - T)/n$, $X = 0$, and $Y = \pm \cos^2 \phi$,
so that e can be found from the XY tables. Zurhellen's second method derives e

from the slopes of the tangents to the velocity-curve at periastron and apastron by

$$\left(\frac{dV}{dt}\right)_0 : \left(\frac{dV}{dt}\right)_{180} = -q^2, \qquad e = \frac{q-1}{q+1}.$$

The first method gives the best results when ω_1 is near $0°$ or $180°$, the second when ω_1 is near $90°$ or $270°$. The computer once more determines the final value of e by weighting. This value determines the mean anomalies and hence the times of latus rectum and the minor axis by $X = 0$, $Y = \pm\cos^2 \phi$, and $X = -e$, $Y = \pm\cos \phi$, respectively, and the curves may again have to be corrected so as to fulfil the conditions used in locating these points. The final values of the three dynamical elements have now been found and for the visual orbit A, B, F, G, and hence a, i, ω, Ω are derived as shown earlier. For the spectroscopic orbit we have ω_1 by

$$\sin \omega_1 = \frac{\bar{V} - V_{+90}}{K} = \frac{V_{-90} - \bar{V}}{K},$$

$$\cos \omega_1 = \frac{V_0 - \bar{V}}{K} = \frac{\bar{V} - V_{180}}{K}.$$

By weighting once more, the computer finds the final values of ω and ω_1, so that $\omega = \omega_1 \pm 180°$ exactly. In the visual orbit Ω may now have to be altered by $180°$, if ω is so altered, and the Thiele-Innes constants recomputed for the final values of ω and Ω, or corrected by

$$\Delta A = +F\Delta\omega, \qquad \Delta F = -A\Delta\omega,$$
$$\qquad\qquad\qquad\qquad\qquad\qquad\qquad\qquad (\Delta\omega \text{ in radians}).$$
$$\Delta B = +G\Delta\omega, \qquad \Delta G = -B\Delta\omega$$

In the spectroscopic orbit,

$$\gamma = \bar{V} - Ke \cos \omega_1 \qquad \text{and} \qquad a_1 = 5022605 \, KP \, \text{cosec} \, i \cos \phi,$$

where a_1 is in kilometers and P in years.

§ 11. CONCLUSION

Experience in orbit determination has shown that, while a working knowledge of some of the standard methods is indispensable, there is no guaranty of the infallibility of any of them in every case that may be met in practice. In difficult cases the computer may be forced to feel his way by trial and error and by taking advantage of peculiarities in the observed motion, devising his own methods, as it were. This applies in particular when the eccentricity is large and the separation falls below the limit of what can be measured for a portion of the apparent orbit near periastron.

A valuable asset to the computer is familiarity with the reliability, or the lack of it, of observations made by different observers, using different telescopes and measuring apparatus on double stars of various degrees of separation, brightness, difference of magnitude, and altitude above the observer's horizon. Such insight is perhaps best obtained by becoming a regular observer of double stars one's self, apart from the fact that orbits cannot be derived unless observations are made first. Lack of observations in critical parts of the orbit is keeping more binaries out of our orbit catalogue than any other single cause, and, unless many more double stars are kept under regular observation than is the case at present, we shall get no warning when these critical parts are being reached.

A word of caution to astronomers using the results of orbit computation for statistical purposes may not be out of place here. It should not be assumed that our orbit catalogues furnish a representative sample of the double-star population. Selection cannot be neglected. The orbital elements frequently conspire in keeping a double star out of the orbit catalogue much longer, or bringing it in much earlier, than would be expected from the ratio of its period of observation to its period of revolution.

Short-period binaries having large eccentricity or high inclination, or both, furnish an example of the first kind of selection. The history of the binary OΣ 341 (ADS 11060) provides perhaps the most striking example. First observed in 1843, it gave no clear evidence of being in motion until 1898, when it was found single with the Lick 36-inch refractor. Burnham (BDS 8353) states: "Hussey suggests that a period of about 240 years will account for the observed positions." Actually, the period is not 240, but 20 years, the eccentricity 0.97, and the inclination 76°. The interval during which the binary's aspect differs perceptibly from that near apastron is only a small fraction of the period and may easily escape detection, unless such a pair is kept under regular scrutiny—and double stars showing little or no motion seldom are. Such escapes, in the case of OΣ 341, happened in 1858 and 1878 and might have continued to happen indefinitely, but for the lucky accident of the 1898 observations. We know a few more binaries of this kind, though not perhaps quite so extreme as OΣ 341, but we simply do *not* know how many more may be hiding themselves in our general catalogues under the cloak of "no perceptible change" and spoiling our statistics. There would seem to be no other way of finding out than by keeping large numbers of close pairs under regular—if need be, annual—observation, especially those known to have a considerable proper motion or parallax. Even if this were done, we might still not be able to compute orbits for them, but we would at least become aware of their existence. The binary A 691 (ADS 9544) has a parallax of 0″.056 and annual proper motion 1″.38. Its maximum separation is twice its parallax. It must have a very short period, but there seems little hope that it will ever appear in our orbit catalogue—except perhaps in the guise of a spectroscopic binary—unless much greater resolving power can be brought to bear on it.

Examples of the second kind of selection—unduly early appearance in the orbit catalogue—are supplied by long-period binaries of large eccentricity, if periastron passage occurs within or near the period of observation. Compare two binaries, each having zero inclination and a period of a thousand years, each having been under observation for a hundred years, but the first having zero eccentricity, the second 0.90, with periastron passage midway during the period of observation. The observed arc will be 36° in the first case and 280° in the second, the binary requiring the remaining 900 years of its period to describe the missing 80°. It will be obvious which of the two will make the earlier appearance in our orbit catalogue. Woolley (1938) puts it thus: "From the orbit catalogue one would derive the absurd law: all binaries with periods over 300 years have passed periastron between 1850 and 1950."

It is not surprising that uncritical use of observational material so strongly influenced by selection has led to unsafe conclusions. The so-called period-eccentricity relation is the best-known example of this. Originally believed to be real, this was shown by later investigators (Barbier 1934; Finsen 1936b; Hopmann 1939) to be explicable by sampling errors and selection, wholly in the case of visual and largely, if not wholly, in the case of spectroscopic binaries. Russell (1928), when applying the eccentricity distribution derived from binaries with reliable orbits to slow-moving pairs, expressed some misgivings, but in a later publication (Russell and Moore 1940) these seem to have disappeared.

Apart from selections inherent in the observational material, selection may also be introduced by subconscious tendencies on the part of the computer. For binaries where the difference of magnitude is zero or so small that the quadrant is in doubt, erroneous orbits having twice the true period have often been derived. There also seems to be a tendency to find the ellipse of minimum period compatible with the observations, especially when using the graphical methods.

REFERENCES

Aitken, R. G.	1932	*New General Catalogue of Double Stars* (Washington D.C.: Carnegie Institution of Washington).
Barbier, D.	1934	*C.R.*, **199**, 930.
Bos, W. H. van den	1926	*Circ. Union Obs.*, **2**, 360.
	1927	*B.A.N.*, **3**, 261.
	1932a	*Circ. Union Obs.*, **3**, 265.
	1932b	*Ibid.*, p. 271.
	1937	*Ibid.*, **4**, 337.
Burnham, S. W.	1906	*A General Catalogue of Double Stars* (Chicago: University of Chicago Press).
Dommanget, J.	1955	*Bull. Astr. Obs. R. Belgique*, **4**, No. 77, 29.
Finsen, W. S.	1936a	*Circ. Union Obs.*, **4**, 225.
	1936b	*M.N.*, **96**, 862.
Fletcher, A.	1931	*M.N.*, **92**, 119.
Hertzsprung, E.	1920	*Pub. Ap. Obs. Potsdam*, No. 75.

Hopmann, J.   1939   *A.N.*, **269**, 81.
I.A.U.   1935   *Transactions*, **5**, 332.
Russell, H. N.   1928   *A.J.*, **38**, 93.
Russell, H. N., and
  Moore, C. E.   1940   *The Masses of the Stars* (Chicago: University of
                                   Chicago Press).
Thiele, T. N.   1883   *A.N.*, **104**, 246.
Wieth-Knudsen, N.   1953   *Ann. Obs. Lund*, No. 12.
Wilson, O. C.   1941   *Ap. J.*, **93**, 29.
Woolley, R. v. d. R.   1938   *Observatory*, **61**, 323.
Zwiers, H. J.   1896   *A.N.*, **139**, 369.

CHAPTER 23

The Determination of Orbital Elements of Spectroscopic Binaries

R. M. PETRIE

Dominion Astrophysical Observatory

§ 1. INTRODUCTION

THE study of close binary stars began with Pickering's discovery of Mizar A in 1882 (Shapley and Howarth 1929). In the intervening years the spectroscopic investigation of double stars has produced a substantial accumulation of orbital data, which in turn has led to a knowledge of the masses, radii, and densities of stars. Studies of stellar structure and stellar evolution rest largely, in the final analysis, on the results of double-star astronomy. Most of the information obtained from binary stars requires as an essential step the deduction of elements from spectroscopic observations of radial velocity. The elements, to be trustworthy and useful, must be determined with care and good judgment. This chapter is therefore devoted to a discussion of the means whereby orbital elements may be found from the spectroscopic observations. It will not include the discussions of anomalies in the apparent motion investigated by Struve and others during the past few years. These extremely important and significant discoveries are not part of the geometrical problems included in this chapter. Taking us far beyond the purely mechanical effects of orbital motion, they are more appropriately discussed in another place.

The determination of elements from a knowledge of the variation in line-of-sight velocities is an attractive problem in the application of celestial mechanics and has been attacked and solved by a number of investigators. The first problem is to find the periodic curve of radial-velocity variation from the original observations. These are the measured radial velocities, determined with greater or less precision, at accurately known times of observation. Finding the period is sometimes very easy, sometimes extraordinarily difficult, and, to the writer's knowledge, there is no general method for insuring success, although several valuable suggestions are to be found in the literature. Usually an unknown number of cycles intervenes between successive observations of recognizable phases —for example, maximum velocity. Thus the short-period examples, by far the most numerous, are the most difficult. Therefore, in contemplating the investigation of a spectroscopic binary, it is of great practical value to arrange for intensive observational coverage over three or four successive nights and, on one night at least, to obtain two or more spectrograms.

Ordinarily, one has a series of observations, a score or so, scattered throughout one or two observing seasons. Unless the period is apparent from a chronological plot, it is usually best to look for a number of well-marked maxima and minima. Each pair of corresponding phases gives a relation $t_2 - t_1 = nP$, where $t_2 - t_1$ is the interval, n is an integer, and P is the period. From a number of pairs, one finds submultiples of the intervals, and that common to all the intervals will give the period. There will often be several values of P satisfying the different intervals unless a very favorable distribution of the observations occurs, and one must choose the correct period from the observations themselves by computing and plotting phases and velocities. There is no general rule, but the best procedure will become evident in practice.

Sometimes it is extraordinarily difficult to choose between two possible values of the period, especially when the radial velocities show considerable scatter. In those cases the only way to be certain is to select dates when the different possible periods predict quite different velocities and to make the critical observations on those dates. This should be done even if it entails deferring the calculation of elements until after another observing season.

One must beware of spurious periods which sometimes correlate the velocities to an astonishing degree when, because of a star's position or other circumstances, the observations are made at nearly integral intervals of a sidereal day. As an illustration we show in Figure 1 recent two-prism (15 A/mm at Hγ) Victoria observations of δ Capricorni, which must be observed close to meridian passage at Victoria because of the star's southern declination. The observations are assembled on periods of 1.023 and 39.5 days, the interval covered by the observations being 106 days. It is obvious that, were these the only observations, one could not choose the correct period, which is found to be the shorter one, as demonstrated by data obtained at other observatories.

The problem of spurious periods of spectroscopic binaries has been discussed recently by Tanner (1948), who gives references to earlier work on the subject. Tanner shows that a number of spurious periods, P_x, are possible, related by expressions of the form

$$\frac{1}{P_x} = 1.0027 \pm \frac{1}{P},$$

where P is the true period.

The obvious escape from the dilemma is to make observations at different sidereal times, if possible. Then the short period will exhibit velocity changes with hour angle, while the longer will not. Tanner systematizes this procedure and gives a criterion which will distinguish between the true and false periods. Examples of spurious periods being adopted are not common, but, nevertheless, Tanner found five cases in his survey. Before proceeding to calculate orbital elements, one should confirm a period by predicting and making a critical observation.

After the period is found and refined, if possible, by reference to early observations, the resulting phase-velocity diagram will resemble a sine-curve unless the eccentricity is rather high. The problem then is to deduce the orbital elements from the amplitude, mean value, and shape of the velocity-curve. The

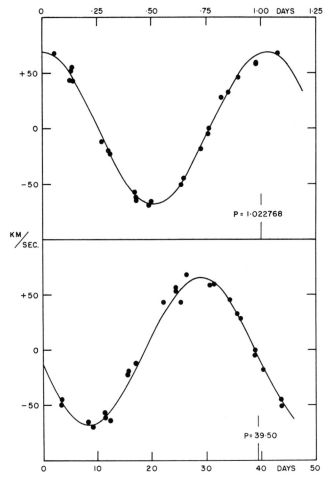

Fig. 1.—Radial velocities of δ Capricorni assembled on two different periods. The observations were made at Victoria over an interval of 106 days. It is not possible to select the correct period from this series of radial velocities.

elements to be determined are P, the period in mean solar days; e, the eccentricity; ω, the longitude of periastron passage in the plane of the orbit, measured from the ascending node; T, the time of periastron passage; K, the amplitude (semi) of the velocity-curve in km/sec; and V_0, the systemic velocity. Additional quantities to be computed from the elements are the projected semi-major axis, $a \sin i$, given by $a \sin i = 13{,}751 \ (1 - e^2)^{1/2} \, KP$ km, and the mass function $m_2^3 \sin^3 i/(m_1 + m_2)^2$, which is given by $1.038 \times 10^{-7} \ (1 - e^2)^{3/2} \, K^3 P \ \odot$. The inclination i, the angle between the orbital plane and the tangent plane, cannot be found from radial-velocity observations and must remain unknown unless the system is also a visual binary or an eclipsing binary.

The elements of the orbit may be deduced from the radial-velocity curve by considering its analytical form. This may be derived as follows: In Figure 2 let $ABCD$ be the tangent plane to the celestial sphere at O, the focus of the elliptical orbit. The orbit plane is defined by $EBFD$, so that the angle FBC is the inclination, i. The direction of motion is from B toward F, DOB is the line of nodes, and B is the ascending node. The major axis of the ellipse extended cuts the orbit-plane circle at P; hence BP is ω.

Let the star be at the point S in its orbit and let OS extended cut the circle EBF at T. Then PT is the star's angular distance from the end of the major axis

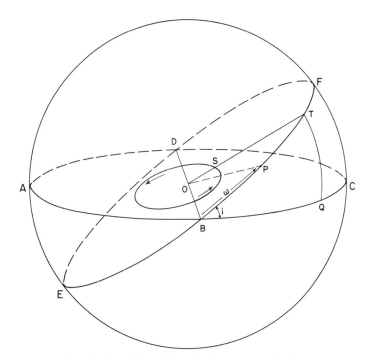

Fig. 2.—Definition of elements for spectroscopic binary

nearest the focus (periastron) and is called the *true anomaly, v*. The angle $BT = v + \omega$ and is called the *argument of latitude, u*.

The measured radial velocity, after allowance for the orbital motion of the earth, is the line-of-sight component of the motion of the star with respect to the tangent plane. The distance of the star from the tangent plane is given by $z = r \sin TOQ$, where r is the radius vector at S. The angles TQO and TQB are right angles. In the spherical triangle TBQ,

$$\sin TQ = \sin i \sin BT = \sin i \sin (v + \omega),$$

and, hence,

$$z = r \sin i \sin (v + \omega).\tag{1}$$

The radial velocity dz/dt hence is

$$\frac{dz}{dt} = \sin i \sin (v + \omega)\frac{dr}{dt} + r \sin i \cos (v + \omega)\frac{dv}{dt}.\tag{2}$$

Now, from the theory of elliptic motion (Smart 1931), we have

$$r = \frac{a(1 - e^2)}{1 + e \cos v}$$

and

$$r^2 \frac{dv}{dt} = [\mu a(1 - e^2)]^{1/2},$$

where $\mu = n^2 a^3$ and n is the mean motion expressed in radians per unit time. We then find that

$$\frac{dr}{dt} = \frac{na}{(1 - e^2)^{1/2}} e \sin v, \qquad r\frac{dv}{dt} = \frac{na}{(1 - e^2)^{1/2}}(1 - e \cos v),$$

and, by substitution in equation (2),

$$\frac{dz}{dt} = \frac{na \sin i}{(1 - e^2)^{1/2}} [\cos (v + \omega) + e \cos \omega].\tag{3}$$

The quantity outside the brackets is plainly the semiamplitude K, and we have defined $v + \omega$ as u. In addition to the orbital motion, the system will have a velocity, V_0, relative to the sun. The final expression for the measured radial velocity, as usually written, then is

$$V = V_0 + K (\cos u + e \cos \omega).\tag{4}$$

§ 2. PRELIMINARY ELEMENTS

There have been devised many excellent methods both analytical and graphical for deducing the elements from the velocity-curve. Most of the methods depend on using special points on the approximate velocity-curve drawn through the observations. For example, if we consider equation (4) for $u = 0°$ and for $u = 180°$, we obviously define the maximum and minimum points on the curve. Calling these velocities A and B, respectively, we have

$$A = V_0 + Ke \cos \omega + K , \qquad B = V_0 + Ke \cos \omega - K ,$$

whence

$$K = \frac{A - B}{2}$$

and

$$V_0 = \frac{A + B}{2} - \frac{A - B}{2} e \cos \omega .$$

Thus, by determining the maximum and minimum points of the curve, we find K at once and may calculate V_0 when e and ω are found. These two elements are deduced from the shape of the curve and from special points on it. The procedure also gives T.

A selection of the various methods is given by Henroteau (1928). Other useful collections are by Curtis (1908) and by Aitken (1935), and individual papers are given in the literature. Evidence of the continued interest in the subject is given by papers as recent as those of O. C. Wilson (1941) and Irwin (1952).

The most convenient and efficient method of obtaining preliminary elements, if one contemplates investigating several binaries, is the use of a series of computed velocity-curves such as those described by King (1920). If one plots, on transparent linen, using a standard scale of co-ordinates, the function $\cos u + e \cos \omega$ for a range of values of e and ω, one may match the observed points with one of the standard curves and find e, ω, and T very quickly. The method enjoys the advantage of utilizing the observed points directly without the intervention of a freehand curve, and one may mentally make allowance for a difference in weights while making the choice of best fit. It is possible, also, by using two or three curves, to make a preliminary adjustment of the elements, noting the residuals from the standard curves, and this adjustment is helpful when one undertakes a least-squares improvement of the elements.

The standard curves supply e, ω, and T directly, while K and V_0 are found from the observed velocity range as outlined above. The standard curves are very readily constructed. One first computes M, the mean anomaly, for a sufficient number of submultiples of the period, using $M = 360/P (t - T)$. The true anomaly v is then given by the table of Schlesinger and Udick (1912) or, for eccentricities in excess of 0.77, by the help of Astrand's table (1890). When v is tabulated against M for the whole range of e, it is a simple matter to form u and tabulate $\cos u$ for the different values of ω. The constant $e \cos \omega$ can then be added quickly to $\cos u$ and the curves plotted. One need compute curves only for values of ω in the first quadrant. Other quadrants are given by rotating the standard curves through 180° and by reversing the transparent linen.

If a study is being made of one velocity-curve only, it is not worthwhile to compute standard curves. In that case, one of the graphical methods referred to above may be used or the interesting analytical method devised by Wilsing and extended by Russell (1902). The analytical method may be especially recommended, as it utilizes the observations directly without the intermediary free-hand curve, which, in certain circumstances, can yield erroneous elements.

The orbital elements as first found from the observations or from a preliminary velocity-curve should be regarded as tentative values to be adjusted or corrected by some refinement. Some improvement can usually be made by inspection of velocity-curves and residuals, but it is virtually impossible to consider the effects of changing all the elements simultaneously and to select the best set without the impersonal and automatic adjustment by the method of least squares. It is common experience that the preliminary set is generally wrong in one element or another, and this is rectified by the least-squares solution. Another aspect of this general method of adjustment is that it supplies the probable errors in the separate elements, an important advantage when we come to investigate the question of changes in the elements. Except in special cases, such as circular orbits, where the amplitudes only are desired or when the observations are very poor, one should always improve the elements by a least-squares solution even if it serves no other purpose than to place them above personal judgment and bias.

§ 3. DIFFERENTIAL CORRECTIONS

The simultaneous adjustment of five or six parameters involves the solution of a set of equations of condition, one for each observation. The radial velocity of a binary may, as shown above, be written as a function of the elements

$$V = f(V_0, K, e, \omega, T, P),$$ (5)

and the change in velocity, produced by changes in the elements ΔV_0, ΔK, Δe, etc., may be written as

$$\Delta V = \frac{\partial f}{\partial V_0} \Delta V_0 + \frac{\partial f}{\partial K} \Delta K + \frac{\partial f}{\partial e} \Delta e + \ldots$$ (6)

if one assumes the changes in the elements to be sufficiently small that the higher-order terms may be ignored. For this reason it is important to obtain a good set of preliminary elements.

Equation (6) is written for each observation, the left member being the observed velocity minus that computed from preliminary elements. The differential coefficients $\partial f/\partial V_0$, $\partial f/\partial K$, etc., are the partial derivatives of equation (5). When these are evaluated, we have the well-known equation of condition derived by Lehmann-Filhés (1894):

$$\Delta V_0 + (\cos u + e \cos \omega)\Delta K + K\left[\cos \omega - \frac{\sin u \sin v(2 + e \cos v)}{1 - e^2}\right]\Delta e$$

$$- K(\sin u + e \sin \omega)\Delta\omega + \sin u (1 + e \cos v)^2 \frac{Kn}{(1 - e^2)^{3/2}}\Delta T \quad (7)$$

$$- \sin u (1 + e \cos v)^2 \frac{K(t - T)}{(1 - e^2)^{3/2}}\Delta n = O - C.$$

Here $t - T$ is the phase reckoned from periastron passage, and n is the mean daily motion defined by $2\pi/P$.

Equation (7), written for each observation or for each normal place, results in a set of observation equations, which, when solved by Gauss's method, give the corrections to the elements. The weights of the unknowns are obtained also, and these, in conjunction with the probable error of a normal place of unit weight, give the probable errors of the elements.

The details of the least-squares solution are lengthy and cannot be given in full here, although the principal features are illustrated by a numerical example given below. An example of the method for the case of five unknowns is given in full detail in Watson's *Theoretical Astronomy* (1868).

The solution is laborious if there are many observations. A large saving in time is effected by combining the observations into normal places, preserving the weights originally assigned to each observation in forming mean phases and mean velocities. While the use of normal places cannot be justified from the point of view of mathematical rigor, they may safely be used if discretion is exercised in forming the normals. The procedure is justified by the saving in labor that results. Generally the observations and normal places will have dissimilar weights, and the weights are allowed to enter into the formation of the normal equations in the Gaussian solution in the usual manner.

Equation (7) contains a term giving a correction to the period through the mean daily motion. It is advisable to omit this term, if possible, in order to shorten the solution and to give a better separation of the unknowns, ΔT and Δn. The observations usually comprise a short interval more or less intensively covered and a few early observations several seasons apart from the main body of information. One can usually obtain a sufficiently accurate period from the long intervals available. If, however, the observations cover only a few cycles, one must, perforce, include the period in the least-squares solution.

If the period is found before the solution is performed, it is usually worthwhile to revise it by the comparison of early and late observations with the final velocity-curve. Here we consider the phase residuals of those observations located on the ascending and descending branches of the velocity-curve, ignoring those near the maximum and minimum points. Let Δt be the phase residual, observation minus curve, of an observation made N cycles from the main body of the material. The correction to the period is $\Delta P = \pm \Delta t/N$, the plus sign being used if the observation is later than the mean date of the observations. Errors in the radial velocity may vitiate the results if only one or two observations can be used, but otherwise this procedure will give a reliable value of the period and a good estimate of its probable error.

A modification of the Lehmann-Filhés equation of condition has been given by Schlesinger (1908), who reduced the labor of forming the differential coefficients by rearranging terms and tabulating certain quantities. Schlesinger's modification has been used by many computers and may be recommended. Note, however, that the unknowns, in this method, are functions of the corrections to the elements in combination; hence additional computations are needed to obtain the probable errors of the separate elements. With modern desk-model computing machines there is little need to depart from the straightforward Lehmann-Filhés equation.

Russell's analytical method, which uses the coefficients of a Fourier series to determine the elements, allows for differential corrections through a least-squares solution. Here, again, the unknowns are functions of the elements, a fact which introduces complications when probable errors are being calculated. It does not appear to be feasible to introduce weights in the solution, and this feature of the method is undesirable.

The different steps in correcting the preliminary elements may be summarized as follows:

a) Compute an ephemeris with the preliminary elements by calculating the radial velocity for the phase of each observation (or normal place). This involves computing the mean anomaly, $M = n(t - T)$; finding v as a function of M and e from the table of Schlesinger and Udick (1912); and then forming $u = v + \omega$, $\cos u$, and $K \cos u$, and, finally, $V = V_0 + Ke \cos \omega + K \cos u$.

b) The residuals O − C from the preliminary ephemeris are tabulated with their weights. Coefficients of the differential corrections as given by equation (7) are computed with preliminary elements. The resulting observation equations are tabulated and weighted, and normal equations are formed. It is advisable to check the differential coefficients very carefully before proceeding with the cross-multiplications and to carry an automatic check column from this point by summing each observation equation.

c) The normal equations are solved simultaneously, and the differential corrections are found and applied to the initial elements. At this stage one may also find the weights of the unknowns by re-solving the normal equations, with the right members being made 1.000 or 0.000 according to the usual rules.

d) The corrected elements are used to compute a final ephemeris. The residuals from the final curve supply the probable error of an observation (or normal place) of unit weight from which we may compute the probable errors of the elements, using the weights of the unknowns already computed. The final ephemeris also gives us the percentage reduction in the sum of the squared residuals, and a comparison of the individual velocities with the final curve gives a good estimate of the probable error of an average plate. In exhibiting the results, the individual velocities should be shown rather than the normal places. The normals ordinarily show small departures from the final curve and fail to give a true impression of the precision of the original observations.

To illustrate the procedure outlined above, we give, somewhat condensed, a solution carried out for a series of observations of the star AR Cassiopeiae. This well-known (eclipsing) binary was discovered at the Allegheny Observatory and investigated with spectrograms obtained in 1908 and 1909. The data discussed here come from twenty-four single-prism spectrograms obtained at the Dominion Astrophysical Observatory between October 17, 1942, and March 1, 1943.

The period of the binary is known with high precision because of the long interval over which it has been observed. We may accept the value of the period as 6.06652 ± 0.00006 days and exclude it from further consideration.

The first observation was made on JD 2430649.751 and the last on JD 2430784.620. The instant of zero phase, which is arbitrary and a matter of convenience, is taken to be 2430648.017, corresponding approximately to the expected value of T. Phases are computed for each of the twenty-four observations with the above zero-phase time and period, and the observations are then combined into ten normal places, as listed in Table 1 and shown in Figure 3. From these observations of velocity and phase we are to determine the orbital elements and to correct them by a least-squares solution.

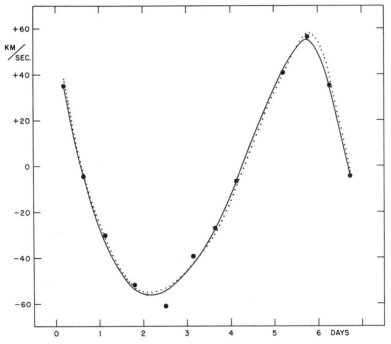

Fig. 3.—Radial-velocity curves of AR Cassiopeiae, with normal places plotted. The dotted curve represents the initial elements, the full curve the final (corrected) elements.

The phases and velocities of Table 1 are plotted, and an estimate of the maximum and minimum values is made. These are $A = +52.6$ km/sec and $B = -59.4$ km/sec, from which the amplitude, K, is 56.0 km/sec. The data are then transferred to a 5×8-inch plot for comparison with the standard velocity-curves drawn on transparent linen. This comparison gives a good representation with

$$e = 0.25 , \qquad \omega = 34° , \qquad T = \text{JD } 2430648.050 .$$

The value of V_0 follows from $V_0 = (A + B)/2 - Ke \cos \omega$. Preliminary elements, hence, are

$$e = 0.25 , \qquad\qquad K = 56.0 \text{ km/sec} ,$$
$$\omega = 34° , \qquad\qquad V_0 = -15.0 \text{ km/sec} .$$
$$T = \text{JD } 2430648.050 ,$$

A trial representation, or ephemeris, is now calculated, using the radial-velocity equation (4). The details are given in Table 2, columns 1–12 inclusive, beginning with the phase t and following through to the computed velocity V_c and the residual O − C.

TABLE 1

OBSERVATIONS OF AR CASSIOPEIAE, NORMAL PLACES

No.	Mean Phase (Days)	Mean Velocity (km/sec)	Wt.	No.	Mean Phase (Days)	Mean Velocity (km/sec)	Wt.
1.....	0.190	+35.0	0.4	6....	3.144	−39.4	0.4
2.....	0.644	− 4.3	.8	7....	3.628	−27.2	.7
3.....	1.127	−30.1	.4	8....	4.216	− 6.9	.7
4.....	1.804	−51.8	.8	9....	5.196	+40.6	.6
5.....	2.502	−61.4	0.6	10....	5.759	+56.3	0.7

Inspection of the residuals in column 11 show at once that they are predominantly positive; the weighted mean is +4.5 km/sec. The preliminary elements have given velocities systematically 4.5 km/sec more negative than the observed velocities. The easiest way to rectify this error is simply to change V_0 from −15.0 to −10.5, thus adding 4.5 km/sec to each value in column 9. When this is done, the second trial values are as in columns 13 and 14. The weighted mean of the residuals is now +0.1 km/sec, and this is quite satisfactory. Furthermore, the residuals in column 14 show no definite correlation either with velocity or with phase, and the preliminary elements, with $V_0 = -10.5$ km/sec, may therefore be adopted. The velocity-curve given by these elements is shown by the dashed line in Figure 3.

The next step is to adjust the preliminary elements by differential corrections conditioned by the residuals. We therefore calculate the numerical values of the coefficients of ΔK, Δe, $\Delta \omega$, etc., appearing in equation (7) for each of the ten normal places, omitting the term in Δn because the period is not to be included. The equations of condition, then, are

1. $1.000 \, \Delta V_0 + 0.850 \, \Delta K + 0.326 \, \Delta e + 0.905 \, \Delta \omega + 1.178 \, \Delta T = -2.140$,

2. $1.000 \qquad\quad + 0.168 \qquad - 1.103 \qquad + 1.139 \qquad + 1.280 \qquad = -3.230$,

3. $1.000 \qquad\quad - 0.402 \qquad - 0.846 \qquad + 0.933 \qquad + 0.769 \qquad = +2.900$,

TABLE 2
PRELIMINARY EPHEMERIS

No. (1)	t (Days) (2)	t−T (Days) (3)	M (4)	v (5)	u (6)	cos u (7)	K cos u (km/sec) (8)	V_c (km/sec) (9)	V_0 (km/sec) (10)	O−C (km/sec) (11)	p (12)	V_c (13)	O−C (14)
1	0.190	0.157	9°32	15°96	49°57.6	+0.643	+36.0	+32.6	+35.0	+2.4	0.4	+37.1	−2.1
2	0.644	0.611	36.26	58.24	92 14.4	−0.039	− 2.2	− 5.6	− 4.3	+1.3	.8	− 1.1	−3.2
3	1.127	1.094	64.92	93.54	127 32.4	−0.609	−34.1	−37.5	−30.1	+7.4	.4	−33.0	+2.9
4	1.804	1.771	105.10	129.89	163 53.4	−0.961	−53.8	−57.2	−51.8	+5.4	.8	−52.7	+0.9
5	2.502	2.469	146.52	158.95	192 57.0	−0.975	−54.6	−58.0	−61.4	−3.4	.6	−53.5	−7.9
6	3.144	3.111	184.62	182.86	216 51.6	−0.800	−44.8	−48.2	−39.4	+8.8	.4	−43.7	+4.3
7	3.628	3.595	213.34	200.96	234 57.6	−0.574	−32.2	−35.6	−27.2	+8.4	.7	−31.0	+3.9
8	4.216	4.183	248.24	225.04	259 02.4	−0.190	−10.6	−14.0	− 6.9	+7.1	.7	− 9.5	+2.6
9	5.196	5.163	306.39	279.22	313 13.2	+0.685	+38.4	+35.0	+40.6	+5.6	.6	+39.5	+1.1
10	5.759	5.726	339.80	326.04	00 02.4	+1.000	+56.0	+52.6	+56.3	+3.7	0.7	+57.1	−0.8

and so on, the right members being the residuals in the last column of Table 2. Before being solved, each equation of condition must be multiplied by the square root of the weights given in Table 1. The ten weighted equations of condition supply the normal equations, by the Gaussian method of cross-products, as follows:

$$6.100x + 0.148y + 0.105z + 0.427u + 0.471v = +0.009 ,$$
$$2.917 - 0.550 + 0.173 + 0.166 = -0.566 ,$$
$$3.305 - 0.741 - 0.853 = -2.659 ,$$
$$2.983 + 2.913 = -6.585 ,$$
$$3.035 = -6.291 ,$$

where $x = \Delta V_0, y = \Delta K, z = K\Delta e, u = -K\Delta\omega,$ and

$$v = \frac{Kn}{(1 - e^2)^{3/2}} \Delta T .$$

TABLE 3

FINAL VELOCITIES AND RESIDUALS

No.	Velocity (km/sec)	O−C (km/sec)	Eq.−Eph. (km/sec)	No.	Velocity (km/sec)	O−C (km/sec)	Eq.−Eph. (km/sec)
1.....	+34.1	+0.9	+0.04	6....	−35.6	+3.8	−0.08
2.....	− 2.4	−1.9	+ .12	7....	−29.3	+2.1	− .13
3.....	−33.8	+3.7	− .02	8....	− 6.3	−0.6	− .12
4.....	−53.8	+2.0	− .04	9....	+42.1	−1.5	− .05
5.....	−54.1	−7.3	−0.06	10....	+55.3	+1.0	+0.13

The solution of the above normal equations gives the following numerical values of the corrections to the preliminary elements:

$$x = +0.218 , \qquad \Delta V_0 = +0.22 \text{ km/sec} ,$$
$$y = -0.327 , \qquad \Delta K = -0.33 \text{ km/sec} ,$$
$$z = -1.458 , \qquad \Delta e = -0.026 ,$$
$$u = -2.253 , \qquad \Delta\omega = +2°.3 ,$$
$$v = -0.337 , \qquad \Delta T = -0.058 \text{ days} .$$

A final ephemeris is now computed with the elements corrected by the values given above. The form is identical with that of Table 2, so it is sufficient to list here only the new calculated velocities and residuals for each of the ten normal places, as in Table 3.

The sum of the squares of the residuals is lowered some 4 per cent by the solution. The rather small reduction shows that the preliminary elements were well chosen and leads one to expect that the solution has converged. The next step, therefore, is to substitute the numerical values of $x, y, z, \ldots$, into the equations of condition and to evaluate Equation minus Ephemeris (see below), as a check on the numerical work and the convergence. The values are included in Table 3, and they are satisfactory in size and distribution. We may therefore accept with confidence the elements as corrected by the solution, these being the "best" elements derivable from the observations according to the criterion of "least squares."

The final computation is the derivation of the probable errors in the elements. The weights of the unknowns, p_x, p_y, p_z, etc., are found by solving the normal equations, again putting the right members equal to 1.000 or zero, according to the usual rule (Brunt 1923). In re-solving the normal equations for this purpose, one finds most of the computing already done in the first solution, since only the right members have been altered. The square root of the weight divided into r_0, the probable error of a normal place of unit weight, gives the probable error of the unknown and hence of the correction to the element. We have

$$r_0 = \pm 0.6745 \sqrt{\left(\frac{\Sigma p \, v \, v}{n - \mu}\right)},$$

where n is the number of observation equations and μ is the number of unknowns. The residuals in Table 3 give $r_0 = \pm 1.56$ km/sec, and the final elements and their probable errors are

$$P = 6.06652 \text{ days} \pm 0.00006, \qquad T = \text{JD } 2430648.044 \pm 0.062,$$
$$e = 0.224 \qquad \pm 0.016, \qquad K = 55.67 \text{ km/sec} \pm 0.93,$$
$$\omega = 36°.3 \qquad \pm 3°.8, \qquad V_0 = -10.27 \text{ km/sec} \pm 0.63,$$

which completes the solution. The velocity-curve computed from the final elements is drawn as the solid curve in Figure 3. Ordinarily, one should plot the individual velocities from which the normal places were derived, but, in order to keep the example simple and straightforward, the normal places are plotted. It may be added that the scatter of the individual velocities about the final curve gives a probable error of a single observation of ± 5.2 km/sec. This is satisfactory for velocities from moderate-dispersion spectrograms of a star like AR Cassiopeiae, whose spectrum contains a few rather poorly defined lines.

Before one accepts a final corrected set of elements, the following test should be applied. Substitute in the equations of condition the unknowns found from the least-squares solution and sum the terms. Add to this sum the final residuals and subtract the preliminary residuals. The result, sometimes referred to as "Equation − Ephemeris," must be nearly zero for each and every equation. It is usually required that each sum shall not exceed 0.1 km/sec, but some latitude may be allowed if K is large.

The test is searching, for it will reveal the existence of an error at any point in the work, including the construction of the preliminary and final ephemerides. Furthermore, it will also tell the computer whether the solution has converged or whether a second approximation is called for. If a numerical error has been made in the solution, it will usually announce itself by a large non-zero sum in the particular observation equation where it was made, flanked by smaller, but non-zero, values in the adjacent equations. This circumstance will assist the computer in locating the error.

If the Equation — Ephemeris shows generally non-zero values and if they exhibit a variation periodic with the orbital period, then a lack of convergence is indicated. This means that the corrections to the elements are large enough that the higher-order terms in equation (6) cannot be neglected. It is instructive to pursue this matter a little further.

The final (corrected) radial velocity, V_f, may be expressed as a Taylor's series expanded in the neighborhood of the preliminary elements V_0, K, e, ..., etc., as follows:

$$V_f = f(V_0, K, e, \omega, T, n)_{\text{initial}} + \frac{\partial f}{\partial V_0} \Delta V_0 + \frac{\partial f}{\partial K} \Delta K + \frac{\partial f}{\partial e} \Delta e$$

$$+ \ldots + \frac{1}{2} \left[\frac{\partial^2 f}{\partial V_0^2} (\Delta V_0)^2 + \frac{\partial^2 f}{\partial K^2} (\Delta K)^2 + \frac{\partial^2 f}{\partial e^2} (\Delta e)^2 + \ldots \right. \quad (8)$$

$$\left. + 2 \frac{\partial^2 f}{\partial V_0 \partial K} (\Delta V_0)(\Delta K) + 2 \frac{\partial^2 f}{\partial V_0 \partial e} (\Delta V_0)(\Delta e) + \ldots \right].$$

Now $f(V_0, K, e, \ldots)_{\text{initial}}$ is the preliminary velocity V_p; so equation (8) may be written

$$\frac{\partial f}{\partial V_0} \Delta V_0 + \frac{\partial f}{\partial K} \Delta K + \frac{\partial f}{\partial e} \Delta e + \ldots + V_p - V_f = -\tfrac{1}{2} [\ ], \quad (9)$$

where the right member represents the second-order (and higher) terms.

The left member of formula (9) is the substitution called Equation — Ephemeris. It is equal to $-\tfrac{1}{2}[\ ]$ and is very small if the second-order terms may be neglected. If they cannot be neglected, then the right member of expression (9) is appreciable, and the substitution indicates the lack of convergence in the solution by non-zero values generally periodic in the period of the binary.

Let us now write the preliminary (uncorrected) velocity in terms of the final (corrected) elements and the differential corrections, which are now $-\Delta V_0$, $-\Delta K$, $-\Delta e$, etc. We then have

$$V_p = f(V_0, K, e, \ldots)_{\text{final}} - \frac{\partial f}{\partial V_0} \Delta V_0 - \frac{\partial f}{\partial K} \Delta K - \frac{\partial f}{\partial e} \Delta e - \ldots$$

$$+ \frac{1}{2} \left[\frac{\partial^2 f}{\partial V_0^2} (\Delta V_0)^2 + \frac{\partial^2 f}{\partial K^2} (\Delta K)^2 + \frac{\partial f^2}{\partial e^2} (\Delta e)^2 \right.$$

$$\left. + \ldots + 2 \frac{\partial^2 f}{\partial V_0 \partial K} (\Delta V_0)(\Delta K) + \ldots \right]$$

or

$$\frac{\partial f}{\partial V_0} \Delta V_0 + \frac{\partial f}{\partial K} \Delta K + \frac{\partial f}{\partial e} \Delta e + \ldots + V_p - V_f = \tfrac{1}{2} [\ ]. \quad (10)$$

The left member of equation (10) is, as before, Equation — Ephemeris, and the right member is very nearly the same as the right member of equation (9) but of opposite sign. This gives a test for lack of convergence as follows:

Compute coefficients of the observation equations with the final elements and make the substitution as before. The non-zero values of Equation — Ephemeris will now be of the opposite sign and nearly the same size numerically as in the original substitution. In practice, one does the computation only for the one or two equations showing the largest departures from zero.

If the solution has not converged, one should repeat the work, deriving corrections to the elements found in the first solution. The new corrections are usually quite small and within the probable errors of the elements. It is often a matter of choice as to whether a second solution is justified. It will depend on the accuracy of the observations and the size of the residuals in Equation — Ephemeris. It is usually worthwhile to make another solution when the largest residual is about 5 per cent of K. A good example of the changes produced by a second solution is given by McKellar (1938) for the binary HD 195986.

§ 4. SPECIAL CASES

The equation of condition (7) and Schlesinger's modification do not give a determinate solution when e is very small. In this case the coefficients of $\Delta\omega$ and ΔT approach equality, and a nearly zero denominator appears in the solution of the normal equations. It was the practice some years ago to evade the difficulty by fixing T and solving for corrections to the other elements. This procedure, however, biased the solution and gave entirely fictitious values of the precision in ω (Luyten 1936), so that one could not rely on the elements derived in this way.

The difficulty was removed by a method given by Sterne (1941b) wherein a preliminary circular orbit is corrected to one of small eccentricity by a full least-squares solution. Sterne avoided the inherent indeterminacy in T (and ω) by adopting T_0, the time of nodal passage, as an element. T_0 is defined with precision even in a circular orbit. Sterne's solution gives corrections to preliminary values of V_0, K, and T_0 and gives, in addition, $e \sin \omega$ and $e \cos \omega$. His equation of condition is

$$\delta V = \delta V_0 + \cos L \, \delta K + \cos 2L \, K \, e \cos \omega + \sin 2L \, K \, e \sin \omega$$
$$+ \sin L \, n \, K \, \delta T_0 - \sin L(t - T_0) \, K \, \delta n , \tag{11}$$

where L is the mean longitude. The method is a valuable contribution to the subject and should be used in all cases where the eccentricity appears to be between 0 and 0.1. Another advantage is the simplicity of the coefficients in equation (11), resulting in a significant reduction in the labor of a solution. It has been found possible to use Sterne's equation successfully even when the final eccentricity is as much as 0.10.

When the components of a spectroscopic binary are comparable in brightness, we observe two sets of spectral lines and obtain two velocity-curves. Such systems are important, for we may derive the mass ratio of the components from the inverse ratio of the amplitudes. The orbital elements in these systems combined with auxiliary quantities—for example, the photometric elements of eclipsing pairs—give us information on stellar masses, radii, and densities and the relation between mass and luminosity.

The spectral lines in a two-spectrum binary may be measured as double near the nodes (Fig. 4). The components merge into a single broad feature as the systemic velocity is approached, and a single line of high contrast is observed in the neighborhood of the systemic velocity. The single sharp-line velocities have sometimes been used in determining elements and are often given high weight. The practice should be abandoned because the lines remain sharp for an appreciable time near the instant of V_0-crossing. Including these observations tends to bias the choice of preliminary elements, and their generally large residuals are likely to give rise to wrong values of e and ω in the solution.

We know from the solution of the two-body problem that the orbits of the components are identical in shape and differ only in size. The values of V_0, e, and T are the same for the two velocity-curves, the values of ω differ by 180°,

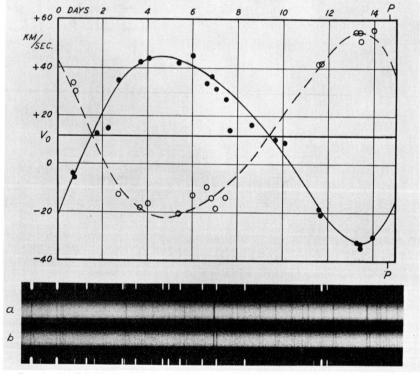

Fig. 4.—Radial-velocity curves and spectra of HD 171978. This is a good example of a binary exhibiting alternately single and double spectral lines. The radial velocities and the curves given by the final elements illustrate the principal features of a two-spectrum binary.

while K_1 is generally not equal to K_2. If we treat the velocity-curves separately, we shall usually violate the above conditions because of the errors of observation. One should therefore adjust the preliminary elements to maintain the proper equality and combine observations of both stars into one least-squares solution to obtain corrected elements. The equation of condition for this kind of solution is given by Harper (1914) from a derivation by W. F. King.

Sometimes the spectral lines of the fainter component are very faint, and the measures are of low precision. Here it is allowable, and even preferable, to derive the orbital elements, except K_2, from the velocities of the brighter component only and then to use the velocities of the fainter to determine K_2. The simple equation,

$$(\cos u_2 + e \cos \omega_2)\Delta K_2 = O - C,$$

may then be used in a least-squares solution.

Distortions of the radial-velocity curve arising in physical effects, such as tidal and rotational distortions of the stars, gravity darkening, or the influence of circumstellar material, do not fall within the scope of this chapter. Some aspects of these problems have been treated by Sterne (1941a) and Kopal (1941), who deduce certain distortions from the true velocity-curve. Each example is a separate problem and must be considered separately. Sometimes it is found that one component does not depart from the geometrical velocity-curve, and elements may be found from its radial velocities. A rather simple case illustrating this is the system HD 190967 (Petrie 1955).

The derivation of preliminary elements and their improvement by a least-squares solution do not usually consume a large fraction of the total time spent in investigating a spectroscopic binary. Nevertheless, it is a laborious process to compute and solve a set of perhaps twenty-five equations in six unknowns. The problem is well suited to the capabilities of high-speed digital computers, and a program for this has been devised by Heard and MacRae (1957). Once the program is prepared for the machine, the final elements and their probable errors are obtained in less than an hour. Future studies of spectroscopic binaries will undoubtedly take advantage of this great saving in labor.

It may be remarked here that the great powers of modern computers render it desirable to devise a method of obtaining accurate final elements directly from the observations. In other words, the computing machine should take the phases and velocities, derive preliminary elements, and proceed to correct them without the interposition of manual computation at any stage. One can see, in a general way, that this procedure is possible, but, so far, the routines appear not to have been specified and applied. The development of a satisfactory method would be a valuable contribution, as it would encourage the detailed and repeated analysis of binary motion, without which the understanding of orbital and other variations cannot be expedited.

§ 5. VARIATIONS OF ORBITAL ELEMENTS

Triple and multiple stars have been found to be rather common in visual-binary surveys, and triple systems are known from purely spectroscopic observations. Algol, λ Tauri, and μ Orionis are well-known examples. The usual arrangement is a close pair, AB, combined with a distant companion, C, and the principal effect is a variation in the systemic velocity of AB. Thus Algol AB has a period of 2.8673 days, while the variation of its systemic velocity is periodic in 1.87 years.

In the usual spectroscopic triple system one star predominates in light, and only one spectrum is seen. In Algol, only the spectral lines of A are ordinarily visible, but the spectrum of C may be seen during the eclipse of A. In λ Tauri the spectral lines of C are never visible, but those of B are seen with difficulty

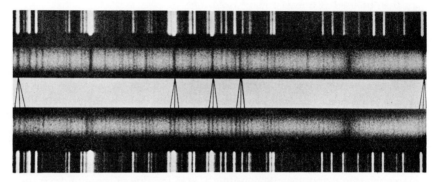

Fig. 5.—Single and triple lines in the spectrum of HD 100018 (ADS 8189). Three components can be seen at the strong iron lines. The outer two lines arise in the short-period (7.4 days) pair, while the visual companion, ADS 8189B, gives the central, little-displaced, line.

upon spectrograms obtained near the nodes. An exceptional case is HD 100018 = ADS 8189, where the three components are comparable in light and consequently triple lines appear in the spectrum (Petrie and Laidler 1952) at times of nodal passage in the short-period orbit, while the lines become single when the close pair has the systemic velocity. This rather spectacular change is illustrated in Figure 5.

The orbital motion of the close pair about the barycenter of the system is usually so slow that the variation of V_0 is easily separated from the orbital elements of the short-period pair. In λ Tauri, however, the periods are 3.95 and 33 days. A recent study of this system by Ebbighausen and Struve (1956) is an excellent example of the method of separating the different orbital motions.

In addition to the variation in V_0, one expects to find other perturbations in the motion of the close pair, particularly a secular change in ω, the orientation of the line of apsides. A change of this kind has been found by Redman (1930) in the system Y Cygni.

A long period of time will be required for the study of perturbations, and we are only now in a position to begin the task. In determining orbital elements it will be necessary to devise a satisfactory method of discussing observations scattered over a rather long interval. It will be difficult to distinguish between uncertainties caused by observational error and actual changes in elements unless one has available a number of compact sets of observations made at intervals of several years.

Orbital changes are possible in binary systems not disturbed by a third body because of the influence of rotational and tidal deformations of the spherical shape. An established variation leads to information on the internal density distribution, and the subject is therefore important in studies of stellar structure and stellar evolution. Theoretical discussions have been given by Cowling (1938) and by Sterne (1939), who agree that the largest perturbation to be expected is a secular advance of the line of apsides. The advance may be detected from

TABLE 4

SUSPECTED VARIATION IN ω IN SPECTROSCOPIC BINARIES

Star	Orbital Eccentricity	Interval (Years)	No. of Orbits
RZ Cassiopeiae............	0.05	22	2
TX Ursae Majoris........	.16	16	4
a Virginis................	.10	42	3
57 Cygni.................	.14	29	3
AR Cassiopeiae..........	0.27	30	2

light-curves or from radial-velocity-curves. The problem is made more difficult, from the spectroscopic side, because of the low orbital eccentricities of the binaries likely to show an effect. It is difficult to be certain of ω—and much more so of the changes in ω—in just those systems which should exhibit them.[1]

At present we know very little about changes in ω in spectroscopic binaries. The fifth catalogue of such binaries (Moore and Neubauer 1948) lists 480 systems with reasonably well-determined orbits. Changes in ω are mentioned for nine of these systems, but several are accompanied by changes in V_0, so that a triple star is indicated. Table 4 lists those binaries in which a change in ω has been mentioned without evidence of a third body.

At first sight, it would appear that several well-established examples are known, but closer inspection tends to weaken this impression. In the case of RZ Cassiopeiae the eccentricity is too small for a firm determination of ω. The eccentricity in TX Ursae Majoris appears to be sufficiently high, but observers differ here, and a value as low as 0.03 has been assigned. The lines in the spectrum of a Virginis are extremely diffuse, and, furthermore, changes in line appearance have been noticed (Struve and Ebbighausen 1934), casting some doubt on the orbital ele-

[1] See also chapter by Z. Kopal in Volume 8 of this series (*Stellar Structure*).

ments. The cases of 57 Cygni and AR Cassiopeiae appear to be more certain, but
even here there are differences in the amount of the change in ω assigned by different investigators. For example, Pearce (1939) found a period for the apsidal
motion of 57 Cygni, from comparison of Allegheny and Victoria orbits, of some
25 years. On the other hand, Luyten, Struve, and Morgan (1939) obtain results
which indicate a period of about 200 years, but they remark that "the period of
apsidal rotation is still unknown." In the case of AR Cassiopeiae a period of the
apsidal rotation of 220 years has been announced (Luyten, Struve, and Morgan
1939), but the second set of orbital elements was derived by a graphical method
and appears to give a value of ω too high if one goes by the value resulting from a
least-squares solution of the same material. The situation is further complicated
by the photometric solution derived by Stebbins (1921). His value of ω is 37°.2,
which, combined with the first spectroscopic value, calls for a short period of
about 120 years. A number of spectroscopic orbits has been obtained by the
writer between 1933 and 1957. The evidence for a forward precession of the
apsidal line is good, but several difficulties remain to be clarified. The spectroscopic information now suggests that the period of the apsidal rotation must be
in excess of 500 years, and this is confirmed by calculations made from the
theoretical formula.

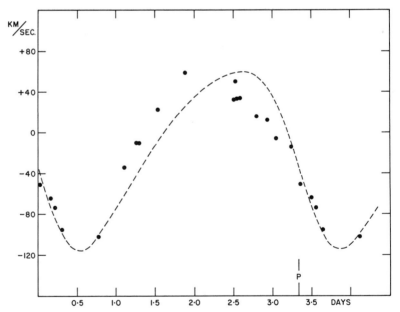

Fig. 6.—Radial velocities of HR 8800 obtained in 1957, compared with a velocity-curve
derived in 1919. The 1919 curve corresponds to ω = 127°. The 1957 observations do not fit the
early curve and define a value of ω of about 210°. The effects shown here correspond to an apsidal
period of about 165 years.

Perhaps the clearest case of probable apsidal motion is given by the binary HR 8800, for which only one set of orbital elements is published. The original elements were derived by Young (1920), who obtained values of $\omega = 126° \pm 7°$ and $e = 0.233 \pm 0.022$. Radial velocities obtained by the writer in 1957 show a marked departure from Young's curve. An eccentricity of about 0.23 is confirmed, but the value of ω must be about 200°, since a preliminary determination yields $e = 0.25$, $\omega = 210°$. The period of apsidal motion is therefore in the neighborhood of 165 years. The evidence described above is presented in Figure 6.

Changes in the amplitude, K, have been announced in one or two systems. The star BD+28°4389 gave a velocity-curve with an amplitude of 79.2 ± 0.6 from a Victoria orbit obtained between 1926 and 1933 (Harper 1933), whereas a Simeis orbit in 1929–1932 (Albitsky 1933) gave $K = 84.8 \pm 0.8$. The difference 5.6 ± 1.0 km/sec appears to be significant.

More striking is the case of δ Capricorni, with a period of 1 day and a circular orbit. An amplitude of 65.7 ± 0.5 km/sec was derived from Yerkes velocities of 1921 (Crump 1921), whereas Victoria and Michigan spectrograms taken between 1933 and 1938 gave $K = 73.4 \pm 0.7$ (Stewart 1958). The difference in K is nine times its probable error.

Another example is ι Pegasi, a star of spectral class F5 with a circular orbit. Orbits from the Lick Observatory in 1904 (Curtis) and from Victoria in 1933–1938 (Petrie and Phibbs 1949) agree exactly in values of K of 48.2 km/sec $\pm$ 0.5, but Miczaika (1951) finds a K of 41.5 km/sec. The explanation here, as in other cases, is obscure.

It is not known how many systems will exhibit orbital changes, for, in the majority of cases, elements have been derived at only one epoch. The subject is in a very unsatisfactory state, and our knowledge of changes is practically nil, apart from a few well-known triple systems. It is apparent from this brief discussion that the existence of changes will not be firmly established without difficulty. New observations will have to be made giving adequate coverage over the cycle. The first-epoch spectrograms should probably be measured again or, at least, re-reduced with a consistent set of wave lengths, homogeneous with those used in the later series. The elements must be determined with every care in the handling of the observational data and corrected by the impersonal criterion of a least-squares solution. In spite of the obvious difficulties, the prospect is not uninviting. Observations made during the next decade are likely to clarify some of the puzzles now confronting us and bring to light additional systems for investigation. The student of binary stars is assured of valuable material in the future from the careful derivation and intercomparison of spectroscopic orbital elements.

REFERENCES

AITKEN, R. G.   1935   *The Binary Stars* (2d ed.; New York: McGraw-Hill Book Co., Inc.), chap. vi.

ALBITSKY, V.	1933	*Pulkovo Obs. Circ.*, **8**, 10.
ASTRAND, J. J.	1890	*Hilfstafeln* (Leipzig: Engelmann).
BRUNT, D.	1923	*The Combination of Observations* (Cambridge: Cambridge University Press), chap. vii.
COWLING, T. G.	1938	*M.N.*, **98**, 734.
CRUMP, C. C.	1921	*Ap. J.*, **54**, 127.
CURTIS, H. D.	1904	*Lick Obs. Bull.*, **2**, 169.
	1908	*Pub. A.S.P.*, **20**, 133.
EBBIGHAUSEN, E. G., and STRUVE, O.	1956	*Ap. J.*, **124**, 507.
HARPER, W. E.	1914	*Pub. Dom. Obs. (Ottawa)*, **1**, 327.
	1933	*Pub. Dom. Ap. Obs. Victoria*, **6**, 203.
HEARD, J. F., and MacRAE, D. A.	1957	*J.R.A.S. Canada*, **51**, 29; *Contr. Dom. Ap. Obs.*, No. 53.
HENROTEAU, F.	1928	*Hdb. d. Ap.* (Berlin: Springer), **6**, 363.
IRWIN, J. B.	1952	*Ap. J.*, **116**, 218.
KING, E. S.	1920	*Harvard Ann.*, **81**, 231.
KOPAL, Z.	1941	*Proc. Acad. Sci.*, **27**, 359.
LEHMANN-FILHÉS, R.	1894	*A.N.*, **136**, 17.
LUYTEN, W. J.	1936	*Ap. J.*, **84**, 85.
LUYTEN, W. J., STRUVE, O., and MORGAN, W. W.	1939	*Pub. Yerkes Obs.*, **7**, 281.
McKELLAR, A.	1938	*Pub. Dom. Ap. Obs. Victoria*, **7**, 115.
MICZAIKA, G. R.	1951	*Zs. f. Ap.*, **29**, 105.
MOORE, J. H., and NEUBAUER, F. J.	1948	*Lick Obs. Bull.*, **20**, 1.
PEARCE, J. A.	1939	*Proc. Amer. Astr. Soc.*, **9**, 268.
PETRIE, R. M.	1955	*Pub. Dom. Ap. Obs. Victoria*, **10**, 259.
PETRIE, R. M., and LAIDLER, D.	1952	*Pub. Dom. Ap. Obs. Victoria*, **9**, 181.
PETRIE, R. M., and PHIBBS, E.	1949	*Pub. Dom. Ap. Obs. Victoria*, **8**, 225.
REDMAN, R. O.	1930	*Pub. Dom. Ap. Obs. Victoria*, **4**, 341.
RUSSELL, H. N.	1902	*Ap. J.*, **15**, 252.
SCHLESINGER, F.	1908	*Pub. Allegheny Obs.*, **1**, 33.
SCHLESINGER, F., and UDICK, S.	1912	*Pub. Allegheny Obs.*, **2**, 155.
SHAPLEY, H., and HOWARTH, H. E.	1929	*A Source Book in Astronomy* (New York: McGraw-Hill Book Co., Inc.), p. 370.
SMART, W. M.	1931	*Spherical Astronomy* (Cambridge: Cambridge University Press), chap. v.
STEBBINS, J.	1921	*Ap. J.*, **54**, 81.
STERNE, T. E.	1939	*M.N.*, **99**, 451.
	1941*a*	*Proc. Acad. Sci.*, **27**, 168.
	1941*b*	*Ibid.*, p. 175.

STEWART, MARYJANE   1958   *J.R.A.S. Canada*, **52**, 11.
STRUVE, O., and
   EBBIGHAUSEN, E. G.   1934   *Ap. J.*, **80**, 365.
TANNER, R. W.   1948   *J.R.A.S. Canada*, **42**, 177.
WATSON, J. C.   1868   *Theoretical Astronomy* (Philadelphia: J. B. Lippin-
                                       cott Co.), chap. 7.
WILSON, O. C.   1941   *Ap. J.*, **93**, 29.
YOUNG, R. K.   1920   *Pub. Dom. Ap. Obs. Victoria*, **1**, 239.

CHAPTER 24

Orbit Determinations of Eclipsing Binaries

JOHN B. IRWIN
Goethe Link Observatory

§ 1. INTRODUCTION

THE observation and analysis of eclipsing binaries has been peculiarly profitable in supplying many important data concerning stars, data that would be difficult to obtain in any other manner. The fruitfulness of this particular branch of stellar astronomy has been well summarized by Russell (1948), who himself made the most fundamental contributions to the theory of the interpretation of eclipsing binary light-curves. Russell's methods not only provided a solution for a previously intractable, important problem but are noteworthy in their demonstration of how a difficult piece of mathematical analysis can be solved in practice by the construction of appropriate numerical tables.

Observations of eclipsing stars may be photometric, spectroscopic, or astrometric. The combination of photometric and spectroscopic observations has been especially rewarding, inasmuch as analysis of the light-curve gives the radii of the components in terms of the separation of the stars, while the velocity-curves, when both spectra are visible, combined with the orbital inclination as deduced from the light-curve, fix both the separation of the stars in kilometers and their individual masses and radii. The spectroscopic observations may also be useful in the interpretation of *light*-curves in providing data concerning relative luminosities, spectral and luminosity classes, mass ratios, orbital eccentricity, times of minima, axial rotations, possible third bodies, and unusual spectroscopic phenomena of many kinds. Unfortunately, spectroscopic observations are time-consuming, usually require large and expensive telescopes, and have, therefore, been made for only a comparatively few eclipsing systems. Seventy per cent of the 2,763 eclipsing stars listed in the second edition of the *General Cata-*

logue of Variable Stars (Kukarkin, Parenago, Efremov, and Kholopov 1958) do not have even the minimum possible spectroscopic information—namely, the spectral type of the brighter component. In contrast, the number of known eclipsing systems is increasing rapidly. For example, the first edition of the *General Catalogue of Variable Stars* (Kukarkin and Parenago 1948) lists only 1,913 eclipsing stars, and the majority of these variables can be observed with precision as to both light and color variation with multiplier phototube photometers attached to relatively small telescopes. This technical advance means that observers now have a wide range of selection in choosing systems of special interest; that there will be an ever increasing number of precision light-curves, with consequent demands for more precise theories; and that interpretation of color and color variations will be of special interest.

The interpretation of any binary-star system is based on a comparison of observations with a model or perhaps a series of increasingly complex models. In the case of a visual binary, the model is a comparatively simple one: two stars, acting like mass points, move in Keplerian orbits under their mutual gravitational attraction. Only occasionally does this simple dynamical model need to be modified because of the presence of a third component or because the photocentric orbit does not correspond to the true orbit. In the case of spectroscopic binaries the simple dynamical model "breaks down" somewhat more frequently; not only may there be a third component causing variations in period and systemic velocity, but also there may be gas streams distorting the velocity-curve, eclipses causing rotational effects, and measurable apsidal motion during the time of the observations. In the case of eclipsing binaries, the simplest model is essentially a geometrical one rather than a dynamical one and is almost invariably found to be inadequate when tested by the best observations. The degree of limb darkening may be unknown, and there may be deviations from a simple cosine law. Periods may vary for a variety of reasons, and an initial assumption of a circular orbit may be in error. Tidal and rotational forces will distort the components into non-spherical shapes, and the surface brightness will vary from point to point on the projected stellar disks in a changing, complex manner due to local gravity, the heating of each component by radiation from the other, and the varying separation of the components in an eccentric orbit. In some cases major deviations from the spherical model are apparent at first glance, even for very poorly observed light-curves, and some deviation is the rule rather than the exception for the most precisely observed light-curves.

The life of a computer of an eclipsing binary orbit is further complicated by the fact that his method of attack is dictated by the nature of his observational material. The simplest possible case would be for observations of an obviously total primary minimum (see Fig. 5) and with light constant outside eclipse and no observed secondary minimum. Even this simple case becomes much more complex if the observations are of the highest precision. For example, the limb-darkening coefficient x need not be assumed but may be derived from the observations, and the shape of the minimum may be substantially distorted because of the non-sphericity of the eclipsing star. For more complicated cases, where observations are made in two or more colors over the entire light-curve and where pertinent spectroscopic material is available, the solution may be lengthy and laborious and proceed by a large number of successive approximations or trials.

For these and other reasons the literature of eclipsing binary orbit determinations is extensive. For example, there have been four monographs written in English on the subject in recent years (Kopal 1946, 1950, 1959; Russell and Merrill 1952). Useful summarizing discussions have been given by Pierce in Hynek (1951) and also by Binnendijk (1960). The reader is also referred to the extensive reports of Commission 42 to be found in *Transactions of the International Astronomical Union* from 1952 on.

A bound volume of the extensive and beautifully constructed Merrill tables (Merrill 1950) weighs 5 pounds. It is obvious that all this material cannot be usefully condensed into one short chapter and that the choice of subject matter presented here must, of necessity, be severely limited. Therefore, the writer proposes to discuss, for the most part, only the basic theory of the simple spherical model, giving tables for the solution of this model that should be adequate for all but the most accurate observations and, finally, two numerical examples. It is hoped that this type of discussion will serve as a useful introduction to the subject for the beginning student who may be somewhat appalled at the amount and extent of the available literature.

Complete tables are presented here for the first time for the half-darkened case ($x = 0.5$). Such tabulations should be of value for two reasons. The majority of eclipsing stars probably have an x lying between 0.35 and 0.65, and a finer division than every 0.2 in x (which has been available up to now) in this range would seem to be indicated. Further, most modern observations are made photoelectrically and are in at least two colors. One would expect x to differ by perhaps 0.1 between the two colors, and it is therefore now possible to choose a combination of either 0.6 and 0.5 or 0.5 and 0.4 for x even in the preliminary solution. The half-darkened tables given here (Tables 1–12A) are based on the fundamental Zessevich (1938, 1940) tables and have been checked in detail by appropriate interpolation of the Merrill tables. I am indebted to Mr. William H. E. Day for performing the computations on the IBM 650 computer of the Indiana University Research Computing Center.

§ 2. THE SPHERICAL MODEL

Our model consists of two spherical stars moving in circular orbits about a common center of mass. The distribution of surface brightness is assumed to follow a cosine law, namely,

$$J = J_c \left(1 - x + x \cos \gamma\right), \tag{1}$$

where J_c is the surface brightness at the center of the disk, x is the coefficient of limb darkening, and γ is the angle between the radius (to the point in question) and the line of sight. A simpler model and one that has been extensively used in the past is the uniform-disk model where $x = 0$. We shall see later that, once the basic tables have been calculated for $x = 0$ and for $x = 1$ (the darkened case), it is a relatively simple matter to develop the theory for the more realistic case of partial limb darkening.

Our initial problem is to be able to predict the light received by a distant observer as a function of time. The motion is uniform in a circular orbit, and, if θ is the longitude in the orbit measured from conjunction—at the time of primary (deepest) minimum—it follows that

$$\theta = \frac{360°}{P}(t - t_0),\tag{2}$$

where P is the period in days and t_0, the epoch of conjunction, is usually expressed in Julian days. The radius of the circular orbit is usually unknown and is taken as our unit distance, so that r_s and r_g, the radii of the smaller and larger (greater) star, respectively, are dimensionless fractions of this distance. The absolute luminosities of the stars are usually not known, so that L_s and L_g, the lights of the smaller and larger stars, respectively, are normalized to

$$L_s + L_g = 1.\tag{3}$$

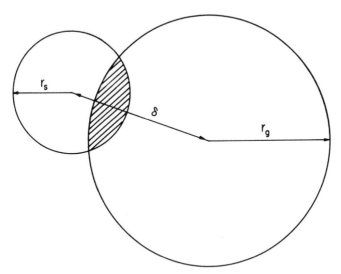

Fig. 1.—The geometry of eclipses. The eclipse is an occultation if the eclipsed area (*shaded*) is on the smaller star. The eclipse is a transit if the eclipsed area is on the larger star.

Let us consider two stars with apparent distance δ between the centers of the disks, as illustrated in Figure 1. The fractional loss of light, f, for a given value of the limb darkening, is clearly a function only of r_s, r_g, and δ. For the uniform case ($x = 0$), f is the ratio of the eclipsed area (*shaded*) to the total area of the eclipsed star; for the more complex darkened case ($x = 1$), f is the ratio of the *light* from the shaded area to the total light of the star being eclipsed. We can, however, change the scale by any factor we choose, inasmuch as we are here interested only in *ratios* of lights or areas. If we choose to divide through by r_g, for example, then we can state that, for a given value of x, f is a function of only two parameters, namely, r_s/r_g and δ/r_g. It is permissible and more convenient to use $(\delta - r_g)/r_s$ as a parameter rather than δ/r_g, so that, if we define

$$k = \frac{r_s}{r_g} \tag{4}$$

and

$$p = \frac{\delta - r_g}{r_s}, \tag{5}$$

we can then state that, for a given value of x, f is a function of only two dimensionless parameters k, the ratio of the radii, and p, the geometrical depth of the eclipse. At first contact (external tangency), $\delta = r_g + r_s$ and $p = +1$; at internal tangency, $\delta = r_g - r_s$ and $p = -1$; for concentric eclipse, $\delta = 0$ and $p = p_c = -1/k$. The geometrical depth p can vary during eclipse from $+1$ at first (or last) contact to a possible minimum of $-1/k$; k is restricted to some value between zero and unity and is equal to unity when the two stars have equal radii. The mathematical expressions for f are complex, and it is a major simplification that f, for a given x, can be tabulated as a function of two parameters rather than three. The light of a star of radius r_1 for the uniform case is

$$^0L_1 = \pi r_1^2 J_c, \tag{6}$$

where the numerical left superscript in the Merrill notation refers to the limb-darkening coefficient expressed in tenths. For the darkened case,

$$J = J_c \cos \gamma = J_c \frac{\sqrt{(r_1^2 - r^2)}}{r_1}, \tag{7}$$

and

$$^{10}L_1 = J_c \int_0^{r_1} \frac{2 \pi r \sqrt{(r_1^2 - r^2)}}{r_1} \, dr = \tfrac{2}{3} \pi r_1^2 J_c. \tag{8}$$

For the partially darkened case,

$$J = J_c(1 - x) + J_c x \cos \gamma, \tag{9}$$

and

$$^xL_1 = (1 - x)\,^0L_1 + x\,^{10}L_1 = \frac{3 - x}{3} \, \pi r_1^2 J_c. \tag{10}$$

The fractional loss of light for the partially darkened case is

$$
^xf = \frac{\displaystyle\int_A J\,ds}{^xL_1} = \frac{\displaystyle\int_A J_c(1 - x + x\cos\gamma)\,ds}{\tfrac{1}{3}(3 - x)\pi r_1^2 J_c}
$$

$$
= \frac{3(1 - x)}{3 - x}\frac{\displaystyle\int_A J_c\,ds}{\pi r_1^2 J_c} + \frac{3x}{3 - x}\frac{\displaystyle\int_A J_c\cos\gamma\,ds}{\pi r_1^2 J_c}.
$$

Inasmuch as

$$
^0f = \frac{\displaystyle\int_A J_c\,ds}{\pi r_1^2 J_c} \qquad \text{and} \qquad ^{10}f = \frac{\displaystyle\int_A J_c\cos\gamma\,ds}{\tfrac{2}{3}\pi r_1^2 J_c},
$$

we have

$$
^xf = \frac{3 - 3x}{3 - x}\,^0f + \frac{2x}{3 - x}\,^{10}f. \tag{11}
$$

Equation (11) may be used to calculate numerically the fractional loss of light for any intermediate degree of limb darkening from tables of ^0f and ^{10}f.

We shall now derive the necessary expressions for ^0f and, in part, ^{10}f. The expressions will be different, depending on whether the smaller star is eclipsed (an occultation) or the larger star is eclipsed (a transit). These two possibilities, in the Russell-Merrill notation, are designated by a superscript of either *oc* or *tr*. For the small star eclipsed (an occultation), it is seen from Figure 2 that

$$
^0f^{oc} = \frac{2}{\pi r_s^2}\left(\frac{\phi_s}{2\pi}\pi r_s^2 + \frac{\phi_g}{2\pi}\pi r_g^2 - \tfrac{1}{2}\delta r_s \sin\phi_s\right). \tag{12}
$$

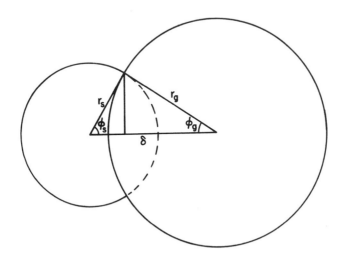

Fig. 2.—The geometry of an occultation used to derive equation (12) for uniform stars

From equations (5) and (4),

$$\delta = r_g(1 + kp),$$ (13)

and therefore

$$^0f^{oc} = \frac{1}{\pi k^2}[k^2\phi_s + \phi_g - k(1 + kp)\sin\phi_s],$$ (14)

where

$$\phi_s = \cos^{-1}\left[\frac{kp^2 + 2p + k}{2(1 + kp)}\right], \qquad \sin\phi_g = k\sin\phi_s.$$ (15)

For the special case of $k = 0$, corresponding to an occultation by a straight-edge, straightforward integration gives

$$^0f^{oc} = \frac{1}{\pi}[\cos^{-1}p - p\sqrt{(1 - p^2)}].$$ (16)

The areas of the two stars are related by the factor k^2, so that, for a transit,

$$^0f^{tr} = k^2\,{}^0f^{oc}.$$ (17)

It is convenient to use a, the fractional loss of light normalized to unity at internal tangency ($p = -1$), and, if τ is the value of f at $p = -1$, then, in general,

$$^xf^{oc} = {}^xa^{oc} \qquad \text{and} \qquad ^xf^{tr} = {}^x\tau\,{}^xa^{tr}.$$ (18)

For $x = 0$,

$$^0a = {}^0a^{oc} = {}^0a^{tr}; \qquad ^0\tau = k^2; \qquad ^0f^{tr} = k^2\,{}^0a.$$ (19)

The evaluation of ^{10}f is more difficult. The first solution by Russell and Shapley (1912) was an ingenious graphical procedure. A 16-inch circle was divided radially into 64 sectors, and, further, 24 concentric circles were so spaced that each of the 1600 small areas corresponded to 1/1600 of the total light of the star. Superposed circles corresponding to appropriate values of k made it possible to evaluate ^{10}f by counting areas and fractions thereof. The resulting tables were systematically incorrect in spots by more than two in the second decimal place (Zessevich 1938) but were adequate for the interpretation of all but the best photoelectric observations. Three different lengthy expressions for ^{10}f involving elliptic functions have been given by Zessevich (1938), Kopal (1946), and Merrill (1950). We shall here derive only the integral for the case of occultation.

It is convenient in Figure 3 to set the radius of the smaller star equal to unity, so that $\delta - r_g = p, r_g = 1/k$, and $\cos\gamma = \sqrt{(1 - r^2)}$. Then

$$^{10}f^{oc} = \frac{\displaystyle\int_p^1 J_c\cos\gamma \times 2r\phi_s\,dr}{\frac{2}{3}\pi J_c} = \frac{3}{\pi}\int_p^1 r\sqrt{(1 - r^2)}\,\phi_s\,dr,$$ (20)

where

$$\phi_s = \cos^{-1}\left[\frac{kr^2 + 2p + kp^2}{2r(1 + kp)}\right].$$ (21)

Two somewhat similar integrals can be derived for $^{10}f^{tr}$, one for partial and one for annular phases ($p < -1$). The accurate evaluation and tabulation of these integrals either numerically or in terms of elliptic integrals constituted a major computational problem; however, at present, it would represent only a few days (or hours) with an electronic computer. There are three special cases in which the integration does not involve elliptic integrals.

For $k = 0$:

$$^{10}f^{oc} = {}^{10}a^{oc} = \tfrac{1}{4}(2 - 3p + p^3).\tag{22}$$

For $\delta = 0$:

$$^{10}f^{tr} = 1 - (1 - k^2)^{3/2}.\tag{23}$$

For $p = -1$:

$$^{10}f^{tr} = {}^{10}\tau = \frac{2}{3\pi}\{3\sin^{-1}\sqrt{k} - (3 + 2k - 8k^2)\sqrt{[k(1-k)]}\}.\tag{24}$$

Merrill (1950) has tabulated $^{10}\tau$ to six decimal places, along with values of $^x\tau$ for $x = $ 0.2, 0.4, 0.6, and 0.8. The latter can be evaluated from

$$^x\tau = \frac{3 - 3x}{3 - x}k^2 + \frac{2x}{3 - x}\,{}^{10}\tau.\tag{25}$$

Zessevich (1940) tabulates in his Table 5 the function $\Phi(k) = 2(^{10}\tau/3k^2)$ to six decimals. Our Table 7 gives $^5\tau$ to six decimal places. Merrill (1950) tabulates a as a function of k and p to four decimals for both transit and occultation for $x = $ 0, 0.2, 0.4, 0.6, 0.8, and 1.0. Zessevich (1938 and 1940) tabulates a to five decimals for $x = 0$ and $x = 1$ and also inverts the tables and tabulates p as a function of k and a to four decimals for the above six values of x. Our Tables 1 and 2 give a as a function of k and p to three decimal places for $x = 0.5$ for both occultation and transit.

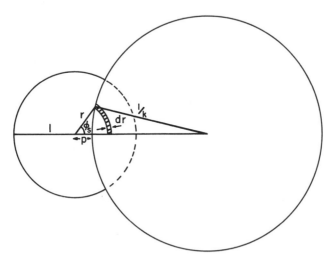

Fig. 3.—The geometry of an occultation used to derive equations (20) and (21) for darkened stars.

Our next task is to express δ in terms of θ so that p can be evaluated as a function of time. The two components of δ are $\sin \theta$ and $\cos \theta \cos i$, so that

$$\delta^2 = \sin^2 \theta + \cos^2 \theta \cos^2 i \tag{26}$$

or

$$\delta^2 = \cos^2 i + \sin^2 i \sin^2 \theta = r_g^2 (1 + kp)^2 . \tag{27}$$

If l is the normalized value of the light received from the whole system, then

$$l = 1 - f_g L_g - f_s L_s . \tag{28}$$

Expressed in magnitudes:

$$\Delta m = m - m_0 = -2.5 \log l , \tag{29}$$

where $l = 1$ and $m = m_0$ outside eclipse.

Merrill (1950) tabulates $\mathfrak{L}(\Delta m)$ (l in eq. [29]) to four decimals as a function of Δm. An abbreviated table of $\mathfrak{L}(\Delta m)$ is given here as Table 13.

This completes the theory necessary to calculate the light-curve—in either light-units or magnitudes or magnitude differences—for the spherical model for any set of elements. The elements are t_0, P, r_s, r_g, i, L_s, $(L_g = 1 - L_s)$, x_s, and x_g. The calculation can proceed as follows. For a given time t, θ is computed from equation (2), and δ is computed from equation (27). The latter calculation is facilitated by a table of $\sin^2 \theta$ to five and six decimals given by Merrill (1950) and given here in abbreviated form as Table 14. The geometrical depth p is calculated from equation (5) (three decimals are usually sufficient), and the appropriate a-table is used to obtain a. Tables of $^5a^{oc}$ and $^5a^{tr}$ are given here as Tables 1 and 2. In the case of a transit, f^{tr} is calculated from equation (18), τ being obtained from previously mentioned tabulations or from equations (24) and (25); l is calculated from equation (28) and Δm or m from equation (29) or with the aid of Table 13. The resulting l (or m) can be compared directly with the observations and

$$\Delta l_{(O-C)} = l_{obs} - l_{comp}$$

evaluated. The procedure is slightly longer for a non-standard value of x. The tables of ^0a and ^{10}a are both used and $^x f$ calculated from equations (25), (18), and (11).

A somewhat more rapid method of representation is possible by using the following equations, which will be derived later:

$$\sin^2 \theta = A + B\psi(x, k, a) , \tag{30}$$

where

$$B = \phi_1 (x, k) r_g^2 \csc^2 i \tag{31}$$

and

$$A = \frac{B}{\phi_2(x, k)} - \cot^2 i \tag{32}$$

and A and B are constants for a particular system but are different for occultation and transit. The quantities ϕ_1, ϕ_2, and ψ are tabulated by Merrill for both
occultation and transit and for six values of x. They are given here as Tables 3,
4, and 5 only for $x = 0.5$. Representation need be made at only ten to twenty
strategically chosen tabular values of a in the ψ-tables and θ calculated from
equation (30); the interpolation for ψ is only k-wise. The relation between l (or
m) and these values of a can be calculated as before and a smooth curve drawn
through the plotted points. To find the light for given epochs of observation,
one solves for ψ from equation (30) and doubly interpolates in the ψ-tables to
obtain a and hence l. This method of representation works for all types of
eclipses, whether total, annular, or partial. The writer normally prefers to use
the very first method of representation given here for the most precise observations, because, although somewhat slower, it represents with the full precision
of the tables at the epoch of observation for *any* value of x; also, because it is

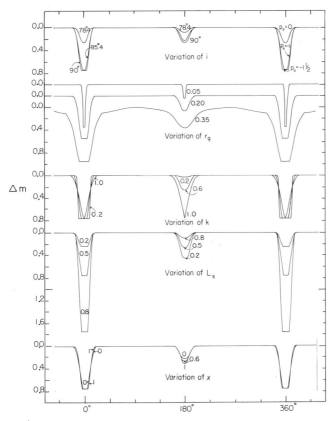

Fig. 4.—Typical light-curves for the case $i = 90°$, $r_g = 0.2$, $k = 0.6$, $L_s = L_g = 0.5$, and
$x = 0.6$. The effects of varying each of these parameters one at a time are shown.

necessary to calculate p for each observation in any event whenever a least-squares solution is to be made with the aid of the Irwin (1947) tables.

It is useful to study typical theoretical light-curves, varying one orbital element at a time. Such curves are given in Figure 4 for the case of $i = 90°$, $r_g = 0.2$, $k = 0.6$, $L_s = L_g = 0.5$, and $x = 0.6$; each of these five elements has been varied in turn. All curves except the one for $r_g = 0.35$, where the ellipticity and reflection effects are pronounced, are based on the spherical model, even though photometric perturbations might just be detectable. The large variation of the depth of secondary minimum with k is suggestive and is of fundamental importance in solutions based on the spherical model.

§ 3. ORBIT SOLUTION FOR THE SPHERICAL MODEL AND TOTAL ECLIPSE

In the previous section we have seen how, given elements of an eclipsing system and with the aid of published tables, a computer can quickly calculate a precise light-curve and compare with observations. A computer's first problem, however, is just the inverse of this, namely, given the photometric observations, what are the elements? In the case of a *spectroscopic* binary, the *shape* of the velocity-curve is a function of only two variables (e and ω), and one can match an observed velocity-curve against a reasonably small set of precomputed standard velocity-curves (King 1920). Inasmuch as p is a non-linear function of the time in our problem, the shape of a light-curve is a function of at least three variables, r_g, r_s (or k), and i, and even more variables if one includes x_s (or x_g). It would therefore seem impracticable to precompute and graph a set of light-curves covering all possible combinations of elements. In point of fact, however, the Russell method precomputes a whole set of tables which can be used numerically to solve quickly any possible system that approximates the spherical model.

A solution using the spherical model is in order, provided that the light outside minima is reasonably constant and the eclipses are symmetrical, equally spaced, and of equal duration. There should be no serious gaps in the observations, although it is quite possible to derive a set of elements from primary minimum alone. It is assumed that P, the period, has been determined and all the observations reduced to one cycle and plotted on an adequate scale.

A freehand curve is drawn as well as possible and t_0, the time of mid-eclipse, determined. This may require some judgment if the minimum is at all asymmetrical, and it may be found useful to fold over—or reflect—the observations about a preliminary value of t_0 and make a further adjustment in its value.

This is a useful device in any case, and it may also be useful to reduce the ordinarily very numerous observations into a comparatively few—but still adequate number of—normal points. The ordinate can be either l or m (or a difference in magnitude between variable and comparison). The abscissa can be either θ, or days, or fractions of a period (phase). If the primary (deeper) minimum shows a constant phase, it is probably a total eclipse. An annular eclipse cannot be very deep unless k is rather close to 1; so that most deep primaries, whether they show a constant phase or not, must, of necessity, be occultations. Because of observational selection, which favors the discovery of deep eclipses, there are probably many more eclipsing stars in our catalogues that have occultations, rather than transits, at primary minimum.

For a total eclipse the loss of light at minimum is obviously L_s. Only the best observations of the most favorable cases can define either x_s or x_g, so that these elements must usually be assumed. Kopal and Shapley (1956) give a list of observed x's for 16 stars, including the sun, and the range is from 0.2 to 0.85. Kopal (1959) gives a table on page 160 of the theoretical values of x as a function of spectral type and effective wave length as deduced by Münch and Chandrasekhar (1949). Neither Merrill nor Zessevich has tables for $x = 0.5$, the choice for the tables presented here, and it might well be that in any particular case some different value should be chosen. The choice is governed by the spectral class, the effective wave length of observation, and whatever observational and theoretical information is available. It is not necessary to set x_s equal to x_g, even in a preliminary solution.

The remaining variables are now three in number, as can be seen from

$$\cos^2 i + \sin^2 i \sin^2 \theta = r_g^2 (1 + kp)^2. \qquad (27)$$

At any time t, θ is a known quantity, and, because $l = 1 - aL_s$, a is also known for any point on the light-curve. Because p is a known and tabulated function of k and a for the chosen value of the limb darkening, the unknowns in equation (27) are i, r_g, and k. In principle, we can solve for these three unknowns if we write this equation for three different θ's. If p_1, p_2, and p_3 correspond to a_1, a_2, and a_3 and θ_1, θ_2, and θ_3, it follows from equation (27) that, by subtracting equations in pairs,

$$\sin^2 \theta_1 - \sin^2 \theta_2 = r_g^2 \csc^2 i [(1 + kp_1)^2 - (1 + kp_2)^2] \qquad (33)$$

and

$$\sin^2 \theta_2 - \sin^2 \theta_3 = r_g^2 \csc^2 i [(1 + kp_2)^2 - (1 + kp_3)^2]. \qquad (34)$$

If we choose permanently a_2 and a_3 to be 0.6 and 0.9, respectively, and if a_1 can take on any value of a and, further, if we divide equation (33) by equation (34), then we can define a function $\psi(x, k, a)$ such that

$$\psi(x, k, a) = \frac{\sin^2 \theta - \sin^2 \theta_2}{\sin^2 \theta_2 - \sin^2 \theta_3} = \frac{(1 + kp)^2 - (1 + kp_2)^2}{(1 + kp_2)^2 - (1 + kp_3)^2}. \qquad (35)$$

Tables of ψ as a function of k and a can be calculated from the right-hand side of equation (35) for occultation or transit and for any specified value of x.

Merrill (1950) gives eleven such tables for $x = 0, 0.2, 0.4, 0.6, 0.8,$ and 1.0. An analysis of equation (35) reveals the elegance of the Russell method. All the geometrical and mathematical complexity is concentrated in the right-hand side of the equation, which can be tabulated once and for all. ψ can be calculated from the light-curve for any value of a, and inverse interpolation in the appropriate ψ-table gives a value of k. Once k is fixed, $r_g^2 \csc^2 i$ can be obtained from either equation (33) or equation (34) and $\cot^2 i$ is obtained by solving equation (27) after division by $\sin^2 i$. From these, one can calculate i, r_g, and r_s.

There is a quicker method, however. If we define

$$A = \sin^2 \theta_2 \quad \text{and} \quad B = \sin^2 \theta_2 - \sin^2 \theta_3, \tag{36}$$

then equation (35) becomes

$$\sin^2 \theta = A + B\psi(x, k, a). \tag{30}$$

If we fix attention on those phases where $a = 0$ and $a = 1$, it can be shown that

$$r_g^2 \csc^2 i = \frac{B}{\phi_1(x, k)}; \quad \cot^2 i = \frac{B}{\phi_2(x, k)} - A, \tag{37}$$

where

$$\phi_1(x, k) = \frac{4k}{[\psi(x, k, 0) - \psi(x, k, 1)]} \tag{38}$$

and

$$\phi_2(x, k) = \frac{4k}{(1-k)^2 \psi(x, k, 0) - (1+k)^2 \psi(x, k, 1)}, \tag{39}$$

where ϕ_1 and ϕ_2 are given in Table 5 for $x = 0.5$ and are tabulated by Merrill (1950) for six other values of x. This short method consists, then, in extracting ϕ_1 and ϕ_2 from the tables—once k is established—and solving for $r_g^2 \csc^2 i$ and $\cot^2 i$ (hence r_g and i) from equation (37).

If, as rarely occurs, errors of observation combine with errors in the assumed model in such a way that $\cot^2 i$ is negative, then adjustments must be made by setting $\cot^2 i$ equal to zero ($i = 90°$), in which case

$$A = \frac{B}{\phi_2(x, k)}. \tag{40}$$

The interested reader is referred to $Ap.\ J.$, **36**, 252–254.

The crux of the Russell method is to establish the value of k first, and, in principle, this can be accomplished by using only three points on the light-curve—$a_2 = 0.6$, $a_3 = 0.9$, and any other $a(= 0.2$ or 0.3 say). Any three-point solution would obviously give too little weight to observations at other points. It is fundamental that the theoretical curve should be the best possible fit to all the *individual* observations—or normals—giving proper weights to all. There should be no long runs of residuals all of the same sign, and the number of positive and negative residuals should be about equal. A study of the literature reveals occasional serious deviations from such principles. Fortunately, in the Russell method, representation by equation (30) is very rapid, and it is possible—even before computing the elements—to "cut and try" and vary A and B (and hence k) by small amounts. Also, spaced points all up and down the free-hand curve can be used, ψ being calculated for each point from the left-hand side of equation (35) and k obtained by inverse interpolation in the table. Russell (1912) suggests giving zero weight to $\alpha = 0$ and 1, at points of external and internal tangency; unit weight to values of k from $\alpha = 0.1$, 0.5, 0.7, 0.8; and double weight for $\alpha = 0.2$, 0.3, 0.4, 0.95, 0.98, and 0.99.

A useful modification of the ψ-method has been given in Russell and Merrill (1952, pp. 59–60), which will usually lead more directly to better values of the preliminary elements. Weighted means of $\sin^2 \theta$ are formed for the points corresponding to $\alpha = 0.05$, 0.10, 0.20, 0.30, with weights 2, 2, 2, and 1; at $\alpha = 0.50$, 0.60, 0.70, with equal weights; at $\alpha = 0.95$, 0.97, 0.985, with weights 1, 2, and 2. If these three means are M_1, M_2, and M_3, respectively, then, from equation (30),

$$M_1 [\sin^2 \theta] = A + BM_1 [\psi],$$

$$M_2 [\sin^2 \theta] = A + BM_2 [\psi], \qquad (41)$$

$$M_3 [\sin^2 \theta] = A + BM_3 [\psi].$$

Successive subtractions enable us to define $R(x, k)$ such that

$$R(x, k) = \frac{M_1 [\sin^2 \theta] - M_2 [\sin^2 \theta]}{M_2 [\sin^2 \theta] - M_3 [\sin^2 \theta]} = \frac{M_1 [\psi] - M_2 [\psi]}{M_2 [\psi] - M_3 [\psi]}, \qquad (42)$$

where R can be calculated from the "observed" M's and can also be tabulated as a function of k alone for a chosen value of x. Inverse interpolation of the calculated R in a table of R gives k, and A and B can be calculated from any two of equations (41) with the third equation as a check. As before, tables of R, M_1, M_2, and M_3 for both occultation and transit and for six values of x are given in the Merrill tables and are given here in Table 6 for $x = 0.5$.

A numerical application of the R-M method is informative, and the one chosen here was also chosen by Russell (1912) and again by Aitken (1935) to illustrate the ψ-method. The light-curve of W Delphini (see Fig. 5) is defined by over 500 visual observations by Wendell (1909 and 1914). The primary minimum is deep, flat-bottomed, and well defined; the depth of secondary is unknown, as no observations fell within 0.27 days of the expected time. The period is 4.8061 days. Russell combined the observations into 59 normals, which are given in Table A. He found the magnitude during constant light to be $9^{m}395 \pm 0.009$; the magnitude at primary minimum to be $12^{m}10 \pm 0.014$; and the epoch of mid-eclipse $0^{d}0015$ earlier than that assumed by Wendell. I have used $12^{m}09$ at totality, and this gives a total change in magnitude of 2.695, corresponding to $L_s = 0.9164$ and $L_g = 0.0836$. The observations were plotted with care on a large sheet of graph paper with a scale of 0.01 inch equal to $0^{m}002$. A freehand curve was carefully drawn, and the ten appropriate phases for both sides of primary minimum were read off the graph. The sequence of calculations is shown in Table B, where use has been made of Tables 13 and 14. The value of

R was calculated from the left-hand side of equation (42) and was 2.043, corresponding to $k = 0.625$ (from Table 6). The three values of $M[\psi]$ for this k were obtained from Table 6 and are given in the last column of Table B. Using equations (41), A and B were found to be 0.03671 and 0.02565, respectively; ϕ_1 and ϕ_2 were interpolated from Table 5 and were 0.4160 and 0.5808. It follows from equation (37) that $r_g = 0.2474$, $i = 85°07$, and $r_s = 0.1546$.

Representation is accomplished through

$$\sin^2 \theta = A + B\psi, \tag{30}$$

and representation can be done before computing the final elements. All tabular values of a in Table 3 were used, and linear interpolation in k by means of a desk calculator quickly gave the necessary 24 values of ψ for $k = 0.625$. The calculated curve was carefully drawn, and the residuals for each normal point, accurate to 0^m001 or 0^m002, were read off the plot and are listed in Table A. The solution appears to be satisfactory, and there is little evidence of systematic runs.

Russell (1912) found k to be 0.528 for an undarkened solution, and Shapley's (1912) darkened ($x = 1$) solution gave $k = 0.703$. Both these solutions gave satisfactory representation, with average residuals comparable to the half-darkened solution. The respective values of r_s are 0.135 ($x = 0$) and 0.170 ($x = 1$), with little change in r_g. In general, a change in x can be almost exactly

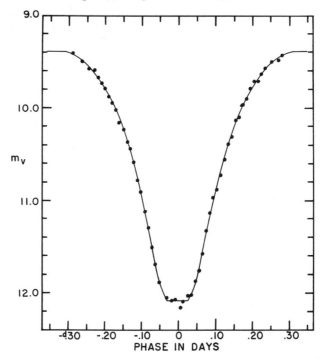

FIG. 5.—Visual light-curve of the primary minimum of W Delphini

compensated for by a change in the radius of the *eclipsed* star. This strong correlation has been graphically exhibited by Irwin (1947) and is the reason that x can be accurately derived only from the best photoelectric observations of favorable systems where the components are well separated and i is close to 90°. The correct choice of x is all-important, and the systematic use of $x = 0$ or $x = 1$ can lead only to systematically incorrect elements.

The depth of the unobserved secondary can be calculated as follows: The maximum geometrical depth, p_0, is equal to (cos $i - r_g$)/r_s and is -1.044; q_0 ($= f_0/a_0$) is 0.424 from Table 12. The loss of light at secondary ($x = 0.5$ assumed here) is 0.424 $L_g = 0.035$, corresponding to a magnitude change of 0^m039. It might be somewhat larger than this because of the reflection effect.

The R-M method is fast and accurate and requires little judgment or experience from the computer. The solution is rigorously tied in to three sections of the

TABLE A

OBSERVED MAGNITUDES AND RESIDUALS

Phase (Days)	m_v	No. Obs.	O−C (Mag.)	Phase (Days)	m_v	No. Obs.	O−C (Mag.)
−0.2894....	9.41	6	−0.009	+0.0560....	11.76	7	+0.016
− .2637....	9.49	5	+ .004	+0.0659....	11.58	8	+ .027
− .2458....	9.58	5	+ .023	+0.0753....	11.33	7	− .031
− .2306....	9.59	4	− .035	+0.0859....	11.14	5	− .024
− .2200....	9.67	5	− .007	+0.0937....	10.97	5	− .040
− .2106....	9.73	8	− .009	+0.1036....	10.88	8	+ .040
− .2007....	9.79	10	− .016	+0.1147....	10.73	8	+ .052
− .1911....	9.88	12	+ .004	+0.1246....	10.56	12	+ .030
− .1817....	9.95	10	+ .002	+0.1351....	10.39	14	+ .001
− .1718....	10.02	8	− .010	+0.1445....	10.31	11	+ .033
− .1615....	10.16	17	+ .036	+0.1546....	10.13	10	− .032
− .1506....	10.23	14	− .017	+0.1641....	10.10	11	+ .032
− .1396....	10.37	14	.00	+0.1744....	9.97	10	− .016
− .1311....	10.44	16	− .039	+0.1847....	9.90	9	+ .003
− .1212....	10.59	17	− .027	+0.1941....	9.79	9	− .041
− .1121....	10.78	14	+ .015	+0.2050....	9.71	8	− .046
− .1013....	10.91	17	− .018	+0.2157....	9.71	6	+ .025
− .0906....	11.12	14	− .002	+0.2242....	9.63	8	− .015
− .0809....	11.30	10	− .003	+0.2345....	9.57	7	− .022
− .0715....	11.51	12	+ .018	+0.2507....	9.50	7	− .021
− .0617....	11.69	10	+ .002	+0.2708....	9.48	7	+ .020
− .0509....	11.88	7	+ .004	+0.2811....	9.43	4	− .003
− .0313....	12.05	5	− .023	+0.94......	9.42	5	+ .025
− .0169....	12.08	4	− .010	+1.90......	9.35	5	− .045
− .0082....	12.07	7	− .020	+2.04......	9.41	7	+ .015
+ .0060....	12.16	5	+ .070	+2.67......	9.38	5	− .015
+ .0139....	12.09	4	.00	+3.04......	9.42	3	+ .025
+ .0261....	12.03	5	− .058	+4.04......	9.44	6	+ .045
+ .0356....	12.02	6	.00	+4.48......	9.36	7	−0.035
+0.0460....	11.87	6	−0.038				

light-curve, and one would expect little deviation at other points. Other good approximate methods of solution can be found in Kopal (1946). It should be pointed out here that a solution of either a total or an annular eclipse can also be made by the Russell χ-method or with the Merrill nomographs, both of these methods to be discussed later in connection with partial eclipses.

There is a certain minimum amount of time necessary for any solution, whatever the method; the observations must be assembled and plotted and residuals calculated. The total time required may be as little as a few hours; this is comparatively insignificant when compared with the time needed either to make the observations, to reduce the observations, to become familiar with the necessary theory associated with any method, or to write up the results. After a good approximate solution has been made, the computer might well consider investing

TABLE B

R-M Calculations for W Delphini

a	l	Δm	m_v	Left Phase (Days)	Right Phase (Days)	θ	$\sin^2 \theta$	Wt.	$M [\sin^2 \theta]$	$M [\psi]$
0.05...	0.9542	0.051	9.446	−0.280	0.278	20.°90	0.1273	2		
.10...	.9084	0.104	9.499	− .261	.257	19.40	.1103	2		
.20...	.8167	0.220	9.615	− .230	.227	17.12	.0867	2	0.10271	+2.573
.30...	.7251	0.349	9.744	− .208	.203	15.39	.0704	1		
.50...	.5418	0.665	10.060	− .168	.165	12.47	.04663	1		
.60...	.4502	0.866	10.261	− .149	.147	11.09	.03700	1	.03705	+0.0135
.70...	.3585	1.114	10.509	− .127	.128	9.55	.02752	1		
.95...	.1294	2.220	11.615	− .065	.063	4.79	.00697	1		
.97...	.1111	2.386	11.781	− .057	.054	4.16	.00526	2	0.00491	−1.2399
0.985..	0.0973	2.530	11.925	−0.048	0.043	3.41	0.00354	2		

more time in making a more refined analytical solution, especially if his observations are considerably more precise than those of Wendell. His primary purposes should be to fit the observations as closely as possible—consistent with a realistic model—giving each observation its proper weight. The method of least squares is designed to do just this, and the general approach is to derive a set of elements by any good approximate method and then to correct those elements by small amounts by means of a differential least-squares solution. A complete discussion will be found in Irwin (1947), and only an outline of the method will be given here. The method is very general and can be applied to all types of eclipses; primary and secondary minima can be solved singly or together, and color observations can be analyzed for differential limb darkening. The quantities, x_s, x_g, and $e \sin \omega$ can be introduced into the solution, as well as other variables, such as the mass ratio. Although a spherical model (or a rectified light-curve) and a circular orbit are usually assumed, the method can be applied with proper care to some distorted systems. A good first approximation to the elements enables one to differentiate the expression $l = 1 - fL_1$ and write the equations of condition in the following form:

$$\Delta l_{(o-c)} = -f\Delta L_1 - L_1\left[\frac{\partial f}{\partial r_g}\Delta r_g + \frac{\partial f}{\partial r_s}\Delta r_s\right.$$

$$\left. + \frac{\partial f}{\partial(\cos^2 i)}\Delta(\cos^2 i) + \frac{\partial f}{\partial x_1}\Delta x_1\right], \tag{43}$$

where the subscript 1 refers to the eclipsed star.

The differential coefficients may be evaluated from Irwin's (1947) tables, where they are tabulated, with modifications, as functions of k and p for $x = 0.0, 0.4, 0.6,$ and 1.0. Other values of x may be employed by using an interpolating equation similar to (11). Other unknowns, such as Δx_2, $\Delta(x_{blue} - x_{red})$, $\Delta(m_s/m_g)$, Δt_0, or $\Delta(e \sin \omega)$, can be introduced into equation (43).

In the case of W Delphini, one would exclude ΔL_1 (L_1 not subject to correction) and perhaps Δx_1, and equation (43) would reduce to three unknowns.

Because of the logarithmic relation between l and m, the weights of the equations usually increase with depth of eclipse. If r_l is the probable error in light-units and r_m is the probable error in magnitudes, then

$$r_l = 0.921\, lr_m. \tag{44}$$

Because the weights vary inversely as the square of the probable error, at a point 2.5 mag. down in a deep eclipse ($l = 0.1$) an observation there would have 100 times the weight of one at the start of eclipse, provided that the probable error in magnitudes remained constant.

There are obvious occasions where the method of least squares should not be used or used only with extreme caution. For example, the observations may be systematically in error, the observations may be too inaccurate to be worth any extra effort, the method may be too laborious, and its application may involve unwarranted assumptions and simplifications. Nevertheless, most modern photometric observations are precise enough, and the tables shorten up the computations to such an extent—along with the use of a modern desk calculator— that there seems to be no reason why the least-squares approach should not be profitably employed even at rather early stages in the calculations. If a light-curve has hidden within it the information that $x = 0.49 \pm 0.03$ and $m_s/m_g = 3.8 \pm 0.4$, only a least-squares solution can extract such data from the observations. The least-squares method is no substitute for good judgment; if wrong assumptions are made (e.g., $x = 0$), incorrect answers will be obtained.

A few remarks concerning the modern observational approach to a star such as W Delphini will now be made. Wendell's observations are some of the best visual observations ever made, with probable errors of the normals of about $\pm 0^m015$. These observations undoubtedly helped to stimulate the development of the basic theory. However, the best modern photoelectric observations of this star would be perhaps ten times as accurate, even though the star is somewhat faint at primary minimum. Observations in the Johnson U, B, V system would establish the interstellar reddening and absorption and the spectral type of the fainter component. Observations of secondary minimum would establish $e \cos \omega$ from the epoch, but this minimum would probably be much too shallow to derive $e \sin \omega$ from the duration; the depth might yield the limb darkening at various wave lengths for the fainter star, although this analysis would be complicated by the reflection effects. Observations between minima would yield the ellipticity and reflection effects, which in turn should establish the mass ratio and perhaps the variation in the gravity-darkening coefficient with wave length. Infrared observations would be especially useful, inasmuch as the secondary minimum would be deeper and the effects due to the distortion of the larger star would be more readily apparent between minima. If the system exhibited no unusual complications, the limb darkening of the smaller star should be obtainable to better than ± 0.04 and differential limb darkening (between different effective wave lengths) with perhaps twice this accuracy. The distortions of the larger star complicate the analysis of both minima, but observations for the hour just preceding totality and the hour just after the end of totality would be especially significant in fixing x_s with high accuracy. The analysis of such a hypothetical light-curve would be lengthy and tedious, but the observations would require it.

The astrophysical approach would be especially important, with due consideration to be given to the photometric perturbations, the mass ratio, the shapes of the two components, the ratio between the photometric and geometric ellipticity, the character of the reflected radiation, etc. Kopal (1955) assumes that W Delphini is a semidetached system (the secondary appears to fill exactly the largest closed equipotential capable of containing it) and from this assumption derives a value of $m_s/m_g = 4.56$.

This large mass ratio requires additional observational verification as outlined above, and, further, it implies that the long axis of the secondary component is about 10 per cent larger than its intermediate axis. The interested reader can find the first-order dynamical theory in chapter iv of Russell and Merrill (1952).

To summarize, both eclipsing-star observer and orbit computer need to be aware of the astrophysical problems and consequences involved in attacking any given system. The initial solution of the light-curve leads to only preliminary elements, which, in turn, can be used to guide the calculations of the dynamical and photometric complications from which new elements can be derived, and so on. These complications usually need to be *calculated*, they cannot normally be obtained directly from the light-curve. The solution is, therefore, one of successive approximations; a preliminary knowledge of the elements is used to derive better elements. A complete discussion is outside the scope of this chapter. The interested reader is referred especially to Kopal (1950, chap. vi) and also Kopal (1959), both of which deal with the computation of the elements of distorted systems. The results of the practical application of Kopal's methods to 83 eclipsing systems may be found in Kopal and Shapley (1956), which is also a most useful reference.

§ 4. SOLUTION FOR ANNULAR ECLIPSES

The solution for an annular primary eclipse alone is complicated by the fact that L_g and L_s are not immediately known and also because $a > 1$ during annular phases, unless $x = 0$. It may be that the loss of light at the total secondary minimum is well defined, in which case L_s is known. Under such circumstances it is clear that the elements derived from primary minimum must be such as to agree with the depth of secondary within the errors of observation. In general, we are here dealing with four—or more—unknowns, and the proper approach would appear to be to get the best preliminary solution by approximate methods and proceed to a least-squares adjustment, with the number of unknowns governed by the nature of the observational material.

At the point of internal tangency, $a = 1$, and if this position on the light-curve is well defined by the observations, the problem is relatively simple. The values of θ for any a can be read from the light-curve and ψ calculated from the left-hand side of equation (35) as before for a series of tabulated a's. Inverse interpolation in the ψ^{tr} tables (Table 4) will give a series of k's, and successive adjustments to A and B—as before—will lead to a final value of k and the other elements. The adjustments to A and B are additionally complicated because the representation must agree with observations throughout annular phases. Whenever k is tentatively adopted, τ should be obtained from the tables, and, because the light lost at internal tangency is observed and is equal to τL_g, the value of L_g can be calculated and compared with the light at secondary minimum.

Another possible approach is the Russell-Merrill R-M method (see eqs. [41] and [42] and Table 6), which may be faster and more precise but would especially need testing against observations during annular phases.

Annular eclipses at primary minimum are especially useful in establishing the coefficient of limb darkening, even though such eclipses are relatively shallow. Further, the deviations from the spherical model are often small because the less massive—and less luminous—star is also the smaller star. An examination of Kopal and Shapley's (1956) Table II of detached systems shows that most of the stars in this highly selected list have annular eclipses (transits) at primary minimum.

Kron's (1939) photoelectric observations of YZ Cassiopeia in the blue are of the highest precision (see Fig. 6), and an approximate solution by the R-M method will be given here to illustrate that method for the case of an annular eclipse. The 27 normal points for primary minimum are listed in Table C and are all of unit weight except 16, which is of three-fourths weight. The point of internal tangency is well defined by the observations at $l = 0.7120$, and a straightforward application of the R-M method gave $R = 2.231$, corresponding to $k = 0.564$. The average residual from this solution was 20 per cent less than that of Kron's, which were derived from a least-squares solution. This value of k, however, fixed $^5\tau$ (Table 7) and hence L_g, whose value of 0.8456 so derived differs sharply from 0.9375 as deduced by Kron from the well-observed loss of light at the (total) secondary minimum. The problem was therefore turned around; $^5\tau$ was derived from L_g, which led in turn to $k = 0.537$ and $R = 2.160$. Now $R = (M_1 - M_2)/(M_2 - M_3)$, so that the required lower value of R can be obtained by decreasing M_1 or M_3 or by increasing M_2. Increasing M_2 changes both numerator and denominator in the right manner. It was therefore decided

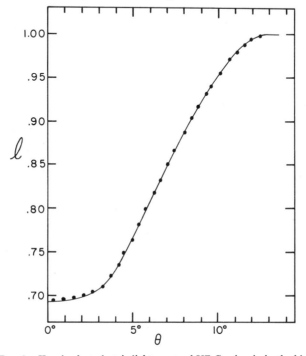

FIG. 6.—Kron's photoelectric light-curve of YZ Cassiopeia in the blue

to change only M_2, and the above equation was solved for M_2, leaving M_1 and M_3 fixed. A better solution could probably have been obtained by making appropriate adjustments to all M's. Whatever the adjustment in an M may be, its effect on $\sin^2 \theta$ and hence θ is readily apparent; in this case the run of positive residuals (and their approximate size) around $\alpha = 0.6$ were predictable. The rest of the auxiliary quantities and the elements can be calculated as before. The results are as follows:

$R = 2.160$, $\quad \phi_1 = 0.3475$, $\quad i = 88°17$,

$k = 0.537$, $\quad \phi_2 = 0.5135$, $\quad L_g = 0.9375$ (from depth of secondary),

$A = 0.012980$, $\quad r_g = 0.14374$, $\quad x_g = 0.5$ (assumed),

$B = 0.007187$, $\quad r_s = 0.07719$, $\quad e = 0$ (assumed).

In order to test the tables severely, the representation was made by two independent methods: (1) graphically from ψ's at tabular a's (Table 4 and eq. [30]) and (2) by the lengthier method of calculating at each point, first, δ and p and then a and l with the aid of Table 2. The two sets of residuals are given in Table C for comparison and are in good agreement. Table 4 and Table 2 are neither so accurate nor so detailed as the corresponding Merrill tables but would seem to be adequate for these observations. The average residual is one-third larger than

TABLE C

OBSERVATIONS AND RESIDUALS FOR YZ CASSIOPEIA

No.	θ	l	O−C		
			Graphical	Table 2 •	Kron
1	0°.330	0.6938	+0.0005	+0.0005	+0.0009
2	0.959	.6958	+ .0011	+ .0016	+ .0016
3	1.531	.6975	+ .0009	+ .0010	+ .0010
4	2.144	.6998	+ .0002	− .0002	− .0005
5	2.643	.7042	+ .0007	+ .0005	+ .0001
6	3.264	.7099	− .0005	− .0004	− .0011
7	3.764	.7224	+ .0014	+ .0014	− .0004
8	4.215	.7352	− .0006	.0000	− .0020
9	4.489	.7487	+ .0037	+ .0037	+ .0017
10	4.996	.7635	− .0008	− .0005	− .0019
11	5.367	.7811	+ .0025	+ .0027	+ .0010
12	5.754	.7989	+ .0048	+ .0046	+ .0029
13	6.245	.8174	+ .0024	+ .0029	+ .0012
14	6.616	.8319	+ .0015	+ .0018	+ .0003
15	7.051	.8500	+ .0025	+ .0023	+ .0007
16	7.414	.8663	+ .0042	+ .0042	+ .0015
17	8.034	.8873	+ .0010	+ .0010	− .0004
18	8.437	.9028	+ .0017	+ .0015	+ .0010
19	8.824	.9164	+ .0020	+ .0015	+ .0006
20	9.292	.9320	+ .0010	+ .0012	+ .0009
21	9.590	.9401	− .0007	− .0002	− .0006
22	10.130	.9550	− .0016	− .0011	− .0015
23	10.663	.9710	+ .0011	+ .0010	+ .0007
24	11.105	.9792	− .0010	− .0006	− .0017
25	11.532	.9874	− .0004	− .0008	− .0013
26	11.919	.9941	+ .0004	+ .0002	− .0002
27	12.475	0.9982	−0.0008	−0.0012	−0.0012

Kron's. In practice, this solution would be quite satisfactory as a basis for the least-squares differential correction which these observations demand. It will be noticed that the method is somewhat more complicated for the annular case as compared with the total-eclipse case.

§ 5. SOLUTION FOR PARTIAL ECLIPSES

The solution of a partial eclipse is complicated by the fact that a is not known from the light-curve directly at any phase, and, further, one usually must deal with both minima. Additional complications ensue, strangely enough, because a wide range of solutions is quite often possible and the elements may be nearly indeterminate. Whatever value of k is initially chosen—and often $k = 1$ is an obvious choice—it may fit the observations so well as to mislead the computer into believing that this is the correct answer. In some cases an apparently partial eclipse may actually be total or annular (refer to Fig. 4).

At any point on the light-curve a comparison can be made between the observed l there and l_0, the light at mid-eclipse. If we define n as

$$n = \frac{1 - l}{1 - l_0},$$ (45)

then

$$a = na_0,$$ (46)

where a_0 is the normalized fractional loss of light at mid-eclipse; its numerical value can be greater than unity; a_0 (or p_0) is one of the unknowns to be determined. From equation (27), at any value of n,

$$\cos^2 i + \sin^2 i \sin^2 \theta(n) = r_g^2 [1 + kp(x, k, na_0)]^2.$$ (47)

At mid-eclipse, $\theta = 0$, and

$$\cos^2 i = r_g^2 [1 + kp_0 (x, k, a_0)]^2.$$ (48)

Subtracting equation (48) from equation (47), we have

$$\sin^2 \theta(n) = r_g^2 \csc^2 i \{[1 + kp (x, k, na_0)]^2 - [1 + kp_0 (x, k, a_0)]^2\}.$$ (49)

If we adopt $n = 0.5$ as a special chosen point, then we can define a function χ such that

$$\chi(x, k, a_0, n) = \frac{\sin^2 \theta(n)}{\sin^2 \theta(\frac{1}{2})}$$

$$= \frac{[1 + kp(x, k, na_0)]^2 - [1 + kp_0(x, k, a_0)]^2}{[1 + kp(x, k, \frac{1}{2}a_0)]^2 - [1 + kp_0(x, k, a_0)]^2}$$ (50)

or

$$\sin^2 \theta(n) = \sin^2 \theta(\tfrac{1}{2})\chi(x, k, a_0, n).$$ (51)

The Merrill tables give χ as a function of k and a_0 for both occultation and transit for five values of x (not $x = 1.0$) and nine values of n (= 0.0, 0.1, 0.2, 0.4, 0.6, 0.8, 0.9, 0.95, and 1.0), a total of 81 tables! Four similar tables are given here (Tables 8–11) for $x = 0.5$ and $n = 0.2$ and 0.8, for both occultation and transit.

For an adopted x, χ can be calculated from the left-hand side of equation (50) for tabular values of n and compared with the appropriate tables. The comparison is more complex than in the case of the method where k could immediately be extracted from the ψ-table by inverse interpolation. Here we are dealing with both k and a_0 as unknowns. In principle, however, three points should provide a solution. For example, if we adopt an x and choose the points $n = 0.2, 0.5,$ and

0.8 on the light-curve, we can calculate χ $(k, a_0, n = 0.2)$ and χ $(k, a_0, n = 0.8)$. Each one of these χ's is a function of k and a_0 only and can be plotted, from interpolation in the tables, as two curves on the k-a_0 plane whose intersection is the solution (see Fig. 7). Once k and a_0 are fixed, equation (48) can be solved for $r_g^2 \csc^2 i$ (where p_0 is obtained from the a-tables), and equation (47) can be solved for $\cot^2 i$. A quick representation may be made by using Merrill's χ-tables for other values of n (if one of his tabular values of x is used) or by calculating A and B from equations (31) and (32), then using equation (30) in conjunction

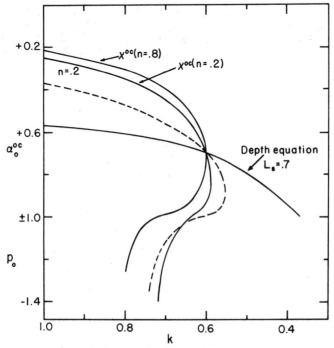

FIG. 7.—The graphical solution for a typical partial eclipse. The dashed line is for χ^{tr} $(n = 0.8)$ from secondary minimum.

with the ψ-tables. The fit should be "perfect" at the four points where $n = 0.2, 0.5, 0.8$, and 1.0.

There may be difficulties; for example, because of incorrectness of the model and/or observational errors, the two χ-curves either may not intersect at all or may intersect twice, and some trial and error is indicated. Further, it may not be clear as to whether the minimum in question is an occultation or a transit, and both hypotheses must be tested in separate plots; again it is possible to get two solutions. If primary and secondary are well observed and the two χ's calculated for both minima, a correct choice should be possible. A much more definitive solution is generally possible, however, by using the relations between the depths of the two minima as follows, in which case only the *depth* of second-ary need be known.

If l_0^{oc} is the light at mid-eclipse of the occultation and l_0^{tr} is the light at mid-eclipse of the transit, then

$$l_0^{oc} = 1 - a_0^{oc} L_s = 1 - a_0^{oc} (1 - L_g) ; \quad l_0^{tr} = 1 - f_0^{tr} L_g ,\qquad (52)$$

and if we eliminate L_g between these two equations, we get the depth equation in the form

$$a_0^{oc} = 1 - l_0^{oc} + \frac{(1 - l_0^{tr})}{q_0},\qquad (53)$$

where

$$q_0 = \frac{f_0^{tr}}{a_0^{oc}} = \frac{\tau a_0^{tr}}{a_0^{oc}}.\qquad (54)$$

For adopted values of x_s and x_g, $q_0 = q_0 (k, a_0^{oc})$, inasmuch as $a_0^{tr} = a_0^{tr} (k, p_0)$, and the implicit assumption is made that p_0 at primary minimum is equal to p_0 at secondary minimum. This implies a circular orbit. For the case of $x_s = x_g = 0.5$, q_0 is tabulated in Table 12 and is given in the Merrill tables for other values of x. Table 12A will be useful in fixing the numerical relation between q_0 and k at internal contact and at central phase. The use of the depth equation is as follows: l_0^{oc} and l_0^{tr} are known from the light-curve, although it may not be known which is which and both assumptions would need to be tested. A useful test, often definitive, is to calculate χ at $n = 0.2$ and 0.8 from observations of both minima. For a circular orbit, χ^{oc} will always be greater than χ^{tr} for $n = 0.8$; the reverse is true for $n = 0.2$. This can be seen by comparing Table 9 with Table 11 and Table 8 with Table 10. For successively assumed values of $q_0 = 1, 0.9, 0.8$, etc., equation (53) is solved for a_0^{oc}, and k can then be extracted from Table 12. This gives a series of values of k and a_0^{oc} which may be plotted along with the χ-curves on a $k - a_0^{oc}$ graph. An example is shown in Figure 7 for a typical case ($a_0^{oc} = 0.7$, $k = 0.6$, $r_g = 0.3$, $x = 0.5$, $L_s = 0.7$). The curves for smaller values of L_s would pass through the solution point with a larger negative slope. In practice, observational errors would tend to shift the two nearly parallel χ-curves from their true position, so that there might be either no intersection or more than one intersection. The depth-curve is more stable in this respect and intersects the χ-curves at less acute angles, giving a much greater degree of determinacy. The χ-curve for $n = 0.8$ from secondary minimum (a transit in this case) is shown as a dashed line. Its computation is somewhat lengthier, inasmuch as inverse interpolations in Table 11 give values of a_0^{tr}, which must be converted to a_0^{oc} by means of equation (54) and with the use of Tables 7, 12, and 12A.

§ 6. THE MERRILL NOMOGRAPHS

There would be some obvious advantages if, instead of choosing k and a_0^{oc} as co-ordinates, new co-ordinates were to be chosen such that the depth equation would be a straight line. This is the basis of the Merrill (1953) nomographs which have been prepared for $x = 0.2, 0.4, 0.6,$ and 0.8. For partial eclipses, the horizontal and vertical co-ordinates are $q_0(1 - a_0^{oc})$ and $q_0 a_0^{oc}$, respectively, and for complete eclipses they are $\tau(1 - a_0^{tr})$ and τa_0^{tr}, respectively. The two intercepts on the axes are calculated from the depths, and a thread or straight-edge gives the intersection with the appropriate χ-curve (for the strategic value of $n = 0.8$). Families of both χ^{oc}- and χ^{tr}- curves are on the nomographs, as well as networks of curves for both k and p_0. The values of χ from both minima will quickly distinguish which minimum is the occultation and which the transit (since χ^{oc} [$n = 0.8$] must always be greater than χ^{tr} [$n = 0.8$] for a circular orbit) and what adjustments need to be made to give a compromise solution. When the point of solution is finally fixed, k and p_0 are read off, and the other elements can be derived as before. Methods for taking a difference of darkening into account are discussed by Merrill. The method is very rapid, easy to learn, and can be applied to total and annular eclipses as well as to partial eclipses. As before, the test of the solution is how well the observations are represented. The computer at this point may wish to evaluate the differential coefficients, using the Irwin (1947) tables, and compare them with the residuals, either making indicated small changes to one element at a time or, better yet, proceeding directly to a general least-squares solution. In general, the χ-method is especially sensitive to the correct choice of the point where $n = 0.5$. The nature of partial eclipses is such that errors of a few thousandths of a magnitude at critical points may cause large errors in derived elements. The use of the depth equation—often a necessity and truly fundamental to the spherical model—unfortunately involves additional assumptions, such as no orbital eccentricity, no third component contributing light, and the correctness of rectification procedures in the case of distorted systems.

§ 7. ORBITAL ECCENTRICITY

Orbital eccentricity can often be ignored either because eccentricities of eclipsing systems are usually small, because the effects are small, or because there is no information regarding secondary minimum or variation of period. The effects can usually be precisely calculated, provided that e and ω are known or can be derived (ω is the longitude of periastron of the star eclipsed at primary minimum). The eccentricity can often be separated into the components of $e \cos \omega$ (tangential eccentricity) and $e \sin \omega$ (radial eccentricity); $e \cos \omega$ can be obtained from the time, t_2, of secondary minimum as compared with t_1, the time of primary minimum. Following Kopal (1946), if $i = 90°$ (central eclipse) and if

$$\psi = \pi + 2 \tan^{-1} \frac{e \cos \omega}{\sqrt{(1 - e^2)}}. \qquad (55)$$

then

$$\frac{2\pi}{P}(t_2 - t_1) = \psi - \sin \psi. \qquad (56)$$

Given $t_2 - t_1$, ψ is evaluated from equation (56) and $(e \cos \omega)/\sqrt{(1 - e^2)}$ evaluated from equation (55). The eccentricity, e, is usually so small that its square can be neglected, or e^2 may be approximated from $e \cos \omega$.

The above algebra can be avoided by the use of Table D, which is calculated from the above two equations.

If i is not equal to $90°$, then the time of mid-eclipse (when δ is a minimum) may not be at conjunction, and the observed values of t_1 and t_2 need small corrections which are to be applied before entering the above table. If η is the correction to the true anomaly in the sense v of conjunction *minus* v of minimum and if ω is the longitude of periastron of the star eclipsed at time t_1, it can be shown (for primary minimum) that

$$\sin 2\eta = \frac{2 e \cos(\omega - \eta)(1 - \sin^2 i \cos^2 \eta)}{\sin^2 i [1 + e \sin(\omega - \eta)]} \tag{57}$$

or, in degrees,

$$\eta \approx \frac{57.3 \, e \cos \omega \cot^2 i}{1 + e \sin \omega}. \tag{58}$$

In general, η is small; for example, $\eta = 3°.2$ for the case $e = 0.25$, $i = 65°$, and $\omega = 0°$. For secondary minimum, replace ω by $\omega + 180°$ in the above formulae.

To find the correction to the mean anomalies and hence to the observed times of t_1 and t_2, the two calculated η's are to be divided by $\partial v/\partial M$. In a practical case, $\partial v/\partial M$ can often be assumed equal to unity but may be numerically evaluated from tables of v as a function of M such as the Allegheny tables by Schlesinger and Udick (1912).

The value of the radial eccentricity, $e \sin \omega$, is difficult to evaluate accurately from light-curves and the most precise observations of secondary minimum are needed. If, for example, primary minimum is at or near periastron and with i equal to $90°$, the duration of secondary minimum is greater than primary minimum. As i is diminished, however, a point is eventually reached where there is no eclipse at secondary whatsoever, i.e., secondary minimum becomes infinitely short. The effects can be calculated in detail from equation (59) below and compared by successive approximations with the observations. It may, however, be found advantageous to use the least-squares method of Wyse, which will be found in Irwin (1947). In this method, the coefficients $\partial f/[\partial(e \sin \omega)]$ are set equal to zero for primary minimum and can be evaluated for secondary from the other differential coefficients. The solution of the normal equations gives $\Delta(e \sin \omega) = e \sin \omega$.

The precise prediction of a light-curve on the spherical model and for an eccentric orbit involves a calculation of δ as a function of the time and would proceed as follows. The separation between centers, δ, is the same as the dimensionless ratio ρ/a in the visual binary case, where ρ is the separation of the components and a is the semimajor axis (both in seconds of arc). It can be shown that

$$\delta = \frac{\rho}{a} = \frac{r}{a} \frac{\rho}{r} = \frac{1 - e^2}{1 + e \cos v} \sqrt{[1 - \sin^2 i \sin^2(v + \omega)]}, \tag{59}$$

TABLE D

$(e \cos \omega)/\sqrt{(1-e^2)}$ FROM THE PHASE OF SECONDARY MINIMUM

$\dfrac{(t_2-t_1)}{P}$	$\dfrac{(e \cos \omega)}{\sqrt{(1-e^2)}}$*	$\dfrac{(t_2-t_1)}{P}$	$\dfrac{(t_2-t_1)}{P}$	$\dfrac{(e \cos \omega)}{\sqrt{(1-e^2)}}$	$\dfrac{(t_2-t_1)}{P}$	$\dfrac{(t_2-t_1)}{P}$	$\dfrac{(e \cos \omega)}{\sqrt{(1-e^2)}}$	$\dfrac{(t_2-t_1)}{P}$
0.50...	0.0000	0.50	0.60...	0.1597	0.40	0.70...	0.3374	0.30
.51...	.0157	.49	.61..	.1763	.39	.71...	.3571	.29
.52...	.0314	.48	.62..	.1931	.38	.72...	.3774	.28
.53...	.0472	.47	.63..	.2102	.37	.73...	.3981	.27
.54...	.0630	.46	.64..	.2274	.36	.74...	.4195	.26
.55...	.0789	.45	.65..	.2449	.35	.75...	.4416	.25
.56...	.0948	.44	.66..	.2627	.34	.76...	.4644	.24
.57...	.1109	.43	.67..	.2808	.33	.77...	.4881	.23
.58...	.1270	.42	.68..	.2993	.32	.78...	.5126	.22
.59...	.1433	.41	.69..	.3181	.31	.79...	.5382	.21
0.60...	0.1597	0.40	0.70..	0.3374	0.30	0.80...	0.5649	0.20

* $(e \cos \omega)/\sqrt{(1-e^2)}$ is negative for $(t_2-t_1)/P < 0.5$.

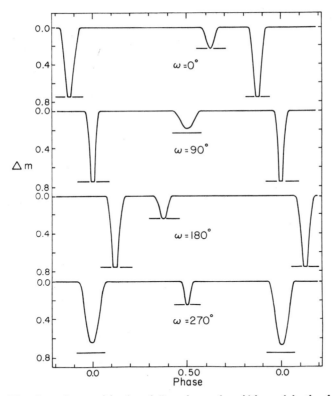

FIG. 8.—The effects of eccentricity ($e = 0.4$) on the epochs, widths, and depths of the minima for different values of ω.

where v is the true anomaly and is related to the mean anomaly M $(= 2\pi[t - T]/P)$ through well-known equations. However, for our purposes it is sufficient to use the Allegheny tables (Schlesinger and Udick 1912), where v is tabulated with respect to M to hundredths of a degree and for e up to 0.77. If T is known, M can be calculated and v extracted from these tables; if e, ω, and i are known, δ can be evaluated from equation (59).

The effects of eccentricity for a typical case are shown in Figure 8, where $e = 0.4$ and p_0 would be -1 (grazing total) if the orbit were circular. The changing depth relations are evident as ω changes, and the widths and epochs of minima vary by substantial amounts. Asymmetries of the eclipses during eclipse are not apparent from the curves and are very small but detectable from the calculations. For this example, corrected values of $(t_2 - t_1)/P$ fit equation (56) within the errors of calculation ($0°.01$), but there is more to this effect than is given by this equation. It is also of interest to consider t_1 and t_2 individually with respect to an average period evaluated over a complete rotation of the line of apsides; such evaluation is most easily accomplished by considering the relation between v and M, using the Allegheny tables. The details will not be given here.

§ 8. CONCLUDING REMARKS

This concludes the discussion of the spherical model. Most of the accurate light-curves and a large fraction of the less accurately observed eclipsing binaries show evident distortions from this model—the light is not constant between minima. It is obvious that some type of correction or rectification must be made to the light-curve so that the rectified light is constant between minima. The Russell method of rectification is discussed in detail in Russell and Merrill (1952), and only very brief remarks will be made here. The model consists of two similar prolate spheroids. The light-curve is analyzed between minima for ellipticity and reflection effects. Correction for reflection is by addition of light and, for ellipticity, by division. Correction to the phase during eclipse is made, but otherwise the solution proceeds by the methods used in the spherical case. After solution, some of the elements need to be modified in accordance with the rectification procedures and assumptions; it may also be that the elements so obtained should be used to give further better rectification to be applied in a second solution.

More complicated procedures, in which the photometric perturbations are individually calculated for the distortion of the eclipsing star, the distortion of the eclipsed star, and gravity-darkening and reflection effects, may be found in Kopal (1950). The calculations of these perturbations are relatively lengthy, but such procedures are often necessary in order to evaluate fully and to attempt to understand the best-observed eclipsing systems.

One of the needs for the near future is for easy-to-use tables of these photometric perturbations so that they may be quickly evaluated in any given case. The separate effects are usually small but non-negligible, and tabulation to only

TABLE 1

$$^5a^{oc}$$

p	k										
	1.00	0.90	0.80	0.70	0.60	0.50	0.40	0.30	0.20	0.10	0.00
+1.0....	0.000	0.000	0.000	0.000	0.000	0.000	0.000	0.000	0.000	0.000	0.000
+0.95....	0.003	0.003	0.004	0.004	0.004	0.004	0.004	0.004	0.004	0.005	0.005
+0.9....	0.010	0.010	0.011	0.011	0.011	0.012	0.012	0.012	0.013	0.013	0.014
+0.85....	0.019	0.020	0.020	0.021	0.022	0.022	0.023	0.024	0.025	0.026	0.027
+0.8....	0.031	0.031	0.032	0.033	0.034	0.035	0.036	0.038	0.039	0.041	0.042
+0.7....	0.059	0.060	0.062	0.064	0.066	0.068	0.070	0.072	0.075	0.078	0.081
+0.6....	0.093	0.096	0.098	0.101	0.104	0.107	0.111	0.114	0.118	0.122	0.127
+0.5....	0.133	0.137	0.140	0.145	0.149	0.153	0.158	0.163	0.168	0.174	0.180
+0.4....	0.179	0.183	0.188	0.194	0.199	0.205	0.211	0.217	0.224	0.230	0.238
+0.3....	0.228	0.234	0.241	0.247	0.254	0.261	0.268	0.276	0.283	0.291	0.300
+0.2....	0.281	0.289	0.297	0.304	0.313	0.321	0.329	0.338	0.347	0.356	0.365
+0.1....	0.337	0.347	0.356	0.365	0.374	0.384	0.393	0.403	0.412	0.422	0.432
0.0....	0.396	0.407	0.418	0.428	0.439	0.449	0.459	0.470	0.480	0.490	0.500
−0.1....	0.457	0.470	0.482	0.494	0.505	0.516	0.527	0.537	0.548	0.558	0.568
−0.2....	0.520	0.534	0.547	0.560	0.572	0.584	0.595	0.605	0.616	0.625	0.635
−0.3....	0.584	0.599	0.614	0.627	0.640	0.651	0.662	0.672	0.682	0.691	0.700
−0.4....	0.648	0.665	0.680	0.694	0.706	0.717	0.728	0.737	0.746	0.754	0.762
−0.5....	0.712	0.731	0.746	0.759	0.771	0.781	0.791	0.799	0.807	0.814	0.820
−0.6....	0.776	0.795	0.810	0.822	0.833	0.842	0.849	0.856	0.862	0.868	0.873
−0.7....	0.837	0.857	0.871	0.881	0.890	0.897	0.902	0.907	0.912	0.916	0.919
−0.8....	0.897	0.915	0.926	0.934	0.939	0.944	0.948	0.951	0.953	0.956	0.958
−0.85....	0.925	0.942	0.951	0.957	0.961	0.964	0.967	0.969	0.970	0.972	0.973
−0.9....	0.952	0.966	0.973	0.976	0.979	0.981	0.982	0.983	0.984	0.985	0.986
−0.95....	0.977	0.987	0.990	0.992	0.993	0.993	0.994	0.994	0.995	0.995	0.995
−1.00....	1.000	1.000	1.000	1.000	1.000	1.000	1.000	1.000	1.000	1.000	1.000

TABLE 2

$${}^{5}_{a}{}^{tr}$$

p	k									
	1.00	0.95	0.90	0.80	0.70	0.60	0.50	0.40	0.30	0.20
+1.0.........	0.000	0.000	0.000	0.000	0.000	0.000	0.000	0.000	0.000	0.000
+0.95........	0.003	0.003	0.003	0.003	0.003	0.003	0.003	0.004	0.004	0.004
+0.9.........	0.010	0.010	0.010	0.010	0.010	0.010	0.010	0.011	0.011	0.012
+0.85........	0.019	0.019	0.019	0.019	0.019	0.019	0.020	0.020	0.021	0.023
+0.8.........	0.031	0.030	0.030	0.029	0.030	0.030	0.031	0.032	0.034	0.036
+0.7.........	0.059	0.057	0.057	0.056	0.056	0.057	0.059	0.061	0.063	0.067
+0.6.........	0.093	0.091	0.090	0.089	0.090	0.091	0.093	0.095	0.099	0.105
+0.5.........	0.133	0.131	0.129	0.128	0.128	0.130	0.132	0.136	0.141	0.148
+0.4.........	0.179	0.175	0.173	0.171	0.172	0.173	0.176	0.181	0.187	0.195
+0.3.........	0.228	0.224	0.221	0.219	0.219	0.221	0.225	0.230	0.237	0.247
+0.2.........	0.281	0.276	0.273	0.271	0.271	0.273	0.277	0.283	9.291	0.302
+0.1.........	0.337	0.331	0.328	0.326	0.326	0.329	0.333	0.340	0.348	0.360
0.0.........	0.396	0.390	0.386	0.384	0.384	0.387	0.392	0.399	0.408	0.420
−0.1.........	0.457	0.450	0.447	0.444	0.445	0.448	0.454	0.461	0.470	0.483
−0.2.........	0.520	0.513	0.509	0.507	0.508	0.512	0.517	0.525	0.534	0.546
−0.3.........	0.584	0.576	0.573	0.571	0.573	0.577	0.582	0.590	0.599	0.611
−0.4.........	0.648	0.641	0.638	0.637	0.639	0.643	0.648	0.655	0.664	0.675
−0.5.........	0.712	0.705	0.703	0.703	0.705	0.709	0.715	0.721	0.729	0.739
−0.6.........	0.776	0.770	0.768	0.769	0.772	0.776	0.780	0.786	0.792	0.801
−0.7.........	0.837	0.833	0.833	0.835	0.837	0.841	0.844	0.848	0.853	0.860
−0.8.........	0.897	0.895	0.896	0.898	0.900	0.902	0.905	0.907	0.910	0.915
−0.85........	0.925	0.925	0.926	0.928	0.930	0.931	0.933	0.935	0.937	0.940
−0.9.........	0.952	0.953	0.954	0.956	0.957	0.958	0.959	0.960	0.961	0.963
−0.95........	0.977	0.980	0.981	0.981	0.981	0.982	0.982	0.982	0.983	0.984
−1.00........	1.000	1.000	1.000	1.000	1.000	1.000	1.000	1.000	1.000	1.000
−1.1.........			1.007	1.014	1.017	1.020	1.021	1.022	1.021	1.020
−1.2.........				1.020	1.029	1.034	1.038	1.040	1.040	1.038
−1.3.........					1.036	1.046	1.052	1.056	1.057	1.054
−1.4.........					1.039	1.054	1.064	1.070	1.072	1.069
−1.6.........						1.063	1.081	1.093	1.098	1.096
−1.8.........							1.091	1.110	1.120	1.120
−2.0.........							1.095	1.123	1.139	1.142
−2.5.........								1.136	1.172	1.186
−3.0.........									1.189	1.219
−3.5.........										1.244
−4.0.........										1.261
−4.5.........										1.271
−1/k.........	1.000	1.003	1.007	1.020	1.039	1.063	1.095	1.136	1.192	1.274

TABLE 3

$_5\psi_{oc}$

α	k												
	0.00	0.10	0.20	0.30	0.40	0.50	0.60	0.70	0.80	0.85	0.90	0.95	1.00
0.00	+2.254	+2.510	+2.797	+3.125	+3.504	+3.947	+4.476	+5.122	+5.936	+6.431	+7.004	+7.679	+8.490
0.02	+2.009	+2.219	+2.455	+2.723	+3.031	+3.391	+3.820	+4.344	+5.004	+5.405	+5.869	+6.417	+7.074
0.05	+1.818	+1.996	+2.195	+2.420	+2.679	+2.981	+3.341	+3.780	+4.331	+4.667	+5.055	+5.513	+6.064
0.10	+1.579	+1.720	+1.877	+2.055	+2.258	+2.495	+2.777	+3.120	+3.552	+3.814	+4.117	+4.475	+4.906
0.15	+1.380	+1.493	+1.620	+1.762	+1.924	+2.114	+2.338	+2.611	+2.954	+3.162	+3.403	+3.687	+4.029
0.20	+1.201	+1.293	+1.394	+1.508	+1.638	+1.789	+1.967	+2.184	+2.456	+2.622	+2.813	+3.039	+3.310
0.25	+1.036	+1.108	+1.189	+1.279	+1.382	+1.501	+1.641	+1.812	+2.026	+2.156	+2.307	+2.484	+2.698
0.30	+0.878	+0.935	+0.998	+1.068	+1.148	+1.240	+1.349	+1.481	+1.646	+1.746	+1.862	+1.999	+2.164
0.35	+0.727	+0.770	+0.818	+0.871	+0.931	+1.000	+1.082	+1.181	+1.305	+1.380	+1.467	+1.570	+1.693
0.40	+0.579	+0.611	+0.645	+0.684	+0.727	+0.777	+0.836	+0.907	+0.996	+1.050	+1.113	+1.186	+1.275
0.45	+0.434	+0.455	+0.479	+0.505	+0.534	+0.568	+0.607	+0.655	+0.715	+0.751	+0.793	+0.842	+0.901
0.50	+0.290	+0.302	+0.316	+0.332	+0.349	+0.370	+0.393	+0.421	+0.457	+0.478	+0.502	+0.531	+0.566
0.55	+0.145	+0.151	+0.157	+0.164	+0.172	+0.181	+0.191	+0.204	+0.219	+0.228	+0.239	+0.252	+0.267
0.60	0.000	0.000	0.000	0.000	0.000	0.000	0.000	0.000	0.000	0.000	0.000	0.000	0.000
0.65	−0.148	−0.152	−0.157	−0.162	−0.168	−0.174	−0.182	−0.191	−0.202	−0.209	−0.217	−0.226	−0.237
0.70	−0.299	−0.306	−0.314	−0.323	−0.332	−0.343	−0.356	−0.370	−0.389	−0.400	−0.412	−0.427	−0.445
0.75	−0.457	−0.465	−0.474	−0.484	−0.495	−0.508	−0.523	−0.540	−0.561	−0.573	−0.588	−0.605	−0.625
0.80	−0.622	−0.630	−0.639	−0.649	−0.659	−0.671	−0.684	−0.700	−0.719	−0.731	−0.744	−0.760	−0.778
0.85	−0.801	−0.806	−0.812	−0.819	−0.826	−0.833	−0.842	−0.853	−0.865	−0.873	−0.882	−0.892	−0.904
0.90	−1.000	−1.000	−1.000	−1.000	−1.000	−1.000	−1.000	−1.000	−1.000	−1.000	−1.000	−1.000	−1.000
0.95	−1.239	−1.229	−1.218	−1.207	−1.194	−1.180	−1.164	−1.146	−1.125	−1.113	−1.099	−1.083	−1.065
0.98	−1.430	−1.409	−1.387	−1.363	−1.337	−1.309	−1.277	−1.241	−1.200	−1.177	−1.150	−1.121	−1.086
0.99	−1.517	−1.490	−1.462	−1.431	−1.398	−1.363	−1.323	−1.279	−1.228	−1.199	−1.167	−1.131	−1.089
1.00	−1.675	−1.636	−1.595	−1.551	−1.505	−1.454	−1.399	−1.337	−1.268	−1.229	−1.187	−1.141	−1.091

TABLE 4

$^5\psi_{tr}$

α	k										
	0.20	0.30	0.40	0.50	0.60	0.70	0.80	0.85	0.90	0.95	1.00
0.00	+3.148	+3.586	+4.073	+4.626	+5.261	+5.994	+6.833	+7.286	+7.746	+8.180	+8.490
0.02	+2.775	+3.128	+3.519	+3.961	+4.470	+5.058	+5.733	+6.098	+6.470	+6.822	+7.074
0.05	+2.480	+2.774	+3.098	+3.465	+3.887	+4.376	+4.939	+5.244	+5.555	+5.851	+6.064
0.10	+2.116	+2.343	+2.594	+2.878	+3.205	+3.584	+4.022	+4.260	+4.504	+4.737	+4.906
0.15	+1.819	+1.998	+2.196	+2.419	+2.677	+2.976	+3.323	+3.513	+3.707	+3.894	+4.029
0.20	+1.559	+1.701	+1.856	+2.032	+2.235	+2.472	+2.746	+2.897	+3.052	+3.201	+3.310
0.25	+1.323	+1.434	+1.556	+1.693	+1.851	+2.036	+2.251	+2.370	+2.492	+2.610	+2.698
0.30	+1.106	+1.191	+1.284	+1.389	+1.510	+1.652	+1.818	+1.909	+2.004	+2.096	+2.164
0.35	+0.901	+0.965	+1.034	+1.112	+1.202	+1.308	+1.432	+1.501	+1.572	+1.641	+1.693
0.40	+0.707	+0.753	+0.802	+0.858	+0.922	+0.997	+1.086	+1.135	+1.187	+1.237	+1.275
0.45	+0.522	+0.552	+0.585	+0.622	+0.664	+0.715	+0.774	+0.807	+0.841	+0.875	+0.901
0.50	+0.343	+0.361	+0.380	+0.401	+0.426	+0.456	+0.491	+0.510	+0.531	+0.551	+0.566
0.55	+0.169	+0.177	+0.185	+0.195	+0.206	+0.218	+0.234	+0.242	+0.251	+0.260	+0.267
0.60	0.000	0.000	0.000	0.000	0.000	0.000	0.000	0.000	0.000	0.000	0.000
0.65	−0.166	−0.172	−0.178	−0.185	−0.192	−0.201	−0.212	−0.218	−0.225	−0.232	−0.237
0.70	−0.330	−0.339	−0.349	−0.360	−0.372	−0.387	−0.405	−0.415	−0.425	−0.436	−0.445
0.75	−0.494	−0.504	−0.515	−0.528	−0.542	−0.559	−0.579	−0.590	−0.602	−0.615	−0.625
0.80	−0.658	−0.668	−0.678	−0.689	−0.702	−0.717	−0.735	−0.746	−0.757	−0.768	−0.778
0.85	−0.826	−0.832	−0.839	−0.846	−0.854	−0.864	−0.875	−0.882	−0.889	−0.897	−0.904
0.90	−1.000	−1.000	−1.000	−1.000	−1.000	−1.000	−1.000	−1.000	−1.000	−1.000	−1.000
0.95	−1.189	−1.179	−1.168	−1.157	−1.144	−1.129	−1.111	−1.100	−1.089	−1.076	−1.065
0.98	−1.318	−1.299	−1.280	−1.259	−1.235	−1.207	−1.173	−1.154	−1.132	−1.109	−1.086
0.99	−1.368	−1.345	−1.322	−1.297	−1.269	−1.235	−1.195	−1.171	−1.145	−1.117	−1.089
1.00	−1.429	−1.400	−1.372	−1.342	−1.309	−1.269	−1.220	−1.192	−1.160	−1.126	−1.091
1.01	−1.517	−1.478	−1.443	−1.408	−1.368	−1.323	−1.267	−1.234			
1.02	−1.610	−1.560	−1.518	−1.477	−1.433	−1.381	−1.318				
1.05	−1.913	−1.828	−1.763	−1.705	−1.645						
1.10	−2.489	−2.334	−2.227								
1.15	−3.145	−2.907									
1.20	−3.876										
1.25	−4.681										
$α_c$	−5.091	−3.436	−2.597	−2.088	−1.747	−1.502	−1.321	−1.248	−1.185	−1.132	−1.091

TABLE 5

k	$^5\phi_1^{oc}$	$^5\phi_2^{oc}$	$^5\phi_1^{tr}$	$^5\phi_2^{tr}$
1.00	0.4175	0.9170	0.4175	0.9170
0.99	.4206	.9079	.4148	.9114
0.98	.4234	.8989	.4127	.9051
0.97	.4261	.8898	.4110	.8982
0.96	.4286	.8808	.4095	.8910
0.95	.4308	.8717	.4083	.8836
0.90	.4395	.8264	.4042	.8438
0.85	.4439	.7813	.4010	.8013
0.80	.4442	.7365	.3973	.7570
0.75	.4407	.6918	.3923	.7117
0.70	.4335	.6473	.3855	.6657
0.65	.4227	.6029	.3766	.6192
0.60	.4085	.5586	.3653	.5726
0.55	.3910	.5142	.3516	.5257
0.50	.3703	.4697	.3351	.4789
0.45	.3464	.4250	.3159	.4319
0.40	.3195	.3800	.2938	.3850
0.35	.2895	.3347	.2688	.3381
0.30	.2566	.2889	.2407	.2910
0.25	.2208	.2426	.2094	.2438
0.20	.1821	.1957	0.1748	0.1964
0.15	.1407	.1481	....	....
0.10	.0965	.0997	....	....
0.05	.0496	.0504	....	....
0.00	0.0000	0.0000	....	....

TABLE 6

k	$^5R^{oc}$	$^5M_1^{oc}$	$^5M_2^{oc}$	$^5M_3^{oc}$	$^5R^{tr}$	$^5M_1^{tr}$	$^5M_2^{tr}$	$^5M_3^{tr}$
1.00	3.880	4.389	+0.0405	−1.0802	3.880	4.389	0.0405	−1.0802
0.95	3.468	4.008	+ .0348	−1.1108	3.690	4.239	.0382	−1.1002
0.90	3.137	3.691	+ .0301	−1.1369	3.458	4.032	.0351	−1.1207
0.85	2.863	3.422	+ .0261	−1.1598	3.230	3.816	.0318	−1.1396
0.80	2.632	3.189	+ .0226	−1.1804	3.016	3.604	.0287	−1.1568
0.75	2.434	2.986	+ .0196	−1.1991	2.820	3.404	.0257	−1.1723
0.70	2.262	2.807	+ .0170	−1.2163	2.641	3.216	.0229	−1.1864
0.65	2.111	2.647	+ .0146	−1.2323	2.478	3.042	.0204	−1.1992
0.60	1.977	2.503	+ .0125	−1.2472	2.329	2.881	.0180	−1.2110
0.55	1.857	2.372	+ .0106	−1.2612	2.193	2.731	.0158	−1.2218
0.50	1.749	2.253	+ .0088	−1.2745	2.069	2.591	.0138	−1.2319
0.45	1.651	2.144	+ .0072	−1.2871	1.955	2.462	.0119	−1.2413
0.40	1.561	2.043	+ .0057	−1.2991	1.849	2.340	.0102	−1.2502
0.35	1.479	1.949	+ .0043	−1.3105	1.750	2.226	.0086	−1.2587
0.30	1.403	1.862	+ .0030	−1.3215	1.657	2.118	.0070	−1.2671
0.25	1.333	1.781	+ .0019	−1.3321	1.569	2.015	.0055	−1.2754
0.20	1.268	1.704	+ .0007	−1.3422	1.485	1.917	0.0041	−1.2838
0.15	1.208	1.632	− .0004	−1.3520	....	....	....	....
0.10	1.151	1.565	− .0014	−1.3615	....	....	....	....
0.05	1.098	1.500	− .0023	−1.3706	....	....	....	....
0.00	1.048	1.439	−0.0032	−1.3796	....	....	....	....

TABLE 7

FRACTIONAL LOSS OF LIGHT AT INTERNAL TANGENCY FOR $x=0.5$
AND SMALL STAR IN FRONT (TRANSIT)*

k	$^5\tau$	k	$^5\tau$	k	$^5\tau$	k	$^5\tau$	k	$^5\tau$
0.00...	0.000000	0.20...	0.037492	0.40...	0.165571	0.60...	0.386747	0.80...	0.683589
.01...	.000068	.21...	.041638	.41...	.174481	.61...	.400032	0.81...	0.699746
.02...	.000286	.22...	.046017	.42...	.183627	.62...	.413508	0.82...	0.715972
.03...	.000666	.23...	.050631	.43...	.193007	.63...	.427172	0.83...	0.732258
.04...	.001217	.24...	.055481	.44...	.202620	.64...	.441020	0.84...	0.748591
.05...	.001947	.25...	.060568	.45...	.212465	.65...	.455047	0.85...	0.764961
.06...	.002863	.26...	.065892	.46...	.222541	.66...	.469250	0.86...	0.781353
.07...	.003970	.27...	.071454	.47...	.232846	.67...	.483624	0.87...	0.797754
.08...	.005272	.28...	.077256	.48...	.243378	.68...	.498164	0.88...	0.814148
.09...	.006775	.29...	.083297	.49...	.254136	.69...	.512866	0.89...	0.830519
.10...	.008483	.30...	.089578	.50...	.265117	.70...	.527725	0.90...	0.846848
.11...	.010399	.31...	.096098	.51...	.276321	.71...	.542734	0.91...	0.863112
.12...	.012526	.32...	.102859	.52...	.287744	.72...	.557890	0.92...	0.879290
.13...	.014869	.33...	.109860	.53...	.299385	.73...	.573184	0.93...	0.895352
.14...	.017428	.34...	.117101	.54...	.311241	.74...	.588612	0.94...	0.911266
.15...	.020209	.35...	.124582	.55...	.323310	.75...	.604167	9.95...	0.926993
.16...	.023212	.36...	.132303	.56...	.335588	.76...	.619841	0.96...	0.942483
.17...	.026439	.37...	.140262	.57...	.348074	.77...	.635629	0.97...	0.957673
.18...	.029894	.38...	.148461	.58...	.360765	.78...	.651521	0.98...	0.972468
.19...	.033578	.39...	.156897	.59...	.373657	.79...	.667511	0.99...	0.986714
0.20...	0.037492	0.40...	0.165571	0.60...	0.386747	0.80...	0.683589	1.00...	1.000000

* For $x \neq 0.5$, use:

$$^x\tau = \frac{3-6x}{3-x} k^2 + \frac{5x}{3-x} {}^5\tau .$$

TABLE 8

$$^5\chi^{oc},\ n=0.2$$

a_0	k										
	1.00	0.90	0.80	0.70	0.60	0.50	0.40	0.30	0.20	0.10	0.00
0.00....	1.778	1.778	1.778	1.778	1.778	1.778	1.778	1.778	1.778	1.778	1.778
0.05....	1.852	1.849	1.846	1.842	1.839	1.835	1.830	1.825	1.819	1.813	1.805
0.10....	1.872	1.868	1.862	1.856	1.850	1.843	1.836	1.828	1.819	1.809	1.798
0.20....	1.910	1.901	1.891	1.881	1.869	1.858	1.845	1.832	1.817	1.801	1.784
0.30....	1.948	1.933	1.917	1.901	1.884	1.867	1.849	1.830	1.811	1.790	1.768
0.40....	1.988	1.966	1.944	1.921	1.898	1.874	1.850	1.826	1.801	1.776	1.750
0.50....	2.036	2.004	1.972	1.940	1.910	1.879	1.849	1.819	1.789	1.759	1.728
0.60....	2.094	2.047	2.003	1.961	1.921	1.882	1.845	1.808	1.773	1.738	1.703
0.70....	2.167	2.100	2.038	1.982	1.930	1.881	1.836	1.793	1.751	1.712	1.673
0.80....	2.266	2.165	2.079	2.003	1.936	1.875	1.820	1.769	1.722	1.678	1.636
0.85....	2.331	2.206	2.102	2.013	1.937	1.869	1.808	1.753	1.703	1.656	1.612
0.90....	2.411	2.252	2.126	2.022	1.934	1.858	1.791	1.732	1.678	1.629	1.584
0.95....	2.514	2.307	2.151	2.027	1.925	1.839	1.766	1.701	1.644	1.593	1.546
1.00....	2.656	2.367	2.160	2.002	1.879	1.778	1.695	1.624	1.564	1.511	1.464
p_0											
−1.10....	......	2.349	2.122	1.956	1.828	1.727	1.644	1.575	1.517	......	......
−1.20....	......	......	2.104	1.924	1.790	1.687	1.604	1.535	1.478		
−1.30....				1.905	1.762	1.655	1.570	1.502	1.445		
−1.40....				1.897	1.742	1.629	1.542	1.474	1.418		
−1.60....				......	1.722	1.594	1.500	1.429	1.373		
−1.80....					......	1.574	1.471	1.396	1.339		
−2.00....						1.568	1.451	1.371	1.312		
−2.50....						......	1.432	1.331	1.266		
−3.00....							......	1.313	1.237		
−3.50....								......	1.219		
−1/k....	2.656	2.349	2.102	1.896	1.721	1.568	1.432	1.310	1.199	......	......

619

TABLE 9

$^5\chi^{oc}$, $n = 0.8$

a_0	\multicolumn{11}{c}{k}
	.00	0.90	0.80	0.70	0.60	0.50	0.40	0.30	0.20	0.10	0.00
0.00....	0.374	0.374	0.374	0.374	0.374	0.374	0.374	0.374	0.374	0.374	0.374
0.05....	.364	.364	.365	.365	.366	.366	.367	.368	.369	.370	.371
0.10....	.360	.361	.362	.362	.363	.364	.366	.367	.368	.370	.372
0.20....	.354	.356	.357	.359	.361	.363	.365	.367	.369	.372	.375
0.30....	.348	.351	.353	.356	.359	.361	.364	.368	.371	.374	.378
0.40....	.341	.345	.349	.353	.357	.361	.365	.369	.373	.378	.383
0.50....	.332	.338	.344	.350	.355	.360	.366	.371	.377	.382	.388
0.60....	.322	.330	.338	.346	.354	.361	.368	.375	.382	.388	.395
0.70....	.307	.320	.332	.343	.353	.363	.372	.380	.389	.397	.405
0.80....	.286	.307	.324	.340	.354	.367	.378	.390	.400	.410	.420
0.85....	.271	.298	.320	.339	.356	.370	.384	.397	.409	.420	.431
0.90....	.252	.287	.315	.339	.359	.377	.393	.407	.421	.433	.445
0.95....	.227	.275	.311	.341	.366	.388	.407	.425	.440	.455	.469
1.00....	0.188	0.262	0.318	0.362	0.399	0.430	0.456	0.479	0.500	0.519	0.536
p_0											
−1.10....	......	0.272	0.340	0.392	0.433	0.467	0.496	0.520	0.542	......	......
−1.20....	......	......	.351	.412	.459	.497	.528	.554	.576	......	......
−1.30....	......	......	......	.424	.478	.520	.554	.582	.605	......	......
−1.40....	......	......	......	.429	.492	.539	.575	.605	.630	......	......
−1.60....	......	......	......	......	.506	.565	.608	.642	.669	......	......
−1.80....	......	......	......	......	......	.579	.631	.670	.699	......	......
−2.00....	......	......	......	......	......	.584	.647	.691	.723	......	......
−2.50....	......	......	......	......	......	......	.662	.724	.764	......	......
−3.00....	......	......	......	......	......	......	......	.739	.790	......	......
−3.50....	......	......	......	......	......	......	......	......	.806	......	......
−1/k....	0.188	0.272	0.352	0.430	0.507	0.584	0.662	0.742	0.824	......	......

TABLE 10

$^5\chi^{tr}$, $n = 0.2$

a_0	\multicolumn{9}{c}{k}
	1.00	0.90	0.80	0.70	0.60	0.50	0.04	0.30	0.20
0.00	1.778	1.778	1.778	1.778	1.778	1.778	1.778	1.778	1.778
0.05	1.852	1.850	1.847	1.843	1.838	1.832	1.825	1.816	1.806
0.10	1.872	1.870	1.866	1.861	1.853	1.845	1.835	1.823	1.808
0.20	1.910	1.907	1.901	1.892	1.880	1.867	1.851	1.833	1.813
0.30	1.948	1.943	1.933	1.920	1.904	1.885	1.864	1.840	1.814
0.40	1.988	1.982	1.968	1.949	1.927	1.902	1.874	1.844	1.812
0.50	2.036	2.026	2.005	1.979	1.950	1.917	1.883	1.847	1.808
0.60	2.094	2.078	2.049	2.013	1.974	1.932	1.890	1.846	1.801
0.70	2.167	2.142	2.099	2.050	1.998	1.946	1.894	1.842	1.790
0.80	2.266	2.225	2.161	2.091	2.023	1.957	1.893	1.833	1.774
0.85	2.331	2.276	2.196	2.114	2.035	1.960	1.891	1.825	1.763
0.90	2.411	2.336	2.236	2.137	2.045	1.961	1.885	1.814	1.748
0.95	2.514	2.408	2.279	2.159	2.052	1.957	1.873	1.797	1.727
1.00	2.656	2.491	2.318	2.169	2.042	1.935	1.843	1.761	1.686
1.01	......	......	2.307	2.153	2.024	1.916	1.823	1.741	1.664
1.02	......	......	2.291	2.134	2.004	1.896	1.802	1.720	1.642
1.03	......	......	......	2.114	1.983	1.874	1.781	1.699	1.620
1.04	......	......	......	......	1.961	1.853	1.760	1.678	1.599
1.05	......	......	......	......	1.939	1.832	1.739	1.657	1.579
1.10	......	......	......	......	......	......	1.641	1.563	1.486
1.15	......	......	......	......	......	......	......	1.484	1.412
1.20	......	......	......	......	......	......	......	......	1.353
1.25	......	......	......	......	......	......	......	......	1.306
a_c	2.656	2.490	2.290	2.094	1.910	1.738	1.579	1.429	1.287

621

TABLE 11

$^5\chi^{tr}$, $n = 0.8$

a_0	k								
	1.00	0.90	0.80	0.70	0.60	0.50	0.40	0.30	0.20
0.00	0.374	0.374	0.374	0.374	0.374	0.374	0.374	0.374	0.374
0.05	.364	.364	.364	.365	.365	.366	.368	.369	.370
0.10	.360	.360	.361	.362	.363	.364	.365	.367	.369
0.20	.354	.355	.356	.357	.359	.361	.363	.366	.369
0.30	.348	.349	.350	.352	.355	.358	.361	.365	.369
0.40	.341	.342	.345	.348	.351	.355	.360	.365	.370
0.50	.332	.334	.338	.343	.348	.353	.359	.365	.372
0.60	.322	.325	.330	.337	.344	.351	.359	.366	.374
0.70	.307	.312	.321	.331	.340	.350	.359	.369	.378
0.80	.286	.296	.310	.324	.337	.350	.362	.373	.385
0.85	.271	.285	.303	.320	.336	.351	.364	.377	.390
0.90	.252	.272	.295	.316	.336	.353	.368	.383	.397
0.95	.227	.256	.287	.314	.338	.358	.376	.393	.409
1.00	.188	.239	.284	.320	.350	.375	.396	.416	.435
1.01	....	....	.294	.331	.362	.388	.410	.431	.452
1.02	....	....	.306	.345	.376	.402	.424	.446	.468
1.03	....	....	....	.358	.390	.416	.439	.461	.485
1.04	....	....	....	....	.404	.430	.454	.476	.501
1.05	....	....	....	....	.419	.445	.468	.491	.517
1.10	....	....	....	....	....	....	.536	.558	.587
1.15	....	....	....	....	....	....	....	.614	.642
1.20	....	....	....	....	....	....	....	....	.683
1.25	....	....	....	....	....	....	....	....	.707
a_c	0.188	0.243	0.306	0.372	0.438	0.507	0.578	0.650	0.702

TABLE 12

$$q_0$$

k

a_0^{oc}	0.20	0.25	0.30	0.35	0.40	0.45	0.50	0.55	0.60	0.65	0.70	0.75	0.80	0.85	0.90	0.95	1.00
0.00	0.040	0.062	0.090	0.122	0.160	0.202	0.250	0.302	0.360	0.422	0.490	0.562	0.640	0.722	0.810	0.902	1.000
0.05	.034	.054	.079	.109	.144	.185	.231	.282	.339	.401	.469	.543	.622	.708	.799	.897	1.000
0.10	.033	.053	.078	.108	.143	.183	.228	.280	.337	.399	.468	.542	.621	.707	.799	.896	1.000
0.20	.033	.052	.077	.107	.142	.182	.228	.280	.337	.399	.468	.542	.622	.708	.799	.897	1.000
0.30	.033	.052	.077	.107	.142	.183	.229	.281	.338	.401	.470	.544	.624	.710	.801	.898	1.000
0.40	.033	.053	.077	.108	.143	.184	.231	.283	.340	.404	.473	.547	.627	.712	.803	.899	1.000
0.50	.033	.053	.078	.109	.144	.186	.233	.285	.343	.407	.476	.551	.631	.716	.806	.901	1.000
0.60	.033	.053	.079	.110	.144	.186	.235	.288	.347	.411	.481	.555	.635	.720	.809	.903	1.000
0.70	.034	.054	.080	.111	.146	.188	.239	.293	.352	.416	.486	.561	.641	.725	.813	.905	1.000
0.80	.034	.055	.082	.114	.148	.191	.243	.298	.358	.423	.493	.569	.648	.732	.819	.909	1.000
0.90	.035	.057	.084	.117	.151	.195	.250	.306	.367	.433	.504	.579	.659	.742	.827	.914	1.000
0.95	.036	.058	.086	.119	.156	.200	.255	.311	.373	.440	.512	.587	.667	.749	.834	.918	1.000
1.00	.037	.061	.090	.125	.166	.212	.265	.323	.387	.455	.528	.604	.684	.765	.847	.927	1.000
p_0																	
−1.1	0.038	0.062	0.091	0.127	0.169	0.217	0.271	0.330	0.394	0.464	0.537	0.614	0.693	0.773	0.853	...	...
−1.2	.039	.063	.093	.130	.172	.221	.275	.335	.400	.470	.543	.619	.697	...	...	...	...
−1.3	.040	.064	.095	.132	.175	.224	.279	.339	.404	.474	.547	.622	...	...	...	...	...
−1.4	.040	.065	.096	.133	.177	.227	.282	.343	.408	.477	.548	...	...	...	...	...	...
−1.6	.041	.067	.098	.137	.181	.231	.287	.347	.411	...	...	...	...	...	...	...	...
−1.8	.042	.068	.100	.139	.184	.234	.289	.348	...	...	...	...	...	...	...	...	...
−2.0	.043	.069	.102	.141	.186	.236	.290	...	...	...	...	...	...	...	...	...	...
−2.5	.044	.072	.105	.144	.188	...	...	...	...	...	...	...	...	...	...	...	...
−3.0	.046	.073	.106	...	...	...	...	...	...	...	...	...	...	...	...	...	...
−3.5	.047	.074	...	...	...	...	...	...	...	...	...	...	...	...	...	...	...
−1/k	0.048	0.074	0.107	0.145	0.188	0.237	0.290	0.348	0.411	0.478	0.548	0.622	0.698	0.775	0.853	0.929	1.000

TABLE 12A

q_0	k_i	k_c	q_0	k_i	k_c	q_0	k_i	k_c	q_0	k_i	k_c
1.00	1.000	1.000	0.75	0.841	0.834	0.50	0.681	0.666	0.25	0.486	0.463
0.99	0.992	0.992	.74	.835	.827	.49	.674	.659	.24	.477	.453
0.98	0.985	0.985	.73	.829	.821	.48	.667	.651	.23	.467	.444
0.97	0.978	0.978	.72	.822	.815	.47	.661	.644	.22	.457	.433
0.96	0.972	0.971	.71	.816	.808	.46	.653	.637	.21	.448	.423
0.95	0.965	0.964	.70	.810	.802	.45	.646	.629	.20	.437	.413
0.94	0.958	0.957	.69	.804	.795	.44	.639	.622	.19	.427	.402
0.93	0.952	0.950	.68	.798	.789	.43	.632	.614	.18	.416	.391
0.92	0.946	0.944	.67	.792	.782	.42	.625	.607	.17	.405	.380
0.91	0.939	0.937	.66	.785	.775	.41	.617	.599	.16	.394	.368
0.90	0.933	0.931	.65	.779	.768	.40	.610	.591	.15	.382	.356
0.89	0.927	0.924	.64	.773	.762	.39	.602	.583	.14	.370	.344
0.88	0.920	0.918	.63	.766	.756	.38	.595	.576	.13	.357	.332
0.87	0.914	0.911	.62	.760	.749	.37	.587	.568	.12	.344	.318
0.86	0.908	0.905	.61	.754	.742	.36	.579	.559	.11	.330	.305
0.85	0.902	0.898	.60	.747	.735	.35	.572	.551	.10	.316	.290
0.84	0.896	0.892	.59	.741	.729	.34	.564	.543	.09	.301	.275
0.83	0.890	0.885	.58	.734	.722	.33	.555	.535	.08	.285	.259
0.82	0.884	0.879	.57	.728	.715	.32	.547	.526	.07	.267	.242
0.81	0.877	0.872	.56	.721	.708	.31	.539	.517	.06	.249	.224
0.80	0.871	0.866	.55	.715	.701	.30	.531	.509	.05	.229	.205
0.79	0.865	0.860	.54	.708	.694	.29	.522	.500	.04	.206	.183
0.78	0.859	0.853	.53	.702	.687	.28	.513	.491	.03	.180	.158
0.77	0.853	0.847	.52	.695	.680	.27	.504	.482	.02	.149	.129
0.76	0.847	0.840	.51	.688	.673	.26	.495	.472	.01	.108	.091
0.75	0.841	0.834	0.50	0.681	0.666	0.25	0.486	0.463	0.00	0.000	0.000

TABLE 13

$\mathcal{L}(\Delta m)$

Δm	0.00	0.01	0.02	0.03	0.04	0.05	0.06	0.07	0.08	0.09
0.0	1.0000	0.9908	0.9817	0.9727	0.9638	0.9550	0.9462	0.9376	0.9290	0.9204
0.1	0.9120	.9036	.8954	.8872	.8790	.8710	.8630	.8551	.8472	.8395
0.2	0.8318	.8241	.8166	.8091	.8017	.7943	.7870	.7798	.7727	.7656
0.3	0.7586	.7516	.7447	.7379	.7311	.7244	.7178	.7112	.7047	.6982
0.4	0.6918	.6855	.6792	.6730	.6668	.6607	.6546	.6486	.6427	.6368
0.5	0.6310	.6252	.6194	.6138	.6081	.6026	.5970	.5916	.5861	.5808
0.6	0.5754	.5702	.5649	.5598	.5546	.5495	.5445	.5395	.5346	.5297
0.7	0.5248	.5200	.5152	.5105	.5058	.5012	.4966	.4920	.4875	.4831
0.8	0.4786	.4742	.4699	.4656	.4613	.4571	.4529	.4487	.4446	.4406
0.9	0.4365	.4325	.4285	.4246	.4207	.4169	.4130	.4093	.4055	.4018
1.0	0.3981	.3945	.3908	.3873	.3837	.3802	.3767	.3733	.3698	.3664
1.1	0.3631	.3597	.3565	.3532	.3499	.3467	.3436	.3404	.3373	.3342
1.2	0.3311	.3281	.3251	.3221	.3192	.3162	.3133	.3105	.3076	.3048
1.3	0.3020	.2992	.2965	.2938	.2911	.2884	.2858	.2831	.2805	.2780
1.4	0.2754	.2729	.2704	.2679	.2655	.2630	.2606	.2582	.2559	.2535
1.5	0.2512	.2489	.2466	.2443	.2421	.2399	.2377	.2355	.2333	.2312
1.6	0.2291	.2270	.2249	.2228	.2208	.2188	.2168	.2148	.2128	.2109
1.7	0.2089	.2070	.2051	.2032	.2014	.1995	.1977	.1959	.1941	.1923
1.8	0.1905	.1888	.1871	.1854	.1837	.1820	.1803	.1786	.1770	.1754
1.9	0.1738	.1722	.1706	.1690	.1675	.1660	.1644	.1629	.1614	.1600
2.0	0.1585	.1570	.1556	.1542	.1528	.1514	.1500	.1486	.1472	.1459
2.1	0.1445	.1432	.1419	.1406	.1393	.1380	.1368	.1355	.1343	.1330
2.2	0.1318	.1306	.1294	.1282	.1271	.1259	.1247	.1236	.1225	.1213
2.3	0.1202	.1191	.1180	.1169	.1159	.1148	.1138	.1127	.1117	.1107
2.4	0.1096	.1086	.1076	.1067	.1057	.1047	.1038	.1028	.1019	.1009
2.5	0.1000	0.0991	0.0982	0.0973	0.0964	0.0955	0.0946	0.0938	0.0929	0.0920

TABLE 14

SIN² θ

θ	0.0	0.1	0.2	0.3	0.4	0.5	0.6	0.7	0.8	0.9
0°.......	0.000000	0.000003	0.000012	0.000027	0.000049	0.000076	0.000110	0.000149	0.000195	0.000247
1........	.00030	.00037	.00044	.00051	.00060	.00069	.00078	.00088	.00099	.00110
2........	.00122	.00134	.00147	.00161	.00175	.00190	.00206	.00222	.00239	.00256
3........	.00274	.00292	.00312	.00331	.00352	.00373	.00394	.00416	.00439	.00463
4........	.00487	.00511	.00536	.00562	.00589	.00616	.00643	.00671	.00700	.00730
5........	.00760	.00790	.00821	.00853	.00886	.00919	.00952	.00986	.01021	.01057
6........	.01093	.01129	.01166	.01204	.01243	.01281	.01321	.01361	.01402	.01443
7........	.01485	.01528	.01571	.01615	.01659	.01704	.01749	.01795	.01842	.01889
8........	.01937	.01985	.02034	.02084	.02134	.02185	.02236	.02288	.02340	.02394
9........	.02447	.02501	.02556	.02612	.02668	.02724	.02781	.02839	.02897	.02956
10........	.03015	.03075	.03136	.03197	.03259	.03321	.03384	.03447	.03511	.03576
11........	.03641	.03706	.03773	.03839	.03907	.03975	.04043	.04112	.04182	.04252
12........	.04323	.04394	.04466	.04538	.04611	.04685	.04759	.04833	.04908	.04984
13........	.05060	.05137	.05214	.05292	.05371	.05450	.05529	.05609	.05690	.05771
14........	.05853	.05935	.06018	.06101	.06185	.06269	.06354	.06439	.06525	.06612
15........	.0670	.0679	.0687	.0696	.0705	.0714	.0723	.0732	.0741	.0751
16........	.0760	.0769	.0778	.0788	.0797	.0807	.0816	.0826	.0835	.0845
17........	.0855	.0865	.0874	.0884	.0894	.0904	.0914	.0924	.0934	.0945
18........	.0955	.0965	.0976	.0986	.0996	.1007	.1017	.1028	.1039	.1049
19........	.1060	.1071	.1082	.1092	.1103	.1114	.1125	.1136	.1147	.1159
20........	.1170	.1181	.1192	.1204	.1215	.1226	.1238	.1249	.1261	.1273
21........	.1284	.1296	.1308	.1320	.1331	.1343	.1355	.1367	.1379	.1391
22........	.1403	.1415	.1428	.1440	.1452	.1464	.1477	.1489	.1502	.1514
23........	.1527	.1539	.1552	.1565	.1577	.1590	.1603	.1616	.1628	.1641
24........	.1654	.1667	.1680	.1693	.1707	.1720	.1733	.1746	.1759	.1773
25........	.1786	.1799	.1813	.1826	.1840	.1853	.1867	.1881	.1894	.1908
26........	.1922	.1935	.1949	.1963	.1977	.1991	.2005	.2019	.2033	.2047
27........	.2061	.2075	.2089	.2104	.2118	.2132	.2146	.2161	.2175	.2190
28........	.2204	.2219	.2233	.2248	.2262	.2277	.2291	.2306	.2321	.2336
29........	.2350	.2365	.2380	.2395	.2410	.2425	.2440	.2455	.2470	.2485
30........	.2500	.2515	.2530	.2545	.2561	.2576	.2591	.2607	.2622	.2637
31........	.2653	.2668	.2684	.2699	.2715	.2730	.2746	.2761	.2777	.2792
32........	.2808	.2824	.2840	.2855	.2871	.2887	.2903	.2919	.2934	.2950
33........	.2966	.2982	.2998	.3014	.3030	.3046	.3062	.3079	.3095	.3111
34........	.3127	.3143	.3159	.3176	.3192	.3208	.3224	.3241	.3257	.3274
35........	.3290	.3306	.3323	.3339	.3356	.3372	.3389	.3405	.3422	.3438
36........	.3455	.3472	.3488	.3505	.3521	.3538	.3555	.3572	.3588	.3605
37........	.3622	.3639	.3655	.3672	.3689	.3706	.3723	.3740	.3757	.3773
38........	.3790	.3807	.3824	.3841	.3858	.3875	.3892	.3909	.3926	.3943
39........	.3960	.3978	.3995	.4012	.4029	.4046	.4063	.4080	.4097	.4115
40........	.4132	.4149	.4166	.4183	.4201	.4218	.4235	.4252	.4270	.4287
41........	.4304	.4321	.4339	.4356	.4373	.4391	.4408	.4425	.4443	.4460
42........	.4477	.4495	.4512	.4529	.4547	.4564	.4582	.4599	.4616	.4634
43........	.4651	.4669	.4686	.4703	.4721	.4738	.4756	.4773	.4791	.4808
44........	.4826	.4843	.4860	.4878	.4895	.4913	.4930	.4948	.4965	.4983
45........	0.5000	0.5017	0.5035	0.5052	0.5070	0.5087	0.5105	0.5122	0.5140	0.5157

two or three significant figures should suffice. Many tables would be necessary, and this would seem to be a task for an electronic computer. In many eclipsing systems, however, and especially for close systems, complications due to gas streams, rings, patches, extended atmospheres, etc., may be of far greater significance than the above-mentioned perturbations. The majority of well-observed light-curves show asymmetries, and there is an increasing list of stars whose light-curves have changed substantially in a few years' time. A deeper insight into complex systems can be obtained from combined spectrographic and photometric observations, but, whether or not such spectrographic observations are available, the photometric observer should endeavor to cover thoroughly the non-eclipse portion of the light-curve and in at least two colors. The use of two colors should be of considerable power, in favorable circumstances, because the geometric elements should be the same in each color. Another use of two colors is to separate out the ellipticity effects of the separate components by discussion of the change with color of the photometric ellipticity between minima, having obtained the colors of each star from the color of the light lost within each eclipse.

A more fundamental approach would be to program the entire solution on an electronic computer and compare the observations by successive approximations to a series of models that are astrophysically more realistic than either the spherical model or the Russell model. Nevertheless, an understanding of the spherical model is of fundamental importance; it is also a useful starting point. For these reasons it is hoped that this chapter will serve as a useful introduction.

REFERENCES

AITKEN, R. G.	1935	*The Binary Stars* (New York: McGraw-Hill Book Co., Inc.), chap. vii.
BINNENDIJK, L.	1960	*Properties of Double Stars* (Philadelphia: University of Pennsylvania Press), chap. vi.
HYNEK, J. A.	1951	*Astrophysics* (New York: McGraw-Hill Book Co., Inc.), chap. 11.
IRWIN, J. B.	1947	*Ap. J.*, **106**, 380.
KING, E. S.	1920	*Harvard Ann.*, **81**, 231.
KOPAL, Z.	1946	*An Introduction to the Study of Eclipsing Variables* (Cambridge: Harvard University Press).
	1950	*The Computation of Elements of Eclipsing Binary Systems* (Cambridge: Harvard College Observatory).
	1955	*Ann. d'ap.*, **18**, 379.
	1959	*Close Binary Systems* (New York: John Wiley & Sons).
KOPAL, Z., and SHAPLEY, M. B.	1956	*Jodrell Bank Ann.*, **1**, 141.
KRON, G. E.	1939	*Lick Obs. Bull.*, No. 499.

KUKARKIN, B. V., and
  PARENAGO, P. P.   1948   *General Catalogue of Variable Stars* (1st ed.; Moscow: U.S.S.R. Academy of Science).

KUKARKIN, B. V., PARE-
  NAGO, P. P., EFREMOV,
  YU. I., and KHOLOPOV,
  P. N.   1958   *General Catalogue of Variable Stars* (2d ed.; Moscow: U.S.S.R. Academy of Science).

MERRILL, J. E.   1950   *Tables for Solution of Light Curves of Eclipsing Binaries* (*Princeton U. Obs. Contr.*, No. 23).

     1953   *Princeton U. Obs. Contr.*, No. 24.

MÜNCH, G., and
  CHANDRASEKHAR, S.   1949   *Harvard Circ.*, No. 453.

RUSSELL, H. N.   1912   *Ap. J.*, **36**, 133.

     1948   *Harvard Mono.*, No. 7.

RUSSELL, H. N., and
  MERRILL, J. E.   1952   *The Determination of the Elements of Eclipsing Binaries* (*Princeton U. Obs. Contr.*, No. 26).

RUSSELL, H. N., and
  SHAPLEY, H.   1912   *Ap. J.*, **36**, 239.

SCHLESINGER, F., and
  UDICK, S.   1912   *Pub. Allegheny Obs.*, Vol. **2**, No. 17.

SHAPLEY, H.   1912   *Ap. J.*, **36**, 269.

WENDELL, O. C.   1909   *Harvard Ann.*, **69**, 86–91.

     1914   *Ibid.*, p. 162.

ZESSEVICH, W.   1938   *Bull. Astr. Inst. Acad. Sci. U.S.S.R.*, No. 45.

     1940   *Ibid.*, No. 50.

Index